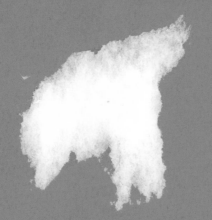

Production and Operations Management

Production and Operations Management

J. William Gavett
University of Rochester

Under the General Editorship of
Martin K. Starr, Columbia University

Harcourt, Brace & World, Inc.

New York / Chicago / San Francisco / Atlanta

Preface

This book is intended for an introductory course in production and operations management. The character of such an introductory course is currently a matter of some controversy. Production, of course, is one of the traditional functions or core areas of business management. The main issue in the controversy is the scope and depth of coverage that should be devoted to the quantitative techniques of operations research and management science. One argument is that the introductory production course should expose the student to operations research, with the emphasis on mathematical techniques and model building. This approach is intellectually sophisticated. However, because of the typical diversity in student backgrounds, mathematical maturity, and career objectives, a softer approach may be more in order. One such approach is to apply the quantitative techniques in the context of production problems and institutional or descriptive models. The term *operations management* connotes, in part, such an approach.

Production management, in some form, is a logical constituent of most engineering curricula. The question therefore arises whether this topic rightfully belongs within the less technical, business school curriculum. Although production has the connotation of being strictly an engineering function, managers make decisions about production matters using economic or even political criteria that are superimposed on the engineer's technological alternatives. There is a *technical* content to the managerial aspects of production management and decision making that is different from the technology of processing materials or providing services. It is this technical content that comprises the substance of business programs in general and production management in particular.

Also, consider the major management problems that exist in nonprofit public institutions and services, such as pollution control, public transportation, solid waste disposal, urban renewal, and hospital administration. These are large-scale systems problems that seem to defy easy formulation or orderly solution. There is a sense of urgency for their solution, and we need to formulate the content and structure of courses related to them. Here again is something that gives meaning to the words *operations management*. This text does more than just allude to these problems, for the reader will encounter a number of examples that have no relation to the traditional factory setting.

The organization of this book is primarily by problem or functional areas. A problem is presented, consideration is given to traditional approaches to it, and then the relevant quantitative techniques and related research are discussed. Many of the problems are tactical, the kind encountered at the "shop" level. This may disturb the student who is anxious to delve into those strategic kinds of problems that preoccupy "top" management. But there must be some substantive knowledge about production detail before one can grapple with policy matters. And more than one top manager has found it useful to be able to talk intelligently to those who must design, plan, and control the more detailed aspects of production systems.

This book is in a certain sense a survey of topics related to production and operations management. It does not exhaust the possible set of relevant topics, nor is any one topic dealt with in the depth required to attain proficiency. Footnotes and bibliographies direct the student to sources for greater penetration of specific topics. The range of topics presented is wide enough to allow the instructor latitude in structuring his course. He may choose to limit the number of topics he will discuss or to limit the depth of their coverage. The text will permit either possibility.

Chapters 1 through 3 are introductory. Chapter 3 discusses some of the conventional models used in production management. The intent is to describe how a model works, rather than to emphasize its mathematical development. This chapter can be used as a reference for later chapters where models are encountered in applications. Chapters 4 through 11 cover subjects that are basically related to the derivation of physical resources-facilities planning and design. Chapters 12 to 18 are mainly related to production planning and control—the management use of the physical resources.

Most chapters include case problems in the text around which the discussion of the substantive material can center. The use of the computer is an element of some of the cases and problems. A knowledge of computer programing, however, is not a requisite. For those students who are familiar with programing, the problems can be structured in the form of logic flow diagrams in varying degrees of detail and approaching programing format.

A survey of a field as dynamic and broad as production and operations management necessarily requires references to many sources of relevant material. Much of the quantitative discussion deals with the contributions of others to the field of management science. Thus I face the risk of omitting acknowledgments where they are rightfully due. Such omissions, if they have occurred, are not by design. The name Richard W. Conway of Cornell University threads its way through the footnotes. Because of my association with him, I am indebted to him for more than is accounted for. Henry P. Goode of Cornell University was kind enough to permit me to reproduce certain of his notes and original class problems. Martin K. Starr of Columbia University, Michael P. Hottenstein of Pennsylvania State University, and Yu Sang Chang of Boston University made many valuable comments and suggestions. Edward J. Carstens of the Eastman Kodak Company contributed some problems and suggestions, and graduate students Paul Brands, Barry Florescue, and Brian Pecon did work that ended up in certain pages of the text. Finally, I am grateful to the editors of *The Journal of Industrial Engineering, Management Science*, and *Operations Research*, as well as others, for permission to reprint and, of course, to the authors whose contributions are reprinted. Without their efforts one might truly question the justification of an academic pursuit of our subject.

J. WILLIAM GAVETT

Contents

8

Flow Processes: Product-Line Design   242

9

Microproduction Systems: Man and Machine   272

10

Facilities Replacement and Maintenance   303

11

Design and Management of Capacity   355

12

Planning Input Data: Work Measurement

13

Controlling Production Quality

14

Production Planning

15

Production and Inventory Control

16
Scheduling and Dispatching

17
Integrated Systems Control

18
Logistics Systems

Appendix

Tables

Index

Production and Operations Management

1
Production Management: An Overview

Production management deals with complex systems of men, machines, materials, and structures, which are designed to produce a product or service of economic value to society. While the management of such systems is part of the more general domain of business administration, we are concerned with production management as distinct from the other major functional areas of marketing and finance. This segregation is historically and pedagogically convenient, but it leaves something to be desired in terms of real-life experience. Although all major areas of business administration are inextricably intertwined in the problems the typical business manager has to face daily, we will discuss only those subjects that can be reasonably isolated under the heading of production.

Production is typically associated with the industrial manufacture of physical goods; we will, however, extend our definition of production to include a variety of services and related activities. The production activity consists of bringing together a restricted set of resources, such as materials, labor, equipment, and structures and "operating" them in some fashion such that a desired product or service results. Thus, we use the term "operations management" to emphasize the dynamic character of the interaction of men and machines.

Most of us have some familiarity with production. Either we have worked in a factory or have a general notion of what goes on inside one. But, more importantly, all of us are elements or variables of operational or service systems. For example, we are customers in retail service systems, patients in hospitals, drivers through toll booths, recipients of library books, maintainers of equipment, and contributors to a wide variety of work situations. We therefore have a first-hand knowledge about how well or poorly such service systems are managed.

Production is a formal and organized human activity. Upon visiting a large manufacturing plant, it is difficult not to be impressed and possibly overwhelmed by the complexity and magnitude of production activities. One is tempted to wonder how such a system of intricate equipment and machines came into being and what makes it run, ostensibly quite smoothly. There is some satisfaction in knowing that the system very likely arrived at its present state through an evolutionary process and that no one masterminded its design as an original problem. And then, the system operates or works because there are many people in the organization, each carrying out, with expertise, a specialized job. Perhaps the most remarkable thing is that their concerted effort yields a productive aggregate effect, although there may be more than a few sour notes in the symphony.

EVOLUTION OF PRODUCTION MANAGEMENT

Simply explaining the production phenomenon as being the result of evolutionary forces, and its workability the product of combined human experience, is, of course, unsatisfactory. (It might be satisfactory if we were viewing the eighteenth-century prototypes of our modern industrial systems.)

Some of the "principles" of industrial and production management appeared on the historical scene before they became the canons of nineteenth- and twentieth-century industrial management. The oldest principle of modern production is that of bringing together the resources of production in an organized fashion, sometimes under one roof, blended with specialization and division of labor. Although Adam Smith was the first to extol its economic virtues, the division of labor was basic in some degree to production long before his time. Venetian shipbuilders, for example, applied the "assembly-line" technique to the outfitting of galleys as early as the fourteenth century.[1] Another example is standardization and interchangeable-part manufacture, which were proposed and tested by the French in the manufacture of musket locks in the 1780's and became the basis for Eli Whitney's more successful applications.[2]

In the pre-industrial revolution era, production technology and management were passed from generation to generation in the secret ways of the guilds. Prior to the nineteenth century, production was a matter of "getting things done" without a formalized theory to support these activities. The practical men concerned with making things and running the shops or factories were never good purveyors of written information about their methods, problems, or lives. Occasionally, however, appeared a chronicler who took the time to expound and illustrate some aspect of industry in his own age, although writing about such things was unusual and perhaps unprofitable.

The French encyclopedist, Denis Diderot, for example, made a successful attempt to penetrate the secrecy of the guilds and preserved in his encyclopedia remarkable pictorial detail of the manufacturing technology of eighteenth-century France. His troubles in obtaining information are described by one of his biographers:[3]

---

[1] F. C. Lane, *Venetian Ships and Shipbuilders of the Renaissance.* Baltimore, Md.: Johns Hopkins Press, 1934, p. 172.
[2] W. F. Durfee, "The First Systematic Attempt at Interchangeability in Firearms," *Cassier's Magazine,* vol. 5, November 1893, pp. 469–77.
[3] Charles C. Gillispie, Ed., *A Diderot Pictorial Encyclopedia of Trades and Industry,* vol. 1. New York: Dover Publications, 1959, pp. XX–XXI.

It proved extremely difficult to find out about a great many trades. Language alone presented enormous difficulties. Each trade had its own barbarous jargon. For some a whole lexicon was needed. Worse, a great many artisans neither understood what they did nor wanted to understand. In their mulish way they preferred working by rote.

Diderot illustrated a French factory system that had been nurtured by the Crown for a century and a half. By the latter half of the eighteenth century, French factories were remarkable systems of water-wheeled power, wooden machinery with metal reinforcing, and an amazing variety of hand tools, all of which were combined with a rationale of labor specialization. Unfortunately, Diderot's explanation emphasized only technique and technology, not management.

When the pace of technology quickened at the end of the eighteenth century, the first notions of an ordered system of managerial concepts and techniques in manufacturing began to appear. The clarion call to recognize things managerial was the notable work in 1832, *On the Economy of Machinery and Manufactures*, by Charles Babbage.[4] Babbage (1792–1871) was a British mathematician, inventor, writer, and apparent scientific jack-of-all-trades. Perhaps he is better known for a noble but abortive attempt to build a computer (or calculating engine, as he called it). Although he personally designed and built some tools for its development, the ultimate lack of financial support, and perhaps the lack of precision of contemporary manufacturing methods, precluded the success of the project. His important book was a product of his tour of factories in England and the continent during the culmination of the industrial revolution. The work ranges, sometimes in a desultory fashion, over a wide variety of topics related to factory management. These included the methods of objectively studying operations, motion and time study (albeit not in those terms), incentive pay, cost analysis, and other topics of more general business concern. As a harbinger of the modern systems analyst, he notes:[5]

> If, therefore, the *maker* of an article wish to become a *manufacturer*, in the more extended sense of the term, he must attend to other principles besides those mechanical ones on which the successful execution of his work depends; and he must carefully arrange the whole system of his factory in such a manner, that the article he sells to the public may be produced at as small a cost as possible.

Babbage was five decades ahead of his time. He was too advanced for the still practical works manager. Until the end of the nineteenth century, the emphasis was on technology and the continued development and use of the machine, and not on its integration into an economic production system. If there was a concern about management problems, the evidence is slim, for there is a paucity of written works on the subject that go beyond the extolment of machinery. Works managers presumably were born with a set of managerial skills; they did not acquire them. And the mechanical engineer had yet to entertain commercial efficiency as a matter of professional concern.

---

[4] Charles Babbage, *On the Economy of Machinery and Manufactures*, 3rd ed. London: Chas. Knight, 1832.
[5] *Ibid.*, p. 121.

By the end of the nineteenth century, things were becoming too complex to predicate production management on the principle that the man closest to the job knew best how to handle it. Consider the description of the Franklin Manufacturing Company plant by G. D. Babcock in 1908, prior to his installing scientific management procedures in the plant.[6] (This plant built automobiles at the rate of about 100 per month.)

> The factory management, which was generally accepted as up to date and well developed, was about as follows: The management ordered the quantity, the form, and the date the product was to be finished. Through the engineering department the detailed part forms, the kind of material, and the combination of assemblies was specified. The foreman and superintendent planned for the time and duration of operations, the kind of machinery and tools, and the general operating method. They also selected and rated the workmen, and supervised their attendance.
>
> From the general car schedules, detailed schedules were made and delivered to the foreman. These were merely copies of the original schedule of finished product, but were dated earlier by one, two, three, or four months. From this dated schedule, any foreman was obliged to plan the procedure for each mechanical operation. With these conditions, it is evident that the scheduling eventually rested in the hands of the stock chasers who represented the assembly floors.
>
> Foremen assigned individual jobs to the workmen, supervised them at their work, and discharged them without appeal on any pretext. They further ordered repairs for machines and equipment, and selected and maintained tools and supplies.
>
> The foremen and workmen decided mechanical methods to pursue at the work, the number of pieces to start on each operation, and the time in which the work could be applied. *The prime responsibility rested on the workman*, with the foreman as a close second. This is evidenced by the considerable workman labor turnover on the charge of "unsatisfactory work," while there was very little change in foremen.
>
> The result of this, as we now see, could hardly be unexpected. The plan of dual responsibility showed the usual weakness of indecision in emergency, lack of correction for faults due to uncertain responsibility, and doubt and distrust due to lack of knowledge. Opinion was pitted against opinion, and a general feeling of indefiniteness permeated the factory.
>
> Dates called for by the management were not kept by the foremen, primarily because of the uncertainty and irregularity in the scheduling of operations. Material shortages were frequent. Tools were unsuitable and lacking. Machines were not best suited to the purpose and were often in poor repair. Neither tools nor machines were standardized, and work could not be exchanged rapidly from one to another. Shortages of parts were constant and serious, and caused a very high ratio of preparation to operating time; through this inefficiency a resultant high peak of workman effort was caused.
>
> The change in the number of employees was frequent. A large percentage of employees were poorly trained and irregular in attendance. The management, the foremen, and the workmen were continuously at odds over results. The purchasing department was forever rushing or holding up orders, and, of course, the people from whom we purchased suffered the same experience.

---

[6] George D. Babcock, *The Taylor System in Franklin Management*. New York: Engineering Magazine Company, 1917, pp. 2–3.

Scientific Management

It was this kind of environment that provided the breeding ground for a significant development in management technique. In 1886, members of the American Society of Mechanical Engineers were strongly advised to consider the economics of production as a proper domain of their professional interests. Henry Towne,[7] president of the Yale & Towne Manufacturing Company, wrote a paper urging the technically trained engineer to concern himself with the economic, financial, and profit-making aspects of works management. Towne's own personal contribution consisted of a departmentalized incentive scheme in his shops. In the meantime, Captain Henry Metcalf was developing a system of routing and costing in the government arsenals.[8]

In 1895, Frederick W. Taylor entered the scene with his famous paper delivered before the American Society of Mechanical Engineers.[9] To the Society, this was merely one more paper on the subject of wage payments and was thus received with indifference. What was overlooked was the fact that the paper reflected the results of concerted, and for that period sophisticated, experimentation in factory work methods. Specifically, it was the result of studies of pig iron handling in the Bethlehem steel yards (see Chapter 12 of this text). More importantly, Taylor's paper was the precursor of more important things, which would constitute the philosophy and methods of scientific management. Taylor was more interested in general shop management problems than he was in advancing simply another wage incentive scheme. As he said in his paper,[10]

> It is not unusual for the manager of a manufacturing business to go most minutely into every detail of the buying and selling and financiering, and arrange every element of these branches in the most systematic manner, and according to principles that have been carefully planned to insure the business against almost any contingency which may arise, while the manufacturing is turned over to a superintendent or foreman with little or no restrictions as to the principles and methods which he is to pursue, either in the management of his men or the care of the company's plant.

His later works, *Shop Management* in 1910 and *Principles of Scientific Management* in 1911, summarized his efforts in this direction. In the *Principles of Scientific Management*, he extolled scientific knowledge and scientific approaches to the regulation of shop work.

By the first decade of the twentieth century, the spirit of scientific management was beginning to take hold. Many contributors to the philosophy of systematic factory management were friends or disciples of Taylor. Henry Gantt, who worked directly with Taylor in his Bethlehem Steel Company experiments, later went on to make original contributions, including improvements in production planning as embodied in his Gantt Charting System. Both Morris Cooke and Harrington

---

[7] Henry R. Towne, "The Engineer as Economist," *Trans. ASME*, vol. 7, 1886, p. 425.

[8] Henry Metcalf, *The Cost of Manufactures and the Administration of Workshops.* New York: John Wiley & Sons, 1885.

[9] Frederick W. Taylor, "A Piece Rate System," *Trans. ASME*, vol. XVI, 1895, p. 856.

[10] *Ibid.*, p. 856.

Emerson spread the gospel as consultants. Cooke became famous for his introduction of the philosophy to university management with many radical ideas that did not endear him to academic and public works administrations. Emerson made important contributions to cost reduction in the railroad industry and became the apostle of efficiency as a national reform movement. Frank Gilbreth made independent studies of jobs in the construction industry, which resulted in his derivation of the principles of motion study and the use of the motion picture to analyze industrial operations.

Management Science

What was "scientific" to Taylor and his disciples in the early part of this century is not scientific by today's standards. Scientific management was mainly system and organization, as well as a certain degree of analysis of things that had been ignored by management in the past. Science is embodied in the method of objective and unbiased investigation of phenomena and the formulation of hypotheses that must be proved multilaterally before they become scientific principles. The closest the scientific managers came to this was probably Taylor's original experiments in work methods and subsequent studies in metal cutting.

The real scientific study of the phenomenon of men and machines would demand a spirit of inquiry and the use of methods similar to those of the laboratory scientist. Babbage's advice to the manager to consider the whole system of his factory pointed to the need for providing the manager with understanding and knowledge of how to go about this task, that is, research in operations.

If the operational characteristics of a whole factory are not scientifically explainable, then at least the behavior of parts of the system might be examined. Before World War II, there were some embryonic beginnings of "scientific" explanations of manufacturing systems, besides the empiricism of the scientific managers. It took World War II, however, to give impetus to the idea of giving a scientific explanation to the behavior of complex factory systems.

As early as 1912, George Babcock formulated some principles for establishing the economical size of a production lot for parts in the Franklin plant. He apparently reduced his principles to a mathematical formula, a cubic equation, that proved infeasible. In 1915, F. W. Harris of the Westinghouse Company used the simple formula

$$\left(Q = \sqrt{\frac{2ds}{ci}} \right)$$

where Q = economic number of a part to produce
d = annual rate of demand for the part
s = cost to set up the process to make the part
c = unit part cost of manufacture
i = annual rate of inventory holding cost

which was the prototype of inventory models. During the next decade, this model was further elaborated on, and the results were summarized in 1931 by F. E. Raymond[11] in *Quantity and Economy in Manufacture.*

In 1928, T. C. Fry[12] of the Bell Telephone Laboratories presented his work on the engineering uses of probability theory. In 1931, his colleague, Walter Shewhart,[13] wrote *Economic Control of Quality of Manufactured Product.* This work presented the methods of statistical quality control and was the basis for the control of various random phenomena in manufacturing and business operations. In the same period (1934), L. H. C. Tippett[14] proposed a scheme for measuring delays in textile operations based on probability theory. His work was later expanded into the modern technique of work sampling.

During World War II and its immediate aftermath, the scientist entered the management arena just as the engineer had done 40 years earlier. The first appreciable use of scientific research into operations was made in Great Britain during the war. The kinds of military operational problems that were investigated included the determination of convoy sizes, optimal size of bombing formations and techniques of bombing, and search patterns for antisubmarine warfare. Much of the work involved building mathematical models of operating systems and required a certain level of scientific and mathematical competence by the investigators. The results of this work formed the foundation of the science of operations.

After the war, this new science began to expand rapidly. In 1947, George Dantzig devised the simplex method for the solution of linear programing problems. In *The Theory of Games and Economic Behavior*, J. J. von Neumann and O. Morgenstern[15] related decision making to economic competition. By the 1950's, the use of mathematical models had expanded into the areas of waiting line or queuing systems, replacement of capital equipment, equipment maintenance, inventory and production planning, etc.

The concomitant development of the electronic computer made the application of these developments in operations research feasible. Not only did the computer make computation of complex problems possible, but by its ability to simulate the variables of complex systems, it also became a model in its own right.

Today, the science of operations has both its theoretical and applied aspects. Much of the theoretical work is of a high level of sophistication and is directed toward the refinement of mathematical models, with little direct relevancy to specific applications. At the applied level, we find operations research practitioners assisting operating managers to make better decisions in a variety of problems. In

[11] Fairfield E. Raymond, *Quantity and Economy in Manufacture.* New York: McGraw-Hill Book Co., 1931.

[12] T. C. Fry, *Probability and Its Engineering Uses.* Princeton, N.J.: D. Van Nostrand Co., 1928.

[13] Walter A. Shewhart, *Economic Control of Quality of Manufactured Product.* Princeton, N.J.: D. Van Nostrand Co., 1931.

[14] L. H. C. Tippett, "Statistical Methods in Textile Research, Use of the Binomial and Poisson Distributions" (a snap-reading method of making time studies of machines and operations in factory surveys), *Shirley Inst. Memoirs*, vol. 13, November 1934.

[15] J. J. von Neumann and O. Morgenstern, *The Theory of Games and Economic Behavior.* Princeton, N.J.: Princeton Univ. Press, 1955.

doing this, they also expose areas where further research of both an applied and a theoretical nature is necessary. Thus, the last two decades have witnessed the beginnings of a true professionalism in the management of operations and businesses.

Automation

The automation of physical production systems is but the culmination of the gradual replacement of human effort and skill by mechanical and electrical devices. Although this kind of automation will continue at an increasing rate, the more pertinent and historically recent development is the automation of some of the aspects of managing production systems. In this area, the computer is now becoming more than just a data processor and computational device: it is providing a cerebral component to the automation of production systems. The computerized and automatic control of certain processes employed in petroleum refining, soap manufacture, bakeries, steel rolling mills, etc., is not uncommon. But beyond that is the use of an "on-line" computer to continuously manage certain aspects of production, such as scheduling jobs, dispatching work through a shop, issuing orders for inventory replenishment, planning future work force levels, and even lending some automation to the design of products and the choice of methods for processing parts. We are in the midst of new developments in this area, and we may expect this use of the computer to be one of the most significant developments in the next decade.

BASIC CONCEPTS

In the remainder of this chapter, we will consider some descriptive concepts, which will provide a framework for the rest of the text.

The Production System

The notion of a *system* is intuitively easy to understand and useful to consider. A system is a *purposeful* collection of elements or objects that, in the *aggregate*, perform some specific and meaningful function. A production system is a complex collection of physical elements (materials, equipment, labor, structures) operated in some manner to provide a product or service. The objects thus collected are characterized by a meaningful wholeness, which is more than the simple addition of the elements.

The system is more than a static arrangement, in the sense that there is *motion* and *dynamic change*. Many of the elements move in a highly predictable and stable pattern. Elements of machines move in fixed paths; materials flow from one point to another along fixed and known paths. With time, changes take place in these motion patterns or in the dimensions of the system, thus giving it a dynamic character.

Both the motion and dynamic characteristics can be described as quantified relationships between the system variables. The variables may be distance, time, weights, costs, or a multitude of others that provide the dimensions of the system. The abstraction of these relationships by quantitative models is an important part of managing such systems.

Besides relating to complex structure, motion, and dynamic change, the notion of a system has other useful meanings. In managing a production system, managers are typically faced with "problems" that are solved by making decisions among alternative courses of action. The *relevant physical production system* contains all the elements or variables the decision maker can change, or over which he has control in making his decision. In contrast, the *environment* of the relevant system contains all the variables over which the decision maker has no control but which nonetheless are affected by and/or do affect his decision. Problems in production are often solved within organizational boundaries of authority and responsibility. Problems, however, do not recognize organizational constraints. They contain relevant variables that cut across organizational lines without regard for who has the authority to alter these variables. Therefore, when we talk about a production or operational system, we refer specifically to the set of elements or variables that constitute the decision maker's domain of interest.

The idea of domain of control works in both a vertical and a horizontal manner. A factory is a hierarchy of systems, subsystems, etc., both in physical structure and in organization of its management. Some of our most pressing problems of physical living are systems problems in that their solution lies in breaking down traditional boundaries of authority and responsibility and providing the decision maker(s) with the relevant set of variables. Eliminating water and air pollution, disposing of refuse, relieving traffic congestion, and removing slums are all systems problems not only because they involve large, complex aggregates of interrelated variables, but because their efficient solutions depend on establishing new domains of decision-making authority for the control of these variables. These are the kinds of operational problems that will, in the future, constitute a major area of production and operations management.

There is an infinite variety of physical production systems that are based on the technology of their processes and outputs. We might compare them in terms of the physical content of their output, such as metal, chemical, food, etc. Or we may classify them in terms of processes, such as extractive, conditioning, analytical, or synthetic operations on materials.

The exact description and knowledge of the technological content of a production system are, of course, important in a specific management problem. However, we want to know those things that are common to the problems of managing a wide variety of technologically different systems. For example, the methods of describing them are common to all systems, and much of this book is therefore directed toward the development of models that describe systems and their behavior. The first section is devoted to more general methods of describing and modeling production systems and decision problems.

Production must be managed in terms of value systems that are independent of the technical character of the product or service. Although the engineer is commissioned to make technical decisions, the ultimate choice of accepting, rejecting, or altering the results of technical innovation and specification must be left to the operating manager. The criteria he uses may be economic, social, political, or other. Finally, we should point out that there is a technical (not technological) content to the production manager's decision making. The essence of this book is to display the technical character of making decisions about production matters.

A MATERIAL TRANSFORMATION PROCESS: The production system usually involves the transformation of physical materials or objects from one state into one or more others. This includes altering shapes, chemical composition, hardness, component composition, and surface finish.

The material transformation process provides the technological basis of production. The point at which resources are collected and employed to generate a specific transformation of material is called an *operation*. This is in contrast to the use of the term to imply a broader scale of activity. Thus, the hammering of a part at a drop forge, the punching of a set of computer cards, the assembly of four wheels to a car, and the packaging of a TV set are specific operations.

To complete a *job*, a sequence of operations is usually necessary. A job is a logical unit of work represented by a completed product or service, the thing that has economic value. The sequence of operations required to complete the job is referred to as a *process*. A simple diagram of a material transformation process is shown in Figure 1.1.

A DEGREE OF REPETITIVENESS: Generally, there is some underlying repetitive pattern to production operations, although the pattern may not be consistent over time. A product is produced in a series of "identical" units, or the service is rendered in successively similar forms. Or, even if successive units of output are not identical, as in structural objects, there is some repetition in the inputs or in the nature of the production activity. In any event, we must consider all sorts of repetitive processes or operations in which the purpose of the operations is to change the properties of physical objects or materials. Our area of interest naturally includes factories for producing consumer goods, such as automobiles, pots, and pans, as well as thousands of other articles that are a normal part of our daily existence. But we should also consider things such as removal of snow from city streets,

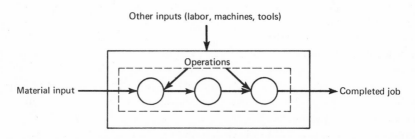

FIGURE **1.1** Material transformation process.

processing of patients in the receiving system of a hospital, replacement of utility poles, disposal of refuse, or handling of books in a library. In each of these, there is a manipulation of materials or objects with some degree of repetition in the output of the operations. Further, we should include the building of structures, the assembly of space vehicles, the repair of a street section, and other "project" types of operations. Here there is repetition in the operations themselves while not necessarily in the output.

INFORMATION PROCESS: Superimposed on the physical system is an information system. This system extracts from and feeds to the physical process both information and data. A production process can be referred to as an increasing information system. The longer the system is permitted to operate before decisions are made relative to the system, the more information is available to the decision maker.

Quantitative information may be collected over an extended time period, processed, and inventoried as a "data base." Such a data base is used for design, planning, and control purposes. Not only are information processes representative of physical production processes in themselves, but the kind of data collected, methods of collection, data-processing techniques and storage, and ultimate use of the data are major factors in designing management control systems.

A MATERIAL FLOW PROCESS: Another characteristic of production systems is the flow of materials or objects. This is another kind of material transformation— the change in spatial relationships between objects in the system. Such a flow of materials is obvious in traffic and transportation service systems, but it also occurs between the machines in a fabrication shop, between the floors of a building, in the harvesting of crops, in the routing of a utility truck and crew, and in the service systems of which we are the customers. The focal point of the flow may be a raw material, some piece of equipment, a person, a paper form, or a product.

The flow of materials is both continuous and intermittent and occurs through a network of machines and equipment. A basic description of production systems is provided by the flow and network characteristics as the flow shop, job shop, and project. (See Figure 1.2.)

Flow shop   In the flow shop type of system configuration, there is a more or less continuous and uninterrupted flow to the object or material that is being processed. Or, conversely, there may be a continuous flow to the process, while the material is geographically stationary. The variety of output of the system is limited, and each kind of output follows roughly the same flow path and sequence of processing steps.

The epitome of the flow shop is the typical "mass production" plant found in the manufacture of consumer goods, such as automobiles and refrigerators. A given unit of output is usually not identified with a particular customer. The facilities or machines are often "special purpose"; that is, they are designed for the exclusive production of one product or a limited number of products.

Besides the obvious mass-production systems, the flow shop is exemplified by the following cases:

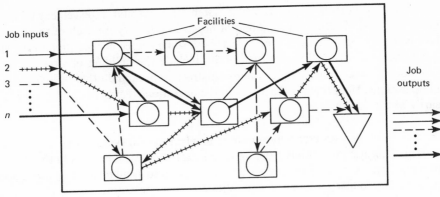

Job shop format

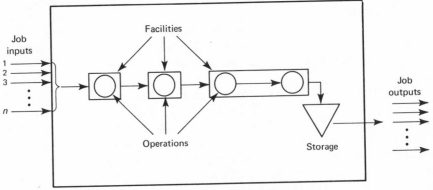

Flow shop format

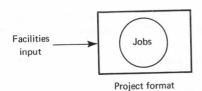

Project format

FIGURE **1.2** Basic flow formats.

1. The processing of customer photographic film. Here the output is identified by customer, but each order follows a common path through a sequence of processing operations.
2. The collection of refuse using a specially designed truck. In this case, the process is mobile; but each "customer's job" is processed by the same facility in a flow sequence.
3. A system for the mass feeding of 5,000 people at a convention. The system is

specially designed to handle a large volume, with a standard menu and possibly a buffet style of serving.
4. A mobile x-ray unit. In this case, the unit is specially designed to take chest x rays and processes the customers in a standard manner.

The job shop   This is the antithesis of the flow shop. The mix of product is high, and production is in terms of batches representing individual jobs produced either to fill customer orders or for inventory replenishment. The flow of a job is intermittent in time, and jobs may follow different paths through the network, or the machines may have to be altered between jobs.

The facilities or machines are jointly shared by many different types of products or jobs. Therefore, the facilities are usually "general purpose" and can be adjusted rather easily to accommodate a variety of output. In the "pure" job shop, no two jobs are exactly alike, and each job requires a unique setup of the facilities for its production. Examples are:

1. A shop for the production of heavy boring mills containing a wide variety of machine tools and facilities and processing several thousand different components.
2. A department of public works truck, which can be adapted for different kinds of jobs, such as hauling dirt, snow plowing, street salting, brush removal, or tree spraying.
3. A general-purpose x-ray clinic having more than one kind of x-ray machine, which can be adjusted for different purposes.

The project   This type of production system is designed to produce only one product or only a limited number of large jobs. It differs from the job shop essentially in the size and scope of the job it can handle. The production resources are brought to the job, which is usually stationary. Examples are the construction or assembly of a space ship, the building of a bridge, the overhauling of large machinery, or the moving of a house from one location to another.

In each of these production systems, the methods and techniques of design, planning, and control are often different. However, there are general concepts that apply equally to all three systems. Most production systems are hybrids consisting of some mixture of two or more of the pure types. With time, a system may be transformed into another type, as, for example, in the case of building construction when prefabricated houses are introduced. We will refer to this classification system when we discuss the various aspects of production management.

Objectives of Production and Production Management

The objectives of production are related both to the production system and to the management function.

FUNCTIONAL OBJECTIVES: Each transformation process has a set of functional objectives, which state the desired qualitative and quantitative characteristics of the output. If the output is a product, then these characteristics are physical properties (weight, color, size, chemical composition) and performance measures (reliability, maintainability, operating effectiveness). The rate, location, timing, and volume of the output are functional specifications. Functional objectives are important in service systems, but sometimes they are more difficult to formulate. For example, a public works supervisor must design and plan a system for removing snow from city streets. The functional specifications include not only the condition of the roads before and after snow removal (by plow, salting, snow throwers), but also the rate at which streets are to be processed for various degrees of snow intensity.

Many of the formal information procedures in a production organization are concerned with transmitting information about functional requirements of production (blueprints, work orders, schedules, etc.).

VALUE OBJECTIVES: The production activity must be designed, planned, and controlled under a constraining system of values set forth by the managers of the organization. These are called the value objectives of the organization in general or, more specifically, the value objectives of a problem. The value objectives are constraining in the sense that they dictate the criteria used in choosing between alternative courses of action.

While the functional objectives of a production system depend on the given process, the value objectives are more or less common to a wide variety of operations. It is possible, therefore, to generalize a set of value objectives for the organization as a whole, as, for example, the general objectives of maximizing profit or minimizing costs. The functional objectives are technically based, whereas the value objectives are related to things economic, social, and political, and, in the final analysis, to the aspirations of the decision makers.

Value objectives are related to specific production problems in *varying degrees*. The problem in setting value objectives for a specific production activity (in design, planning, or control) is the determination of the degree to which these objectives should be realized in carrying out the ensuing activity, because many value objectives are conflicting. Thus, maximizing customer service in street snow removal is conflicting with minimizing the costs of the operations.

Basic Management Functions in Production

The notion of a system has given us one way of looking at the physical structure of production. We now need a simple framework within which to discuss the activities of managers in managing production systems. The following list of basic functions may appear far too scant. Nevertheless, it will form the basis for the organization of this book.

THE ORGANIZATIONAL FUNCTION: First, managers organize themselves into collective bodies in order to carry out their individual jobs and tasks. This involves the delegation of responsibilities and authority for decision making to the members of the organization. In general, we will not concern ourselves with formal organization structures, except to describe later the typical organization of management tasks in a manufacturing situation.

Although we shall not discuss the subject of organization theory, we should point out that organization is here important to the extent that it affects the way managers solve problems and make decisions. Looking at problems from a systems point of view requires consideration of organizational constraints. This we have noted earlier. In discussing problems of management, however, we will implicitly assume that organization is not a constraint in making the kinds of decisions involved.

Finally, organization refers to people and not to the arranging of the physical components of a production system. The latter is the function of design and planning.

THE VALUE SYSTEM: Another thing managers do is set a system of organization values.

Value objectives can be stated in very general terms for the organization as a whole or quite specifically with respect to given problems. For example, the maximization of profit, the maximization of service to the customer, or the perpetuation of the organization are general value objectives set forth by the people in the organization. But in making decisions about specific aspects of production, the manager needs to know the relative importance of different and often conflicting objectives.

Goals are statements about the extent to which an objective is to be satisfied. Examples are a maximum limit placed on scrap or spoilage, a profit target, a cost limit, or a tolerable limit of customer complaints. As we shall see, part of the difficulty in making decisions is that of trying to quantify a system of human values. In the final analysis, it sometimes boils down to the way people feel about what is important in their own lives, as well as the corporate life.

THE DESIGN FUNCTION: Managers are responsible for creating the physical production system. This includes machines, equipment, materials, information devices, buildings, etc.

One may argue that this is technology and, therefore, an engineering function. But the point is that decisions about physical structure go well beyond merely technological considerations. Whether or not a man is an engineer, physicist, purchasing agent, plant engineer, or foreman is not the issue. The question is, what do people do to create something as complex as a modern factory?

Design is a management concept and not a function carried out on a drafting board. For example, the choice of a new machine and its purchase from an outside vendor is part of the process of creating the physical structure of production.

THE PLANNING FUNCTION: Planning is the function of specifying how the physical structure and systems will be utilized over time. That is, planning specifies how the physical resources are to be *allocated* to various outputs in some given time span. The physical nature of the resources, their operational characteristics, and the physical attributes of their output are matters of design.

The distinction between planning and design becomes admittedly vague when we extend the time scale or the planning horizon. The choice of a new plant site is really a design problem, even though one might easily say that it is part of the long-range planning in the company. However, this is an unimportant distinction and is really a semantic argument. All we want to accomplish here is to decide on a rational way to divide the content of our subject.

Obviously, we cannot simply divorce design from planning. A system cannot be designed unless something is known about the way it will be utilized in time. For example, there is no use trying to decide on the kind of street cleaning machine to buy unless we know how many streets there are and how often they are to be cleaned. Both plans and designs are mutually constraining, and interrelating the two at any one time is not a particularly easy thing to do. Often they are carried out sequentially so that a system is designed to meet a set of plans and plans are made to utilize a set of physical resources.

THE CONTROL FUNCTION: Once designs and plans have been specified, the purpose of control is to operate the system accordingly. Part of control is to detect deviations from standard performance or to notice when the functional specifications are not being satisfied. Furthermore, control involves the remedial adjustments of the system to correct the deviations. Besides making adjustments, remedial action can include changes in the designs and plans.

Control is also concerned with the way value objectives are being satisfied. A dynamic control system detects not only how well goals are being met, but also when the weights assigned to values should be changed and what kind of remedial action should be taken. For example, the manager of an automobile repair shop wishes to control the flow of jobs through the shop. A good control system should help him predict the loads on the shop, what weights should be assigned to measures of effectiveness (such as work in process, job completion times, and facility utilization), and what rules he should use to dispatch the jobs in the shop, as well as to control the quality of work done.

The Human Factor

We would be remiss if we did not include human relations in the domain of management interests. Indeed, the issue of managing people as individuals and as groups permeates the decision-making environment in most production problems. The history of production management is fraught with examples of failures in the implementation of designs and plans due to the mismanagement of the human variable.

The subject has both its technical and its humanistic elements. Employee selection, placement, training, motivation, remuneration, etc., are technical subjects aptly dealt with by behavioral scientists and to which the student is hopefully exposed in related courses. The subject is much too broad and of such substantive material that a casual rendering in this book seems quite out of place. In our models of production management, we consider, perhaps too casually, employee performance to be a predictable system parameter.

The humanistic element and the ethical and philosophical issues we leave to the reader to pursue elsewhere. This writer has no suggestions concerning where the matter might start or leave off.

The Decision-Making Process

In the literature of modern management science, more has been written about decision making than any other phase of management. What is common to the basic management functions is the process of making a decision. Each of the previous basic functions can be partially described in terms of what managers do in the process that leads to a decision among alternative courses of action.

In this book, we want to focus on the kinds of decisions that managers make in designing, planning, and controlling production operations. But we also want to discuss various aspects of decision making independently of the specific problem with which the decision maker deals.

Decision making is a problem-solving process. In the past decade, there has been considerable interest in the thinking processes of decision makers as problem solvers. There is no clear-cut sequence of mental activities that takes place in some uninterrupted order that culminates in a decision. However, in concept, we will structure the decision-making process in terms of the following phases, even though they are not necessarily recognizable in an operating situation.

1. The recognition of an *economic need* for some future course of action. This economic need might be a new product or service, the improvement of an existing operation, the need to maximize some value objective, or, more simply, the recognition of a *symptom* of inadequate performance or satisfaction of objectives.
2. The statement and definition of a specific *problem.*
3. The *analysis* of the problem or the accumulation of knowledge about the problem.
4. The *synthesis* of alternative courses of action.
5. The *evaluation* of alternatives leading to the choice among alternatives.
6. The *implementation* of the chosen course of action.

Each of these phases is present to a greater or lesser extent in all the types of production problems that we will discuss and where decisions must be made. We will dwell on some of these phases in greater detail in later sections. At this point, we will only examine their general meaning and relate them to the efficiency of production decisions.

SYMPTOMS OF PROBLEMS: Most production problems arise out of an existing system of operations. A production system is usually the result of a process of evolutionary changes that have taken place over a period of time. Therefore, problems arise out of existing *situations*. More specifically, initially there are symptoms of difficulty, rather than problems. Symptoms include such things as low worker morale, high levels of scrap or spoilage, and under-utilization of resources, or more general things, such as low profits and high costs. Symptoms are *not* problems. Symptoms must be translated into problem statements, which direct management in an efficient way toward making decisions that relieve the symptoms.

For example, the statement that machines are not being fully utilized merely says that a value objective (maximizing machine utilization) is not being adequately met. The problem statement defines the scope of things the manager will have to consider in making a decision about design, plans, or controls, which *may* result in better utilization of machines.

In certain cases, problems may be generated by the formal investigation of the way economic needs are being met, without waiting for some symptom to trigger decision-making action. A formal program of cost reduction in a plant may lead to decisions to improve a process, even though the present methods appear to be adequate. The kinds of alternatives considered in such cases may be better than those considered under the duress of remedying acute symptoms of difficulty.

THE STATEMENT OF THE PROBLEM: The proper statement of the problem sets the stage for the analysis, synthesis, and evaluation of alternatives. The statement of a problem leading to a decision about production systems asks the following questions:

1. What course of action must be taken such that the following set of functional objectives are satisfied subject to maximizing the following set of value objectives or goals?
2. What should the value of a decision variable X be subject to the following set of restrictions on its value and subject to maximizing the following set of value objectives?

The statement of the problem recognizes the need to choose between alternative courses of action or to decide what the quantitative value of a certain decision variable should be. It also includes a statement about both functional and value objectives.

The decision is a solution to the problem. If the problem is stated incorrectly, then the value of the solution is measured with respect not only to the incorrectly stated problem, but also to the problem as it should have been stated. In other words, a poor solution to the correct problem may be better than a good solution to the wrong problem.

The statement of a problem is related to the concept of systems. The problem defines the domain of variables the decision maker wishes to consider. We therefore make the following general rule: In stating a problem, it is desirable to make the *scope of the problem as large as possible* and, therefore, *initially* admit as many decision variables as possible. This permits the decision maker to consider a wider variety of first-order alternative courses of action than if the problem is constrained. Eventually, problems must be constrained into a hierarchy of sub- and sub-subproblems, each containing a progressively restricted domain of variables. But the local, tactical, or sub-problems are relevant if they are fractionated from a good first-order alternative.

THE ANALYSIS OF THE PROBLEM: Analysis is the phase of breaking down the problem to determine the relevant variables and their qualitative or quantitative relationships. The cliché is "getting the facts" or "studying the situation."

In this sense, analysis is a destructive process. The most difficult part of analysis is that of determining which variables are relevant and critical, and how they interact to explain the dynamic "behavior" of the system under study. This often involves the construction of a "model" that the decision maker can use to find out which variables are critical and how they will be affected by the decision.

Included in analysis is the determination of the *criteria* that will be used to evaluate alternative courses of action. The criteria are the concomitants of the functional and value objectives of the problem.

SYNTHESIS OF ALTERNATIVE SOLUTIONS: This phase of decision making is the opposite of analysis. Here, the purpose is to derive a set of alternative courses of action, as well as to set forth the range of values that some dimension of the system can assume. Much of the synthesis phase is a creative act and, therefore, part of the decision-making function to consider ways of efficiently generating a set of uniquely different alternatives.

As we have suggested earlier, the matter of creating alternatives is related to how problems are stated. An unconstrained problem statement permits the decision maker to consider a wide range of alternatives. The value of an alternative is *relative* to other alternatives and is, therefore, a function of the number of alternatives and the degree of their differences.

EVALUATION OF ALTERNATIVES: The choice among a set of alternatives is based on the degree to which they satisfy the criteria. Evaluation is partially a matter of analysis, as well as of judgment. Evaluation consists of predicting what will happen to the objectives, or measures of effectiveness, if a given alternative is chosen. Again, models are useful and necessary for this purpose.

In cases where the decision is to determine an optimal value for some variable (size of inventory, number of machines to purchase, floor space, when to schedule a job), analysis and evaluation proceed jointly, and the synthesis or creative phase is absent. That is, determining the optimal size of an inventory problem is not a creative act, except perhaps in designing a model to find the optimum.

IMPLEMENTATION: Implementation is the phase of installing or making operational the results of the decision. In a sense, it is not part of making the decision but is nevertheless a critical segment of problem solving. Many well-conceived plans and designs fail when an attempt is made to implement them in a going organization and to relate them to an existing system.

When a decision results in changes to a physical system, a good deal of time must be spent in "debugging" the new installation. But more important sometimes is the matter of getting persons in the organization to accept the changes. This often requires a review of the system of rewards in order to encourage the kind of behavior that is compatible with the expected performance. The solution of many production problems, particularly in the area of tactical controls, involves determining "decision rules" that are to be used by people in the organization who make recurring or repetitive decisions about some aspect of production (such as deciding on inventory levels or scheduling jobs through a shop). The implementation of these rules requires an assessment of the way the decisions are currently being made by the individuals for whom the rules are designed. Not only does this clarify where the decision rules are different from current performance, but it also exposes the points where the individual concerned must be trained to alter his attitudes and habituated responses.

These various phases of decision making give us another framework in which to discuss production management functions. They certainly are not explicitly carried out in the sequence suggested. The way in which managers make decisions is highly complex and certainly a function of the individual. In general, managers are usually sensitive to the variables that interact with their decision. Furthermore, they are usually cognizant of the important criteria used in making their choices. Experience, judgment, and intuition are extremely important ingredients of decision making; and it would be highly fallacious to suggest that good decisions are made only when the decision-making process is made highly formal and objective in terms of structure and techniques.

CASE PROBLEM 1.1 A farmers' and ranchers' cooperative operates a feed pellet mill in a distribution center serving a large rural area. The mill grinds various mixtures of hay, feed, and grains, supplements them with various diet additives, and then converts the mixture to pellets of varying size. The raw materials are trucked to the distribution center by the farmer or rancher in loose or baled form. The individual farmer's lot is then processed into pellets, bagged, and loaded directly back on the farmer's truck or held in temporary storage for later delivery.

Figure 1.3 is a schematic diagram showing the individual steps in the process. Each step is described in the flow-process chart shown in Figure 1.4 in the sequence of steps performed.

The use of pellet feeds has proved to be profitable for the farmer due to the reduced requirements for space, the ease of handling materials, the flexibility in choosing feed mixes, and the opportunity to use his own raw materials.

The manager of the cooperative has been concerned about the service for several reasons. The volume of business has increased to a point where additional capacity is warranted. An additional mill would require an investment of at least $35,000, including power-generating equipment (150 hp). In addition, extra space would be required in the plant. Furthermore, the company's insurance carrier has strongly recommended the installation of a dust control system to reduce the fire hazard.

Also, the efficiency of the actual service needs improvement. Often a farmer is held up while he has to wait for his order to be accepted. Then he may not wish to wait until the order is processed, thus requiring the storage of his order until he can pick it up or until it can be delivered by the cooperative.

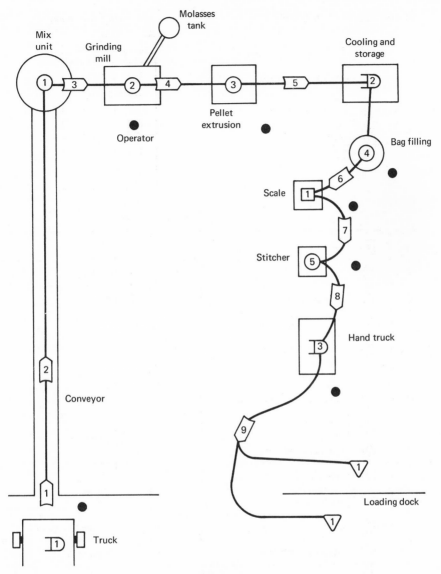

FIGURE **1.3**   Flow diagram for feed pellet mill.

Each individual farmer's order usually must be run independently through the mill, since each order differs in composition. The system is adaptable to a wide variety of ingredients. In order to encourage the farmer to use the variety of his own raw materials, the manager thinks that additional storage and premixing facilities should be installed near the unloading dock. This would permit the farmer to make several truck runs of different grains or feeds and to temporarily store his "mix" until his order could be processed.

FLOW PROCESS CHART

Process ___Feed and Hay Pellet Process___   Dept ___Retail warehouses___

Part ___Feed & Hay___

Process Begins At ___Unloading Dock___

Process Ends At ___Loading Dock___

Details of (proposed / present) method

Number of Symbols	
◯	5
⇨	9
▢	1
D	3
▽	1

Step	Symbol	Description	Pick up lay down	Feet moved	Notes
1	▢1	on truck			
2	⇨	loaded on conveyor	1	3	by hand
3	⇨2	conveyor belt to storage		30	
4	◯1	mix additives			
5	⇨3	conveyor belt to grinding mill		4	
6	◯2	grind feed			
7	⇨4	conveyor to extrusion mill		6	
8	◯3	pellet extrusion			
9	⇨5	to cooling and storage		6	
10	▢2	cool and store			
11	◯4	bag filling			
12	⇨6	transfer bag to weighing scale	1	6	by hand, operator b
13	▢1	weigh bag for billing			operator b
14	⇨7	transfer bag to stitcher	1	6	by hand, operator b
15	◯5	bag stitching			operator c
16	⇨8	transfer bag to hand truck	1	6	operator c by hand
17	▢3	temporary storage on hand truck			
18	⇨9	to truck—loading dock		25	operator d
19	▽	inventory			

Total   92

FIGURE **1.4**   Flow-process chart for pelletizing process.

Suppose you are the manager's assistant, and he asks you to "consider" what might be done to the pelletizing operation. Assume that he gives you a day or so to outline what you are going to do. That is, submit a *preliminary report* outlining what general or specific things you are going to investigate. Indicate, for example, any "first-order" solutions to the problem and why they might appear to be worthwhile investigating in detail. Keep in mind that the purpose of the preliminary report is to tell the manager what you intend to do with your time over the next several weeks in which you will be working on the problem, rather than to submit the details of a final solution.

ORGANIZATION FOR MANUFACTURING

Because manufacturing is a highly structured organization for production, we present a brief description of typical functions in a manufacturing organization. This is done in Figure 1.5, which depicts standard functions found in most firms producing a large product mix in the job shop format. This type of organization has partially determined the framework of material presented in this book.

This organization is structured around the tasks that must be carried out to develop and design a product and then design and control the processes for its production. Each of the areas shown in Figure 1.5 is a vital component of a manufacturing organization and is more than simply a staff or advisory function. Most of the areas constitute sequential stages in a process concerned with the economical development of a product from its inception as an idea to the issuance of the work or shop order to produce one or more of its parts. Besides guiding the development of new products or processes, these functions are continually involved in improving the design of existing parts, operations, or processes.

In each of these functions, both technical and economic decisions are made recurrently. We are then interested in these decisions, how they are traditionally made, what kind of information is needed to make them, and what kinds of quantitative approaches may be taken, especially with reference to the economic decisions. We will not elaborate on the details of these functions here but defer them for the appropriate chapters. We should, however, note the following things.

The organization for bringing a new product into production, as well as sustaining the production of literally thousands of parts, is indeed complex. The fact that such organizations and production systems work can be partially attributed to the skills of systematic and organized management, which was instituted some 60 years ago in response to the complexities exemplified by the Franklin plant (page 4). But the complexities of today's manufacturing plants are of another order of magnitude. The current advancements in production organization design seem to derive from integrated information systems centering on the use of the electronic computer. This is more than data processing. The traditional organization functions are being scrutinized to determine where recurring design, planning, and control decision making can be incorporated into automated and integrated information systems.

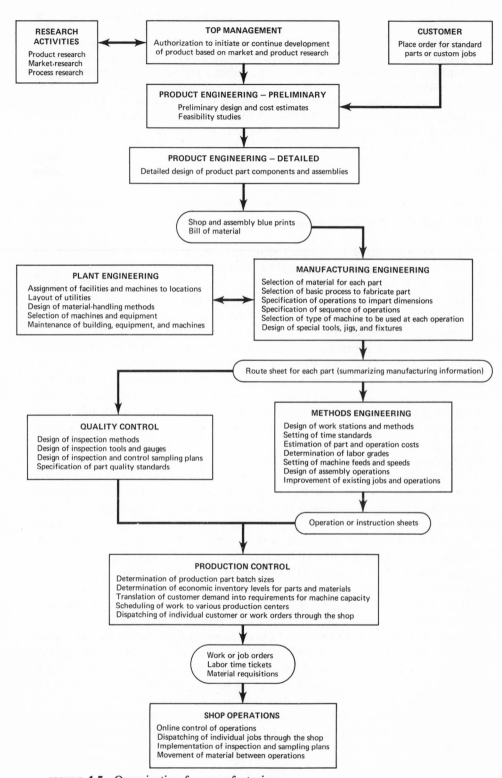

FIGURE **1.5** Organization for manufacturing.

Behind the successful automation of some of the managerial functions in manufacturing or production lies the necessity of conducting research into operations. We wish to conclude this chapter with a brief discussion of this important topic.

RESEARCH INTO OPERATIONS

Most of the production functions we have described are the outgrowth of the tenets of scientific management. The generic term *industrial engineering* historically connotes those activities related to the conversion of a product design into manufacturing specifications, methods and plant engineering, and manufacturing control. Individual firms may attach a more specific meaning to the term, but that is irrelevant here.

Historically, the industrial engineer conducted research into operations. Much of this research, however, was of an empirical nature and was related to the technical design of man-machine systems. Furthermore, it did not draw upon a specific body of theoretical knowledge to any large extent.

In contrast, modern operations research includes the development of a special theory, a science of operations. This body of knowledge consists mainly of a structure of mathematical and analytical models to explain the behavior of man-machine, operational, and business systems. Another difference is in the kinds of persons involved in the activity. Operations research typically attracts those trained in mathematics or basic sciences who have the ability to conduct scientific research in the classical sense. Also, operations research now focuses on areas where managers must make decisions involving complex operating systems, whether they be in production, marketing, finance, or any other part of the business. Finally, research involves risk in achieving a payoff. It is inherently a wasteful process. Since he is conducting research in the literal sense of the word, the operations researcher must to some degree be immune to operating pressures and to the requirement of immediately producing profitable results, even though his efforts are long term and are directed to an ultimate payoff to the firm.

In many firms today, industrial engineering consists in applying the methods of management science to a wide variety of operating problems. In some firms, these operations research activities are labeled departments of operations research, operations analysis, or systems and procedures. The backgrounds of the persons employed in these organizations, the kinds of problems they work on, and the level of sophistication of their techniques may vary. The unifying concept is the spirit of research, even if it is directed toward the practical goal of helping managers make better decisions.

The Manager and Operations Research

Certainly, management is more than a science of operations research. The production manager who has the responsibility and authority to make decisions about production matters is not a management scientist. For one thing, the demands placed upon him by his job do not allow him to approach every problem by utilizing a formal scientific procedure. He must often rely on his experience, intuition, and judgment, supported by limited information or data. It is probably also fairly safe to say that he does not have the training and scientific skills required to behave "scientifically." Such skill includes both familiarity with the existing body of theory and the techniques related to a given problem, as well as the methodology or approach to be taken.

Regardless of who performs the functions that may be classified as operations research or management science and in what degree they exert their efforts, the line manager is faced with a particular problem. He must make the ultimate decision of whether or not to accept the advice and institute the changes suggested by the researcher. Furthermore, the staff function may be a part of his administrative domain. This is true both in product and process research. But in the case of operations research, recommendations often have a direct bearing on how the manager is going to make a decision about some aspect of the company operations. Operations research therefore impinges directly on the management function itself, although it can never replace the human judgment, which must ultimately be a part of every decision. For example, the manager must set the value system used to guide his decision, although even in this case the scientist may be helpful.

The gap that can exist between the existence and development of a body of theory on the one hand and the practical application of the theory on the other hand may be a very formidable one. There is the problem not only of implementation, but also that of communication among the researcher, the manager, and the persons in the organization who are affected by the changes, which contribute to widening the gap.

The person who conducts research in operations (at the applied level) has the task of communicating his suggestions and results in a manner the manager can understand. But the solution of management problems by the methods of science often involve complicated and complex methods, which are not easy to convey to those who lack the requisite training. The manager, therefore, must assimilate enough knowledge so that he can comprehend the objectives and general methods of the researcher, as well as make an intelligent appraisal of the proposals offered.

CASE PROBLEM 1.2   The Theta Printing Company produces printed business forms in very large volumes. The company operates five plants throughout the country. Each plant has a battery (from 10 to 20) of large rotary presses that turn out a great variety of jobs.

A *job* consists in printing a specific paper form for some customer. Each job printed by the company is made to customer specifications but within a range of standard sizes, grades of paper, print type, etc. The operation of a press system is essentially as follows:

1. Every two days a press is assigned a "batch" of jobs, each job, as noted, being for a specific customer.
2. The press is loaded at the rear with a large roll of a given type of paper. The paper is webbed through the press rolls. When the press is started, the paper moves continuously through the rolls, which print duplicates of the paper form

on the web. At the front end of the press, each individual form is cut from the web, resulting in a stack of individual sheets of the form. Sometimes several jobs are "ganged" on one printing plate so that an individual sheet may contain several orders. A *job* is then represented by one order or a gang of orders.

3. When one job is completed, the press is shut down and set up or "made ready" for the next job. The make-ready task includes changing the roll of paper if necessary, changing the plates, rewebbing the paper through the press, changing ink, and making press adjustments.

4. The press is operated by a highly skilled pressman who is paid by the hour and who belongs to a craft union. He may or may not have an apprentice helping him.

At a general meeting of plant managers at the corporate home office in New York City, it was decided to investigate the problem of press downtime. It was agreed that all the plants experienced a significant amount of idle press time. Upon the advice of the director of the newly formed Operations Analysis Department in the corporate office, the Vice President of Manufacturing urged that a study be made of the problem.

Shortly later, Mr. White, manager of the Syracuse plant, scheduled a meeting to discuss the problem of press downtime. This meeting included himself; Mr. Preston, the Printing Department superintendent; Mr. Spencer, the general press foreman; Mr. Lewis, the plant industrial engineer; and Mr. Boyd, from the corporate Operations Analysis Department. It was agreed that the causes of press idleness were varied and that several approaches could be taken. By the conclusion of the meeting, Mr. White authorized the following steps to be taken:

1. Mr. Boyd was to make a preliminary study of the actual operation of changing over the press between jobs with a view to improving the methods of doing the task. He also agreed to make a "work sampling" study to determine the actual proportion of time the presses were idle for various reasons.

2. Mr. Preston agreed to make a study of the way jobs were assigned to the presses and the way jobs were sequenced.

3. Mr. Spencer was to work with Mr. Boyd in determining the extent of maintenance downtime and how this might be reduced through preventive maintenance and scheduling.

Mr. Boyd thought he could bring some "theory" to bear on the job changeover problem, but he wished to spend some time in the plant observing the press operations.

Several months later, the same group met to discuss their progress. The work sampling study revealed that a major proportion of downtime was due to job changeovers, the amount being higher than expected by Preston and Spencer. It was felt that some progress could be made in the scheduling function by paying closer attention to batching like jobs for a given press. Preston explained, however, that the scheduler was very experienced, and he felt he did a good job in this respect.

Boyd entered the picture by suggesting that the downtime due to job changeovers might be "significantly" reduced by better sequencing. Both Preston and Spencer pointed out that the pressmen probably did an adequate sequencing job and that this was a part of the craft of their job. Both men were hesitant to tamper with the pressmen's jobs, particularly if things were "working well." But neither Spencer nor Preston knew "exactly" how pressmen decided in what sequence the members of a job batch would be sequenced through the press. At the end of the meeting, Boyd requested that they meet again in two days and said he would pursue the sequencing issue.

Two days later, the group listened to Boyd's explanation of the theoretical content of the sequencing problem. The substance of Boyd's explanation is outlined below. While he did a good job in exposing the group to the theoretical problem, he also generated some misgivings among those present. As Preston noted, "All of that mathematical stuff is O.K., but who's going to try and explain this stuff to the pressmen? I'm not sure I understand it myself." Spencer was plainly worried about having Boyd probe around the place "with all his formulas." White was also concerned. He had to ultimately decide how far he should let Boyd pursue his "theories." Boyd had noted that he had a way of finding the "optimal" sequence for any batch of jobs. But the question was, how practical would his method really be? But White felt that Boyd had made a good point when he said that he could not see how a pressman could choose a good sequence from among n factorial ($n!$) possibilities. It was certainly possible to have as many as ten jobs scheduled for a press in one batch. White decided that he would mull the thing over and have another meeting with Boyd later on. In the meantime, he would ask Spencer to find out, if possible, how the pressmen were now making the sequencing decision.

In his discussion, Boyd structured the sequencing problem as a special case of the "traveling salesman" problem.[16] The structure was:

1. There is a batch of n jobs waiting to be processed by a press.
2. For each pair of jobs, there is a particular make-ready time, which is a function of the dissimilarity between the jobs. There are $n(n-1)$ such paired job times. These are conveniently displayed in the following matrix for an example involving six jobs, including Job A, which is already on the press. The X's in the first column of the matrix mean that no job can precede A. As an example, it takes 2.5 time units if Job 4 follows Job A, or 1.8 time units if Job 1 follows Job 3, etc.

Job i \ Job j	A	1	2	3	4	5
A	X	3.0	2.8	2.2	2.5	1.7
1	X	X	1.7	2.3	1.8	0.9
2	X	3.4	X	3.5	2.7	1.9
3	X	1.8	1.2	X	1.2	2.2
4	X	2.5	2.4	3.6	X	2.5
5	X	1.5	2.6	3.4	2.6	X

Setup time required if Job j follows Job i.

3. A complete sequence will result in a total press downtime. For example, the sequence A–4–2–1–3–5 requires a total of $2.5 + 2.4 + 3.4 + 2.3 + 2.2 = 12.8$ time units. Note that a sequence time involves selecting one and only one time from

---

[16] The problem is as follows. A salesman has a trip to make in which he must visit a number of cities, say, for example, five. He must arrange a tour that includes passing through the five cities and returning to his home town. A tour consists of a given sequence or order in which the cities will be visited. The problem is to determine a tour that will minimize the total distance traveled, given that there is a known distance between every pair of cities. If we let a job correspond to a city and let setup time correspond to distance, and if we do not require that the tour end at the starting point, then we have the job sequencing problem.

each row and column (except column 1) of the matrix and then adding them together.

4. There are $n!$ (n factorial) possible sequences to choose from. In this example, there are 5! or 120 possible ways of ordering the jobs through the press. If the batch size is 10, then there are 10! (or 3,628,800) possible sequences.

5. The problem is to find the sequence that results in the minimum total press down-time (sequence time).

Problems

1.1   The following is a list of institutions or entities with which most of us are familiar. One might expect to find operational or production systems associated with each entity. Cite some examples, including the aspects of material transformation, repetitiveness, and flow.

(a) department store
(b) hotel
(c) cemetery
(d) state tree nursery
(e) regional garage for state highway department
(f) emergency ward of a hospital

1.2   The township of Glen Oaks has a population of 30,000 people and is a rapidly expanding suburban area adjacent to a large city. The issue in question is the collection and disposal of home refuse and garbage in this township. Suppose you are involved in this question in either one of the following capacities:

1. If you have a liberal outlook on life, you can assume that you are a recently elected town supervisor. Your election platform included a pledge to ensure sound management of the taxpayer's dollar. One of your pet projects is to "examine" the whole matter of refuse disposal.

2. If you are conservative and feel that services of this kind should be performed by a private enterprise, you can assume that you want to set up a business and bid for this service. Your primary objective is to make an adequate return on your investment.

(a) In either case, explain in what ways your problem is a production systems problem. Give an example of a hierarchy of systems and subsystems problems in designing a system for refuse collection.

(b) Make a list of "first-order" ideas for solutions to the design of a refuse collection and disposal system.

(c) Suppose that one of your first-order solutions is to collect by truck and dispose at a sanitary land dump. Make a list of desirable truck design features that consider the truck collection problem from a systems point of view.

1.3   Make a list of possible functional and value objectives for the following operations:

(a) An electric utility company has to replace a utility pole next to a main highway.

(b) A foreman of an inspection department must design a method for manually inspecting two dimensions of a batch of 5,000 of a certain part.

(c) The assistant principal of a town high school must plan the routing and scheduling of the school's ten school buses.

(d) A plant engineer in a large machine shop must design a method for collecting scrap and cuttings at each machine in the shop and disposing of it in a large bin at one end of the shop.

1.4 The City of Maplewood has a hospital that serves a county wide area. Suppose you are on the Board of Governors of the Hospital and are the head of a special committee to study some of the hospital services. Your agenda includes possible investigations of 1) the processing of patients admitted to the emergency section of the hospital and 2) the custodian's (housekeeping) operation.
(a) In what way are these two operations production systems?
(b) For each one of these production processes, prepare a general outline of steps that you and your committee will take in your investigation. You should give some thought to the order in which these steps will be taken.

1.5 Southside hospital is located in a metropolitan area (750,000 population). It is the oldest of six hospitals serving the area. You have recently joined the administrative staff of the hospital. Your first assignment is to investigate ways of expanding and improving the hospital's laundry service. A preliminary study by the board of directors has led to the belief that the present facilities can be expanded to twice the size if necessary by adding space at one end. Outline the steps you might take in carrying out the preliminary phases of your investigation.

1.6 Do Case Problem 1.1 on page 20.

1.7 In Case Problem 1.2 on page 26, assume the position of Mr. White. What would you discuss in your meeting with Mr. Boyd? Consider particularly the practical issues in the problem.

Bibliography

BOWMAN, EDWARD H., and ROBERT B. FETTER, *Analysis for Production Management*, 3rd ed. Homewood, Ill.: Richard D. Irwin, Inc., 1967.

BUFFA, ELWOOD, *Modern Production Management*, 2nd ed. New York: John Wiley & Sons, 1965.

BUFFA, ELWOOD, Ed., *Readings in Production and Operations Management*. New York: John Wiley & Sons, 1966.

CHURCHMAN, C. W., R. ACKOFF, and E. L. ARNOFF, *Introduction to Operations Research*. New York: John Wiley & Sons, 1957.

COOKE, MORRIS L., "Academic and Industrial Efficiency," Carnegie Foundation Bull. No. 5, 1910.

DOOLEY, A. R., et al., *Casebooks in Production Management: Basic Problems, Concepts and Techniques*. New York: John Wiley & Sons, 1964.

EMERSON, HARRINGTON, *The Twelve Principles of Efficiency*. New York: Engineering Magazine Co., 1911.

GANTT, H. L., *Work, Wages and Profits*. New York: Engineering Magazine Co., 1910.

GILBRETH, FRANK B., *Bricklaying System*. Chicago, Ill.: Clark Publishing Co., 1909.

MC GARRAH, ROBERT E., *Production and Logistics Management*. New York: John Wiley & Sons, 1963.

MILLER, D. W., and M. K. STARR, *Executive Decisions and Operations Research*. Englewood Cliffs, N.J.: Prentice-Hall, Inc., 1960.

MORRIS, W. T., *The Analysis of Management Decisions*, rev. ed. Homewood, Ill.: Richard D. Irwin, Inc., 1964.

SASIENI, M., A. YASPAN, and L. FRIEDMAN, *Introduction to Operations Research*. New York: John Wiley & Sons, 1966.

2

Evaluation
of Alternatives

A GOOD DECISION

In Chapter 1, we examined some of the simple concepts involved in the decision-making process. We followed the individual steps in the process from the recognition and formulation of a problem through the creation or synthesis of alternatives, their evaluation, and finally the implementation of one of these alternatives. In this chapter, we will discuss in greater detail the phase of evaluating alternatives and making a choice between them. Although this is only one step in the decision-making process, it has been the object of much analytical and quantitative treatment during the past several decades.

Making good decisions involves more than just the efficiency or effectiveness of a choice between alternatives. In defining a "good" decision, we might consider the following points.

1. A good decision must provide a satisfactory solution to the *pertinent problem*. This stresses the need to define the problem correctly, since it is possible to find a good solution to the wrong problem.
2. A good decision results from a choice from a spectrum of possible alternatives. Efficiency, in this sense, depends on the ability of the decision maker to generate a variety of alternative solutions. That is, it is possible that the decision maker is inefficient in developing a set of uniquely different and original ideas but efficient in his choice from this limited set of alternatives. This is related to the issue of problem definition and the synthesis of ideas. For example, a company chooses to process a metal part on an automatic machine, this being the least-cost method among the alternatives considered. Subsequently, an engineer proposes a different material for the part, thus cutting the cost in half, even when requiring a different process.
3. A good decision considers the economics of the decision-making process itself. The expenditure of design and planning resources must be balanced with the incremental effects of applying these resources. The decision must be made at some cutoff point in time; the "optimal" cutoff point is reached

when the marginal costs of added design or planning time is equal to the marginal benefits in the improvements in alternatives.

4. If a problem is correctly stated and the list of alternatives is reasonably exhaustive, then a good decision results in satisfactory outcomes. That is, the actual results of the decision lead to at least some minimum satisfaction of the objectives. When the outcomes of a decision are a matter of risk and uncertainty, the efficiency of the decision is partially at the mercy of variables not under the control of the decision maker. But even these risks can be evaluated to some extent in the process of making the choice.

While all of these points will be discussed in some degree in later chapters, we will assume in this section that the matter of problem definition and alternative generation has been satisfactorily performed. Our problem, then, is to examine the manner in which the choice is made among the admissible list of alternatives.

VARIABLES IN DECISION MAKING

To begin with, every decision includes the assessment of variables of one kind or another. Euphemistically we may caution the decision maker to "look at all the facts," "weigh all the variables in the situation," or "look at the problem objectively." But how one is to do these things efficiently and systematically is another matter. Having made a good decision, the decision maker may simply pass the matter off as having used his experience, good judgment, and intuition. If his batting average is high, we might base decision making on these three ingredients and hope to maintain on the payroll decision makers with such capabilities. Experience may be reliable if the decision concerns a matter that has appeared in similar form in the past and conditions affecting the outcomes are the same. In the final analysis, most decision-making situations call for subjective judgment. This means leaving to the individual the assessment of those variables which cannot be manipulated in quantifiable form, or whose values cannot be predicted, or which represent risk. As for intuition, we know too little about it to argue its complete abolition in favor of more objective means.

Given that, in theory, human decision making is a complex phenomenon, the best we can do here is to examine some of the more objective ways of choosing among alternatives. First, we should consider the types of variables with which the decision maker must deal.

Alternatives

The first variables the decision maker must consider are the *alternatives*. In the absence of alternatives, one is constrained to only one future course of action, and therefore no decision is possible. Situations in which this type of constraint appears to exist are cases where the consequences of all but one alternative are so costly as to preclude their serious consideration as alternatives.

Alternatives are *controllable* by the decision maker. This is in contrast to other kinds of variables that affect his choice but over which he has only partial or no control. In design, planning, or control problems, the alternatives are sometimes referred to, respectively, as design variables, planning variables, or control variables. For example, in designing a storage system for raw materials, the design variables are the configuration of the bins, the location of the bins, the system of coding, and the handling of the materials. Or, in planning production for the coming year, the planning variables are the inventory levels, employment levels, and various other ways of varying production capacity in the months when it is needed.

In a very general sense, alternatives assume two basic forms. First, they can consist of a finite and discrete set of uniquely different *courses of future action* that may be taken to meet a set of objectives. In many cases, these alternatives are the result of creative synthesis. That is, the possibility of their admission to the evaluation process depends on the ability of the decision maker or analyst to conceive of them in a creative sense. Examples of these alternatives are:

1. Alternative methods for clearing the university campus lawns of leaves, including the possibilities of rotary sweeping, leaf blowing, vacuum system, mulching, hand raking, etc.
2. Alternative policies with respect to the use of research funds of a company, including the type of products or processes that should be researched.
3. Alternative methods of handling material in a plant, including fork-lift trucks, conveyors of various sorts, or hand trucks.
4. Alternative methods of converting salt water into fresh water.

In these cases, the alternatives differ with respect to a set of nonhomogeneous attributes including shapes, configurations, materials, or ways of processing materials. The criteria for choosing between them are usually multiple and perhaps difficult to quantify.

In the second case, the alternatives may be a scale of *dimensional values* for some given system. The decision variable is a quantity, and the problem is to select an ideal or optimal value of the dimension. The alternatives are noncreative but rather an explicit range or set of values on the particular scale of interest. Examples are:

1. The optimal size of inventory for a part carried in finished goods stock.
2. The number of fork-lift trucks required to service a production facility.
3. The optimal speed of a conveyorized assembly line.
4. The optimal assignment of machines to locations in a shop in order to minimize material handling costs.

In many of these cases, the choice is made on the simplified basis of a single quantifiable criterion, which identifies the optimal value for the dimension in question. The scale of the dimension may be either continuous, such as conveyor speed, or discrete, such as the number of fork-lift trucks or the number of possible assignments of machines to locations.

The distinction between the two types of alternatives (courses of action and dimensions) is useful to keep in mind when discussing the selection of a best or optimal alternative. Also, the kinds of models that are used to evaluate an alternative may differ. For example, in choosing among a set of discrete alternative courses of action, we usually rank the alternatives in terms of some criterion and choose the alternative that ranks highest on the scale. When choosing an optimal dimension, we might try to develop a logical-analytical expression, hopefully mathematical, of the relationship between the dimensional value and the criterion. Such a relationship will then identify the optimal or an ideal value in a direct fashion without the need to examine all possible values.

States of Nature

The second variables are called *states of nature*. These are variables that influence the decision, but are only partially or not at all under the control of the decision maker. States of nature are such things as volume of demand for the output of a production system, the state of the weather, the possibility of worker resistance to a proposed change, the breakdown of a machine, an action taken by the government, or the death of a key supervisor.

EVENTS: In a given decision problem, there may be one or more critical variables representing states of nature. Each variable may have a vector of values. For example, suppose that we are trying to decide on the best size for a certain production facility. Two important states of nature might be the volume of demand for the output and the possible actions taken by competitors. Each of these has a scale of mutually exclusive values, including the range of possible demands and the set of possible actions taken by a competitor. An *event* is one of the alternative values on the scale of possibilities for a given state of nature. Thus, in the case above, an event is a particular value of demand or a particular action taken by a competitor.

Since events are only partially controllable, usually indirectly, or more likely uncontrollable, one of the problems of decision making involves the prediction of events and their value. The degree of predictability of an event is one method of classifying the type of decision. If the value for a state of nature is known with certainty, then there is only one possible event for that state of nature, and the problem is called *decision making under certainty*. For example, in trying to select between two alternative methods for processing a metal part, the volume of demand for the part is a critical variable. If the demand is known with certainty, then the choice is relatively easy to make.

If the events are known probabilistically, then the decision is one of *decision making under risk*. Here we attach a probability to each event and use this information in some way to make the choice.

If the future occurrence of the events is unpredictable, this condition is known as *decision making under uncertainty*.

Outcomes

An outcome of a decision is an expression of the consequence of an event occurring *given* that a certain alternative is chosen. There is an outcome for every paired combination of alternatives and events. The outcome can be expressed in words or as a number representing some important objective. Usually, of course, the outcome is an expression of the effect of the alternative–event combination on the critical objectives of the problem.

We should note that a good deal of analytical work may be required to determine outcomes. We must know the effect of choosing an alternative and having a certain event occur on the various measures of outcome. For example, in trying to choose between the two alternative methods of processing a metal part, suppose that the outcome is expressed in terms of processing cost. If the events are a range of demands for the part, then, for each alternative, we must find out the effect of demand on processing cost.

From this description of the three elements of decision making, we see that a good decision maker has the ability to conceive of possible alternatives, visualize the critical states of nature, attach a vector of events for each state, and then assess the outcomes for each alternative–event pair. How he does this is a matter of considerable academic interest.

Decision Matrix

So far we have said nothing about the way the choice will be made, given that we have alternatives and states of nature and their events and outcomes. The accumulation of information about the three types of variables is useful only in constructing a basis for making the choice. In the following discussion, we will assume that there is only one state of nature and its associated vector of events. Furthermore, we assume that the events are unaffected by the choice of alternative.

The decision matrix is a handy way of classifying the information about the three types of decision variables. The general form of the matrix is as follows: Let

A_i = the ith alternative from a list of admissible alternatives, $i = 1, 2, \ldots, n$

E_j = the jth event for a given state of nature, $j = 1, 2, \ldots, m$

O_{ij} = the outcome for which the ith alternative is chosen and the jth event occurs

Then

$$O_{ij} = f(A_i, E_j)$$

The decision matrix has the form shown in Figure 2.1.

	E_1	E_2	$\ldots$	E_j	$\ldots$	E_m
A_1	O_{11}	O_{12}	$\ldots$	O_{1j}	$\ldots$	O_{1m}
$\vdots$	$\vdots$	$\vdots$		$\vdots$		$\vdots$
A_i	O_{i1}	O_{i2}		O_{ij}		O_{im}
$\vdots$	$\vdots$	$\vdots$		$\vdots$		$\vdots$
A_n	O_{n1}	O_{n2}	$\ldots$	O_{nj}	$\ldots$	O_{nm}

FIGURE **2.1** Decision matrix.

	E_1 (Storm strikes)	E_2 (No storm)
A_1 (Dismiss the crews)	Call back crews into service Delay service to customers without power Save standby cost Explanation to boss	Success!
A_2 (Place 5 crews on standby)	Power breakdowns corrected faster Overtime standby cost	Loss due to overtime for standby crews Explanation to boss

FIGURE **2.2**   Decision matrix for utility storm damage decision.

Now let us take a simplified example as follows. Suppose an electrical utility has in charge of power-line maintenance crews a supervisor who is faced with the following decision. Periodically during the summer months, electric storms cause interruptions in the power supply of the area by tripping switches or blowing fuses and causing varying amounts of damage to the power lines. On a certain day, the weather report indicates that a severe thunderstorm may possibly strike the area in the next two hours. It is now 4:30 P.M. The alternatives faced by the supervisor are A_1, to let the maintenance crews go home because it is now normal quitting time and then call them back to work if the storm strikes the area, and A_2, to keep five crews on standby status. The state of nature is the storm and the events are E_1, the storm will strike, and E_2, the storm will not strike. There are four possible outcomes, each a function of the alternative chosen and the storm event.

We now construct a decision matrix, as shown in Figure 2.2, in which we simply express the outcomes in verbal form.

In this example, of course, you can easily think of ways to make the situation much more complex. And there is good reason to suppose that the manager would not go about making his decision explicitly in this manner. We are simply trying to explain a method by using a simplified problem.

The decision matrix in this form does not do much to help the decision maker, except to systemize the information that he needs to make a decision. There is nothing here to tell him how to make the decision or what the decision criterion is. We might improve the matrix in a number of ways.

1. We might impose some subjective probabilities to the storm event. If the probability of the storm occurring is much higher than not occurring, then the supervisor will concentrate his analysis of the outcomes in the first column. If the probability of the storm is 1.00, then the decision is made under certainty.
2. An objective choice could be made if we could quantify the outcomes in terms of some single measure of effectiveness. The two major costs involved are the direct cost of crew overtime on standby and the lost revenue due to power breakdowns. Nonquantifiable factors are the customer complaints,

the reaction of the supervisor's superiors to his decision, and the reaction of the crews to the decision.

3. The measures of effectiveness or costs might be sensitive to one or more variables. A better critical variable might be a scale of storm severity, rather than the two mutually exclusive events. Or, the costs might be sensitive to the number of crews involved, in which case the alternatives would be dimensional, namely, the number of crews kept on standby. Both of these cases are refinements in the scale of the two variables.

4. The dimensionality and size of the decision matrix can be increased by considering either additional states of nature or additional kinds of alternatives. An additional state of nature might be the location of the storm. If the storm is concentrated, then its location with respect to a highly industrialized area versus a residential area might have an effect on the costs of the plan. In this case, the alternatives might consider both the number of crews and a mix of truck and crew sizes. Again, this refinement in extending the problem dimensions is important only if the outcomes or costs are sensitive to it.

CRITERIA

The criteria that form the basis for a choice among alternatives spell out the conditions under which a chosen course of action or dimension is considered to be optimal. As soon as an objective is stated, there must be some criterion that will measure the degree to which that objective is satisfied by any alternative. For instance, the objective of maximizing "worker morale" in the design of an assembly line is rather useless unless there is some way of measuring the degree to which worker morale is affected by alternative designs. Of course, the decision maker may ultimately use his intuition, judgment, and experience in ranking alternatives, but this lends little to the discussion.

The term "measures of effectiveness" is used interchangeably with the term "criteria." The former term, however, places the emphasis on measurement and quantification.

Just as there are two types of objectives, there are two types of criteria. *Value criteria* reflect the degree to which an alternative satisfies the value objectives. Cost, profit, worker morale, safety, space, scrap, spoilage, and service are all measures of value that may be minimized or maximized, as the case may be, with respect to some problem.

Functional criteria measure the efficiency with which an alternative satisfies the functional objectives. These are particularly relevant to design problems, where function and performance of a product or process are often measurable.

In design problems, the two kinds of criteria are often incompatible, so that various levels of function or performance yield different profits, costs, spoilage, etc. In cases where a significant range of performance can be tolerated, the problem becomes one of a tradeoff of performance versus cost. Cost-effectiveness studies involve the analysis of this kind of relationship and are important in the design of large-scale industrial, military, or institutional systems.

Multiple Criteria

Very few decisions, except those devised in textbooks, involve the assessment of alternatives in terms of a single criterion. Usually there is a set of multiple criteria or measures of effectiveness that must be evaluated. In this lies part of the complexity of decision making.

For example, the public works department of a city wishes to purchase a general-purpose truck. The choice among alternative makes and models includes their evaluation in terms of initial cost, cost of operation, flexibility for a variety of uses, facility of maintenance, ease of handling in traffic, vendor relationship, etc.

The matter of multiple criteria lies at the heart of the problem of trying to relegate decision making to a quantifiable science. If one alternative is superior to all other alternatives with respect to all criteria, then no problem exists, and the choice is apparent. But the usual case is to have incompatible objectives such that the choice must be based on a weighted balance of the incompatible criteria.

Incompatibility of Objectives

Incompatibility of objectives (and criteria) exists in three ways. The first is related to the hierarchal characteristics of an organization and its production problems. The objectives chosen by a decision maker in the lower echelons of the company may be incompatible with the objectives of a higher order of control. This type of inconsistency is between levels or objectives in an organization. For example, consider the supervisor of the power-line maintenance crews. He might plan a storm maintenance program that minimizes the direct cost of operating crews assigned to storm damage. This might be incompatible with the company objective of maximizing service (or in this case of minimizing the time that customers are without service). Or take the case of a firm that transforms hay and feed into pellets. A paramount objective of the firm might be to provide faster service to customers. The manager of the warehouse operation might redesign the pellet-making process with the thought in mind of simply reducing his own direct labor costs. His choice among alternative improvements may have no influence at all on the service. His choice is then suboptimal with respect to the company's objective.

A second incompatibility is related to a given decision problem in which the decision maker is confronted with a set of objectives and criteria, some of which are incompatible. Thus, in deciding on the number, capacity, and location of refuse incinerators for Monroe County, the minimization of capital investment on the one hand and the minimization of collection costs on the other hand are incompatible. Or, minimizing the time the customer is without service and minimizing crew costs are conflicting objectives in planning the storm control procedure for the utility. Incompatibilities of this kind appear over and over again in a multitude of production and operating problems at all levels of the company.

The third kind of incompatibility reflects the "futurity" of the decision. The *decision horizon* is that period into the future over which the decision maker projects his problem. The criteria are a function of the decision horizon. Short-term objectives differ from long-term objectives, and therefore there is a temporal incompatibility of objectives, which are resolved only by selecting the decision horizon. For example, looking at the effect on short- and long-term profits, a paper company might consider alternative methods of and sites for cutting pulp wood on company-owned land. A longer planning horizon might consider uses of the land for recreational purposes, the future trends in raw material availability on the open market, etc. Then, of course, over time the decision maker can change the set of criteria or their weights due to a change in his outlook or learning or a change in environment.

OPTIMAL DECISIONS: The term optimal is related to incompatibility of criteria in the three senses mentioned above. An optimal decision is one that results in the most judicious balance of all conflicting objectives or criteria. In theory, a choice can be called optimal only if it can be established quantitatively that the most desirable balance of criteria has been established. A suboptimal solution is one in which this has not occurred.

Suboptimization occurs when a decision is optimized with respect to a set of suboptimal or organizationally local criteria, or when a decision is optimized with respect to an incomplete set of objectives or when short-term objectives are incompatible with long-term objectives. In practice, most decisions are suboptimal simply because these conditions probably exist to some degree in most problems. However, when we speak of an optimum solution or decision in a theoretical problem or example, we will mean the choice of that alternative which maximizes an objective and is identifiable in a quantitative sense.

A model in decision making may be used not only to help predict the outcome of an alternative, but also to directly identify an optimal choice among alternatives. As a matter of fact, since optimal must be rigorously defined and determined, the only way this can be done is to express the problem quantitatively. Throughout this book we will be concerned with the kinds of models that are useful in making optimal decisions for various types of production and operating problems.

The resolution of incompatibilities in the organizational sense is a matter of good communications and eventual agreement between the various levels in the organization. We will say no more about this kind of suboptimization but will rather dwell on the issue of resolving conflicts at the individual problem level, given a fixed decision horizon. When incompatible objectives exist in this fashion, then the choice must be made such that there is composite satisfaction of the objectives. When the set of incompatible criteria can all be expressed in terms of a single common measure, then the optimum decision is that alternative which maximizes or minimizes the common denominator.

We should use the word optimal with care. If objectives are positively stated, with corresponding measurable criteria, and they are in conflict, then, in theory, an optimal alternative exists. The challenge is to determine that optimal alternative by analytical means. Usually we are concerned with determining optimal dimensions of a system based on a single criterion, rather than with optimal courses of action. Alternative courses of action may be evaluated according to a set of criteria, and the best or most effective in the alternative set can then be chosen. In the case of a dimension, where a single criterion is used, the optimal alternative is established and verified by analytical means. Too often we hear people say they made an optimal decision, when in fact they made no effort to verify the conditions under which an optimal choice would exist. Their choice is more often a good or effective one.

Decision Rules

The collection and analysis of data related to a decision does not indicate how the decision is to be made. For instance, the decision matrix spells out various outcomes for alternative–event pairs, but it does not tell how to make the decision.

A decision rule states how the decision should be made. In problems where there is a single criterion or measure of effectiveness, the choice to maximize or minimize the criterion value is made under a condition of certainty. Many of the decisions that are made in the course of operating a production system are of this kind. They are localized or tactical decisions and are made day in and day out by the operating personnel. Examples are inventory levels for parts, production batch sizes, sequencing of jobs through a machine, the assignment of personnel to jobs, etc. Many of these decisions can be made on the basis of decision rules, which indicate how a decision should be made under a given set of circumstances. The rules assume that the conditions guiding the decision are known with certainty, and when these conditions are identified in a particular form, they signal a given decision. This is analogous to reflex action in biology, and as it has been stated, "When you put your finger on a hot stove, you don't need a philosopher to suggest the relative merits of alternative courses of action."

Decision rules of this type can often be incorporated into a computerized operation. For example, when price, volume of demand, setup costs, and inventory holding costs for a part are fed into the computer, the computer calculates the optimal production batch size for the part. Of course, the computer cannot create the models; someone has to program it for the model that leads to the optimal decision.

In less routine situations, where one deals with alternative courses of action in more strategic problems, the choice must again be based on a decision rule. This might include the minimization of expected cost, minimization of the maximum possible loss, or some other rule that reflects the decision maker's proneness to gamble in situations of risk or uncertainty.

MAKING THE CHOICE UNDER CERTAINTY

A decision is made under certainty when the decision matrix consists of a list of alternatives and outcomes corresponding to a *single* event for each state of nature. Rarely is any decision made under certainty, since completely accurate predictions or forecasts of future events and their values are highly improbable. Therefore, the models that assume the condition of certainty are only approximations of the real-life decision-making situation. When the condition of certainty is assumed, the decision maker implicitly or explicitly chooses the event that is most likely to occur "if everything goes according to Hoyle." In the "final analysis," even if the model assumes the condition of certainty, the decision maker can always allow for contingencies in a number of ways. One of these is to always avoid a risky choice if his judgment or intuition tells him to do so. There are other ways, which we will examine later.

Suppose, as an example, that we wish to make a choice of methods for clearing the university campus lawns of leaves in the fall. We have the following alternatives:

A_1 hand raking and removal by truck (present method)
A_2 rotary sweeper towed by tractor; removal by truck
A_3 vacuum sweeper unit towed by tractor; removal by truck
A_4 leaf blower towed by tractor; removal by truck
A_5 mulching unit towed by tractor; no removal necessary

For the states of nature we might assume the following:

S_1 demand for the service: This is reasonably constant although the exact dates and daily volume are variable.

S_2 mechanical failure: This is a function of the type of equipment. We might assume some expected failure rate for each individual mechanical alternative and include this in the list of outcomes.

S_3 kind of raw material: Suppose that the campus contained only elm trees, which are now dying off from Dutch elm disease. There is the possibility (as one member of the board of trustees mentioned) of replacing them with blue spruce, or some other coniferous species, thus reducing the leaf removal requirement. In this case, we make an assumption about the life of the leaf removal operation.

We could go on listing other states of nature and assuming a single event for each one. The list of outcomes would then contain the results of assuming the most likely event for each of these states of nature in terms of the measures of effectiveness.

If the measures of effectiveness can be expressed as a single measure, such as the total annual cost of operating the system, then the choice is made by simply ranking the alternatives and choosing the one representing minimum cost. This is the formalized decision rule. But, as we have noted, things do not always work out quite as neatly. The measures of effectiveness usually cannot be reduced to a single quantitative measure. The decision maker must ponder the "intangibles" or irreducibles and allow for the risks and possible errors in the analyst's work.

Ranking by Paired Comparison

When all measures of effectiveness cannot be quantified in terms of a common denominator, then we may rank the alternatives on an ordinal scale of judgment.

Suppose the decision maker is confronted with the following list of outcomes for each of the lawn cleaning alternatives.

Outcomes

Alternative	Capital cost	Operating cost	Degree of lawn cleanliness	Other factors
A_1	None	$3,000	Very good	No layoff of existing personnel
A_2	$500 (second-hand equipment, good condition)	$2,000	Fair—cannot get clean corners	
A_3	$2,500	$500	Very good	Highest maintenance cost. Leaves in bags for easy trucking to dump

After studying the above information plus certain intangibles, the university business manager constructs the following preference matrix.

	A_1	A_2	A_3	A_4	A_5
A_1	—	*	0	*	0
A_2	0	—	0	*	0
A_3	*	*	—	*	0
A_4	0	0	0	—	0
A_5	*	*	*	*	—

the asterisk means that the alternative labeling the row is preferred to the alternative labeling the column and the zero means that the alternative labeling the column is preferred to the alternative labeling the row.

In general terms, if there are m alternatives, then there will be $m(m - 1)/2$ paired comparisons. Let r be the ranked position of an alternative, $r = 1, 2, \ldots, m$. Therefore, each alternative will be preferred $m - r$ times. In our example, the ranking is

Rank (r)	Alternative	$m - r$
1	A_5	4
2	A_3	3
3	A_1	2
4	A_2	1
5	A_4	0

An inconsistency, called intransitivity, can occur when the preference matrix has unequal numbers of asterisks and zeros. For example, suppose that A_1 was listed as being preferred to A_5. This would be inconsistent with the paired comparisons, $A_3 * A_1$ and $A_5 * A_3$. Thus, the procedure of paired comparisons as we have shown brings to light such inconsistencies and forces the decision maker to review his judgments.

Our example would probably be better if we made a quantitative comparison of the cost data based on a single criterion, such as rate of return or equivalent annual costs of operations, thus giving some consistency to the cost data and narrowing down the variety of outcomes that the decision maker must review.

Sensitivity of Outcomes

An outcome is a function of both alternatives and events. The sensitivity of an outcome is the degree to which it responds to a change in either alternatives or events. If the outcomes are insensitive to all alternatives or events, then the implication is that the choice is unimportant. In the previous case, noise is an important measure of effectiveness in the campus environment. It is relatively insensitive to four of the five alternatives, and we might eliminate alternative 4 immediately if the decision maker places high priority on that measure of effectiveness.

Alternatives and events are *critical* when outcomes are sensitive to changes in them. Therefore, one of the problems in designing a decision-making model is to determine the critical variables and ignore uncritical ones. If we synthesize multiple criteria into a single measure of effectiveness, the criticalness of the independent variables may not be apparent until the final measure is constructed and evaluated. In a later section we will discuss models and model building and the use of models to determine sensitivity and critical variables.

At this point, we will consider the implication of sensitivity of outcomes. There are probably many situations, particularly at the tactical decision-making level, where outcomes are quite insensitive to either the alternative chosen or to the events or to both. In other words, it does not really matter what alternative is chosen; the difference is inconsequential, providing the alternative does not represent some obviously nonsensical extreme. It is like trying to find the best route to drive home from work. Of a half-dozen feasible routes, one may result in minimum distance or time, but it is not significantly different from other alternatives.

In such cases, the search for the "optimum" is usually academic, and the expenditure of resources to find the best alternative is greater than the savings implicit in its discovery. The only reasonable argument for concentrating on the search for an optimum is the aggregate effect of repeating the process a large number of times. But in such cases, we may presume a degree of precision in the estimate of data and prediction of outcomes that is not realistic.

We mention this because much of our theoretical analysis of various types of decisions leads to such a degree of refinement. Nature is kind enough to the decision maker to permit him to make nonoptimal or suboptimal decisions without the hazard of severe consequences in many practical situations. If this were not the case, then only management scientists could make the world go around.

At the other extreme, many decisions involve situations where the outcome is so obviously sensitive to choice that no elaborate analysis is needed to suggest the choice that should be made.

The Holy Grail of the objective analysis of a decision is to find a hidden payoff that is obvious from neither experience, judgment, nor intuition. The determination of an optimal decision may, in fact, offer aggregative savings over the choice that might be made by common sense or more superficial decision making, even though the consequences of the latter are not severe. The importance of sensitivity analysis is to indicate the potential payoff from consideration of alternatives, events, and outcomes.

MAKING THE CHOICE UNDER RISK

When the decision maker is not sure of the outcome of his decision but may attach probabilities to the possible outcomes, then the condition known as *decision under risk* occurs. For the moment, we will not be concerned about how the probabilities are obtained. They may be the result of empirical studies of historical data, predictions, or the judgment of the decision maker.

The probabilities that express the risk are usually associated with *events*. Thus, we have a new variable P_j, which is the probability that the jth event will occur. Since the events are mutually exclusive, $\sum_j P_j = 1$. In the decision matrix, the probabilities are usually listed with the events to which they correspond. The problem is to consider the different ways the probability information can be useful to the decision maker.

Getting back to the power-line maintenance crew supervisor and his storm problem, suppose he is able to construct the following decision matrix. Each event now has a probability of occurring, and the outcomes are evaluated in terms of cost.

	E_1 Storm strikes $P_1 = 0.4$	E_2 No storm $P_2 = 0.6$
A_1 (Dismiss the crews)	$5,000	$0
A_2 (Place 5 crews on standby)	$3,500	$1,800

Now the question is one of using the information to make a choice in terms of some *decision criterion*.

The subject of decision making under risk and uncertainty is theoretically complicated simply because there is no standard way of dealing with these two conditions. In the final analysis, the issue is a matter of the personal preferences of the decision maker, based upon his own personal responses to risky situations. All this is dealt with by decision theory, and the best that we can do here is to touch upon only the most elementary notions. The issue seems to be important if the possible gains or losses for any decision are large relative to the resources owned by the decision maker at the time of the decision. This, of course, is reasonable in most situations of risk and gamble. A possible loss of $10,000 compared to a chance of gaining $30,000 will be viewed differently by a small businessman with limited resources and by a large corporation with assets in the millions. Then, also, the matter is important if the outcomes involve a wide spread of possible losses or gains. The rule for choosing an inventory level for a part involving possible gains and losses in the range of $500 will probably differ from the rule that would be used to choose among alternative product development programs, where thousands or millions of dollars are at stake.

In the particular problem of the utility company, the absolute amounts are not great relative to the total resources of the firm, and the range of losses or costs cannot be considered especially large. However, we will use this example for our discussion of alternative decision rules.

Expected Cost

One decision criterion is minimization of the expected cost. Each alternative has an expected cost, which we can express as

$$E(A_i) = \sum_{j=1}^{2} O_{ij}P_j$$

In this case, we have the two expected costs

$$E(A_1) = (0.4)(\$5,000) + (0.6)(0) \quad = \$2,000$$
$$E(A_2) = (0.4)(\$3,500) + (0.6)(1,800) = \$2,400$$

On this basis we would choose alternative A_1, although the difference between the two alternatives is not large.

The expected cost model is appropriate in repetitive situations. If the supervisor must make this decision a large number of times, then over the long run, the cost of the operation will be minimized by minimizing expected cost, even though in a single situation the choice of alternative A_1 might not be the best. However, we might assume that each potential storm condition presents a new decision matrix with different probabilities and costs, so that blind adherence to minimizing the expected cost criterion might result in disaster.

MINIMAX RULE: Another approach is to minimize the maximum risk in the following sense. If the storm strikes, the minimum cost that can be incurred is $3,500. Therefore, the marginal cost of having chosen A_1 is $1,500. If no storm occurs, the minimum cost is $0 and the marginal cost of choosing alternative A_2 is $1,800. The maximum risk of making the wrong decision is therefore $1,500, and if we wish to minimize this maximum risk, the choice is A_1.

The danger in employing this decision rule is that it ignores the absolute differences in the outcome values. For example, if the matrix contained the following figures, then A_2 would still be chosen using the minimax rule, whereas A_1 now appears more appealing, since there is a possibility of avoiding a cost of around $800 by choosing A_1.

	E_1	E_2
A_1	$825	$0
A_2	$800	$800

MAXIMUM GAIN: Another possibility is to shoot for the maximum gain. This is an optimistic outlook. If A_1 is chosen, then the supervisor has a chance of incurring no cost at all, which might look good on his budget review. But by doing this he exposes himself to the possibility of a $1,500 extra storm cost.

THE COST CRITERION

Perhaps the most pervasive objective criterion in production decisions is the minimization of cost. It is generally understood that costs are classified in different ways, depending on their use in a variety of managerial situations.

Because we are interested in decision making, we need to consider at this point the various concepts of cost that are pertinent to the evaluation of alternatives.

Relevant Costs

The most important cost concept in decision making is that of *relevant costs*. Each alternative in a set of proposed designs or plans has a particular structure of relevant costs. For a given alternative design, plan, or course of action, a relevant cost is one that will be incurred in the future if the alternative is chosen. Or, to put it differently, the cost is *escapable if the alternative is not chosen*. Complementary costs are those which are irrelevant or inescapable or whose value is independent of the choice between alternatives.

For example, in the utility storm problem, the direct labor costs of repairing a damaged power line, if the storm occurs, is the same whether the crews are on standby status or alerted after the storm occurs. They are inescapable. However, the crew cost while the crews are on standby status is obviously relevant to the problem.

The concept of relevant costs is recognized under different names, depending on the type of decision to be made.

VARIABLE VERSUS FIXED COSTS: When the decision variable is the production volume in a certain time period, the *variable costs* are those which change with the output volume. In contrast, *fixed costs* remain unchanged with variations in output volume. In salting the streets of a city during the winter, the variable costs are the costs of the salt, overtime labor, or additional labor costs, gasoline, and supplies. Fixed costs include truck depreciation, supervisory costs (unless supervisors are paid overtime), and conversion of the trucks for salt dispensing if it is done once at the beginning of the season.

LONG-TERM VERSUS SHORT-TERM COSTS: A cost may be inescapable in the short run but escapable in the long run. The distinction depends on the future time period with which the decision is concerned. In planning a long-term procedure for salting city streets, the purchase of alternative pieces of equipment admits equipment depreciation as an escapable cost, and on a short-term plan, the present equipment may be held fixed. As the planning horizon is lengthened, a whole new set of escapable costs is admitted for evaluation. Renting additional warehouse space adds *short-term costs*. Building a new warehouse adds *long-term costs*. Thus, a cost that is irrelevant on a short-term basis is relevant on a long-term basis.

OUTLAY VERSUS OPPORTUNITY COSTS: *Outlay costs* are those which appear in the books of the company. *Opportunity costs*, on the other hand, never appear formally in the accounting records of the firm. When a decision involves the commitment of a scarce resource to a certain course of action, the opportunity costs are the profits foregone by not using the resource for some other purpose. The cost of assigning utility crews to storm damage must consider the losses that occur by not using the crews in normally scheduled projects. Opportunity costs are therefore pertinent when the decision involves the commitment of a restricted resource or input to the chosen alternative.

CAPITAL AND OPERATING COSTS: If a decision involves an initial outlay of cost that will subsequently be amortized or depreciated over the life of the system, then this initial cost is a *capital cost*. Capital expenditures may recur periodically in the life of the system. *Operating costs*, in contrast, are annual expenditures or disbursements made during the system life. The distinction is somewhat academic when we are comparing alternatives based on disbursements over the life of the system or plan. Capital expenditures can be converted into equivalent annual costs, and annual operating costs can be converted into a single equivalent disbursement.

DIRECT OR TRACEABLE VERSUS INDIRECT COSTS: A *direct cost* is one that can be traced directly to or identified directly with some product, process, department, or system. In the design sense, the direct cost is one that can be traceable to a particular alternative, whereas the *indirect cost* cannot. Relevant costs are of both types. Material is a highly traceable cost since its actual consumption in production can be identified with a given operation or process. The cost of supervision is less so, and while a given alternative may influence the future costs of supervision, this cost is difficult to identify.

JOINT VERSUS SEPARATE COSTS: When the input of a given set of resources results in more than one kind of output or when several kinds of outputs share a common resource, the costs of the output are *joint costs*. If the consumption of the common resource can be identified with each kind of output, the costs of the output are *separate costs*. The classical example is the division of some raw material into a number of joint products, such as the processing of a hog into a variety of end products or the distillation of crude oil into a variety of products. The term *common cost* signifies the same concept only usually with reference to overhead costs. Where joint costs occur, the problem is one of allocating the joint cost to the various outputs, usually for purposes of output pricing and inventory evaluation. In decision making, the economies of operation may have to be examined in terms of the total operation, since allocation may be purely arbitrary.

HISTORICAL VERSUS FUTURE COSTS: *Historical costs* are those which have occurred in the past. All decisions involve *future costs*. Historical costs may be used as a basis for predicting future costs but with a good deal of caution.

The central problem of costing alternatives is therefore the choice of the relevant costs. Accounting records typically collect costs for purposes of assessing the financial status of the company. In decision making, there is the temptation to use accounting costs, since they are usually easier to obtain. The collection of relevant costs involves the reclassification of accounting records including selection, deletion, and re-ordering of costs into the appropriate dichotomies. Also it involves the estimation or prediction of costs that never appear in the accounting records. In general, it is often better to make a decision based on rough estimates of the relevant costs than to rely on a highly refined and precise estimate of costs, which accounting records supply but which are not relevant to the set of alternatives.

CAPITAL INVESTMENT DECISIONS

Many production decisions involve the commitment of a capital expenditure, or initial outlay of money, for new equipment, buildings, or other resources. The comparison of alternatives related to the acquisition of capital equipment is a part of capital investment theory. Since the subject is generally treated as a segment of accounting or finance, we will only review the basic model here. Furthermore, the subject is presented in more detail as it relates to facilities replacement (Chapter 10) and capacity decisions (Chapter 11).

Compound Interest and Equivalence

Each alternative investment will generate a stream of relevant future receipts and disbursements. The fact that monies are spent or received in the future requires that the time value of the dollar be accounted for if exactness in the analysis is desired. Using interest formulas and compound interest factors derived from them, it is possible to convert, at any future time, a given single amount of money, or a series of unequal amounts, or combinations of both into amounts or series of amounts that are equivalent at a specified rate of compound interest. Similarly, future amounts may be converted into equivalent present amounts. The amounts in question may be present or future investments, annual costs, savings, receipts, or any other kind of disbursement.

The compound interest factor is the coefficient that permits the calculation of equivalency. Using the following notation, we list these factors for reference. Let

i = rate of interest per annum in percent
n = number of interest periods, assuming an interest period to be one year
P = present worth of a future series of payments or receipts
S = future sum of money in interest periods from the present date that is equivalent to P at the interest rate i
R = uniform annual series. This is the end-of-year annual payments or receipts in a uniform (equal) series continuing for the coming n periods. The entire series is equivalent to P at the interest rate i.

SINGLE PAYMENTS: The single payment formulas are concerned with finding P given S, or vice versa.

1. Present worth factor—single payment $[PWF(s)_i^n]$
   To find P given S:

$$PWF(s)_i^n = \frac{1}{(1 + i)^n}$$

$$P = S[PWF(s)_i^n]$$

2. Compound amount factor—single payment $[CAF(s)_i^n]$
   To find S given P:

$$CAF(s)_i^n = (1 + i)^n$$
$$S = P[CAF(s)_i^n]$$

UNIFORM ANNUAL SERIES: Any stream of receipts or disbursements can be converted into an equivalent stream of uniform receipts or disbursements made at the end of each year. This uniform annual series can in turn be converted into a single starting or ending period payment.

3. Present worth factor—uniform series $[PWF(u)_i^n]$
   To find P given R:

$$PWF(u)_i^n = \frac{(1 + i)^n - 1}{i(1 + i)^n}$$

$$P = R[PWF(u)_i^n]$$

4. Compound amount factor—uniform series $[CAF(u)_i^n]$
   To find S given R:

$$CAF(u)_i^n = \frac{(1 + i)^n - 1}{i}$$

$$S = R[CAF(u)_i^n]$$

5. Sinking fund factor $[(SFF)_i^n]$
   To find R given S:

$$(SFF)_i^n = \left[\frac{i}{(1 + i)^n - 1}\right]$$

$$R = S[(SFF)_i^n]$$

6. Capital recovery factor $[(CRF)_i^n]$
   To find R given P:

$$(CRF)_i^n = \left[\frac{i(1 + i)^n}{(1 + i)^n - 1}\right]$$

$$R = P[(CRF)_i^n]$$

Tables giving the values of each of the six factors are readily available in a number of sources, including financial, accounting, and engineering economics textbooks. Several tables of factor values are contained in the Appendix.

The Discounted Cash Flow Model

There is a variety of methods of comparing alternatives using both approximate and exact formulas. The discounted cash flow model is a generally used formula for comparing production investment alternatives. Its advantages include the fact that it is an exact method, permits the evaluation of unequal annual receipts and disbursements, and can be readily adapted to computer applications.

We use the following notation:

i = rate of interest per annum in percent
P = initial investment made at the present time
T = life of the investment
v_t = receipts or savings occurring in period t, where $t = 1, 2, \ldots, T$
c_t = disbursements made in period t

Then, the present worth of the net income from an investment is

$$PW = \sum_1^T \frac{(v_t - c_t)}{(1 + i)^t} - P = \sum_1^T (v_t - c_t)[PWF(s)_i^t] - P$$

In this case, we assume that receipts and disbursement occur at the end of discrete periods. A more general form of the model considering the continuous discounting to present worth is

$$PW = \int_0^T [v(t) - c(t)]e^{-it}\, dt - P$$

where both receipts and disbursements are functions of time. Then discounting will take place instantaneously in time. Consider the expansion of the term $(1 + i)^t$, where t is number of interest periods (years) and i is annual rate of interest.

$$(1 + i)^t = 1 + \frac{ti}{1!} + \frac{t(t - 1)i^2}{2!} + \frac{t(t - 1)(t - 2)i^3}{3!} + \cdots \tag{1}$$

As the discount period is reduced, i will decrease and the number of interest periods will increase.

That is, as $i \to 0$ and $t \to \infty$, the binomial series, Equation (1), approaches

$$1 + \frac{ti}{1!} + \frac{t^2i^2}{2!} + \frac{t^3i^3}{3!} + \cdots \tag{2}$$

Equation (2) is the expansion of e^{it}.

Single or alternative investments may be evaluated on the basis of their present worths or rates of return.

Problems

2.1   In the following general situations, what might be problems involving alternative courses of action and problems involving alternative system dimensions?
(a) An electrical utility company is considering the installation of underground power lines rather than overhead transmission.
(b) The Erie Metal Supply Company is considering building a warehouse for inventorying 35,000 different types of nonferrous metals.

(c) The New York Telephone Company wishes to establish a method for scheduling its fleet of small customer-service trucks.

(d) The Theta Transit Corporation wishes to establish an "economical" system of public bus transportation for the City of Rochester.

(e) A gas utility company wishes to design a procedure for economically collecting information from customer gas meters.

(f) The Gamma Gear Company is considering a new layout of the general production shop.

(g) The United States Forest Service has a research group to consider the ways of reducing the number of forest fires.

2.2 In considering the following alternatives, make a list of possible incompatible objectives related to each decision.

(a) The Erie Metal Supply Company is going to build a new warehouse. The alternatives are a single-story warehouse or a two-story warehouse. Both alternatives have equal capacity.

(b) The Gas Department of the Atlantic Utility Company considers two alternative ways of obtaining customer meter information. One is to have metermen read the meters each month, and the other is to mail a meter-reading card to each customer at the time he is billed. The customer reads his own meter and returns the information on the card to the company.

(c) The Theta Transit Corporation considers two bus systems. One is to use a fleet of 50 type X buses, and the other is to use a fleet of 75 type Y buses, which are smaller than type X.

2.3 In Problem 1.5, you were asked to investigate the hospital laundry situation. Construct a decision matrix with word descriptions of alternatives, states of nature, events, and outcomes.

2.4 A gas company has a service man who answers various customer complaint calls during the course of the day. He travels around the city in a small truck. At the beginning of the day, he is given a list of jobs to take care of at various locations in the city. Give the decision rule he might use in selecting the order in which he will service the jobs if the criterion is to

(a) Minimize the travel time between jobs.

(b) Minimize the time the customer must wait for the service.

(c) Minimize the danger to the customer of fault in the gas system.

(d) Maximize the number of jobs he can complete in a day (assuming that he can be given more jobs when he is through with the first batch).

2.5 Mrs. Hedley owns and manages a small factory in northern Vermont in which she produces her famous high-protein chicken fat cookies known throughout New England. Her formula is known only to her and she daily supervises personally the mixing of each batch of ingredients. Realizing that her age precludes the continuation of the operations in this manner, she turns the business over to her son. In order to find out exactly what her formula is, he has a detailed chemical analysis made of the product, which yields the following information.

The cookies are made of two ingredients, chicken fat and a ground nut syrup. Each standard portion of cookie mix must contain at least 180 grams of protein, 50 grams of fat, and 100 grams of carbohydrate. One kilogram (1,000 grams) of the chicken fat contains 200 grams of carbohydrate, 100 grams of protein, and 100 grams of fat. One kilogram of the ground nut syrup contains 300 grams of protein and 100 grams of carbohydrate.

The price of the ground nut mixture and chicken fat vary over time, and, therefore, the new manager wishes to determine at the beginning of each day a least-cost mixture of the two ingredients for the day's production of cookies, commensurate with maintaining the minimum quality standards. Determine a decision rule that can be applied each day by the production manager of the plant, who has been with the company for the last ten years and has only a high-school education.

2.6 The Clinton Township Water Authority has been asked to consider supplying water to several surrounding townships. The Authority has two alternatives confronting it:

A_1 expand the facilities

A_2 do not expand the facilities

There are two events. Either 1) the Authority will be granted a contract to supply water or 2) it will not. The outcomes are:

O_{11} a future profit of $200,000

O_{12} a loss of $70,000

O_{22} nothing

O_{21} a gain of $40,000 through a contract with a township in county Y

The probability of the two events are: the contract will be awarded $= 0.40$, and the contract will not be awarded $= 0.60$.

Discuss the decision in light of various decision rules.

2.7 The production manager of a steel fabrication business needs some steel to complete an important rush order. The steel can be purchased from a vendor in Buffalo, N.Y., 300 miles away. There are two alternative methods of getting the steel to the manager's plant.

A_1 send the company truck and a crew to Buffalo for the steel and get it back in two or three days

A_2 let the vendor truck it to the shop with a variable time of delivery

Suppose that the critical variable is the delay time, in days, in receiving the steel. The cost outcomes are:

Day of delivery Days delay	Friday 2	Saturday 3	Monday 5	Tuesday 6
A_1	500^{0.5}$	700^{0.5}$	0	0
A_2	100^{0.30}$	0	500^{0.6}$	1250^{0.1}$

Note in this example that the events and their probabilities depend on the alternative. Which alternative would you choose and why?

2.8 In the following situations, designate the relevant cost concepts involved, and give examples of each.

(a) The Atlantic Gas and Electric Company wishes to improve the reliability and efficiency of the meter-reading system. Two alternatives are under consideration. 1) Schedule the meters to be read by the company representative every other month rather than every month. 2) Replace the present multidial meters with a directly read number type of meter, and have the customer read the meter, record the value on a post card, and send it to the company.

(b) The Bonbon Candy Company maintains a system of 20 retail candy shops in a five-county district. Every two days the shops are supplied by a truck from the factory. Each shop manager must place an order for the amount of each type of candy he wishes to stock over the two-day period.

(c) The Erie Metal Supply Company is considering two alternative warehouse designs: 1) a conveyorized multistory warehouse and 2) a single-story warehouse using fork-lift trucks.

(d) The Quincy Quarry Company produces six different grades of gravel in its pit operation using a single stone crusher. The price of the gravel is based on unit cost.

(e) The Pacific Electric and Gas Company has a utility pole replacement policy. When a pole is replaced, it is presently scrapped at the company yards or transported free of charge to any location near to the point of replacement. The Perfect Piling Company offers to buy the old poles, which they will subsequently treat and use for piling.

Bibliography

ALEXIS, MARCUS, and CHARLES Z. WILSON, *Organizational Decision Making*. Englewood Cliffs, N.J.: Prentice-Hall, Inc., 1967.

BARISH, N. N., *Economic Analysis for Engineering and Managerial Decision Making*. New York: McGraw-Hill Book Co., 1962.

BOWMAN, E. H., "Consistency and Optimality in Managerial Decision Making," *Management Science*, January 1963.

DEAN, JOEL, *Managerial Economics*. Englewood Cliffs, N.J.: Prentice-Hall, Inc., 1951.

FISHBURN, PETER C., "Decision Under Uncertainty: An Introductory Exposition," *J. Ind. Eng.*, July 1966.

GRANT, EUGENE L., and W. GRANT IRESON, *Principles of Engineering Economy*, 4th ed. New York: Ronald Press, 1960.

MILLER, DAVID W., and MARTIN K. STARR, *Executive Decisions and Operations Research*. Englewood Cliffs, N.J.: Prentice-Hall, Inc., 1960.

MORRIS, WILLIAM T., *The Analysis of Management Decisions*. Homewood, Ill.: Richard D. Irwin, Inc., 1964.

TAYLOR, GEORGE A., *Managerial and Engineering Economy*. Princeton, N.J.: D. Van Nostrand Co., 1964.

TERRY, HERBERT, "Comparative Evaluation of Performance Using Multiple Criteria," *Management Science*, April 1963.

3
Model Building

THE FUNCTION OF MODELS

One of the distinctive features of *homo sapiens* is his ability to reconstruct the real world about him in the form of models. We model the real world in so many varied ways that we take the process for granted. The experience we gain by using models helps us to minimize the risk we face in carrying out some activity or function in real life. And even if the risk is not completely removed, at least some of the anxiety about the results of our actions is dispelled.

In making decisions related to the design, planning, or control of production systems, managers are constantly faced with the problem of predicting the future behavior of the system under a variety of possible alternative-event combinations. For example,

1. The manager of a large machine shop wants to know the effect on shop performance of using alternative methods of handling material (fork-lift trucks, hand trucks, overhead crane).
2. The manager of the cooperative pelletizing process would like to know the effect on farmer wait time of inventorying both raw materials and standard finished mixes.
3. The manager of a county public works department wants to know the relationship between the number and location of proposed refuse disposal incinerators and the costs of refuse collection and disposal.

In order to have any understanding of how a system, under design or planning, will behave relative to cost, quantity and quality of output, or other performance measures, the manager can do one or a combination of three things. First, he can obviously implement the design or plan and then observe its operating characteristics under actual conditions. This avoids the wearisome task of trying to figure everything out ahead of time, and the experience gained can be used to make subsequent adjustments to the system in order to approach ideal performance. Second, he can rely upon his experience with systems that are similar to the one being planned (if any exist). The propriety of this approach depends on the similarity between the present and proposed systems and the reliability of his experience. Third, he can construct a model of the proposal and experiment with varying alternatives and probabilistic events.

Today, a great deal of reliance is placed on experience gained from years of contact with real-life situations. But this experience sometimes lacks reliability when we deal with sudden and complex changes. A good example of this is the space industry, where model-building has been a prime requisite. Our present industrial and technological life is changing at such a rapid pace that experience tends to be short lived, and we are forced to take recourse in research, experimentation, and model building before taking action.

One way of classifying models is in terms of their general purpose. Three general purposes for models are suggested below:

1. *Models for communication*   The earliest models of production (other than written reports) were used to communicate the specifications of designers and planners to those who had to decide on and implement the design and plans; the models were thus used to systematically present detailed information. Examples are schematic diagrams, process charts, scheduling charts, and graphs.

2. *Models for decision making*   Most models are used to supply the manager with information to assist him in making decisions. Certain models indicate, in a more or less direct fashion, the best choice from a set of alternatives in terms of some stated criterion. The term *decision model* is often applied to the method of summarizing the gains or losses associated with each one of a set of discrete alternatives. These models may assume that the *outcome* of the choice is known with certainty or, in contrast, that the choice involves a risk due to the probabilistic character of some of the variables in the problem. *Optimizing* models are a special type of decision model that determine the optimal value of some design or planning variable. These models usually deal with a continuous set of alternatives or with a very large set of discrete alternatives. The variable may be either a monetary expression of cost or profit or some nonmonetary dimension of the system.

3. *Descriptive models of operations*   Certain models may simply describe the behavior of the variables comprising a system. Such models may be used to collect information that will subsequently be applied to a decision model or to aid the decision maker in choosing between alternatives. Models can also be classified in terms of their general type or form, rather than by their use. A given type of model may be used for any one or more of the purposes outlined above.

Schematic-Diagrammatic Models

These models may be diagrams, sketches, drawings, or layouts, which show some fixed relationship between the elements of a system. Examples are blueprints, route sheets, flow charts, and instruction sheets. Such models usually indicate a static relationship among the elements. They may be quantitative in that they indicate the dimensions of the system, but usually they indicate only a spatial relationship between elements, such as in a flow diagram, template plant layout, or assembly drawing. Their principal use is as an aid in communicating the physical features of a design or method. Or they may be used in analyzing a system to find ways of improving the design. Their general limitation is the fact that they do not represent the dynamic behavior of the real system. For instance, a diagrammatic layout of the shop with two overhead cranes may indicate the spatial relationships between the crane and machines in the shop. It does not give an insight, however, into the operating behavior of the shop in terms of inventories, machine utilization, or rate of work flow, as influenced by the operation of the cranes.

In order to overcome the objections to the static models, a system may be modeled in a number of ways to portray the dynamic characteristics.

Mathematical Models

Sometimes a system may be represented as an equation or as a set of equations. Quantitative relationships between system variables can be analyzed in an experimental sense. Also, optimum solutions to problems can be determined. However, accurate mathematical expressions of real-life situations are often difficult to establish, and other kinds of models must be used or a certain degree of error must be accepted in the mathematical results.

Analog Computer

An analog computer is a physical system that is a direct analog of a second system of dissimilar form. The analog is usually a mechanical, electrical, or hydraulic system, and its physical components are analogs of the elements of the system studied. An analog computer is a special-purpose computer, since it pertains only to a specific system. The physical components of the analog computer may be manipulated in any way to study the effect on the other elements of the system.

Pilot Plants

A pilot model is a small-scale replica of a real production system. Pilot models or pilot plants are used extensively in the chemical industry to predict the performance characteristics of a chemical manufacturing system. In the case of metal-working industries or plants having a discrete unit of output, pilot plants have little meaning except when an actual existing production system is used to experiment with changes in designs and plans. Obviously, this approach is usually unreasonable because of disruptions in existing production. However, on off-shift periods, it may be possible to utilize an existing production system to experiment with minor changes.

Hand and Digital Computer Simulation

Most models analyze operations and in effect simulate operations. This is particularly true of analog computers, pilot plants, and certain mathematical models. Another type of simulation involves keeping track of the status of a system at various points in time. The relationships between the variables of the system are known but are perhaps too complex to express neatly by a set of equations. The problem is to assign certain values to a number of independent variables and then to determine the values of the dependent variables in the system. The method is more arithmetical than mathematical, and the status of the system as represented by the dependent variables can be kept track of by hand on paper or by a digital computer. Business games are of this type, where the independent variables are decision or playing variables, and the financial statements, inventory levels, etc. (the dependent variables), represent the status of the system after the decisions have been made. Monte Carlo simulation deals specifically with stochastic processes or systems involving random inputs or outputs. We will consider this type of simulation in more detail later in this chapter.

A third way of classifying models is in terms of the kind of thing they model. Production and operating systems have certain common attributes, even among firms producing highly dissimilar products. Examples are waiting-line models, resource allocation models, assignment models, etc. We will briefly review some of these models in the remainder of this chapter.

MATHEMATICAL PROGRAMING MODELS

Mathematical programing models are employed to optimize the use of a set of limited resources for which there are competing demands. The problem is stated in the form of a set of mathematical equations in which the unknowns are the amounts of resources to be applied to specific demands. The kinds of problems amenable to programing solutions are represented by the following examples:

1. A certain machine shop has a variety of lathes. In a certain time period, a set of jobs is assigned to the lathe department for processing. Each job may be routed alternatively to more than one type of lathe. There is insufficient lathe capacity to assign each job to the lowest cost process. The problem is to determine the optimum assignment of jobs so that total processing costs are minimized.

2. A saw mill produces a variety of end products. The input to the mill is a variety of types and sizes of logs. The problem is to decide how the logs are to be allocated to the production of the end products. Each end product will have a given cost, depending on the log type and process, and a given market price. The objective is to maximize the profit of the output over a given time period.

3. A food processing company has five processing centers located in different cities in the country. The company also maintains ten warehouses located at different points in the country, which receive the output of the processing centers. There is a given cost of shipping the product from each processing center to each warehouse. The problem is to determine a minimum cost assignment of products from processing stations to warehouses, such that the demands of the warehouses are satisfied.

4. A company produces a set of products with seasonal variation. The problem is to decide on a production plan that will designate month by month how much of each product is to be produced, amounts of overtime, inventory level, and employment levels, such that the total cost of the plan is minimized.
5. An oil company wishes to determine an optimum plan for its refinery operations, given estimates of external conditions, such as market demands for end products, crude oil availability, etc., and given internal company directive, such as refinery unit construction, minimum contracted crude, etc.

There are a variety of mathematical programing models that depend both on the nature of the problem and on the variables. Linear programing applies to models in which the set of equations are linear. Integer programing applies to the special case where the solution variables can assume only integer values. Nonlinear programing obviously refers to cases where some or all of the equations are nonlinear. Dynamic programing entails optimizing a sequence of decisions, where a decision at one stage in the sequence affects subsequent decisions. Further embellishments include the consideration of risk or uncertainty in the values of the programing variables.

In this chapter, we will consider only linear and dynamic programing.

Linear Programing

THE SIMPLEX METHOD: The simplex method is a general method for determining an optimal solution to the following kind of problem.

1. There is a set of variables $x_1, x_2, \ldots, x_n$ whose values are to be determined.
2. Only non-negative values are allowed, that is, $x_j \geq 0; j = 1, \ldots, n$.
3. There are one or more joint linear restrictions on the values that x_i can assume. These are of the form

$$a_{11}x_1 + \cdots + a_{1j}x_j + \cdots + a_{1n}x_n \leq b_1$$
.
.
.
$$a_{i1}x_1 + \cdots + a_{ij}x_j + \cdots + a_{in}x_n = b_i$$
.
.
.
$$a_{m1}x_1 + \cdots + a_{mj}x_j + \cdots + a_{mn}x_n \geq b_m$$

There are m such restrictive equalities or inequalities, and some of the a_{ij} may equal zero.

4. Each unknown has an associated value coefficient c_j. Then, a total value z can be assigned to any solution such that

$$z = c_1x_1 + \cdots + c_jx_j + \cdots + c_nx_n$$

An optimal solution is one for which z is maximum, the restrictions are satisfied, and all values of x are non-negative.

EXAMPLE 3.1   A wood-working firm makes two products, clothes pins (A) and screw-driver handles (B), which are processed on each of three machines M_1, M_2, and M_3. It is assumed that the demand for each product exceeds the capacity of the three-machine system. The problem is to determine how much of each product to produce in a given time period in order to maximize marginal profit, given the restriction in the machine system.

Let

x_A = number of units (times 1,000) of A produced in time t
x_B = number of units (times 1,000) of B produced in time t

The basic time data of the system are tabulated as follows:

Machine	Hours to produce 1,000 units of product		Capacity of machine in hours for period t
	A	B	
M_1	4	6	240
M_2	8	4	240
M_3	2	3	150

The profit margin on each product is $24 per 1,000 units for A and $30 per 1,000 units for B. The objective function is

maximize $z = 24x_A + 30x_B$

subject to the constraints

$$4x_A + 6x_B \leq 240$$
$$8x_A + 4x_B \leq 240$$
$$2x_A + 3x_B \leq 150$$
$$x_A, x_B \geq 0$$

The first three inequalities show that the total hours worked by each machine cannot exceed the capacity of the machine. The last expression shows that the number of each product produced must be equal to or greater than zero.

The problem is represented graphically in Figure 3.1. Feasible production combinations of A and B lie within the shaded area $0A'CB'$. Any combination of x_A and x_B, that lies outside the shaded area violates one or more of the restrictions.

Now consider the objective function for $z = 2,000$ (dotted line). The optimum solution lies at the point at which the objective function first intersects the shaded area as z is decreased. Normally, the intersection of the objective function and the solution space (shaded area) occurs at one of the extreme points of the solution space. In this case, it occurs at C, which therefore represents the optimum combination of x_A and x_B. We make the following comments about this simple case, which may not be obvious in a more complex problem.

1. At point A', only A is produced in the amount $x_A = 30$, yielding a total margin of $(24 \times 30) = \$720$. No more than $30A$ can be produced, because this is the limit of M_2 capacity. In this program, both M_1 and M_3 will have idle capacity. For instance, M_1 could produce 60 units of A in order to fill its capacity of 240 hours.

2. At point B', only B is produced in the amount of $x_B = 40$, giving a total margin of $\$1,200$. Here M_1 is the limiting factor.

3. At point C, a mix of $x_A = 15$ and $x_B = 30$ is produced, giving a total margin of

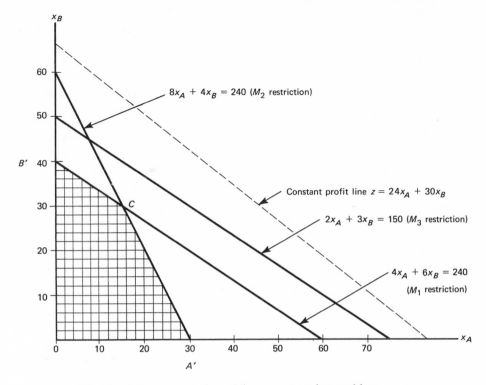

FIGURE **3.1** Graphic representation of linear programing problem.

$1,260, which is the optimum program. The quantities of A and B at C are determined by solving the simultaneous equations that intersect at that point.

If there were three unknowns (products in this case), then the graphic solution would be in three-dimensional space, and the optimum would be an extreme point in a convex polyhedron.[1]

The simplex method is used to evaluate systematically the extreme points of a convex set in n-dimensional space and to identify the optimum. The first step is to convert the restrictions to equalities,

$$4x_A + 6x_B + w_1 = 240$$
$$8x_A + 4x_B + w_2 = 240$$
$$2x_A + 3x_B + w_3 = 150$$

where w_1, w_2, and w_3 are called *null products* (or slack variables). They each represent the idle hours on the machine whose number is their subscript. For instance, a unit of w_1 is the production of an idle hour on M_1. Or, when x_A and x_B are zero, M_1 produces 240 hours of idle time. Since they are unknowns, $w_1, w_2, w_3 \geq 0$.

The problem is structured in the form of a tableau, which represents a feasible

---

[1] A polyhedron is convex if no point on any line segment connecting any two points of the polyhedron lies outside the polyhedron.

solution to the problem. In the tableau shown in Figure 3.2, the unknowns are listed across the top row, each labeling a column. The unknown variables in the first column (labeling the rows) are those which have positive values in the current solution, and their values are listed in the last column at the end of the corresponding row. The remaining variables have zero values. Note that in a system of m equations and n unknowns ($m < n$), a feasible solution will consist of m of the variables having positive values and $n - m$ having zero values. The values c_j in the bottom row indicate the contribution to profit resulting from the introduction into the system of a unit of the variable labeling the corresponding column. The contribution is indicated as negative if the profit is increased. The remaining values in the tableau represent the quantity of the product, labeling the row, that will be removed from the system by introducing one unit of the product labeling the column.

Figure 3.2, therefore, represents the situation where neither A nor B is produced, and each machine is idle to the limit of its capacity. This corresponds to point 0 on the graph, and only the "null" products are being produced.

Assume that a unit of A is introduced into the system. The result according to Figure 3.2 will be a reduction of four units of w_1, that is, four less idle hours in the first machine, as well as a reduction of eight and two units of products w_2 and w_3, respectively. Also, the profit margin will be increased by \$24. The maximum number of units of A that can be introduced into the system is $x_A = \frac{240}{8} = 30$. In other words, this is point A' on the graph, where M_2 is the limiting factor. Machines 1 and 3 are not limiting factors since $\frac{240}{4}$ or 60 units of A can be produced on M_1, and $\frac{150}{2}$ or 75 units of A can be produced on M_2. If 30 units of A are introduced, w_2 is excluded from the system, and this is indicated by the arrows in the first tableau. This results in Tableau 2 in Figure 3.3.

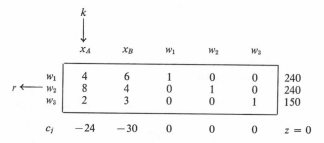

	x_A	x_B	w_1	w_2	w_3	
w_1	4	6	1	0	0	240
w_2	8	4	0	1	0	240
w_3	2	3	0	0	1	150
c_j	-24	-30	0	0	0	$z = 0$

$k \downarrow$

$r \leftarrow w_2$

FIGURE 3.2   Basic solution.

	x_A	x_B	w_1	w_2	w_3	
w_1	0	4	1	$-\frac{1}{2}$	0	120
x_A	1	$\frac{1}{2}$	0	$\frac{1}{8}$	0	30
w_3	0	2	0	$-\frac{1}{4}$	1	90
c_j	0	-18	0	3	0	$z = 720$

$k \downarrow$

$r \leftarrow w_1$

FIGURE 3.3   Second solution.

The values in Figure 3.3 are calculated by using two algorithms. The column of the variable being introduced is called the kth column. The row of the displaced variable is called the rth row.[2] In Figure 3.2, the column under x_A and the row containing w_2 are the kth column and rth row, respectively. We further let i represent the ith row and j the jth column, where i and j may be any row or column. Then,

a'_{ij} = the value in the square of the ith row and jth column of the *new* tableau

a_{ij} = the corresponding value in the preceding tableau

We now state the two algorithms as follows:

$$a'_{rj} = a_{rj}/a_{rk} \tag{1}$$

$$a'_{ij} = a_{ij} - (a_{rj}/a_{rk})a_{ik} \tag{2}$$

Applying algorithm (1), we find for the second row, from left to right $\frac{8}{8}, \frac{4}{8}, \frac{0}{8}, \frac{1}{8}, \frac{0}{8}, \frac{240}{8}$. In the first row we have the elements a'_{ij}: $4 - (\frac{8}{8})4$, $6 - (\frac{4}{8})4$, $\ldots$, $240 - 240(\frac{240}{8})4$. The reader can check the remaining values in Figure 3.3.

Figure 3.3 indicates that the profit may be increased by introducing units of B. This is revealed by the fact that the amount under the column x_B is negative (indicating that the increment in profit is positive if a unit of B is added). But to introduce one unit of B requires that one-half unit of A not be produced on M_2. The net effect on the profit is:

Introduce one unit of B	$30
Lose one-half unit of A	$-$$12
Net result	$18

Notice also that introducing an idle hour (w_2) on M_2 would displace $3 of margin, since $\frac{1}{8}$ of a unit A would be displaced ($\frac{1}{8} \times \$24 = \$3$).

Figure 3.4 results from the introduction of B in place of w_1 [again applying algorithms (1) and (2)]. This tableau indicates that the optimum has been reached (point C on the graph), since further introduction of a product results in either no change in margin or in a loss. The tableau can be analyzed for further information about the system:

1. There are 30 idle hours of capacity left on M_3. Note that this machine could have been ignored in the tableaus because its capacity to produce a mix of A and B exceeds either one or both of the other machines. However, its inclusion in the model permits an evaluation of its idle capacity, as well as its relation to the system.
2. The amount 4.5 in the bottom row in column w_1 indicates that the first machine M_1 is a critical machine. Any idle time resulting from a machine breakdown, absence of material, and the like will result in a loss of $4.5 per hour. Tableau 3 shows that by introducing an idle hour on M_1,
   (a) Production of B should be reduced by $\frac{1}{4}$ of a unit.
   (b) This releases temporarily 1.5 hours on M_1 ($\frac{1}{4}B$ times 6 hours per unit = 1.5 hours).
   (c) Also, one hour on M_2 releases ($\frac{1}{4}B \times 4 = 1$).
   (d) This means that more A can be produced on M_2, or $\frac{1}{8}$ of a unit of A to be exact. Note that the tableau points out that introducing one unit of w_1 brings back into the system $\frac{1}{8}$ unit of A.
   (e) $\frac{1}{8}$ of a unit of A requires the use of $\frac{1}{2}$ hour on M_1, resulting in a net loss in time of 1 hour on this machine.

---

[2] The kth column and rth row are called the *pivot* column and row, respectively.

	x_A	x_B	w_1	w_2	w_3	
x_B	0	1	$\frac{1}{4}$	$-\frac{1}{8}$	0	30
x_A	1	0	$-\frac{1}{8}$	$\frac{3}{16}$	0	15
w_3	0	0	$-\frac{1}{2}$	0	1	30
	0	0	4.5	0.75	0	$z = 1{,}260$

FIGURE **3.4**   Optimum solution.

(f) The net loss in margin, as shown by the "shadow price," is \$4.5, or $\frac{1}{8}A \times \$24 - \frac{1}{4}B \times \$30 = -\$4.5$. The sign should be reversed to comply with the tableau rule.

This points out that if M_1's capacity were impaired, a considerable amount of production of B would be sacrificed, while production of A would be increased. It also suggests that a methods study be made on M_1 to remedy this critical situation.

3. If the capacity of a machine is increased by, say, an extra shift with no changes in the time or cost structure, the results are still indicated by the tableau, except that the arithmetic signs are reversed. Suppose that one extra hour of capacity is added to M_2. The tableau indicates that $\frac{1}{8}$ unit of B would be displaced in favor of adding $\frac{3}{16}$ units of A with a net gain of \$0.75. The new optimum is symbolically at point C' on the graph (Figure 3.5). The maximum increase in capacity on M_2 that can take place with these attendant results is 240 hours (a total capacity of 480 hours),

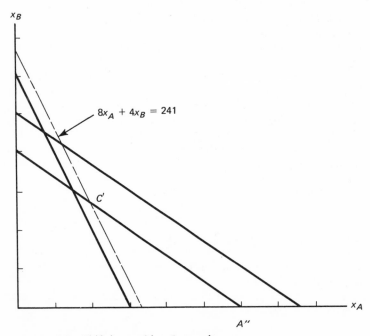

FIGURE **3.5**   Shift in machine 2 capacity.

beyond which point the capacity of M_1 must also be increased if profits are to be increased. This is point A'' on the graph.

The above analysis points out the fact that the linear programing model can be used to evaluate the effects of changes in one or more of the system parameters on the objectives. These include such things as changes in machine rates and capacities, prices, and the introduction of alternative processes. In some cases, the use of linear programing in this sense may be more important than the specification of a definite program.

THE DUAL OF THE SIMPLEX: We refer to the problem just solved as the *primal* problem. The dual formulation of the simplex problem involves in general the following:

1. If the primal is a minimizing problem, the dual is a maximizing problem, and vice versa.
2. The coefficients of the primal objective function are the constraint constants of the dual problem.
3. The constraint constants of the primal become the objective function coefficients of the dual.
4. The constraint matrix of the primal is transposed to become the constraint matrix of the dual.

In our previous example, the primal problem was

maximize $(24x_A + 30x_B)$

subject to

$$4x_A + 6x_B \leq 240$$
$$8x_A + 4x_B \leq 240$$
$$2x_A + 3x_B \leq 150$$
$$x_A, x_B \geq 0$$

Now the dual formulation is

minimize $(240p_1 + 240p_2 + 150p_3)$

subject to

$$4p_1 + 8p_2 + 2p_3 \geq 24$$
$$6p_1 + 4p_2 + 3p_3 \geq 30$$
$$p_1, p_2, p_3 \geq 0$$

Consider what the dual means in terms of the example. In the last tableau of the primal problem, we noted that the "scarce" resources were M_1 and M_2. The "value" of these resources in terms of lost profit if their capacity was reduced, or increased profits if capacity was added, was indicated as the shadow prices ($\$4.5$ and 0.75). The purpose of the dual formulation is to focus attention on just this feature, that is, the contribution to profit made by the resources rather than the products (activities). The problem is formulated in the simplex, where the objective is to minimize the opportunity or foregone profits by not using the resources in an optimal way. Thus, the variables p_1, p_2, and p_3 are the marginal profits to be

	p_1	p_2	p_3	p_A	p_B	α_1	α_2	
α_1	4	8	2	1	0	1	0	24
α_2	6	4	3	0	-1	0	1	30
c_j	-240	-240	-150	0	0	∞	∞	
α_1	0	$\frac{16}{3}$	0	-1	$\frac{2}{3}$	1		4
p_1	1	$\frac{2}{3}$	$\frac{1}{2}$	0	$-\frac{1}{6}$	0		5
c_j	0	-80	-30	0	-40	∞		
p_2	0	1	0	$-\frac{3}{16}$	$\frac{1}{8}$			0.75
p_1	1	0	$\frac{1}{2}$	$\frac{1}{8}$	$-\frac{1}{4}$			4.50
c_j	0	0	-30	-15	-30			$z = 1,260$

FIGURE **3.6**   Three tableaus in dual simplex.

gained by adding an hour to the capacity of the machine corresponding to the subscript.

Applying the simplex to the dual, we have three tableaus (Figure 3.6) leading to the optimum. Slack variables p_A and p_B are added to equalize the constraints. However, since the variables cannot assume negative values, we must add two artificial variables α_1 and α_2 to permit a starting point for the iterations. These variables are assigned infinite cost coefficients and drop out of the solution.

Compare the dual with the primal solution. Both objective functions are equal ($z = 1,260$). The c_j values of the variables not in the solution (basis) of the dual are exactly equal to the negative values of the variables in the basis of the primal. The solution values of the dual are exactly equal to the negative of the c_j values of the variables not in the basis of the primal.

The Distribution Method

A special class of linear programing problems is called *distribution* or *transportation* programing problems. The terms reflect their common use in optimizing the shipment of goods in a factory warehouse system, but the method has more general applicability. In general terms, the problem takes this form:

1. There is a set of *m origins* (locations). At each origin there is a resource that is available in some stated quantity.

2. There are *n* *destinations*. Each destination requires a certain quantity of the resource.
3. The total quantity of the resource available at the origins is exactly equal to the total amount of the resource required at the destinations.
4. Each origin-destination pair has an associated linear cost coefficient. This is the cost of allocating a unit of the resource from the origin to the destination.
5. The objective of the problem is to determine the optimum allocation of the resource from the origins to destinations, such that the total cost of the allocation is minimized and the total availability of and requirement for the resource are satisfied. In symbolic notation, the problem is stated as follows:
Let

i = index of the origin, $i = 1, 2, \ldots, m$
j = index of the destination, $j = 1, 2, \ldots, n$
c_{ij} = cost of allocating one unit of the resource from origin i to destination j
a_i = availability of the resource at origin i
b_j = requirement of the resource at destination j
x_{ij} = amount of the resource allocated from origin i to destination j

Then, the objective is

$$\text{minimize} \sum_i \sum_j x_{ij} c_{ij}$$

$$\sum_j x_{ij} = a_i; \sum_i x_{ij} = b_j; x_{ij} \geq 0$$

$$\sum_i a_i = \sum_j b$$

EXAMPLE 3.2   The Oliva Oil Company has three processing plants located at origins O_1, O_2, and O_3. The output of the plants is shipped to district bulk storage tanks located at destinations D_1, D_2, D_3, and D_4. The total quantities produced by each plant and required by each storage facility in a given time period and the shipping cost coefficients are conveniently represented in Figure 3.7.

For example, Plant O_1 produces 18 (1,000 bbl). The cost of shipping from O_1 to D_1 is $80 (1,000 bbl). The requirement of Tank D_1 is 10 (1,000 bbl).

	Destinations (storage tanks)				a_i Available quantity (1,000 bbl)
	D_1	D_2	D_3	D_4	
O_1	80	50	40	30	18
Origins O_2 (plants)	70	80	60	50	18
O_3	100	60	80	60	14
Required b_j quantity (1,000 bbl)	10	12	12	16	50

FIGURE 3.7   Initial cost-quantity tableau.

		Destinations					
		D_1	D_2	D_3	D_4		
	O_1	[80] 10	[50] 8	[40]	[30]	18	
Origins	O_2	[70]	[80] 4	[60] 12	[50] 2	18	Total cost = \$3,180
	O_3	[100]	[60]	[80]	[60] 14	14	
		10	12	12	16	50	

FIGURE **3.8** First trial solution.

A solution to the problem will consist of a schedule of shipments from the origins to the destinations. Figure 3.8 shows a first feasible trial solution in which six cells of the tableau have positive entries (nonzero cells); the remaining are zero cells. It can be shown that the optimum solution will not have more than $m + n - 1$ nonzero cells and possibly less.

The *stepping-stone* method of solution is now demonstrated. The first trial solution is developed by starting in the upper left-hand corner cell of the tableau and making entries systematically, working toward the lower right-hand corner and meeting the requirements and availabilities at each step. This will yield the first trial solution (Figure 3.8). The c_{ij} values are shown in the upper right-hand corner square of every cell.

The search for an optimum solution involves examining the matrix of the trial solution to determine if the use of a zero cell would result in a reduction in cost. The use of a zero cell requires adjustments to be made in some of the nonzero cells, since the row and column restrictions must be satisfied. For every zero cell used, at least three, and possibly more, of the nonzero cells must be changed. The net change in total cost is determined by an increase in cost for those cells in which the quantity is increased and a reduction in cost for those cells in which the quantity is reduced. The amount of change is such as to drive one of the previous nonzero cells to a zero value.

Suppose we wish to examine the desirability of using the route from O_2 to D_1.

1. Increasing O_2D_1 by one unit will increase the cost by \$70.
2. O_1D_1 must be decreased by one unit in order to satisfy the column restriction, with a savings of \$80.
3. Since O_1D_1 is decreased by one unit, then O_1D_2 must be increased by one unit to satisfy the first row restriction of 18 units. The cost is increased by \$50.
4. Now O_2D_2 must be decreased to satisfy the second column restriction of 12 units. This saves \$80. It will also satisfy the second row restriction by offsetting the initial increase in O_2D_1.
5. The net savings of adding a unit to O_2D_1 is \$40. The maximum that can be assigned to O_2D_1 is four units, the maximum by which cell O_2D_2 can be reduced. The result is shown in Figure 3.9.

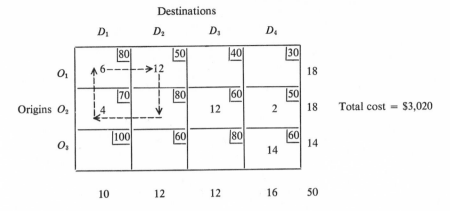

FIGURE **3.9** Second trial solution.

If one proceeds in this fashion, examining all zero cells to determine if a net advantage will be realized, the optimum solution will be obtained when the point is reached where no net advantage can be obtained. This means either proceeding in the fashion outlined above, that is, selecting a zero cell that results in a net advantage, or by examining all zero cells at each step and selecting the one that will result in the greatest advantage for an assignment.

The remainder of the problem steps are shown in Figure 3.10. In each step, all zero cells are examined for the maximum cost reduction. The x cell is the one to which an assignment will be made, and the boldface quantities are those that must be changed by the assignment.

THE MODIFIED DISTRIBUTION METHOD (MODI): The MODI method differs from the distribution method only in the manner in which the zero cells are evaluated; it is more efficient for hand computation.

In Figure 3.11, we reproduce the tableau for the first trial solution of the previous problem (circled numbers).

To each row and column of this tableau a value is added as follows:

1. First assign an arbitrary value of zero to row one.
2. Next assign the remaining values for the rows and column such that the sums of the row and column values correspond to the costs in the *nonzero* cells. For example, starting with zero, the value of column 1 row 1, the first column value must be 80, since $0 + 80$ equals the cost of the assigned cell O_1D_1.
3. The value of row 1 and column 2 must add to 50, the cost of O_1D_2; therefore, the column 2 value is 50.
4. The values of row 2 and column 2 must add to 80; therefore, the value of row 2 is 30.
5. In a similar fashion, the remaining row and column values can be determined using the costs for the assigned cells.
6. Now for each *zero* cell, enter the sum of the appropriate row and column

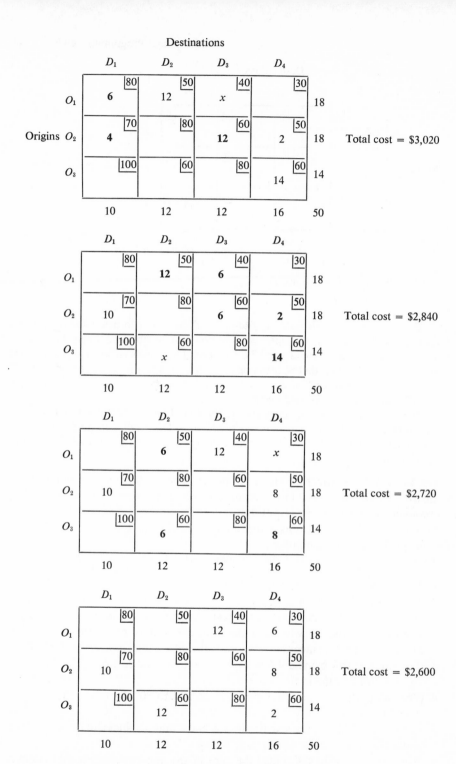

FIGURE **3.10** Final four trial solutions leading to optimum.

	Destinations				Quantity available	Row value
	D_1	D_2	D_3	D_4		
O_1	[80] (10)	[50] (8)	[40] 30	[30] 20	18	0
Origins O_2	[70] 110	[80] (4)	[60] (12)	[50] (2)	18	30
O_3	[100] 120	[60] 90	[80] 70	[60] (14)	14	40
Quantity required	10	12	12	16	50	
Column value	80	50	30	20		

FIGURE **3.11**   First trial solution—MODI.

values. These sums are compared with the cost coefficients of each cell. The cost coefficient is the *cost of assigning* a value to the cell. The sum in the cell is the cost of *not using the cell*. For example, it costs $100 to use cell O_3D_1, but it costs $120 not to use that cell, and therefore a net improvement of $20 can be gained for every unit assigned to that cell.

The procedure now continues in the same manner as before (Figure 3.12). The zero cell that is chosen is the one for which a maximum improvement is realized. In this case, it is O_2D_1, which yields a maximum savings of $40 (110 − 70) for each unit assigned.

New row and column values are generated. The procedure continues until, for

	Destinations				Row value
	D_1	D_2	D_3	D_4	
O_1	[80] (6)	[50] (12)	[40] 70	[30] 60	0
Origins O_2	[70] (4)	[80] 40	[60] (12)	[50] (2)	−10
O_3	[100] 80	[60] 50	[80] 70	[60] (14)	0
Column value	80	50	70	60	

FIGURE **3.12**   Second trial solution—MODI.

every zero cell, the sum of the row and column values is equal to or less than the cell's cost coefficient.

VARIATIONS IN THE MODEL AND METHOD: Sometimes degeneracy may be encountered in the solution. This occurs when a feasible solution has less than $m + n - 1$ individual allocations (nonzero x_{ij} values), but the allocations are nevertheless independent. A set of allocations is independent if it is impossible to increase or decrease any individual allocation (x_{ij}) without either changing the position of allocations or violating the row and column restrictions (a_i, b_j).

For example, assume that we have the following trial solution to a problem of three origins and four destinations.

	D_1	D_2	D_3	D_4	
O_1	10	4			14
O_2		8	6	4	18
O_3				10	10
	10	12	6	14	

By shifting an allocation to cell O_1D_4, we end up with less than $m + n - 1$ nonzero cells as follows:

	D_1	D_2	D_3	D_4	
O_1	10		ϵ	4	14
O_2		12	6		18
O_3				10	10
	10	12	6	14	

In this case, it is impossible to determine the row and column values by the *MODI method*. This problem is solved by introducing an infinitesimal allocation ϵ to the number of zero cells necessary to increase the number of nonzero cells to the required $m + n - 1$. In our example, we add an ϵ to cell O_1D_3. The ϵ can be shifted around without affecting the remaining real allocations and permits the calculation of row and column values in the modi method. It drops out of the final solution with no effect on its value.

Various things can be done to give the general model flexibility.

1. If the total requirements of the destinations are less than the total availability at the origins ($\sum_j b_j < \sum_i a_i$), then a dummy destination (k) can be added to absorb the added availability. The cost c_{ik} will be set inordinately high for

all i. Similarly, an additional dummy origin can be added for the situation, $\sum_j b_j > \sum_i a_i$.

2. If all a_i, b_i, and c_{ij} have a common and positive divisor Z, then the problem remains unaltered if the division is carried out before computation. The real solution is obtained by the product Zx_{ij} after computations are completed.

3. A fixed cost y_{ij} may be added to any element of the cost matrix such that

$$y_{ij} = \begin{cases} 1 \text{ if } x_{ij} > 0 \\ 0 \text{ otherwise} \end{cases}$$

A number of approaches have been suggested for handling this situation,[3,4] but we will not consider them.

The Linear Assignment Problem

The linear assignment problem is a special case of the distribution problem in which the solution values x_{ij} can be only zero or one. The general formulation is

i = index of origin, $i = 1, 2, \ldots, n$

j = index of destination, $j = 1, 2, \ldots, n$

c_{ij} = cost of assigning the resource at origin i to destination j

Note that the number of origins must be the same as the number of destinations. If this is not the case in a real problem, then dummy rows or columns must be added. Furthermore, there is only one unit of a resource at each origin and required by each destination. There is a solution matrix

$$X = \{x_{ij}\} \quad \text{where} \quad x_{ij} = \begin{cases} 1 \text{ if } i \text{ is assigned to } j \\ 0 \text{ otherwise} \end{cases}$$

The objective function is

$$\text{minimize} \sum_{i,j}^{n} x_{ij}c_{ij} \quad i = 1, \ldots, n; j = 1, \ldots, n$$

subject to

$$\sum_i x_{ij} = 1; \sum_j x_{ij} = 1$$

A number of methods are used to solve this problem. The following example is solved by the method of branch and bound. This method has more general applicability to combinatorial problems and therefore should be demonstrated.

BRANCH AND BOUND: Before discussing an example of the assignment problem, it would be well to say a few words about combinatorial problems in general. Many production problems involve the search for a solution from among a large number of discrete alternatives. For example, in the linear assignment problem, there are $n!$ possible solution matrices, each involving a unique assignment of the n origins to the n destinations. Other examples are:

[3] M. L. Balinski, "Fixed Cost Transportation Problems," *Naval Research Logistics Quarterly*, vol. 8, no. 1, March 1961.

[4] P. S. Dwyer, "Use of Completely Reduced Matrices in Solving Transportation Problems with Fixed Charges," *Naval Research Logistics Quarterly*, vol. 13, no. 3, September 1966.

1. A printing press operator must decide on the sequence with which n jobs are to be processed by the press. There are $n!$ possible sequences from which to make a choice.
2. In arranging machines in a shop, there are n machines to be assigned to n locations on the shop floor. There are $n!$ possible arrangements of the machines in the locations.
3. A finite number of n jobs are to be processed on m machines in the same order of machines. There are $(n!)^m$ possible schedules to choose from.
4. A part is processed at n different machines. The problem is to decide at what point between operations the part should be inspected. There are 2^n possible inspection arrangements.

Certain combinatorial problems can be structured as *integer* linear programming problems in which the variables can take on only non-negative integer values. However, the solution of such problems is not as straightforward as the simplex method, and alternative methods may have to be used, such as *branch and bound*.

The branch and bound technique is a method of partitioning the large set of possible solutions to a combinatorial problem into successively smaller subsets until a subset containing only the optimal solution is identified. We will now apply it to a linear assignment problem.

EXAMPLE 3.3   A city public works department has five street-cleaning vehicles of varying ages and capacities. There are five territories to each of which only one street-cleaning vehicle will be assigned. The problem is to decide on an optimum assignment of the five vehicles to the territories such that the total cost of the street-cleaning operation is minimized. Let the five vehicles be labeled A, B, C, D, and E and the five territories I, II, III, IV, and V.

The cost of cleaning the streets in a given territory will depend on the type of vehicle that is assigned to the territory, the difference in the size of the territory, the adaptability of the equipment to the type of streets, and the distances involved in disposing of the refuse. The costs (say, in thousands of dollars per year) are summarized in the form of the matrix shown in Figure 3.13a. For instance, the cost to clean the streets in territory III with vehicle A is $4,000.

Territories

	I	II	III	IV	V			I	II	III	IV	V
A	7	18	4	14	19		A	2	15	0	12	8
B	5	3	9	2	14		B	0	0	5	0	3
Vehicles C	9	15	11	8	12		C	4	12	7	6	1
D	17	20	13	26	22		D	12	17	9	24	11
E	10	6	8	7	11		E	5	3	4	5	0

(a) $C = c_{ij}$ (1,000 dollars) -5 -3 -4 -2 -11 $\Sigma = 25$
(b) Column reduction

FIGURE **3.13**   Steps in solution of linear assignment problem.

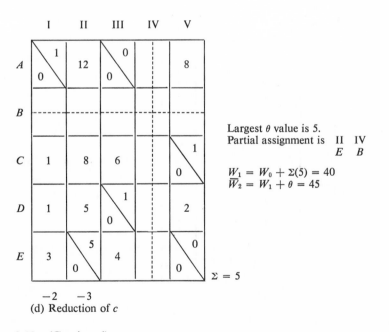

$W_0 = 10 + 25 = 35$

Partial assignment is   IV,
                          B
which has largest θ value = 5.

$\overline{W}_1 = w_0 + \theta = 40$

(c) Row reduction

Largest θ value is 5.
Partial assignment is   II   IV
                          E   B

$W_1 = W_0 + \Sigma(5) = 40$
$\overline{W}_2 = W_1 + \theta = 45$

(d) Reduction of c

FIGURE 3.13   (Continued)

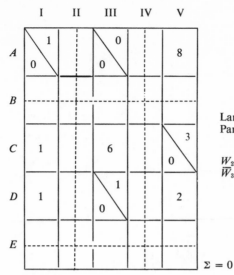

Largest θ is 3.
Partial assignment   II   IV   V
                     E   B   C

$W_2 = W_1 + \Sigma(0) = 40$
$\overline{W}_3 = W_2 + \theta = 43$

(e) Reduction of d

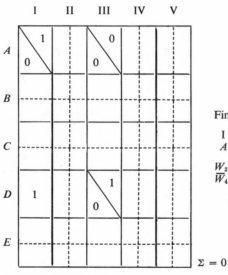

Final assignment

I   II   III   IV   V
A   E   D   B   C $S(\text{Min}) = 40$

$W_3 = W_2 + \Sigma(0) = 40$
$\overline{W}_4 = W_3 + \theta = 41$

(f) Reduction of e

FIGURE **3.13**   (Continued)

	I	II	III	IV	V
A	7	18	4	14	19
B	5	3	9	∞	14
C	9	15	11	8	12
D	17	20	13	26	22
E	10	6	8	7	11

Original matrix with $B - \text{IV} = \infty$

(g)

	I	II	III	IV	V	
A	2	15	2 / 0	7	8	
B	2 / 0	3 / 0	5	∞	3	
C	3	11	6	0 / 0	0 / 0	−1
D	3	8	2 / 0	10	2	−9
E	5	3	4	0 / 0	0 / 0	
	−5	−3	−4	−7	−11	

Partial assignment   II
B

$\overline{W}_6 = \overline{W}_1 + \theta = 43$

$\Sigma\ 30 + 10 = 40 = \overline{W}_1$

(h) Reduction of g.

	I	II	III	IV	V	
A	0		0	7	8	
B						
C	1		6	0	0	
D	1		0	10	2	
E	3		4	0	2	Σ = 2
	−2					

$W_6 = \overline{W}_1 + \Sigma(2) = 42$
$W_6 > W_4$

(i) Reduction of h.

FIGURE 3.13 (Continued)

A complete assignment is set forth as a solution matrix $X_k = x_{ij}, k = 1, 2, \ldots, n!$. The cost of the kth assignment is S_k and consists of the sum of five values taken one and only one from each row and each column of the cost matrix. Thus, for the assignment

	I	II	III	IV	V
A	1	0	0	0	0
B	0	0	1	0	0
C	0	1	0	0	0
D	0	0	0	0	1
E	0	0	0	1	0

the total cost is $S_k = 60$.

We could enumerate all of the 5! assignments, cost each one, and then select the minimum. A heuristic rule might be simply to examine the matrix and make a number of trial-and-error solutions and pick the minimum. This would not guarantee getting the optimum, particularly if the matrix were larger. We will now proceed to obtain systematically the minimum or optimum by the *branch and bound* method using the following steps:

1. *Reduce the original matrix*   The reduction of the matrix consists in first subtracting the minimum from every column of the matrix and then subtracting the minimum from every row of the matrix that has been column reduced. This is shown in Figure 3.13b and c with the amounts subtracted shown below each column and to the right of each row. Now the matrix *has at least one zero in every row and column*. The total amount that has been subtracted from the matrix is 35. We will explain the other numbers in the zero elements later.

2. *Set the initial lower bound*   Since the original matrix has been reduced by 35, *any solution will cost at least 35*. This is because any solution must contain a value from every row and column of the matrix, and the reduction includes values from each row and column unless the row or column already has a zero in it.

Let W_0 be the amount by which the initial matrix is reduced. Then W_0 is called an *initial lower bound* on the problem. No solution can have a cost less than W_0. This would be the optimum value, provided that in Figure 3.13c the position of the zeros were such that they defined a solution. In our example, selecting the partial assignment B-I means that territories II and IV cannot be serviced by B and therefore must be serviced by some other vehicle, resulting in additional cost over and above the 35.

3. *Set first node in decision tree*   The various stages leading to an optimum solution are depicted in the form of a decision tree in Figure 3.14. A *node* in the tree represents a subset of assignments, each subset defined in a particular way. The first node at the start represents the set of all 5! assignments. Next to it is placed the lower cost bound on that set. The following steps involve a successive partitioning of this initial set until the optimum assignment is found.

4. *First partitioning*   We now make a partial assignment of one vehicle to one territory. This first partial assignment might logically correspond with a zero element

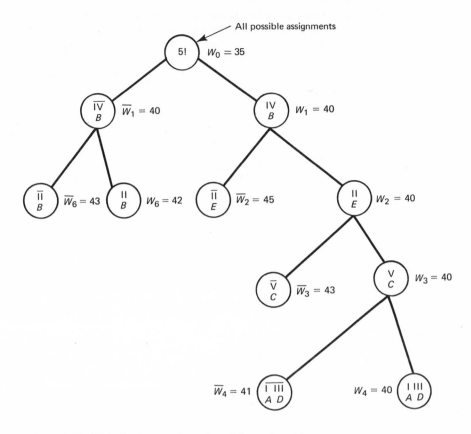

FIGURE **3.14** Solution tree to branch-and-bound problem.

in Figure 3.13c. That is, we might logically assign B-I, or B-II, or A-III, or any other pair that labels a zero element. In order to make a choice between the zeros, we do the following:

(a) In the corner of each zero element, place the sum of the minimum value in the row and the minimum value in the column containing the zero element. For instance, consider element B-I. The minimum value in the column is 2, and the minimum value in the row is 0. The value above the diagonal line is 2, which we will refer to as the θ value.

(b) The θ value is the minimum cost of *not* making the partial assignment defined by the zero element. For instance, if we do not choose to assign B to I, then I must be serviced by another vehicle. The lowest alternative cost is to assign A to I at a cost of 2, and B will have to be assigned to another territory. The lowest cost alternatives are either II or IV at an additional cost of zero.

(c) We now choose the partial assignment for which the zero element has the highest θ value. This is the assignment of B to IV with a θ value of 5. By making this partial assignment, we avoid the maximum cost (5) of not making it.

The first partial assignment results in a partitioning of the $n!$ set into two subsets, say X_1 and $\overline{X}_1$. Subset X_1 contains all the assignments that have the partial assignment B-IV. $\overline{X}_1$ contains all the assignments that do not have the partial assignment B-IV. Thus, at the first branch, the tree is divided into these two subsets:

$$X_1 = \left(\begin{array}{c}\text{IV}\\B\end{array}\right) \quad \text{and} \quad \overline{X}_1 = \left(\begin{array}{c}\overline{\text{IV}}\\B\end{array}\right).$$

5. *Lower bounds on the first branch*   We now attach lower bounds to each of the two mutually exclusive subsets. For the set $\overline{X}_1$, the lower bound is equal to that of all assignments, 35, plus the minimum cost of not assigning B to IV. This was already found to be 5. Therefore, the lower bound is $\overline{W}_1 = 35 + 5 = 40$. We determine the lower bound of the assignment B-IV by reducing the matrix in Figure 3.13c. First, row B and column IV are deleted. The resulting submatrix must be reduced by 2 in the first column and by 3 in the second column, giving a total of -5. Now the lower bound on X_1 is $35 + 5 = 40$. This is shown in Figure 3.13d.

6. *Make the second branching*   At this point, we could branch out of either the node $\left(\begin{array}{c}\text{IV}\\B\end{array}\right)$ or the node $\left(\begin{array}{c}\overline{\text{IV}}\\B\end{array}\right)$. Each has the same lower bound. In general, we would choose the node with the smallest lower bound as the branch point. We will continue the branching from $\left(\begin{array}{c}\text{IV}\\B\end{array}\right)$. In Figure 3.13d, we again assign θ values to each of the zero elements of the matrix and then choose the element that has the highest θ value, in this case E-II. The subset $\left(\begin{array}{c}\text{IV}\\B\end{array}\right)$ is now partitioned into two sub-subsets $\left(\begin{array}{c}\text{II}\\E\end{array}\right)$ and $\left(\begin{array}{c}\overline{\text{II}}\\E\end{array}\right)$. The sub-subset $\left(\begin{array}{c}\text{II}\\E\end{array}\right)$ contains all the assignments that have B-IV and E-II as partial assignments. The sub-subset $\left(\begin{array}{c}\overline{\text{II}}\\E\end{array}\right)$ contains all assignments that have B-IV, but not E-II, as a partial assignment.

7. The process continues branching to the right until we reach a node that contains a full assignment

	I	II	III	IV	V
A	1	0	0	0	0
B	0	0	0	1	0
$X = C$	0	0	0	0	1
D	0	0	1	0	0
E	0	1	0	0	0

with a total cost of 40. This is optimum, because no other node in the tree system contains a lower bound less than 40. However, there might be more than one optimal value in this problem, since we still have the node $\left(\dfrac{\text{IV}}{B}\right)$ with a lower bound of 40.

We therefore need to branch from this node in search of a second optimum. We do this by the following steps.

(a) We return to the original matrix and place infinity (∞) in the element B-IV, since no assignment can contain this partial assignment (Figure 3.13g).

(b) We then reduce this matrix, obtaining a total of 40, which should agree with $\overline{W}_1$, Figure 3.13h.

(c) Next we assign θ values to the zero cells and make a partial assignment based on the maximum θ value. This will be B-II, selected at random from those elements having $\theta = 3$.

(d) We then partition the subset $\left(\dfrac{\overline{\text{IV}}}{B}\right)$ into two sub-subsets $\left(\dfrac{\text{II}}{B}\right)$ and $\left(\dfrac{\overline{\text{II}}}{B}\right)$.

(e) The reduction of the matrix in Figure 3.13i results in a lower bound on the node B-II equal to 42; since this is greater than W_4, the optimum, there can be no node following $\left(\dfrac{\text{II}}{B}\right)$, and there is therefore no reason to continue.

Dynamic Programing

Certain problems appear as a sequence of decisions to be made over a period of time, where a decision made at one point in the sequence affects the decisions at subsequent points. We wish to find a policy or a particular sequence of decisions that optimizes an objective function for the entire period in question. In this case, the optimal policy is not found by a simple summation of optimal decisions made independently at each point in the sequence. To solve this kind of problem, we use the method of dynamic programing.

To demonstrate the method in simple terms, we will select a problem from a certain class of combinatorial problems, which have the theme 2^n and which appear in a number of forms in production problems. Suppose we have a set $K = \{k_t | t = 1, 2, \ldots, n\}$, where k_t is an "object" ordered by the subscript t. The object may be a physical item, positions in time, or sequential stages in a process. Then there are 2^n possible subsets, each subset containing combinations of the original set K. An element of K either belongs to the subset (1) or it does not (0). Thus, for $n = 3$, the subsets are $(0, 0, 0)$, $(1, 0, 0)$, $(0, 1, 0)$, $\ldots$, $(1, 1, 1)$.

The values 1, 0 can correspond to two alternative choices that can be made at each stage of an n-stage decision process. Some examples are the following:

1. A particular part has four operations performed on it in sequence, each operation being performed by a different machine. We wish to decide where to place inspection stations in the sequence. An inspection station can be located after each operation (1) or not (0). Of the 16 possible location sequences, which is best?

2. There is a finite set of n containers. Each container has a certain volume equal to s_i, $i = 1, 2, \ldots, n$. Each container also has an economic value v_i. The containers are to be loaded into a truck to be carried to some destination. The truck has a volume restriction H. Given that $\Sigma\, s_i > H$, the problem is to choose from among the set of n objects a unique subset of n' objects, which will maximize the total value in the truck subject to the restrictions in the truck capacity. This is called the "loading or knapsack" problem.

3. A machine has a predicted productive life of exactly five years. At the end of each year, a decision is to be made either to make a general preventive maintenance repair of the machine or to permit it to run for one more year without preventive maintenance. The preventive maintenance operation costs a fixed amount. The cost of permitting the machine to run one more year is a function of the age of the machine. In which years should preventive maintenance be performed?

Consider the last example concerning the preventive maintenance of the machine. Let the decision variable be X_t such that

$$X_t = \begin{cases} 1 \text{ if the machine is given preventive maintenance at the end of year } t; \\ \quad\quad t = 1, \ldots, 5 \\ 0 \text{ if the machine is not given preventive maintenance} \end{cases}$$

Also, let

P_t = cost of preventive maintenance made at the end of period t
  = $\$100 + \$10(t)$
Q_t = cost of permitting the machine to run from the end of year $t - 1$ to the end of year t without preventive maintenance being performed at the end of year $t - 1$
  = $\$50 + \$25(t - 1)$

Now it is clear that the cost in any period t is a function of the decision made at the previous period, $t = 2, \ldots, 5$. Therefore, we may start with period 5 and determine the maintenance costs as a function of the previous year's possible decisions. For each period, we can conveniently represent the costs in the form of a matrix:

$$C(t) = c(X_{t-1}, X_t)$$

1. *Period 5.* There is only one possible decision in period 5, and that is not to perform preventive maintenance since it is the last month. Therefore,

$C(5) = c(X_4, 0) =$

X_4 \ X_5	0
1	0
0	150

where $c(1, 0) = 0$, since $P_5 = 0$; and $c(0, 0) = 150$, since $Q_5 = \$50 + \$25(4)$.

2. *Period 4.* We have a cost matrix $C(4) = c(X_3, X_4)$ where the element $c(X_3, X_4) = $ minimum $\{c(X_4, X_5)\} + P_4 + Q_4$. For example, the element $c(1, 1) = 0 + \$100 + \$10(4) + 0 = \$140$.

$C(4) =$

X_3 \ X_4	1	0
1	0 140 0 $\overline{140}$	150 0 0 $\overline{150}$
0	0 140 125 $\overline{265}$	150 0 125 $\overline{275}$

minimum $c(X_4, X_5)$
P_t
Q_t

3. *Period 3.* For period 3, the element of the matrix is $c(X_2, X_3) = $ minimum $\{c(X_3, X_4)\} + P_3 + Q_3$, where $X_4 = 0, 1$.

$C(3) =$

X_2 \ X_3	1	0
1	140 130 0 $\overline{270}$	265 0 0 $\overline{265}$
0	140 130 100 $\overline{370}$	265 0 100 $\overline{365}$

Continuing in a like manner, the costs for the remaining two periods are

$C(2) =$

X_1 \ X_2	1	0
1	265 120 0 ――― 385	365 0 0 ――― 365
0	265 120 75 ――― 460	365 0 75 ――― 440

$C(1) =$

X_0 \ X_1	1	0
0	365 110 ――― 475	440 0 ――― 440

The optimum policy corresponds to the total cost of $440. This was obtained by setting $X_1 = 0$, $X_2 = 0$, $X_3 = 0$, and $X_4 = 1$.

NETWORK MODELS

A network model is a general way of structuring some kinds of production problems. The obvious situations are those involving a system of material flow. A network consists of a set of elements (factories, operations, stations) that are interconnected by a set of links (roads, conveyors, pipelines). One characteristic is the nature of the flow through such networks. We might wish to determine, for example, the maximum rate of flow or the shortest or fastest route through the system. Some examples are the following:

1. A network of railroads connects a set of cities, and we want to determine the maximum rate at which goods can be shipped through the network from one city to another.
2. A network of roads and highways connects factories and warehouses, and we want to find the shortest route for the trans-shipment of materials between any two factories and/or warehouses.

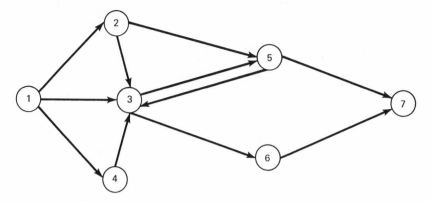

FIGURE **3.15**   Network of nodes and arcs.

Other kinds of production problems can also be represented by the network format. We will first discuss the network model in terms of material flow and then extend it to other applications.

Network theory consists of a rigorous definition of network structures and algorithms for determining the desired measures of network flow. We will briefly consider only the essential features of this theory.

LINEAR GRAPH: A linear graph is displayed in Figure 3.15. It is a collection of branches consisting of a set N of nodes $n_1, n_2, \ldots, n_N$ and a set A of arcs. An arc is an ordered pair (n_i, n_j). The directed arc n_i, n_j extends from node i, the origin, to node j, the terminal, and is displayed by a directional arrow between the two circles representing the nodes.

A *connected graph* is one in which any node j can be reached from any other node i via branches in the graph.

A *directed* path between two nodes n_i and n_j is the sequence of nodes and arcs connecting i and j. Thus, $n_1, (n_1, n_2), n_2, (n_2, n_5), (n_5, n_3), n_3$ is a directed path between node 1 and node 3.

A path between two nodes i and j consists of a sequence of nodes and arcs such that either n_k, n_{k+1} or n_{k+1}, n_k is chosen for any pair of nodes in the sequence i, $i + 1, \ldots, k, \ldots, j - 1$. The sequence $n_1, (n_1, n_3), n_3, (n_4, n_3), n_4$ is a path where (n_1, n_3) is a forward arc and (n_4, n_3) is a backward arc.

Cuts

Suppose we partition the set N into two disjointed subsets P and Q, such that $Q = N - P$. In Figure 3.16, the partition yields $P = (1, 2, 3, 4)$ and $Q = (5, 6, 7)$. Then let (P, Q) be the set of forward arcs (n_p, n_q), where $n_p \in P$ and $n_q \in Q$. Thus, in Figure 3.16 $(P, Q) = \{(2, 5), (3, 5), (3, 6)\}$.

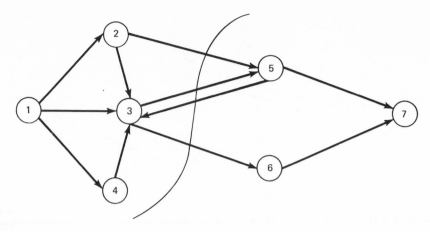

FIGURE **3.16** A cut in a network.

Every directed path from a node $n_i \in P$ to a node $n_j \in Q$ contains an arc $n_i n_j \in$ (P, Q), and (P, Q) is a cut separating P from Q or any n_p from n_q.

Capacity

The capacity of an arc n_i, n_j is defined by a non-negative number $c(i, j)$. Figure 3.17 shows a capacitated directed network with the arc capacity shown next to each arc.

Given this type of network, we are interested in determining the value v of the flow between a node s, called the source, and a node r, called the sink.[5] This flow is a function $f(i, j)$ of the set A and has these properties:

1. The flow between two nodes i and j cannot exceed the capacity, or $f(i, j) \le c(i, j)$ for all $(i, j) \in A$.
2. The net flow from the source must equal v, or $\sum_j f(s, j) - \sum f(j, s) = v$.
3. The net flow through any node other then s or r is zero, or $\sum f(i, j) - \sum f(j, i) = 0$.
4. The net flow from the sink is equal to $-v$, or $\sum f(i, r) - \sum f(r, i) = -v$.

In a capacitated directed network, the capacity of a cut in (P, Q) is

$$c(P, Q) = \sum_{i \in P, j \in Q} c(i, j)$$

From Figure 3.17,

$$c(P, Q) = c(2, 5) + c(3, 5) + c(3, 6) = 17$$

Since every directed path through the cut from $s = 1$ to $r = 7$ must contain one of the arcs in (P, Q), the flow from s to r cannot exceed 17.

---

[5] A *source* is a node with no arcs entering it, and a sink is a node with no arcs leaving it.

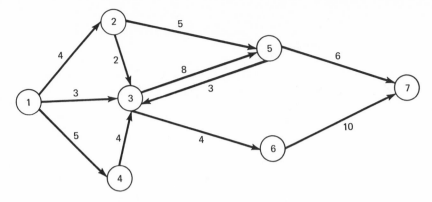

FIGURE **3.17**   Capacitated network.

Maximal-Flow Minimal-Cut Theorem

Let (P_0, Q_0) be the minimum cut for which $c(P, Q)$ is a minimum. Then the Maximal-Flow—Minimal-Cut theorem states that if v_0 is the value of a maximum flow s to r and $c(P_0, Q_0)$ is the capacity of the minimum cut separating s from r, then

$$v_0 = c(P_0, Q_0)$$

The Ford-Fulkerson Algorithm

We now wish to determine the maximum flow in a capacitated directed network. As an example, we will use the network in Figure 3.17. The algorithm is due to Ford and Fulkerson and is based on a labeling and scanning process.[6] The steps of the solution are traced in Figure 3.18. Note that we have changed nodes 1 and 7 to read s and r, respectively.

We introduce the notion of flow in a branch or arc as $f(i, j)$ in the direction of node i to node j. Each arc has an associated number pair. The first number of the pair is $c(i, j)$, and the second number is $f(i, j)$. To begin with, we set $f(i, j)$ equal to zero for all arcs.

Step 1. Assign an initial flow to the system corresponding as closely as possible to a maximum flow as can be determined by sight. In this case, we assign a flow of 4 to the path s-4-3-5-r. Note that the arc (4, 3) has been *saturated;* that is, $c(i, j) - f(i, j) = 0$. No labeling has taken place.

Step 2. Labeling is now applied to certain nodes. Label node s $(-, \infty)$. We now *scan* node s by considering all nodes terminating the arcs (s, j). Consider node 4, for example. We can move one more unit to it through arc $(s, 4)$; therefore, we label

---

[6] L. R. Ford and D. R. Fulkerson, *Flows in Networks.* Princeton, N.J.: Princeton University Press. 1962.

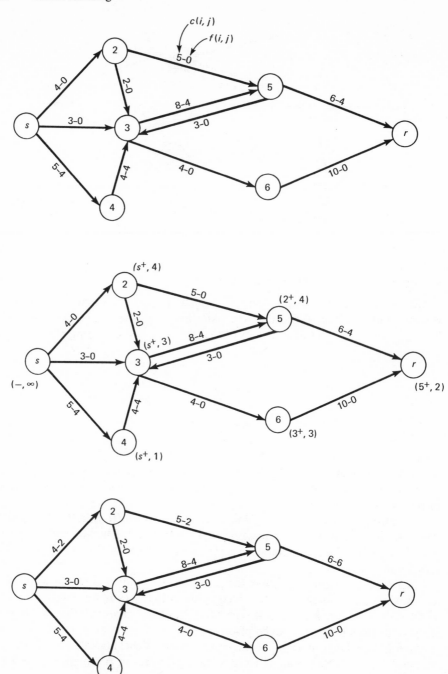

FIGURE **3.18** Steps in maximal flow algorithm.

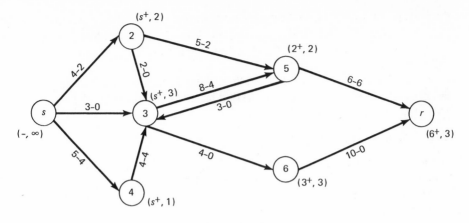

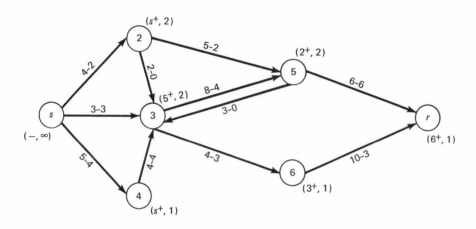

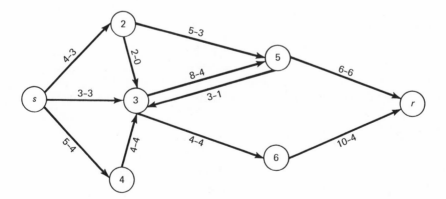

FIGURE **3.18**   (Continued)

the node $(s, 1)$, where the first number represents the node from which the transfer or flow is made and the second number the amount. More generally, if $c(s, j) > f(s, j)$, label j for each of the nodes with (s^+, δ_j), where $\delta_j = c(s, j) - f(s, j)$. The source has now been scanned.

Now shift to any node j that has been labeled but not scanned (e.g., $j = 2$). For each node k of the set of arcs (j, k) that has not been labeled, if $c(j, k) > f(j, k)$, apply the label (j, δ_k), where

$$\delta_k = \min [\delta_j, c(j, k) - f(j, k)]$$

For example, node 5 is labeled $(2^+, \delta_2)$. Each node is therefore labeled with the minimum amount that the arc terminating at it can carry, or the amount available at the origin node.

Now j has been scanned.

The process is repeated for each labeled but unscanned node until either 1) the sink r is labeled (a breakthrough) or 2) the sink r is not labeled, and no more labels can be applied. In case 2), the algorithm is terminated and maximum flow is attained. In case 1), we apply the flow-augmenting process to increase flow.

Step 3. In the example, we now apply the flow-augmenting process. The sink has been labeled $(5^+, 2)$. Now $f(i, r)$, $i = 5$ is replaced by $f(i, r) + \delta(r)$ or $(4 + 2)$. If the sink label is (i^-, δ_r), then the flow is augmented by $f(i, r) - \delta_r$. Then, if node i is labeled $[i - 1^+, \delta_i]$ or $[i - 1^-, \delta_i]$, then $f(i - 1, i)$ is augmented by $+\delta_r$ or $-\delta_r$, respectively. The process is repeated until the source is reached. In this case, we have added two units of flow to the branch s-2-5-r.

Step 4. After all first cycle labels are deleted, step 2 is repeated.

Step 5. The flow is augmented a second time by adding $+3$ to the directed path s-3-6-r, and then the third label scanning cycle is completed.

Step 6. The flow is augmented a third time by adding one unit to the directed path s-2-5-3-6-r. Since no additional flow can be added to the network, the problem is now completed.

Shortest Route

Suppose we have a network as shown in Figure 3.19, where each arc has an associated number $d(j, k)$, which is the distance between nodes j and k. We wish to find the shortest path between the source s and the sink r. Given a total of n nodes in the network, Bellman[7] proposes a recursive algorithm of the following type:

$$a_j^1 = d(j, r) \quad \text{and} \quad a_j^i = \underset{k}{\text{minimum}} \ \{d(j, k) + a_k^{i-1}\}$$

where $1 \leq j$, $k \leq n$ and $2 \leq i \leq n - 1$. The symbol a_j^i is the minimum distance between nodes j and r for a path of $i + 1$ nodes including r. Each step of the algo-

---

[7] R. Bellman, "A Routing Problem," *Quart. of Appl. Math.*, vol. 16, 1958, pp. 87–90.

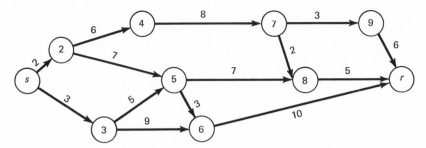

FIGURE **3.19**   Network with arc distance.

rithm consists in calculating in order of ascending i the vectors $a^i = a_1^i, a_2^i, \ldots, a_n^i$ until either

$$a_s^p = a_s^{p+q} \text{ for all } q$$

or

$$q = n - 1.$$

The calculations of the a^i vectors, leading to the shortest path s-3-5-8-r for the network in Figure 3.19, are given below.

i	j	k	d_{jk}	a_k^{i-1}	a_j^i	Path
1	9	r	6	0	6	9–r minimum
	8	r	5	0	5	8–r minimum
	6	r	10	0	10	6–r minimum
2	7	9	3	6	9	7–9–r
	7	8	2	5	7	7–8–r minimum
	5	8	7	5	12	5–8–r minimum
	5	6	3	10	13	5–6–r
	3	6	9	10	19	3–6–r minimum
3	4	7	8	7	15	4–7–8–r minimum
	2	5	7	12	19	2–5–8–r minimum
	3	5	5	12	17	3–5–8–r minimum
	s	3	3	19	22	s–3–6–r minimum
4	2	4	6	15	21	2–4–7–8–r minimum
	s	2	2	19	21	2–5–8–r
	s	3	3	17	20	s–3–5–8–r minimum
5	s	2	2	21	23	s–2–4–7–8–r minimum

Minimum path is s-3-5-8-r, for which $a_s^4 = 20$.

A Transportation Problem

A special kind of transportation problem is the following. There are three processing plants located at origins O_1, O_2, and O_3, and their output is piped to district bulk storage tanks located at destinations D_1, D_2, D_3, and D_4. The quantity

	D_1	D_2	D_3	D_4	
O_1	$c(1, 1)$		$c(1, 3)$		a_1
O_2		$c(2, 2)$		$c(2, 4)$	a_2
O_3	$c(3, 1)$	$c(3, 2)$	$c(3, 3)$		a_3
	b_1	b_2	b_3	b_4	

FIGURE **3.20** Tableau format for capacity transportation problem.

that can be shipped between plant and tanks is restricted by pipeline capacities. We want to find a schedule of shipments in thousands of barrels a day to maximize the output of the plant system.

The problem is formulated in general terms as follows. Figure 3.20 is a tableau in which the $c(i, j)$ values represent the restriction in flow from origin i to destination j. Cells with no entries indicate that flow is impossible. The plant capabilities and tank demands are shown as a_i and b_j, respectively. If x_{ij} is the daily flow of material from origin i to destination j, we have

$$\text{Maximize} \sum_i \sum_j x_{ij}$$

subject to

$$x_{ij} \leq c(i, j)$$
$$\sum_j x_i \leq a_i$$
$$\sum_i x_j \leq b_j$$

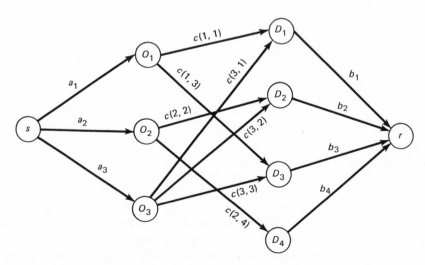

FIGURE **3.21** Network representation of capacity transportation problem.

The problem can now be formulated as a maximum flow network problem (Figure 3.21). The source s and sink r represent dummy nodes from which a_i and b_j values flow, respectively. This assures that the sum of the flow from an origin node does not exceed the capability of the origin. Similarly, the requirements of a destination cannot be exceeded.

RANDOM PROCESSES

A second class of models involves the description of the random nature of processes. In the remainder of this chapter, we will consider some useful and common models of random processes and then continue with the subject of random variability in the next chapter.

Queuing Systems

We speak of a queuing system, or waiting line, when *customers* arrive sequentially over time at a *service* facility to receive the service. Owing to the inability of the service facility to handle the flux of customer arrivals, a waiting line of customers forms at various times. We wish to formulate a quantitative description of the waiting-line system.

Our daily existence is replete with waiting-line situations. We are all familiar with the experience of having to queue up or wait in line for some service, whether it be for theater tickets, checkout lines in supermarkets, stoplights, or barber shops. The waiting-line phenomenon appears frequently in industrial and production systems. For example, an individual machine establishes a waiting line, where the customers are the various jobs assigned to the machine. A set of machines forms a network of waiting lines through which jobs must work their way to completion. In contrast, a single operator tending a group of machines is a service facility. The machines periodically require his attendance with the possibility of a queue of machines waiting for his service.

THE STRUCTURE OF A QUEUING SYSTEM: A queuing system is described in terms of four characteristics.

1. *Customer arrival pattern*   The queuing system can be described by the manner in which the customers arrive at the service operation. Customers can arrive either at regular intervals or at random points in time. In the latter case, we are interested in the probability distribution of the random arrival variables. This can either be the rate of arrival, that is, the number of customers arriving in a stated time interval, or the interval of time between successive arrivals.

2. *Service pattern*   The first element of the service mechanism is the service time. This can either be a constant or a random variable, and again, in the latter case, we are interested in the probability distribution of the service times.

3. *Number of channels*   The second element of the service function is the format of the service stations. A single-channel queue is one in which there is only a

single station to which the arriving customer can go. A multiple-channel queue permits a customer to be serviced at any one of a number of stations in parallel (like a multichaired barber shop) or by a sequence of stations (like the physical examination for military service). Besides these two basic formats, one can describe a wide variety of combinations of channel formats.

4. *The service priority*   The final characteristic is the priority with which customers are serviced. We naturally think of first come, first served as the fair and democratic way of servicing customers in most service systems dealing with the public. However, in industrial situations, we might find other priority rules to be more advantageous. For example, in the case of the machine to which a number of jobs has been assigned, we might sequence the waiting jobs through the machine on the basis of the dates on which they are due for completion, thus giving priority to the job with the earliest due date. Or, if there is a group of trucks waiting to be unloaded at a receiving dock, we might take the smallest loads first to minimize the number of trucks waiting in the yard.

Variations in each of the four major characteristics permit a wide variety of queuing situations. *Queuing theory* is a body of knowledge containing analytical or mathematical models that explain the behavior of queuing systems. As we shall see, queuing problems, however, can be handled by means other than mathematical models. Therefore, the solving of queuing problems is not the exclusive domain of queuing theory.

SYSTEM VARIABLES: If either the arrival and/or the service time is a random variable, the queuing system behaves as a random process. The purpose of queuing theory, or other methods of studying waiting lines, is to examine and describe the random character of the system in terms of the distribution of certain system variables. These variables include:

1. *The system state*   The state of the system pertains to the queue or the waiting line itself. The number of customers waiting in the line at any given time is a random variable. Therefore, the nature of the waiting-line distribution including the mean number of customers in the line, symbolized as $\bar{n}$, and the probability of n, or $P(n)$, are state variables.

2. *Customer waiting time*   We may also be interested in the average time a customer must wait in line, this time we will call $\bar{w}$.

3. *Idle time of service facility*   If the rate of service exceeds the rate of arrivals, then the service facility will experience some idle time. A measure of this idle time is the percent utilization of the facility.

Queuing Problems

Queuing problems are often encountered in situations where some economic objective must be satisfied. Queuing models are descriptive in the sense of quantifying the system variables. Therefore, the information they yield is usually an input to a decision or optimizing model of some type. Some typical problems are indicated in the following table.

Service facility	Customer	Objective	Design or control variable
Material stockroom	Machine operators	Minimize the total cost including the number of stockroom attendants and machine operator wait time	Number of checkout stations
Truck unloading at dock	Incoming delivery trucks	Minimize investment in loading docks and truck waiting time	Number of docks
Tollbooths on super-highway tollgate	Vehicles	Minimize number of toll-booths with a constraint on queue lengths	Number of tollbooths
Maintenance men	Machine requiring adjustment or repair	Minimize the idle time of men and machine	Number of maintenance men
An operation B in a product-line layout	Parts arriving from previous operation A	Optimize the space for work in process between the operations, or minimize downtime of operation A	Storage space between operations A and B

In these examples, the common objective is to minimize both an expenditure in service resources and costs associated with the customer or queue. The economic problem is to optimize the design variable such that the sum of service-customer costs are minimized.

While the costs of the resources may be direct and relatively easy to determine, the costs related to the customer or queue are more difficult to assess. This is especially true when the customer has the option of leaving the queue and seeking service elsewhere. In the industrial cases that we have cited, this does not apply, and the costs of having idle customers (delivery trucks, machine operators, machines, or operations), which are also resources, may be measured.

In general, queuing problems involve changing the design or control variables representing one or more characteristics of the queuing system and then measuring the performance of the system after making the changes. In most of the above examples, the design variable is the number of channels in the queue. In the product-line problem, the variable is the space to handle the queue. In dispatching jobs through a network of machines, we might be interested in the effect of changing the service priority rules on the performance measures for the shop as a whole. Both service and arrival patterns can be changed by design scheduling or planning with resultant effects on the economics of the system.

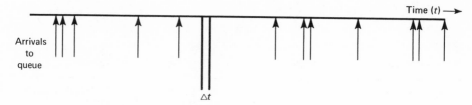

FIGURE **3.22**   Random arrivals to a queue.

To summarize, then, we must remember that it is one thing to analyze the queuing system and still another to translate the results into a decision model. Various analytical cost models have been proposed for minimizing the expected cost of a queuing system under certain assumptions.[8] For complex problems involving the perturbation of several design variables trial-and-error solutions using simulation or queuing theory are necessary.

Queuing Theory

Queuing theory pertains to the mathematical treatment of waiting lines. Because of the many variations in the four general characteristics of waiting lines, this is a large and expanding subject. It will suffice, for our purposes, if we examine only a few of the simpler kinds of queuing situations.

THE SINGLE-CHANNEL QUEUE: The single-channel queue, together with certain assumptions about the arrival and service mechanisms, is the simplest case to handle mathematically. In this situation, we assume that customers arriving at the system remain in the system until they are served. We make the following additional assumptions:

1. *Arrival pattern*   The arrivals to the system are *completely random*. Here, completely random has a more specific meaning than chance phenomenon. It means that the number of arrivals per a unit time is Poisson distributed with a mean arrival rate designated as λ.

The arrivals constitute a Poisson process in this sense. Suppose that a finite interval of time t is broken down into a succession of m infinitesimally small units of time Δt. Now assume that the probability of a success (a customer arrival) occurring in Δt is a constant p. Then, in the interval t, the number of arrivals will be binomially distributed. But as both Δt and p approach zero and m approaches infinity, the number of arrivals in t approaches a Poisson distribution.

For a given length of time, then, the arrival pattern is as shown in Figure 3.22.

Now consider carefully the assumption of Poisson arrivals. If X is the random number of arrivals per unit time, then

---

[8] Frederick S. Hillier, "Economic Models for Industrial Waiting Line Problems," *Management Science*, vol. 10, no. 1, October 1963, pp. 119–30.

$$P(X = x) = \frac{\lambda^x e^{-\lambda}}{x!}$$

where, again, λ is the mean arrival rate. Remember, the mean arrival rate is a constant of proportionality, that is, average number of arrivals per a unit of time. For a very small increment of time Δt the mean arrival rate is then $\lambda \Delta t$. Then

$$P(x = 0) = e^{-\lambda \Delta t} = 1 - \lambda \Delta t - \frac{(\lambda \Delta t)^2}{2!} \cdots [9]$$

$$P(x = 1) = \lambda \Delta t e^{-\lambda \Delta t} = \lambda \Delta t \left[1 - \lambda \Delta t - \frac{(\lambda \Delta t)^2}{2!} \cdots \right]$$

$$P(x = 2) = \frac{(\lambda \Delta t)^2}{2!} e^{-\lambda \Delta t} = \frac{(\lambda \Delta t)^2}{2!} \left[1 - \lambda \Delta t - \frac{(\lambda \Delta t)^2}{2!} \cdots \right]$$

Neglecting all higher order terms in Δt, we have

$$P(x = 0) = 1 - \lambda \Delta t$$

$$P(x = 1) = \lambda \Delta t$$

$$P(x > 1) = \text{negligible}$$

Then the probability of one arrival in the interval Δt is a constant $\lambda \Delta t$ and is therefore *independent of the time of the previous arrival*. This is the definition of completely random arrivals.

Corresponding to the Poisson arrival rate is a distribution of times between successive arrivals. It can be shown that this is a negative exponential distribution in which the probability of t time units between successive arrivals is $f(t)$, and

$$f(t) = \lambda e^{-\lambda t}$$

The Poisson arrival distribution is found in real life when the population of potential customers to the queue system is large and each customer acts independently of every other. Examples are cars arriving at toll booths, the rate of fire alarms received by a fire department dispatching station, the rate at which bees arrive at the hive, or the rate of accidents in a plant. In these cases, we might experience a bunching of events followed by periods of inactivity; the saying, "It never rains but it pours," is a cliché that recognizes this phenomenon.

2. *Service pattern*   Our second assumption is that service times are also exponentially distributed with a mean service time of $1/\mu$ and a corresponding Poisson service rate with a mean of μ. Letting Y be the service time random variable, we have

$$f(y) = \mu e^{-\mu y} \qquad (y \geq 0)$$

Again consider a time interval Δt. Suppose a customer has been in service for a time y_0. The probability of the customer service being completed in the interval Δt is the conditional probability

---

[9] $e^{-a} = 1 - \dfrac{a}{1!} - \dfrac{a^2}{2!} - \cdots - \dfrac{a^n}{n!}$

$$P(y_0 \leq Y \leq y_0 + \Delta t \mid Y \geq y_0)$$

$$= \frac{P(y_0 \leq Y \leq y_0 + \Delta t)}{P(Y \geq y_0)}$$

$$\sim \frac{\mu e^{-\mu y_0} \Delta t}{e^{-\mu y_0}} = \mu \, \Delta t$$

Therefore the time of completion of a service is independent of the length of time the service has been in progress.

We should note that the rate of service is the potential rate and should not be confused with the number of units departing from the system per unit time. The latter must equal the arrival rate, assuming that customers can be serviced faster than they arrive.

The assumption of exponential service times is probably less tenable than the same assumption for interarrival times. However, this assumption permits easier development of the set of equations that describes the queuing system.

3. *Priority rule*   The third assumption is that the customers arriving at the queue are serviced on the basis of "first come, first served."

4. *Steady state*   When a queuing system starts up, with no customers in the queue, a transient state exists over some initial period. During this period, the parameters and probabilities of the state variables are changing with time. When the system finally settles down and reaches the steady state, these parameters become constants. Therefore, we are interested mainly in developing these steady-state distributions.

The parameters of the steady-state model are as follows. Let

n = the number of customers in the system including the one being serviced
$\bar{n}$ = mean number of customers in the system
σ_n = variance of n
ρ = λ / u; $0 \leq \rho < 1$ (called traffic intensity)
$P(n)$ = probability of n customers in the system
$\bar{w}$ = average waiting time including service time
p = percent idle service time

It can then be shown (see Appendix) that

$$P(0) = 1 - \rho$$
$$P(n) = \rho^n(1 - \rho) \qquad (n > 0)$$

$$\bar{n} \quad = \frac{\rho}{1 - \rho}$$

$$\bar{w} \quad = \bar{n}/\lambda = \frac{1}{\mu - \lambda}$$

$$p \quad = P(0) = 1 - \rho$$

EXAMPLE 3.4   Security Savings Bank proposes to leave one teller on duty during the period from 1 to 2 P.M. each weekday. Suppose that the customer arrival rates are Poisson distributed and the service time is exponential with means of $\lambda = 10$ per hour and $1/\mu = 0.05$ hours, respectively. The traffic intensity ρ is therefore 0.50.

$$\bar{n} = \frac{0.5}{1 - 0.5} = 1$$

$$\bar{w} = \frac{1}{10} = 0.10 \text{ hours}$$

$P_0 = 0.5$
$P_1 = 0.25$
$P_2 = 0.125$
$P_3 = 0.062$
$P_4 = 0.031$

Variations in the single-channel queue include modifications to the arrival and service patterns and to the service priority. For example, arrivals can be modified by a system of customer scheduling or by assuming that customers will leave the system if the queue is of a certain length. Service time parameters can be altered in terms of lower means or reduced variance, particularly in response to the size of the queue. Priorities can be changed to give pre-emptive priority to customers whose cost per unit of time in the queue is high. Or, priorities may be assigned on the basis of the estimated time to service the customer, such as servicing first customers with short service times.

MULTIPLE-CHANNEL QUEUES IN PARALLEL: Many waiting-line situations consist of a number of finite service channels arranged in parallel. For completely random arrivals and service times and no departures from the system except for service, the customer will be serviced upon arrival if a channel is idle. If the number of channels or service stations is s, then a waiting line will form only when $(n - s) > s$.

If $\rho = \lambda/\mu s$, where μ is the service rate for a channel (i.e., $\mu_i = \mu$ for $i = 1, \ldots, s$), then the steady-state variables are a function of a series K, where

$$K = 1 + s\rho + \frac{(s\rho)^2}{2!} + \cdots + \frac{(s\rho)^{s-1}}{(s - 1)!} + \frac{(s\rho)}{s!(1 - \rho)}$$

and, without proof,

$$P(0) = 1/K$$

$$P(n) = \frac{(s\rho)^n}{n!K} \quad \text{for} \quad 0 < n < s - 1$$

$$P(n) = \frac{s^s\rho^n}{s!K} \quad \text{for} \quad n \geq s$$

Formulas of this kind are cumbersome to use in specific cases, and we may refer to predetermined tables of the kind shown in Figure 3.23.

EXAMPLE 3.5   Suppose we assign two tellers to the bank between 1 and 2 P.M. What is the effect on customer waiting time? Using Figure 3.23, we first calculate the constant $U = \lambda/\mu s = 0.25$. Starting at the bottom of the chart at $s = 2$, we follow the vertical line until it crosses the line corresponding to $U = 0.25$, then read horizontally to the left-hand column to determine the value of $\bar{w}\mu = 0.65$. Solving for $\bar{w}$, we obtain 0.0325 hours.

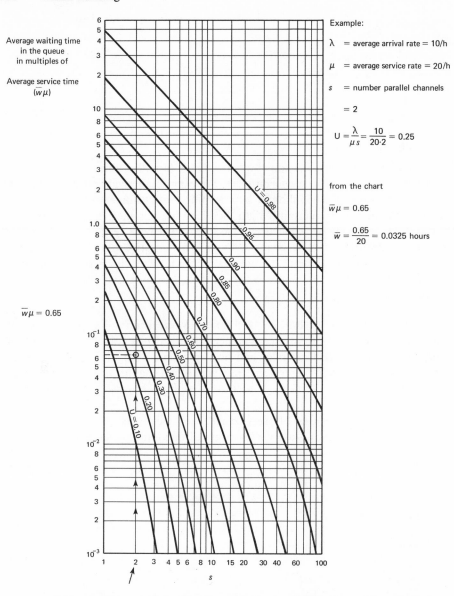

Average waiting time
in the queue
in multiples of

Average service time
$(\bar{w}\mu)$

$\bar{w}\mu = 0.65$

Example:

λ = average arrival rate = 10/h

μ = average service rate = 20/h

s = number parallel channels

$= 2$

$U = \dfrac{\lambda}{\mu s} = \dfrac{10}{20 \cdot 2} = 0.25$

from the chart

$\bar{w}\mu = 0.65$

$\bar{w} = \dfrac{0.65}{20} = 0.0325$ hours

FIGURE **3.23** Average waiting time for arrivals to waiting line with unlimited Poisson distributed arrivals, exponential service times, and random or arrival order of service. From E. V. Krick, *Methods Engineering.* New York: John Wiley & Sons, 1962.

SEQUENTIAL QUEUES: In industrial situations, we are faced with cases in which the customer is serviced by a number of stations in sequence. This is particularly true of a job shop, where a "job" proceeds through a series of operations on different machines. Each machine is an independent service center, and the jobs arrive at it randomly from other machines in the system. Each machine may have a queue of jobs competing for the machine. Another example is an assembly line with inventories permitted between each of the successive stations in the line. In this case, all customers (parts) go through every operation in the line. We will examine these situations in Chapter 8.

FINITE POPULATIONS: Another variation is the case of the finite population. In the preceding examples, we have assumed a large population of customers. An example of a finite population occurs in the problem of "machine interference." In this situation, there is a given number of machines that are to be serviced by an operator. The machines are essentially automatic, but they must nevertheless be attended to at various times, such as unloading and loading, adjusting, etc. At any given point in time, more than one machine may require attention, and, therefore, idle machine time and lost production will result. A problem might be to determine the number of machines to be assigned to a single operator to balance the machine and operator idle times. We will consider this question in Chapter 9.

Monte Carlo Simulation

Mathematical models of random processes can be difficult or impossible to construct when the state variables are a function of a complex system of random variables. In such cases, it is usually possible to construct a simulator of the process that reproduces the random inputs to a system and measures the random outputs of the transformed system. The term *Monte Carlo simulation* applies specifically to random or stochastic processes.

The Monte Carlo method is essentially an arithmetical operation, which includes the following major steps:

1. A random system or stochastic process is described in terms of a set of variables, which may include constants as well as random variables.
2. The process is simulated by recording the time sequence of random events as they occur, including inputs to the system and resulting outputs.
3. Time is advanced until some random "event" occurs in the system. The effect of this event on the state of the system is determined by arithmetical operations.
4. Time is then advanced to the next event, and the process is repeated until some desired cumulative sampling time period is satisfied. At this point, the simulation is completed, and various system state parameters are calculated, based on the sampled information.

This method of modeling a system is extremely flexible and can be tailored to a wide variety of possibilities. Since it can become a massive arithmetical operation, it is usually done by computer, although in elementary cases it can be done on paper.

EXAMPLE 3.6   The manager of Brinkley's Food Market decides that it might be a good idea to try window service for food marketing, something like the bank across the street, which provides window teller service. He is interested in the performance of the system in terms of the waiting time of the customers, the size of the queue behind the window, and the idleness of the window attendant who will have only that job to do. We provide the following Monte Carlo simulation of the proposed system.

1. *Variables*   First, we describe the system in terms of the following variables:

ARRIVE = the time of arrival of a customer
     A = a random variable, which is the time between arrivals of successive customers (interarrival time)
LEAVE = the time that a customer leaves the system after being serviced
     S = a random variable, which is the time to service a customer
  WAIT = the cumulative waiting time of customers in the queue
   IDLE = the cumulative time the attendant is idle
     N = the length of the waiting line
     M = the total number of customers that arrive at the system over the length of the study
CLOCK = a designation of cumulative lapsed time
   END = the total amount of simulated time desired

We may note that END represents the actual period to be simulated, such as a day, week, or longer. WAIT, IDLE, and M are cumulative measures over this time period.

2. *Generation of random variables*   The second step is to specify the method for generating the values of the random variables. The method depends on both the kind of distribution and the computational facilities. Suppose, for example, that the two random variables are

S is normally distributed with mean 7 min and variance 4 min
A is exponentially distributed with mean 9 min

(a) *Normal distribution*   A straightforward method is to use a table of random normal deviates. Assuming that we anticipate simulating no more than k customer arrivals, we generate k random service times as follows:

Sample	z	S
1	1.4	9.8
2	−1.05	4.9
3	1.50	10.0
4	−0.45	6.1
5	−0.50	6.0
6	1.80	10.6
7	0.40	7.8
8	−0.15	6.7
9	−2.60	1.8
⋮	⋮	⋮
k	−0.15	6.7

1) Select a value z from a table of random normal deviates.
2) Convert the z value to a random service time S, where

$$S = 2z + 7$$

3) Repeat the process k times to obtain a table of k random service times.

Another approach to generate normal random deviates is to use the Central Limit Theorem in the following way.

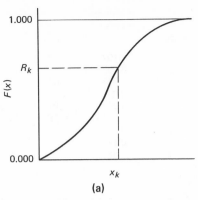 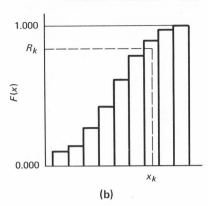

(a)   (b)

FIGURE **3.24**   Distribution functions. (a) Continuous variable. (b) Discrete variable.

1) Generate a set of n random numbers, $x_1, \ldots, x_n$ from a uniform distribution with range R, mean μ, and variance $R^2/12$.

2) Calculate the mean of the set of n sample numbers, $\bar{x} = \sum_{1}^{n} x_i$.

3) According to the Central Limit Theorem, $\bar{x}$ is normally distributed with mean μ and variance $R^2/12n$. Then a random normal deviate is calculated as

$$z_j = \frac{\bar{x} - \mu}{\sqrt{\dfrac{R^2}{12n}}}$$

If it is desired to generate a normal random variable from the distribution with mean $\bar{y}$ and variance σ_y, then the variable is

$$y_j = \bar{y} + z_j \sigma_y$$

(b) *Any distribution*   We may generate a random variable x from any distribution by using its distribution function $F(x)$. For either a continuous variable or discrete variable (Figure 3.24), the following steps are performed.

1) Select a random number R_k between 0.000 and 1.000, and enter the scale $F(x) = R_k$.

2) Read the corresponding value x_k from the inverse function

$$x_k = F^{-1}(R_k)$$

In the case of the interarrival times A, which are exponentially distributed, we apply the above method using a table of natural logarithms for the numbers between 0.0 and 1.0. Figure 3.25 shows a plot of the number x, lying between 0 and 1.0, and the negative ln (x). This corresponds to the complement of the distribution function for a negative exponentially distributed random variable with mean of 1.0. The use of this distribution to generate interarrival times is explained below.

1) Select a random number x_i between 0.000 and 1.000 from a table of random numbers.

2) Let $t = -1.00 \ln x$.

3) Multiply t_i times 9.00, the mean interarrival time; that is, $A_i = 9.00t_i$.

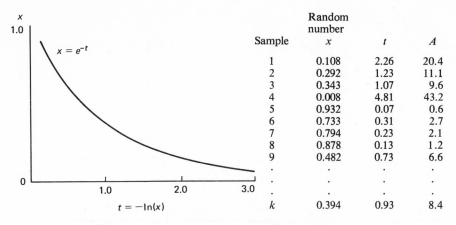

Sample	Random number x	t	A
1	0.108	2.26	20.4
2	0.292	1.23	11.1
3	0.343	1.07	9.6
4	0.008	4.81	43.2
5	0.932	0.07	0.6
6	0.733	0.31	2.7
7	0.794	0.23	2.1
8	0.878	0.13	1.2
9	0.482	0.73	6.6
.	.	.	.
.	.	.	.
.	.	.	.
k	0.394	0.93	8.4

FIGURE **3.25**   Natural logarithmic function for interarrival times.

4) Repeat steps 1, 2, and 3 a total of k times to obtain a table of k interarrival times.

3. *Manual simulation*   The method of simulating the first eight arrivals is shown below:

	Service request No.	1	2	3	4	5	6	7	8	...	k
ARRIVE	(Arrival time of a service request)	20.4	31.5	41.1	84.3	84.9	87.6	89.7	90.9	...	1,262.8
WAIT	(Waiting time for customer)	0	0	0	0	5.5	8.8	17.3	23.9	...	16.0
	(Cumulative waiting time)	—	—	—	—	5.5	14.3	31.6	55.5	...	506.2
N	(Number in queue)	0	0	0	0	1	2	3	3	...	0
LEAVE	(Completion time of service)	30.2	36.4	51.1	90.4	96.4	107.0	114.8	121.5	...	(1,284.6) = END
IDLE	(Idle time for attendant)	20.4	1.3	4.7	33.2	0	16.7	0	0	...	—
	(Cumulative idle time)	20.4	21.7	26.4	59.6	59.6	59.6	59.6	59.6	...	301.0

1. Select the first of the set of interarrival times. Assuming the study starts at 0.0 minutes, the first arrival is at 20.4 minutes.
2. Select the first of the set of service times. The completion time for the first customer is 20.4 + 9.8.
3. There are zero customers in the queue, and therefore the waiting time is zero.
4. Select the second interarrival time, 11.1 minutes. The arrival time of the second customer is 20.4 + 11.1 = 31.5 minutes. The service time is 4.9 min. Therefore, the completion time for the customer is 36.4. The idle time of the operator is 31.5 − 30.2 = 1.3 minutes.

5. Continue this process until a sample of k arrivals has been examined.

6. Note that when the fifth customer arrives, the fourth customer is still being serviced, and therefore the queue length is 1 and the customer wait time is 5.5 minutes.

4. *Calculate the measures of performance*   At the conclusion of the simulation, we may calculate the following measures of performance:

Average Number in the System = WAIT/END.

Average Waiting Time per Customer = (WAIT/AVERAGE NO. IN QUEUE).

Note that we could make a frequency distribution of number in queue directly from the results shown in the row labeled N. We could also obtain a distribution of waiting time per customer by making that calculation directly as we proceeded through the simulation.

LOGIC DIAGRAM: It can be seen that a manual simulation of any complex stochastic system would be cumbersome. Most simulations are performed on high-speed computers, and it is surprisingly easy to program a simulator for an elementary problem such as our example.

The logical steps in the simulation can be depicted in the form of a logic flow diagram. A logic flow diagram for the case discussed is shown in Figure 3.26. The next step is to translate this into a program language.

CHANGING THE PARAMETERS OF THE MODEL: If a computer is used, it will automatically generate the required arrival and service times, as well as any other stochastic variables desired. And, of course, it can make the calculations, store the information, and compute the performance measures at the end of the study. It also permits us to study the effect of changes in the parameters of the model.

The parameters of the model include the things we hold constant in the particular study, such as the type of distribution, the mean and variance of any one of the stochastic variables, the number of channels, etc. In general, we are interested in the "sensitivity" of the particular measures of performances to changes in any one of the parameters. The only way we can do this is to study the system under different sets of parameter values—something like a controlled experiment.

We will refer to the use of the Monte Carlo method in a number of situations in later sections. One word of caution: a Monte Carlo simulation can be a very expensive way of obtaining information, although in a very complex situation, it is often the only way of obtaining the necessary information about a system. There are, however, many cases, perhaps less involved, where an analytical solution will yield the desired information.

A Finite Markov Chain Process

A Markov chain is a way of explaining the random changes that can take place over time in a process or facility. The characteristics of this time-induced random process are:

1. The process moves through a successive set of states over time. Thus, at any given point in time, the process can be in only one of a set of mutually exclusive states, $s_1, s_2, \ldots, s_i, \ldots, s_r$.

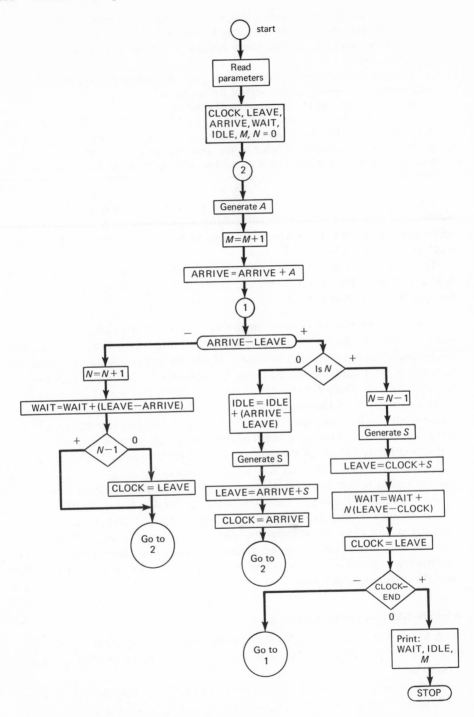

FIGURE **3.26** Logic flow diagram.

2. A step is a point in time when the process shifts from one state s_i to another state s_j. This may include the process remaining in the same state at a particular step.
3. At any given step, the probability that the process will shift from s_i to s_j depends on the value of i at the beginning of the step.
4. There is a probability transition matrix, $P = \{p_{ij}\}$, where p_{ij} is the probability of the process shifting from state i to state j at any step. Thus,

i \ j	s_1	s_2	. . .	s_r
s_1	p_{11}	p_{12}	. . .	p_{1r}
s_2	p_{21}	p_{22}	. . .	p_{2r}
$\vdots$	$\vdots$	$\vdots$		
s_r	p_{r1}	p_{r2}	. . .	p_{rr}

$$p_{ij} \geq 0$$
$$\sum_j p_{ij} = 1.00$$

A row containing non-negative elements that add to 1.00 is called a probability vector.

For example, the town of Glendale is divided into three police precincts A, B, and C. We are concerned with the random movement of police cruiser 1, which is headquartered in precinct A. There are two other cruisers on duty at any one time, one of which is headquartered in each of the other precincts. The movement of the cruiser throughout the three precincts (it aids the other cars if necessary) yields a probability transition matrix, where the probabilities relate to transition changes in location every half hour.

$P =$

	A	B	C
A	0.5	0.1	0.4
B	0.1	0.3	0.6
C	0.3	0.4	0.3

We might ask, what is the probability that cruiser 1 will be in a specific precinct after n stages, given that it was in precinct A at the start of the process? The two-step tree in Figure 3.27 shows the second-stage probabilities, given that the cruiser started in precinct A. The probability of being in precinct B at the end of the second step is

$$p_{AA}p_{AB} + p_{AB}p_{BB} + p_{AC}p_{CB} = (0.5)(0.1) + (0.1)(0.3) + (0.4)(0.4) = 0.24$$

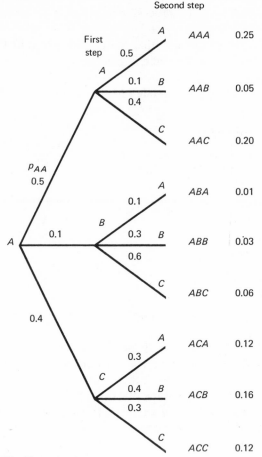

Second step

First
step   0.5
A

0.1 B

0.4

p_{AA}
0.5

0.1

B

0.3 B

0.6

0.4

0.3

C

0.4 B

0.3

A

AAA   0.25

AAB   0.05

C

AAC   0.20

A

ABA   0.01

ABB   0.03

C

ABC   0.06

A

ACA   0.12

ACB   0.16

C

ACC   0.12

FIGURE **3.27** Two-step tree.

We can represent the second-step probabilities in a matrix $P(2) = (p(2)_{ij})$, where $(p(2)_{ij})$ is the probability of being in state j at the end of 2 steps, given that the process started in state i.

The interesting thing is that the probability transition matrix for the nth step is equal to the nth power of the initial transition matrix, that is, $P(n) = P^n$.

For our example,

	A	B	C
A	0.5	0.1	0.4
B	0.1	0.3	0.6
C	0.3	0.4	0.3

$P(2) = P^2 =$ (above) $\times$

	A	B	C
A	0.5	0.1	0.4
B	0.1	0.3	0.6
C	0.3	0.4	0.3

$=$

	A	B	C
A	0.38	0.24	0.38
B	0.26	0.34	0.40
C	0.28	0.27	0.45

A regular Markov Chain is one in which some power of the probability transition matrix P_n has only positive elements. This means that after a certain number of steps, there is a positive chance of being in any one of the states, regardless of the starting state. For regular Markov chains, we can state the following:

If P is an $r \times r$ probability transition matrix, then

1. $P^n \rightarrow T$ as n approaches ∞, where T is an $r \times r$ matrix with each row consisting of the same probability vector W.
2. For any probability vector X with r elements, $XP^n \rightarrow W$, where W is a probability vector that is the same for all choices of X.
3. For any column vector Y with r elements, $P^n Y \rightarrow Z$, where Z is a column vector with all elements having the same number z. The value of z depends on the value of Y.

For our example,

	A	B	C
A	0.305	0.280	0.415
B	0.305	0.280	0.415
C	0.305	0.280	0.415

$$\lim_{n \to \infty} P^n = B$$

Problems

3.1 The Malenke Manufacturing Company produces two products, Divits and Thorps, in three departments. If it is assumed that the company can sell any quantity of either product, what is the optimum production program, given the following information?

	Divit	Thorp
Sales price, $ per unit	3.00	3.00
Variable costs, $ per unit	2.44	2.20
(material, labor, and variable overhead)		
Marginal profit, $ per unit	0.56	0.80
Standard hours per unit		
Dept. 1	0.10	0.90
Dept. 2	0.50	0.10
Dept. 3	0.60	0.60
Dept. capacity-hours		
Dept. 1		900
Dept. 2		800
Dept. 3		1,000

3.2 The following is a flow diagram for the processing of lumber by a large lumber company. The company must determine the allocation of the three kinds of source material to the nine kinds of final product, including the sale of standing timber. The

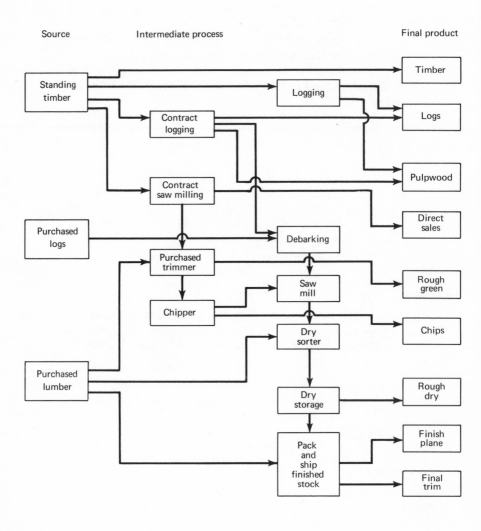

decisions must be based on the final product profits, the capacity of the intermediate processes, and the limitations in the material sources. How would you set this up as a linear programing problem? Give examples of the decision variables and the different kinds of constraints.

3.3

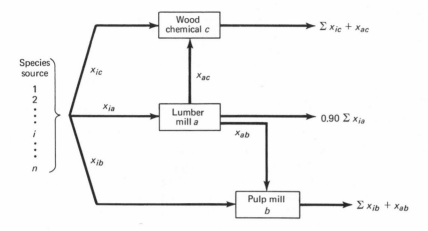

A forest products company operates three mills: a lumber mill a, a pulp mill b, and a wood chemical mill c. The raw material consists of different species of trees or wood located on company-owned tree farms or purchased on the market. Let

i = index indicating a tree species—source for a raw material
Q_i = maximum quantity of raw material i available in a given time period
H_j = the capacity of mill j in units of raw material for the given time period, $j = a, b, c$
P_{ij} = the marginal profit from a unit of raw material i used in mill j

Note that mill a produces a byproduct, which is 10% of the volume of its input. This raw material can be used by mills b and c. For the period in question, the problem is to determine the allocation of raw materials to the mills, assuming the demand exceeds the capacity of the mills.

1. Structure this problem as a linear programing problem.
2. Assume the following information and solve the problem.

$i = 1, 2$
$Q_1 = 800; Q_2 = 2,000$
$H_a = 1,000; H_b = 1,200; H_c = 500$
$P_{1a} = 12; P_{1b} = 8; P_{2a} = 10; P_{2b} = 5; P_{2c} = 3; P_{ab} = 6; P_{ac} = 5$

Note that mill c cannot use raw material 1. The profit margins P_{1a}, P_{2a} account for 90% of the yield at mill a.

3. Considering the solution to part 2, where in the system would you suggest that capacity or resources be increased and by how much, assuming your wish to maximize profit and demand is sufficient? How much would the price of a ton of product 1-a and 1-b be reduced to force complete utilization of species 2?
4. Create and define a hypothetical linear programing problem.

3.4

	Market I	Market II	Market III	Market IV	Market V	Plant capacity
Plant A	20	15	10	6	13	100,000
Plant B	5	10	15	20	25	80,000
Plant C	6	12	8	8	11	70,000
Market requirements	60,000	40,000	30,000	70,000	50,000	

The above matrix indicates the total planned requirements of each of five markets (for example, market III usually requires 30,000 units per month). It indicates the distribution cost of sending a product from the plant to the market (for example, it costs $10 to send a unit from plant B to market II). It indicates the plant capacities, which must not be exceeded (for example, plant C cannot produce more than 70,000 units a month).

Your task is to find the best plan for shipping from plants to markets while staying within your plant's capacity. "Best" in this case is the lowest cost method.

3.5   Problem 3.4 is given with some added complications. The plants now have higher capacity as a result of manufacturing improvements. The market, however, has not changed, so we are in an over-capacity situation. The following table shows how our costs vary as the capacity utilization changes:

Capacity utilization (%)	Unit costs ($ per unit)
100	$100
90	105
80	115
70	125
60	150
50	180

All plants must operate at 50% capacity or higher. The 100% capacity for the plants is now: Plant A = 120,000 units/month, Plant B = 100,000, and Plant C = 100,000. Find the lowest cost method of meeting requirements taking into account both plant efficiency and transportation cost.

3.6   Using network theory, find the optimum allocation of the output of the following three plants to four tank farms, given a restriction in the capacity of a network of pipelines in terms of thousands of barrels per time period.

	F_1	F_2	F_3	F_4	a_i
P_1	10		20		50
P_2		30	50	5	70
P_3	10			20	30
b_j	20	30	80	30	

3.7 Assignments are to be made of one each from six origins to six possible destinations. The costs associated with each possible assignment are shown in the matrix below. Find the assignment program that minimizes total cost.

Origin

		1	2	3	4	5	6
	a	26	40	18	27	35	17
	b	20	23	46	14	31	21
	c	23	38	32	21	24	40
Destination	d	35	16	50	30	23	19
	e	27	18	34	23	17	44
	f	36	22	53	37	37	28

Costs

3.8 Suppose that in the problem on page 74 there are certain restrictions regarding the assignment of trucks to territories. The cost matrix below contains X's to indicate that the vehicle labeling the row cannot be assigned to the territory labeling the column. Find the optimum assignment.

Territory

Vehicle	I	II	III	IV	V
A	X	18	4	X	19
B	5	3	9	2	X
C	X	15	11	X	12
D	17	20	X	X	22
E	10	X	X	X	11

3.9 In the dynamic programing problem (page 82), suppose that the cost of permitting the machine to run one more year without preventive maintenance is $Q_t =$

$50 + $25(k), where k is the number of years since the year of the last preventive maintenance and including year t. What is the best schedule of preventive maintenance?

3.10

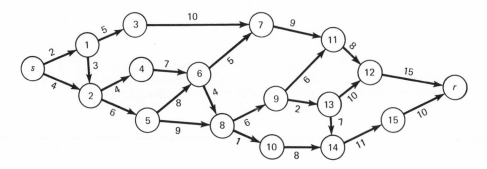

Find the shortest route from the source s to sink r.

3.11   Plot a graph that shows the relationship between λ/μ (traffic intensity) and $\bar{n}$ (average number in system) for a single-channel queue, assuming Poisson distributed arrival service rates of 10 and 9, respectively.

3.12   Police Car 54 is assigned to an outlying district of the Bronx. The precinct captain complains that the car is always arriving late to the scene of its calls. He claims that the car's officers, Toody and Muldoon, are taking too many coffee breaks. The officers defend their position by saying that they have too many jobs to handle per hour, and some calls have to wait because the captain will not assign another car to the district. Attach some quantitative measures to the situation by using queuing theory. You can make the assumption that police calls arrive exponentially and that the service rate is Poisson distributed. Your preliminary analysis shows that the rate of calls to the car has a mean of 10 per hour and the mean service rate is 15 calls per hour. Can you defend Toody and Muldoon? How long does the customer actually wait for Toody and Muldoon on the average before they arrive on the scene? What is the percentage utilization of the two patrol cars? That is, what is the average percentage of time that they are busy?

3.13   The Apogee Interspace Trucking Company maintains and operates a large fleet of space freight ships, which deliver materials between various plants and space stations. The company has an installation of four unloading stations on Planet X. This has been incapable of handling the traffic of ships arriving at the Planet to be serviced. The problem is to determine the economical number of stations, assuming that the annual cost of operating a station is $1,000,000 (excluding depreciation, which we will assume to be negligible). The cost of waiting time for a vehicle is $500 for every hour of vehicle wait time. A study of arrivals by industrial engineers yields the following frequency distribution for a sample of 200 arrivals. The service times are exponentially distributed with a mean of five vehicles per week. What is the economical number of stations to have?

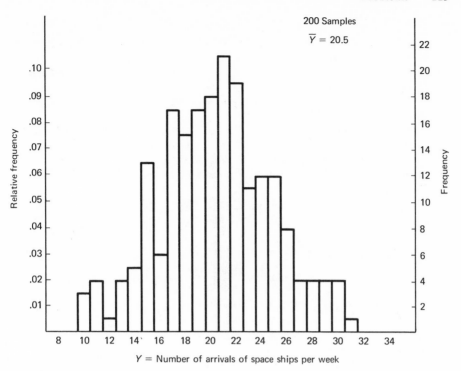

200 Samples

$\overline{Y} = 20.5$

Y = Number of arrivals of space ships per week

3.14 Smedley's Farms is a high-quality tree nursery where customers are given special service in the sense of being waited on without undue delay. Business is increasing such that the manager is concerned about having sufficient help to maintain this quality of service. Sampling of last year's business, together with a forecast of the coming spring business, results in the customer service statistics shown below. Inter-arrival times are negative exponentially distributed with a mean of 10 min. Using simulation, derive customer wait time and serviceman idle time statistics for a relevant range of number of servicemen.

Service time (minutes)	Probability
5	0.02
10	0.15
15	0.20
20	0.30
25	0.20
30	0.05
35	0.05
40	0.03
	1.00

Bibliography

BELLMAN, R., and S. DREYFUS, *Applied Dynamic Programming.* Princeton, N.J.: Princeton Univ. Press, 1962.

BOWMAN, EDWARD H., and ROBERT B. FETTER, *Analysis for Production Management.* Homewood, Ill.: Richard D. Irwin, Inc., 1961.

BUFFA, ELWOOD, *Models for Production and Operations Management.* New York: John Wiley & Sons, 1963.

CHORAFAS, DIMITRIS, *Systems and Simulation.* New York: Academic Press, 1965.

CHURCHMAN, C. WEST, RUSSEL L. ACKOFF, and E. LEONARD ARNOFF, *Introduction to Operations Research.* New York: John Wiley & Sons, 1958.

CONWAY, R. W., "Some Tactical Problems in Digital Simulation," *Management Science*, October 1963.

COX, D. R., and WALTER L. SMITH, *Queues.* New York: John Wiley & Sons, 1961.

DANTZIG, G. B., *Linear Programming and Extensions.* Princeton, N.J.: Princeton Univ. Press, 1963.

ELMAGHRABY, SALAH E., *The Design of Production Systems.* New York: Reinhold Publishing Corp., 1966.

FORD, L. K., and D. R. FULKERSON, *Flow in Networks.* Princeton, N.J.: Princeton Univ. Press, 1962.

HILLIER, FREDERICK S., "Economic Models for Industrial Waiting Line Problems," *Management Science*, October 1963.

HILLIER, FREDERICK S., and GERALD J. LIEBERMAN, *Introduction to Operations Research.* San Francisco: Holden-Day, Inc., 1967.

KUHN, H. W., "The Hungarian Method for Assignment Problem," *Naval Research Logistics Quarterly*, vol. 2, 1955.

LITTLE, J. D. C., et al., "An Algorithm for the Traveling Salesman Problem," *Operations Research*, vol. 11, 1963, pp. 972–989.

MORSE, P. M., *Queues, Inventories and Maintenance.* New York: John Wiley & Sons, 1958.

SAATY, T. L., *Elements of Queuing Theory with Applications.* New York: McGraw-Hill Book Co., 1961.

SHELTON, JOHN R., "Solution Methods for Waiting Line Problems," *J. Ind. Eng.*, July–August 1960.

VAJDA, S., *Mathematical Programming.* Reading, Mass.: Addison-Wesley, 1961.

4
Design and Improvement:
An Overview

INTRODUCTION

This chapter considers some of the concepts underlying the activities involved in designing and improving production systems.

Design is relevant to those situations where a decision leads to either the origination of or change in the specifications of the physical elements of a system. It is concerned with specifying shapes, sizes, configurations, speeds, energy requirements, equipment, spatial arrangements, and so forth. There is, therefore, a technological content to much of design based on engineering and the basic sciences.

From a management point of view, there is more to design than the literal translation of ideas into physical realities by the application of technical skills. First, design problems must usually be solved in the context of strong economic and other nontechnical criteria. The determination of value objectives as both guides to the designer and as the bases for the ultimate decisions to accept or reject proposals is a management responsibility. That is, the proposal for a new machine, the design of a process, or the suggestion to alter a product design ultimately requires a management decision of acceptance or rejection.

Second, design change or improvement involves the expenditure of organization resources in research and development, product engineering, industrial engineering, or other less formalized activities. Obviously, the allocation of financial resources to these activities, as well as their actual administration, is a complex management problem.

Rather than attempt a synopsis of various technical functions, we prefer to examine more general concepts related to solving design problems. Although we are interested in the physical aspects of production systems, our discussion applies equally well to both products and services, the outputs of these systems.

INITIAL DESIGN VERSUS IMPROVEMENT

Design can be considered from the point of view of the degree of novelty of the design problem. Initial design is the designing of a system "de novo" or without any reference to an already existing or operating system. It is pertinent to the design of new plants, processes, or systems to make a new or different product. In contrast, redesign or improvement implies alteration of an existing and operating production system. Pure design "de novo" is rare since almost every new design is based upon some existing knowledge and technology.

Improvement consists in altering an existing system by varying degrees. Although some of these changes may be dramatic, many consist of minor, but when taken collectively, important changes in the operations. These include changes in work methods, arrangement of facilities, flow of work, and handling of materials, tools, machines, and equipment.

These two concepts are important in the way design problems are handled. In the case of improvement, the designer always has the present system upon which to perform a critical analysis as the basis for leading to the improvement. The designer is an agent of a continuous evolutionary process, which, in some ways, is easier to carry out than the initial creation of a new and complex system. On the other hand, there are certain disadvantages to the availability of an existing system as the basis of a design problem. We will dwell on this point later when discussing the creation of alternative design solutions. We should, however, note here that any design problem may be tackled conceptually as an initial design problem if the designer is willing to block out any reference to existing practice when he attacks the problem.

Besides the psychological implications of the two approaches, we should note these general economic implications. The more gradual evolutionary changes implied by improvement are being replaced by the necessity for more dramatic and sudden mutations in production methods. Technological changes of a major kind, in both products and production methods and variations in consumer demand, are occurring so rapidly that major and rapid changes in production are necessary. These include the construction of new plants, the revamping of entire existing processes, or the introduction of radically new and different pieces of machines and equipment. The initial capital investments are large and the inherent risks of obsolescence ever present. The shift is therefore from the emphasis on a continued introduction of many minor improvements in operations to the initial design of complex systems whose economic life may be limited, and which will be subjected to major revision at some predictable future time.

ORGANIZATION FOR IMPROVEMENT

Since much of production design has to do with improving an existing system, we should consider some issues related to managing improvement in a going organization.

Constraints on Improvement

Improvements in a production system are introduced for many reasons. Generally, they might be classified as the desire to reduce the costs of operations, improve the quality of output, or increase capacity. In spite of its connotation, there is no virtue in the objective of maximizing the amount of improvement to a production system. While cost reduction and efficiency are intrinsically admirable goals, there is the notion that the changes that they introduce might proceed at an optimal rather than a maximum rate. Changes that occur too often in production may be costly and disruptive to an otherwise profitable operation. Also, there is usually some constraint on the resources that can be applied to generating, developing, and implementing ideas for change and improvement. At the other extreme, there is little reason to condone the perpetuation of operations that are obviously inefficient and costly, even if the eventual change may require a readjustment on the part of personnel affected by the changes. It can often be observed that a concerted and formal effort to reduce costs in an organization is a drastic response to current conditions, rather than a consistent and perpetual policy.

In practice, there is very real organizational and personnel resistance to formal or informal attempts to reduce costs or improve a going operation. These are related to the pervasive human reactions to change.

1. Inherent in all cost-reduction efforts is the implication that the improvement will result in job layoffs. This is not without reason, because layoffs are a fact in the history of technological advances. Not more than a decade ago, the notion of technological unemployment was considered by many to be an idle lament of unreasonable critics of our technological society. Today, the threat seems much less idle. The effects of large-scale mechanization on unemployment are fully evident in certain cases. There is reason to suggest that there may be some optimal rate at which improvement should take place such that the objective of minimizing unemployment would assume importance.

In isolated and local cases within individual firms, layoffs need not be, and often are not, the critical factor. Most progressive organizations will defer proposed changes in operations until normal job attrition reduces the labor content to the number of operators required in the proposed system. Furthermore, job transfers with opportunities for retraining provide added insurance against the layoff threat in the improvement of operations.

However, not all of these guarantees are present in every company, and, even if they are, there is often the natural aversion to change, which is manifested in many ways by both labor and management.

2. From the viewpoint of management, the possibility of a change, especially of a major type, poses a threat to the manager whose area of responsibility and authority is the scene of the change. This threat to his own security resides in his implicit concern that he will not be able to cope with the real or imagined complexities of the new system. This assumes for the moment that the change is being suggested by technical staff personnel or imposed upon the manager by superiors. In today's world, where many changes do, in fact, involve the implanting of radically new and different methods, equipment, and techniques, this threat is

quite real. Furthermore, there exists a very real communications barrier between the technical specialist and the operating manager, because the latter sometimes cannot comprehend the language, as well as the technology, of the specialist.

Again, this sort of resistance can be dealt with by an enlightened management, which recognizes the problems and threats to the security of those whose positions are in the vortex of a major change. Where top management is impetuous in forcing changes, we can expect nothing but an underlying resistance, especially from older and entrenched supervisors.

3. Even when the change may not precipitate a traumatic situation for line managers, the feeling of loss of prestige may accompany the suggestion by someone else for an improvement in the manager's area of responsibility. There is the implicit suggestion that maybe the manager should have thought of the improvement himself, or that the improvement points out an inefficient operation. A wounded pride can be the source of strength for resisting change.

4. When the organization, business, or system is ostensibly operating smoothly, there is little impetus for cost reduction, improvement, or change. In many firms, the success of the firm resides in the profitability of the product that is produced and not particularly in the astuteness of the management controlling the operations. Every change has its inherent risk, and there must be very real and cogent arguments for courting the risk if the ship is sailing smoothly. Cost-reduction programs are typically embarked upon during periods of economic crises or stress for the department, division, or company as a whole.

5. There is often the tacit feeling that cost reduction is synonymous with the curtailment of service. From the budgetary point of view, this may often be the case in times of economic austerity. It is particularly true in the operation of nonprofit or government institutions, where services are often geared to the budget. Ideally, a sustained program of cost reduction should have as its goal the improvement of services, as well as the reduction in resources, required to provide a certain level of service.

Besides the prevailing human attitudes toward change, a program of cost reduction can be limited by the amount of funds that can be invested in the proposals and in the human resources needed to effect the program. Technical know-how may also be lacking either on the part of the line organization or in the form of staff assistance. Furthermore, a system of supervisory incentives to improve costs may be weak or lacking altogether as a part of job specifications.

Formal Organizational Approaches

Many companies are organized in some manner and degree to effect redesign and improvement in operations. These include the availability of staff resources and/or the specification of cost reduction as a part of the line supervision job. In nonmanufacturing or service institutions, reliance is placed mainly on line supervisors to make desired changes.

The manner in which management uses the resources of the organization to increase efficiency and reduce costs depends on a number of factors. These include the size of the organization, the technological content of the product, the general policies of the organization, the types of costs being reduced, the urgency of the needed results, the techniques used, and the training and background of the managers.

In Figure 4.1, we introduce some of the traditional ways in which organizations approach cost reduction. The system of classification is very elementary and is not offered as a principle of organization.

Two general approaches are suggested for the management of costs. The first is *cost control.* Cost controls are management's efforts to keep costs within certain prescribed limits. The major functions of cost control are embodied in budgeting, cost accounting, and standard cost systems. At the local operating level, costs are controlled through the use of labor time standards, inspection and quality control standards, various production and inventory controls, and direct line supervision. In these areas, the emphasis is to keep the costs in line with those specified by the standards of good performance. By keeping the operations under surveillance through a control procedure, the areas where costs are out of line are flagged, and both designs and plans may be changed to improve the situation. It must be emphasized that in the final analysis, the control of costs resides with the supervisors or managers who are responsible for the consumption of the resource that is translated into the cost. In this section, we will be interested not in cost control but rather in the ideas behind cost reduction.

The other major approach is that of actual *cost reduction.* Figure 4.1 points out three approaches to cost reduction in an organization. These three approaches are not mutually exclusive in any given company, and two or more of them may be taken by a given division of the organization.

TECHNIQUE-ORIENTED APPROACHES: In American industry, production improvements have traditionally been carried out by industrial engineering departments, as

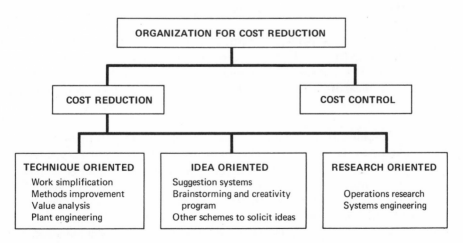

FIGURE **4.1**   Basic approaches to cost reduction.

well as by line managers. The function of industrial engineering has evolved over the past sixty years as an attempt to constantly improve and redesign industrial production operations. Much of the work has centered on techniques for analyzing some aspect of the production system, such as jobs, operations, or processes, with the purpose of finding ways to improve them. In recent years, a significant part of industrial engineering has come to include operations research and systems analysis.

Work simplification refers to the continued search for better ways to perform work, usually where the human being is an element of the work situation. Work simplification places emphasis on the participation of both line supervisor and worker in the process of job improvement. Formal work simplification programs are designed to motivate the line organization in job improvement and to provide training in the necessary skills to effect such improvement. Thus, the major contribution is made by employees and line managers in the analysis of their own jobs and those they supervise.

Methods engineering is a formalized industrial engineering function. It includes the planning of the processes to manufacture a product or provide a service, the use of motion study, work measurement, and the design of jobs and operations. While employee participation in improvement is important, the initiative for a change rests with the engineer. Furthermore, the technical content of the problem may require engineering talent, which the line employee cannot provide.

Product redesign and value analysis emphasizes the analysis of a product and its components to determine if the redesign of the part will lead to a cost reduction. This refers to such things as changes in materials, basic processes required, surface finishes, dimension tolerances, use of standard materials and components, and so forth.

Plant engineering categorizes those improvements related to building and facilities such as machine replacement, design of material-handling systems, location or layout of machines, equipment and utilities, and the maintenance of such systems. Improvements in these areas are strategic in character and typically involve significant capital expenditures.

IDEA-ORIENTED APPROACHES: The generation of ideas is an important part of all cost-reduction endeavors. However, certain approaches place emphasis on the generation of ideas to initiate improvements. Suggestions systems, for instance, are used to elicit ideas from employees. Formal programs are used to teach creative thinking or to direct creative effort toward some specific problem.

RESEARCH-ORIENTED APPROACHES: These are usually highly formalized and carried out under the heading of operations research, management science, or systems engineering. Research of a sophisticated nature is carried on into some phase of the company operations. The intent is usually to help managers make better decisions about their operations. In many cases, the problems are complex and involve planning and control, as well as design problems.

Regardless of the organizational approach that is taken to cost reduction, there is an underlying theme when the function of design or redesign is involved. We wish to examine this general theme, rather than concentrate on the differences between the organizational approaches. In spite of the names we attach to the sections of the organization that do the work, or regardless of the specific techniques used, there are common and basic concepts that are important to understand. As the science of management evolves, we find fewer differences between the approaches and techniques of modern industrial engineering, operations research, and systems engineering.

THE DESIGN PROCESS

The History of a Project

One way to examine the design function is to describe the life history of a design project—that is, what happens to the system being designed, be it a piece of equipment or a production process. The "flow" of a design project would start with an initial stage involving, to begin with, nebulous ideas and generalities and would end with a system spelled out in detail in the form of models, blueprints, charts, etc.

The *design process* is executed within some organizational framework. The process is structured into various *stages* that subdivide the total design activity in time and allocate the manpower requirements. The stages are arranged on a hierarchic scale. That is, there is a basic sequence to the stages, and the project evolves from one stage to the next in progressive degrees of detail.

Notice that we could apply our discussion to a one-man project in which the problem is elementary but nevertheless implicitly flows through the stages, even though these stages may be recognizable only to the individual.

The purpose of each stage is to force the evolution of the system from a single idea to a series of detailed and precisely defined subsystems. That is, the incipient design problem fans out into subproblems and sub-subproblems, depending on its complexity. In the case of complex systems such as machines, processes, or entire plants, the design process is highly organized with different functions contributing to each stage.

Within each stage in the development of the system, the designers execute a methodology involving various phases including the statement of problems, the analysis of problems, and the synthesis of alternative designs and their evaluation leading to design decisions.

Each stage, depending on the scope of the problem, may involve the work of different individuals and groups in the organization. In the initial stages, basic economic and marketing decisions are important if we are dealing with a product, and, therefore, the people involved may include marketing managers and accountants, as well as engineers. In the final stage, we might expect the project to center around the activities of engineers, technicians, and line managers—people who will have to implement the design and make it operate.

While there is a general flow to the stages in time, the process is reiterative. There is a feedback of information from later stages to cause a re-examination of

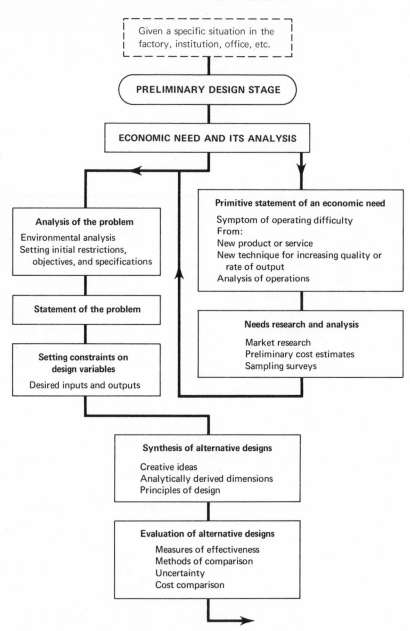

FIGURE **4.2**   Major stages in the design process.

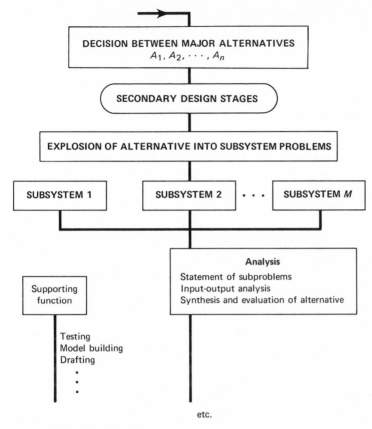

FIGURE **4.2**   (Continued)

the decisions made in the earlier stages. But feedback loops are most likely localized, and there may be milestones in the flow after which prior decisions will not be changed.

Figure 4.2 is a graphic description of the design process and the major phases of the methodology. These stages and phases may be explicit only in major design projects, but they constitute what might be carried out implicitly by those who deal with elementary design problems.

Design—A Decision-Making Process

Describing design in terms of the life process of a project provides an anatomical structure to the design function. Within each of the development stages, a multitude of decisions are made, ranging from the initial decision in the beginning to embark upon a project down to the hundreds of technical-economic decisions in the final stage related to the system details. We can therefore use the decision-making process to describe the designer's methodology.

The question of distinguishing phases is less important than some conceptual understanding of the content of these phases and why they might be considered different from each other. We will do this in the subsequent pages. We should keep in mind that we will be discussing both the concepts of stages and phases.

THE DETERMINATION OF AN ECONOMIC NEED

The design process represents the expenditure of design resources, which include all the costs directly and indirectly related to the development of the system. Obviously, if the process itself is to be efficient, two things must be considered. First, there must be a control over the expenditures through the administration of the design activities. Second, there must be a reasonable degree of assurance that the resources are spent on the design of a system that will eventually be technically feasible and economically beneficial to the firm or institution.

The recognition of a potential economic need is the first step in the design process. It is a long step from the amorphously defined economic need to the ultimate decision to commit technical resources to a specific design problem. The way in which a need is recognized is related to organization. We should consider the following points, keeping in mind that we are interested in design of production systems.

1. It is quite obvious that the decision to manufacture a new product or to provide a new service, even though vaguely defined at first, is tantamount to the commitment to a new production system. In these cases, the economic need is implicitly linked to that of the product or service. The validity of the need for a new product or service is established by the functions of market research and analysis. These activities provide the information and data about the demand that will be placed on the production system. First, they provide the basis for specifying the functional requirements of the product or service, which in turn are translated through product design to functional specifications for the production system. Second, they provide the basis for specifying the quantities of various outputs from the system at various times.

2. It is more likely that the impetus to a production design problem commences with the recognition of *symptoms* of inadequate performance in existing systems. Thus, the manager is faced with the unassailable fact that costs are too high, quality is not up to specifications, work in process inventory is too large, capacity is insufficient to meet an anticipated demand, etc. The problem, then, is essentially to redesign the present system in order to meet a pressing and obvious economic need.

3. We may agree that when the technical manpower resources of the organization are involved in meeting the type of pressing needs described above, this leaves something to be desired. The action precipitated by obvious symptoms of difficulty often results in less than long-term optimal solutions to design and improvement problems. A more ideal situation exists in an organization when the

recognition of economic needs for the redesign of *production systems* arises from objective analysis or research into the operations of the firm. The extraction of potential problems through the analysis of operations may permit a more carefully planned project leading to more effective and long-term solutions to the problems before they appear as overt symptoms of difficulty. In a progressive organization containing competent professional personnel, this approach to recognizing economic needs often leads from the knowledge of new techniques and methods. This is to say that a continued search of the environment of the firm for new methods, materials, devices, machines, etc., leads to the ultimate use of these new factors in the company.

4. When the economic need is linked to the discovery of a new method, material, or device, there is an inherent danger that the problem exists merely to satisfy the desire to implement the innovation in question. We need to stress the point that the economic need and the design problem that ensues should exist independently from the ultimate solution or design chosen. The discovery of a new technique might trigger the study of an economic need, but it should not be the foreordained solution to a problem defined after the fact of a solution.

5. When a new product is not directly involved, analysis focuses on the need for an existing system. Any system, whether in a factory or institution, presumably is presently operating to meet some economic need. The problem, of course, is the fact that the economic need may have arisen in the past and does not exist today in the same form or degree. Production systems are creatures of habit. There is good reason today to believe that some production processes, jobs, or operations exist to fulfill a function no longer needed. Thus, secretaries fill out paper forms that end up in files having been used by no one; a drill press operator drills two holes in a part that serve no purpose; a lathe operator finishes a part surface that is later covered up in an assembly; an assembly operator assembles the bolt, two washers, and nut, only to have them disassembled at a later operation before being used. Therefore, *prior to the redesign of a production system, it is imperative that the need for the operation, process, or system be verified.*

THE ANALYSIS OF THE PROBLEM

The recognition of an economic need gives broad direction to the design process. The statement of a design problem gives it specific direction. The preliminary design stage commences with the intuitive or vague feeling that a need may be consummated. The conclusion of the stage is marked by a clear-cut statement of a problem, an understanding of the restrictions or constraints on the problem, a statement of desired outputs of the system, as well as objectives and criteria or measures of effectiveness. Thus, a positive framework is provided within which the project can evolve into a detailed set of specifications.

Before a clear-cut problem statement can be made, a good deal of analytical work is required. We can now examine some of the characteristics of this work.

Environmental Analysis

The purpose of environmental analysis is threefold. First, it is necessary to segregate the system from its environment. Second, it is necessary to determine the factors in the environment of the system that are relevant, that is, have a bearing on the design decisions. Third, it is necessary to convert the environmental factors into quantified restrictions on the problem.

The system is the set of design variables over which the designer has control and to which he will assign values and qualities. The differentiation of the system from its environment is something that must unfold as the project progresses in time. For example, the problem of designing the feed-pelletizing system (page 20) involved, first of all, the determination of the scope of the problem, which eventually involved factors outside the physical limits of the warehouse. It is sometimes obvious at the start that certain factors will always be beyond the control of the designer. Environmental analysis involves a search of the state of technology, company policies, competition, legal aspects, natural environment, capital sources, human resources, etc., to determine in each of these domains which factors of environment are relevant to the situation.

When the relevant factors are recognized, it is necessary to quantify them wherever possible such that they become a list of valid constraints on the design problem. It is quite easy to see how a lack of capital becomes a constraint on the problem. It is less easy to see the same thing in the realms of company policies, politics, and human factors. It cannot be stressed too often that factors within these areas may prove to be significant restrictions on the design problem. For example, the choice of the type of machine to use in a production system may be limited in a certain plant not by capital restrictions, but by company relationships with vendors of such machines. Or, in another plant, the alternative of introducing a labor-saving device may be inadmissible because of a company–union agreement. These types of restrictions are peculiar to a given situation, and the most we can do is recognize that they exist and occasionally dominate the purely economic aspects of the problem.

We should recognize that the determination of environmental restrictions on the problem must be *valid*. An invalid restriction is one the designer places on the problem as a matter of *assumption*, rather than after validating that it is impossible or unfeasible to remove it. In the feed-pelletizing problem, the assumption that the system must be confined to handling bags is invalid if, in fact, the choice of bulk handling is highly feasible.

It is in the nature of restrictions to limit the number of possible and alternative solutions to the problem, and it is axiomatic that in the preliminary stages of design we wish to maximize the number of possible incipient solutions. Conversely, it should be the purpose in this stage to recognize valid restrictions before too much time is expended in developing alternative solutions, which obviously fail to consider these restrictions. In any event, assumptions are the standard ingredients of textbook problems, but in real-life situations, there is no authority that can arbitrarily set forth assumptions without verifying them. This is not to argue the matter of imposing authoritative specifications under which the designer must operate. It is management's ultimate responsibility in the early design stages to assist the designer in finding the valid set of restrictions.

One important consideration is the amount of manpower that can be budgeted for the project, as well as time limitations. The planning of the project and the scheduling of its activities evolve simultaneously with the system. We will discuss project scheduling in Chapter 16.

Objectives and Criteria

An important part of problem analysis is the setting up of objectives and criteria. We have discussed objectives and criteria in previous sections, but we might note here that each design problem will have its own set of weighted value objectives. These include:

1. *Profit.* Profit is a function of price, cost, and volume of output. In the design of production systems, both volume and cost may be important criteria. Profit must be carefully defined as to its desired rate, dependence on taxes, desired interest rates, etc.
2. *Cost.* When both volume and prices are independently fixed, then cost becomes the important criterion. In the early design stages, cost may be expressed in monetary terms. In the later and more detailed stages, local criteria will consist of indices of cost, such as space, amount of material handling, material required, etc.
3. *Flexibility.* This is important in considering future changes in the specifications for the system. How well can the system be adapted to changes in rate of output, product design, product mix, etc.? This is a difficult criterion to quantify, especially in monetary terms.
4. *Compatibility.* This refers to the ease with which the design can be incorporated into its environment. One factor, for instance, is the facility with which human operator skills can be transferred in the new system. Compatibility often requires a good deal of analytical work to determine the relationship between the design and other elements of the system.
5. *Obsolescence.* The rate at which a design will become obsolete due to technological changes in the product or production methods may influence the decision. This requires some knowledge of the state of developments in various technical sectors. In order to be a useful criterion, some estimate must be made of the advantages of any stream of future technological advances, which is admittedly difficult.
6. *Realization.* A series of alternatives may be evaluated in terms of the costs required to develop and implement the design. The costs of development may be included as a variable in the cost criterion or evaluated separately.
7. *Other criteria.* Simplicity, safety, operator fatigue, operator job satisfaction, and ease of supervision are only a few from a longer list of possible objectives.

Alternative designs will also be judged by the efficiency with which they satisfy functional objectives. In many design problems, functional specifications are rigidly defined such that choice among alternatives is based on value criteria, assuming that all alternatives equally satisfy the functional requirements. Otherwise, a trade-off between value and function is necessary.

Problem Statement

Most textbooks submit the aphorism that "problems must be clearly stated before they can be solved." This recommendation is void of meaning unless the reader is advised of exactly how the problem should be stated. We reiterate what we said in Chapter 1, namely, that the statement of the problem is to clarify and specify the functional and value objectives, as well as constraints on their values.

THE BLACK-BOX APPROACH TO PROBLEM ANALYSIS: A potential production system can be structured as a black box whose physical contents and operating characteristics are the subject of the design problem. The black box differentiates the domain of design (decision) variables from the system's environment. The following example considers this approach to problem analysis.

EXAMPLE 4.1   Within the context of a dynamic cost-reduction program, the following problem has emerged from the Field Operations Section of a large utility company. The Field Operations Section consists of such activities as repairing power lines, pole replacement, equipment installations, etc. From a work-sampling analysis of various operations, it was determined (among many other things) that a significant cost was engendered in delimbing trees around power lines in off-highway and off-road areas.

The initial problem statement is as follows: "Design a ground-operated method for economically delimbing trees up to a height of 50 feet."

The initial problem statement does little to delimit the problem relative to finding a solution.

The purpose of the black-box approach is to bring into better focus the distinction between environmental factors, specifications, and the design variables.

1. *Economic need:* This has been initially established as the need to reduce the costs of delimbing and trimming trees around power lines and installations.
2. *Desired outputs:* These consist of the list of output specifications spelled out to any degree of refinement; for example,
   (a) Tree is void of limbs at selective points on trunk.
   (b) Limb must be removed close to trunk to avoid disease-attracting stumps.
3. *Undesired outputs:* These are anticipated outputs that are not specified, for example, limbs hanging on wires, scarred tree trunk, limbs scattered on the ground, falling limbs, possible damage to wires or servicing equipment.
4. *Known or desired inputs:* Nonhuman power source, human control at ground level, power source for mobility between work areas, fuel meter, etc.
5. *Constraints on inputs and outputs:*
   (a) Maximum limb diameter is 4 inches
   (b) Maximum of two men to operate and control
   (c) Minimum horsepower requirement at cutting point is 2 hp
   (d) Minimum fuel capacity equal to 1 hour running time
   (e) Joint use of power source with other activities where possible
   (f) Minimum rate of cutting is x square inches per second.

6. *Constraints on system:*
   (a) Units should be portable and not weigh over 100 lbs if transported by hand. They must be operated from ground level. The minimum time between cutting device sharpening or replacement is 8 hours; maximum capital expenditure is $2,000.
   (b) Easily stored in truck.
7. *Design criteria:* Payoff period for capital expenditure must be 2 years maximum, mobility of unit, ease of handling from ground, ease of maintenance in field of operations.

While we can elaborate on any one of the points listed above, the general idea is there. The problem is framed so that the designer is in a position to consider alternative designs to fill the black box.

THE SYNTHESIS OF ALTERNATIVE DESIGNS

Given a statement of the problem and a set of valid restrictions, the designer is in a position to give serious attention to the derivation of alternative solutions.

A Good Decision

Everything we have said in previous chapters about a good decision applies to the derivation of a good design. We can raise the following question: With respect to a given design problem, is there a "best" solution that exists in theory and that should be identified by the designer? If there is one potentially best solution, then the problem of synthesis would be to search for it and identify it from among a large number of possibilities. This would be like searching in a crowd for a person whose features are known. On the other hand, if "best" is merely academic and unidentifiable, then the problem of synthesis is to search for a solution that is satisfactory in terms of the criteria used and is "good" relative to the other possibilities considered in the search.

Design synthesis involves the concept of "courses of action." There is a trial-and-error derivation of a finite set of discrete alternative courses of action. This trial-and-error process we refer to as *creative synthesis*. Superimposed on the trial-and-error process are problems of dimensional design in which an optimal value of some dimension is sought. In these latter cases, the alternatives are not synthetically created. The creative part of the optimal seeking process may lie in the derivation of methods of finding optimum. In this section, we wish to consider some of the aspects of creative synthesis.

Creative Synthesis

The essence of creative thinking is the derivation of unique alternative courses of action. For example, in the case of the tree saw, the designer's task is to think of a set of alternative devices that would permit a ground-controlled unit to cut tree limbs as high as 50 feet in the tree. Creative thinking on his part might yield various ideas. Probably he would dwell on versions of a gasoline-driven electric power generator or air compressor, which would in turn supply power to a cutter on the end of a long pole. Then, the type of cutter must be innovated. This could include a simple circular blade, a small chain saw, or perhaps a low-speed milling cutter or grinder. Note that the problem can be subdivided into subsystems, including the original power source, the system for transmitting power to the limb, and the system for cutting the limb. A creative genius might upset the apple cart entirely by dreaming up a chemical that, when applied locally to the limb, would cause eventual separation. Or another idea might be to use a laser beam applied from the ground and focused on the limb joint. Here we are dealing with more or less unique and discrete alternatives, which, as far as we can see, have not been derived by a methodical and logical mental process.

Finding the "best" by creative synthesis with its trial-and-error approach seems wasteful, since we become involved in dealing with alternatives that we will subsequently discard in favor of the one chosen. Theoretically, we might like to transcend this trial-and-error method and derive the "best" by an analytical approach, involving the application of a series of logical steps that would constrict our activity to a direct path leading to the best.

The "efficiency" of creative synthesis can be considered from several angles. The first is the matter of constraints on the problem. If the problem and its constraints are carefully stated as previously prescribed, then we presumably confine the derivation of alternatives to those pertinent to the problem. Second, many solutions to design problems consist in applying principles or rules of design that lend some systematization to the process of arriving at a solution. Design rules may be incorporated in checklists or in operational rules that guide the creative part of the design. Therefore, both problem definition and design principles are in a sense constraints on creative activity. It can be argued, however, that the idea of efficiency is irrelevant in the creative phase of design and that creative thinking is inherently a wasteful process. That is, only through the derivation of a large number of ideas are one or a few good ideas likely to be realized. Therefore, we should investigate the characteristics of the idea-generating process in terms of improving the quality of performance, rather than concentrate on minimizing the time or resources devoted to the synthesis phase.

In creative synthesis, we deal with ideas for solutions to problems. The derivation of ideas for solutions pervades all stages of a design problem. In the preliminary stages of design, when economic needs are translated into statement of problems, objectives, and criteria, there may be a derivation of ideas for possible solutions. In some cases, the process may be triggered by the idea itself. But the incipient idea is a stimulus to analysis and problem formulation, rather than a predetermined solution to a problem that has yet to be defined. Once the problem is defined, system and environment segregated, and constraints recognized, the designer may direct his attention to the derivation of alternative solutions with some impunity from the hazards of dwelling on solutions to the wrong problem.

IMPROVING CREATIVITY: In managing design effort, one of the problems is to increase the efficiency of the creative process, both in individuals and organizations. The need is to remove road blocks and create an environment conducive to idea generation.

Various formal techniques are used to promote the creative potential in an organization. These include training sessions, which promote an individual's understanding of creative activity, particularly the nature of individual psychological and emotional inhibitors and social or cultural constraints. Then there is the efficient use of activities such as *brainstorming sessions*, which generate interaction among individuals in a group problem-solving situation. A good deal has been written about the human creative process by psychologists, engineers, and managers, so the reader may pursue the subject from a variety of viewpoints.

Finally, we must be careful to point out that creativity is not a substitute for the total design or problem-solving process. Generating ideas can be easy relative to the total job of evaluating and eventually implementing a final design. The widespread proliferation of ideas in an organization and outside the context of a well-structured problem can often do nothing but add fuel to the resistance to changes by those who end up having to evaluate, analyze, and implement.

EXAMPLE 4.2 We now refer to the case of pelletizing grain and feeds (page 20). The economic need in this example is that of converting grains and feeds into pellets for storage at the farm or ranch site. The kinds of solutions depend on the statement of the problem and the constraints placed on it. Suppose that we initially minimize the number of constraints and view the problem as a black box.

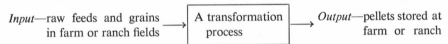

Input—raw feeds and grains in farm or ranch fields → | A transformation process | → *Output*—pellets stored at farm or ranch

Presenting the problem in this general form permits us to consider a wide variety of alternative courses of action. In the list of first-order solutions we can include the possibility of installing the production equipment on the body of a large truck and processing the materials directly at the farm or ranch. Figure 4.3 shows such an arrangement.

In contrast, the imposition of constraints, such as the assumption that materials are transported to and from the existing location by the customer or that the present layout of equipment is fixed, must lead to the statement of different problems and consequently different solutions.

Parametric Design

The problem of parametric design is to relate the quantifiable dimensions of a system to the design criteria. This is done first by establishing economic boundaries on design variables prior to the synthesis of a solution and then by optimizing the dimensions of a creative course of action.

PRELIMINARY DESIGN LIMITS: In the preliminary design stages, it is often necessary to impose limits on the problem dimensions based upon cost or other criteria.

FIGURE **4.3**   One solution to the pelletizing problem. Courtesy of Dodgen Industries, Inc.

For example, suppose we wish to design a production system for a new product or service. If the price, projected demand, and product life are known, together with a minimum rate of return on investment, then a first-order limit on capital expenditure can be set. If the problem is one of improving a system, then, given a desired rate of return on invested capital, a schedule of potential capital investments can be made for a possible range of cost savings.

The feasibility of creative ideas can often be assessed by initial "back-of-the-envelope" calculations if the designer has available standard cost-estimating data. It is surprising how easy it is to ignore preliminary estimates of this kind by pursuing a course of action in some detail before it is recognized that the whole line of attack is unprofitable. The issue is simply one of determining whether or not a certain idea is feasible.

OPTIMIZING DESIGN VARIABLES: Within the context of a first-order creative design solution, there is the need to establish the initial values of critical design variables. For example, suppose an analysis of refuse collection and disposal problems in the greater Baxter County area indicates that disposal by incineration is more economical than using sanitary landfills or building composting plants. The secondary design stage involves determining the following parameters: the number of incinerators to service the towns within the area, their capacities, and their locations. These are critical design variables, and, given the volume of demand for the service, we wish to optimize their values.

Figure 4.4 shows how parametric design might be carried out to determine these values. For a given number and capacity of incinerators, a model establishes the optimum location and compiles collection or transportation cost information.

The relationships between capacity, investment, and operating costs are established using standard or historical cost information. Finally, investment, operating, and transportation cost information are combined to derive a total cost model from which an optimum number and capacity of incinerators is revealed. Within these aggregate results, the more exacting details of design are pursued.

This kind of approach to synthesizing a design is often difficult to carry out. One must establish valid relationships between the design variables and the measures of effectiveness, such as profit, cost, volume of transport, weight, etc. And even if the functional relationships are understood and can be modeled, the derivation of the data to feed the model may be a demanding task. The only alternative is to fragment the design and independently design each fraction and hope that the combined effort is effective.

COST/EFFECTIVENESS: The term *cost/effectiveness analysis* describes the general function of relating cost to design parameters and system effectiveness. The term originated with application to military systems. This kind of analysis has become a formalized approach in the design of complex systems, particularly where alternative designs, or courses of action, yield different functional capabilities and performance.

CASE PROBLEM: The city of Bayburgh (pop. 400,000) is plagued each spring by a disease known to the townfolk as "street pox." The symptoms of this malady are city streets full of potholes and broken pavement resulting from periodic thaws and freezing. The period in question is about 8 weeks commencing in early February and ending in late March but depending on the weather, of course.

The potholes are repaired during this period by five-man crews who shovel cold asphalt into the holes from a dump truck and press the mixture with a power roller. In an average year, some 7,400 tons of asphalt are used for this work at $34 per ton. Labor assigned to the job consists of 15 crews at a cost of $100 per day per crew for wages. A work week is 6 days.

The manager of public works claims that the situation can be improved by spending more money for the general resurfacing of city streets. The present resurfacing budget is $500,000 per year, which pays for about 33 miles of resurfacing normally done during the summer months. At this rate, it takes about 20 years to resurface the 560 miles of city streets. He notes,

"If, instead of resurfacing 30-odd miles each year, we could do 60 miles, we could recover every street in ten years. If you doubled the budget for resurfacing and continued at that rate, after five years potholes would be reduced 25% and after ten years at least 50%."

The Public Works Department also has a proposal for improving the method of filling potholes. This consists of an integrated vehicle, which cleans the hole, heats it, puts a hot asphalt fill in it, and then presses it with a roller. This gives a much more permanent fill to the hole. The machine vendor claims that over a 10-year period the number of potholes occurring in a season would be reduced by 50%. This assumes

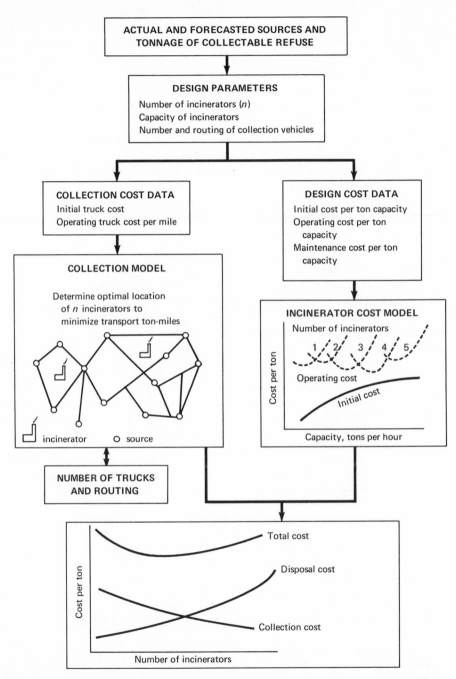

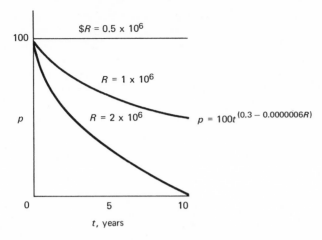

FIGURE **4.5**   Percentage of street potholes as a function of time for various levels of resurfacing investment.

that the department would use eight machines, each priced at $8,000. Each machine will require a crew of four men.

An analyst in the Budget Bureau is asked to evaluate the "possibilities." In the course of discussions with public works engineers, he formulated a model that relates the "decay" percentage of potholes per year to time for various annual expenditures in road resurfacing. The model is shown above (Figure 4.5).

R = annual expenditures in road resurfacing in dollars
t = time in years
p = percent annual potholes where 100% equals normal number (for R = $500,000)

Using this model, he started an analysis of the alternatives, including a resurfacing policy, if that alternative should ultimately be selected by the city manager.

Problems

4.1   The year is 1970. In response to public demands, governments at all levels in the United States have intensified their efforts to control pollution in its many forms. There is noticeable pressure to process normal refuse other than by sanitary landfill, due to the increased scarcity of land sites. The use of community incinerators continues to receive objection from nearby residents because of their feeling that the air is unduly polluted in spite of scientific tests that show that the pollution is negligible. The Consolidated Electric Company is a producer of home appliances. It has appointed a team to consider the feasibility of producing a "device" for processing refuse in the home. The suburban resident presently pays about $50 to $60 a year for refuse collection, usually by private contractors. Consider this as a system design problem and structure the problem in terms of the discussion in this chapter.

4.2   Monroe County in upstate New York contains a large city (400,000 population), 19 townships, and 30 villages. Each government entity, that is, city, village, town, county, and state, maintains a fleet of public works vehicles. Presently, each entity operates its own vehicle garage and maintenance facilities. A group of students in a production course in the graduate business school at a local university has undertaken to investigate the economics of public works fleet maintenance. The hypothesis is made that fleet maintenance might be centralized to some degree, rather than decentralized as it is now. That is, one or more centralized maintenance facilities might be designed to be shared jointly by the various government agencies. Assuming you are a member of the project group, prepare an initial report that would set forth the general framework of the study. That is, how might the study proceed, what data should be collected, how might they be used, etc.? Your report might be used as the basis for making initial assignments to the people in the group.

4.3   What design features of an office building would you recommend to minimize the cost of interior cleaning?

4.4   Suppose you are in a value analysis group for the Genesis Company, a heavenly organization, which has created the earth and its inhabitants. The function of the value analysis group is to consider if the effectiveness of the human body can be improved by changing locations of any one or more of these four organs—eyes, ears, nose, mouth—to any other part of the body. What changes would you suggest, and what are their advantages and disadvantages?

4.5   The Southeastern Gas Corporation wishes to locate a 600,000 ft³ natural gas storage tank in a large city. The tank is a globe about 10 building stories high. The ideal location is near a residential area of the city. However, the proposed location has been objected to by the citizens and clubs in the area because of its being a possible eyesore. Resistance to the location was overcome by a suggestion made by the company president. The suggestion cost about $6,800 but resulted in the location being enthusiastically approved by the citizens. What do you think the idea was?

4.6   You are the manager of a trucking firm. One of your trucks is delivering a load of perishable foods to an important customer. You get a call from the driver. He has stopped in front of an underpass and found that his load height is about one inch higher than the underpass height. Also, his refrigeration system has broken down. If he detours, it may cost the whole load in spoiled goods plus a late delivery. What do you tell him to do?

4.7   The White Engine Company has experienced pilferage by employees of their electric-powered hand tools, which are used extensively in their shops (drills, grinders, hammers, wrenches, sanders, screwdrivers, etc.). The loss amounts to several thousand dollars a year. The items are very inviting to the home shop owner. Your job is to suggest ways of reducing this cost.

Bibliography

ALGER, JOHN R. M., and CARL V. HAYS, *Creative Synthesis in Design.* Englewood Cliffs, N.J.: Prentice-Hall, Inc., 1964.

ASIMOW, MORRIS, *Introduction to Design.* Englewood Cliffs, N.J.: Prentice-Hall, Inc., 1961.

ENGLISH, J. M., "Understanding the Engineering Design Process," *J. Ind. Eng.*, November–December 1964.

FIELDS, DAVID S., "Cost/Effectiveness Analysis: Its Tasks and Their Interrelations," *Operations Research*, May–June 1966.

GHISELIN, BREWSTER, *The Creative Process—A Symposium*. Berkeley, Calif.: University of California Press, 1962.

GORDON, WILLIAM, *Synectics*. New York: Harper and Row, Publishers, 1961.

HALL, ARTHUR E., *A Methodology for Systems Engineering*. Princeton, N.J.: D. Van Nostrand Co., 1962.

HILL, L. S., "Towards a Coordinated Approach to the Structuring of Cost and Design Models," *Operations Research*, July–August 1965.

HEUSTON, M. C., and G. OGAWA, "Observations on the Theoretical Basis of Cost Effectiveness," *Operations Research*, March–April 1966.

NADLER, GERALD, "An Investigation of Design Methodology," *Management Science*, June 1967.

NEWTON, NORMAN T., *An Approach to Design*. Reading, Mass.: Addison-Wesley Press, Inc., 1951.

VON FANGE, EUGENE K., *Professional Creativity*. Englewood Cliffs, N.J.: Prentice-Hall, Inc., 1960.

WOODSON, WILLIAM S., "Creative Techniques—A Comparative Analysis," *J. Ind. Eng.*, March–April 1964.

5
Product Design
and Process Capability

THE CONSUMER SYSTEM

The purpose of a product or a service is to satisfy an economic need for the consumer. The product or service may be designed to meet the specific needs of a given customer, or it may be designed to satisfy the needs of a class of consumers in some average sense. We can briefly note at this point that one of the basic problems of product planning and design is the degree to which the product will meet the specific desires of an individual customer. On the one hand, the custom-made products, while meeting the exact needs of the individual, are costly; and the infinite variety of individual human tastes precludes an economy of custom-made goods. On the other hand, the "mass" produced product satisfies the expected desires of the population of potential customers. The broad economic issue and challenge are, therefore, the production of variety without sacrifice of economy.

Regardless of the specificity of the ultimate customer, the product designer must evaluate alternative designs in terms of criteria that reflect the attractiveness of the product to the future buyer. These criteria may be classified in two general ways.

1. *Function and reliability* First, the product must perform some specific function or meet a set of functional specifications. For example, a refrigerator must keep food at a certain temperature, a nut and bolt must hold two parts together under some maximum load, a saw must cut wood of specific dimensions, and so forth. Then, the product must perform this function with reliability, which refers to some specified or desired functional life. Both function and reliability comprise the major technical content of the product design problem.

2. *Appearance and performance in the consumer system* Besides functioning with reliability, the product must have esthetic appeal, and it must also be designed as an input to a consumer's operating system or living environment. The refrigerator should have an appealing appearance and also be adapted to the home kitchen system. For example, its top may be used to store items, the food shelves must be easily loaded and unloaded, and the direction of the door opening should accommodate its location in the kitchen. Consider a chain saw. Obviously, it must

140

cut wood, but it must also fit into the system in which it will be used. This involves ease of handling and maintenance in the field, resistance to breakage under rough usage, etc. The same applies to service systems, where the designer must consider how to maximize the accommodation of the customer in the service system. A cleaning establishment may do a good job of cleaning but be poorly designed to service the customer when he deposits and picks up his cleaning.

A product may be functionally well designed but lacking in terms of market appeal and adaptability to the consumer's operating needs. In the long history of product development until recent times, it has been significant how appearance and performance in the consumer operating system have lagged behind the developments in function. Today, the competitive advantage of a product often lies in a superior appearance or adaptability to the consumer's operating needs. As examples, you might consider a half-dozen consumer items that you frequently use and evaluate their design from these various points of view.

PRODUCT DESIGN AND MANUFACTURABILITY

The product is the output of a production system. The functional specifications for a production operation are embodied in the dimensions and attributes of the product that is to be made.

The functional or output specifications for a production process are manifested as a set of blueprints, diagrams, drawings, or lists. The fundamental nature and cost of a production system is initially controlled in these stages of product design and development. This is less obvious but just as true for service operations. For example, the cost of cleaning a hospital is a function of the design of the structure and its rooms. The cost of handling items in a warehouse depends on the design of the shelves and their relative locations.

The control of production costs in the product design stages depends on the existence of alternative product or structure designs, which on the one hand satisfy the functional criteria and on the other hand reflect the different production costs. If such alternatives do not exist, then the issue of cost control is academic.

This problem is extremely important from an organizational point of view. The ideal situation exists when all criteria, including function, reliability, appearance, performance, maintenance, and manufacturing variables are considered in the product design stages. This implies that product design should be a coordinated effort between the various organizational groups concerned with the problem. The worst situation obtains when product or structure design proceeds as an additive endeavor. This is to ignore a systems approach, which begs an optimal design. Instead, each set of criteria is considered independently and in some sequence by separate professional groups, first function and reliability, then performance, followed by manufacturing and maintenance considerations. If this is the case, then there is either a good deal of design change or an inordinate amount of redesign and improvement after the product has been released for production and sales.

Alternative Designs

We can gain some perspective of the problem by considering the following example. Figure 5.1 shows four alternative designs for a machine bracket.

Design 1 is a casting requiring certain machining operations. The weight of the part is 40 lb, and the unit cost is $11.70.

Design 2 is made from 8-gauge sheet stock and formed by press brake and shear. This reduces the weight by 22 lb, and the cost is $6.14.

Design 3 is fabricated from steel by welding and flame cutting, resulting in a part weighing 31 lb with a unit cost of $4.60.

Design 4 is formed from a single strip of steel and welded for strength. The unit cost is $3.18, and the weight is 10 lb.

INITIAL DESIGN VERSUS EVOLUTIONARY IMPROVEMENT: While the foregoing examples show the dramatic reduction in cost and weight with no sacrifice to function, the important issue is the way in which the design function is managed. We are familiar with the fact that the cost of a product may be reduced over time by the application of a series of improvements to both the product design and the production process. However, in the initial design stage, an attempt should be made to *force* the evolution of improvements in the actual design stage. This is consistent with the objective of the design process, which is to seek the "best" or most effective design. Obviously, if the cost is reduced through an evolution of design changes after the first design is placed in operation, then there is an opportunity cost, which is the savings lost because the "best" design was not conceived prior to producing the item.

For example, in the design of the machine bracket, let us assume that Design 4 emerges as the result of a cost-reduction program long after the part has been placed into production using an inferior design. The relevant question is, why was Design 4 not conceived in the initial design stage? If, with some additional expenditure of

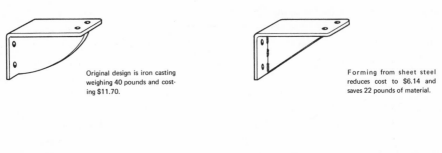

Original design is iron casting weighing 40 pounds and costing $11.70.

Forming from sheet steel reduces cost to $6.14 and saves 22 pounds of material.

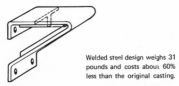

Welded steel design weighs 31 pounds and costs about 60% less than the original casting.

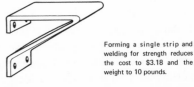

Forming a single strip and welding for strength reduces the cost to $3.18 and the weight to 10 pounds.

FIGURE **5.1**   Alternative designs of a machine bracket.

design time, Design 4 was potentially attainable, then the principle is that the company had an opportunity cost of $8.52 for every unit produced with the inferior design. However, one might defend the evolution of design in the form of successive improvements.

1. Designs 3 and 4 could not have been conceived initially because they involved technological factors that were not a part of the designer's repertoire at the time the problem was assigned to him. Many improvements, of course, originate because of the emergence of some new technology.
2. It may be argued that improvements are much easier to make on something that already exists, which is the essence of evolution. It is psychologically demanding to conceive of a new product, or ideas, and then destroy them in an effort to find something better. We are familiar with this aspect of creative design.
3. In most design projects, the design time and resources are limited to such an extent that the designer does not have the opportunity to converge on an "ideal" design. The cost of delaying the project is imputed to be higher than the opportunity costs of not having the ideal design.

In spite of these arguments, there is reason to believe that, in many initial product design problems, insufficient attention is paid to the matter of achieving an ideal design through the forced evolutionary process. However, in many progressive firms, the problem is recognized and a certain degree of coordination exacted in the design stages. Presently, the problem is a matter of the ability to direct the efforts of the people involved to consider a range of possible areas where the design of a product can be altered to improve production costs without a significant sacrifice of function, appearance, or performance. It is an area that might well be subjected to operations research, and, in particular, it might be determined how the memory capacity of computers can systematically operate on the wide variety of material and process information that must be assessed in tackling the problem. At the present time, the wide experience of production processing that the production engineer brings to the problem is extremely important. He can often spot a minor change in part design that will save a few cents per part—a significant saving in the aggregate.

Principles of Product Design for Manufacturability

When a part design is analyzed for economic production, certain principles may be used to guide the analysis. In general, production design may center on the following factors.

BASIC PROCESSES AND MATERIALS: The previous example incorporates the principle of examining different alternative basic processes with or without the use of different materials. The economics of a particular process depend on the volume of the part that is to be produced. Two or more processes are competitive usually at only a confined range of volume. Consider the example shown in Figure 5.2.

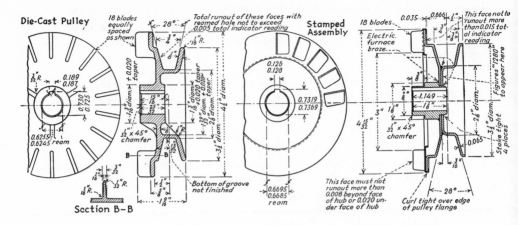

FIGURE **5.2**   Pulley-ventilating fan. From *Handbook on Designing for Quantity Production* by H. Chase. Copyright 1944 by McGraw-Hill, Inc. Used by permission of McGraw-Hill Book Company.

This shows two designs for a combined pulley and ventilating fan for a lighting generator. The design in the left of the figure is a single integral die casting, while the design in the right consists in welding four stamped parts together. The two designs are compared in Table 5.1 with respect to certain attributes.

TABLE **5.1**   Comparison of two designs.

Item	Die casting[b]	Stamping[b]
Weight	Double the weight of the stamped part	—
Die cost[a]	$580	$1,200
Total unit cost[a]	$0.17	$0.14
Total annual volume	300,000 units	300,000 units
No. of operations	4	8
Production rate	—	50% greater than with die casting
No. of components	1	4

[a] Cost based on volume given.
[b] Both parts meet the engineering specifications.

We note that at the volume given, 300,000 units, the stamped part is superior in terms of unit manufacturing cost as well as in other factors, such as rate of output and weight. On the other hand, it requires more components than the die casting and also a more expensive die. We might expect a range of costs for each method, depending on the demand for the parts. Thus, at another volume, the cost advantage might shift from stamping to die casting.

In cases of this type, the decision between alternative product designs may be complicated by a difference in the degree to which functional specifications or other criteria are met. In the case shown, both designs meet functional specifications equally well. However, we might be faced with the situation in which die casting has some distinct advantage over stamping in its ability to meet other than production criteria. Then the decision is a case of tradeoff or determining if losing the advantage in functional performance is worth the savings in production costs.

In situations where the demand for an item is extremely high and production resources are limited, two or more alternative designs may be accepted for production. For instance, in the case of the fan, it might be advantageous to produce the product both ways in order to meet demand. Or, the alternatives might allow a degree of flexibility in the utilization of the shop. This is the same thing as having two or more routes specified for the part. Such a situation is probably not possible in cases where both alternative designs require a significant capital investment in process tools, such as dies or fixtures.

ALTERNATIVE AND CHEAPER MATERIALS: The design may be improved by the use of a different material that may increase strength, reduce weight or cost, etc. Figure 5.3 shows the substitution of plastic for metal in the design of a small part.

STANDARD MATERIALS AND PARTS: The use of standard materials and parts often results in significant cost savings. Figure 5.4 shows the substitution of standard parts in a small part design resulting in a reduction of part cost by 50%.

SIMPLIFICATION OF DESIGN: Simplification means the reduction in the number of components of a product, as well as reduction in complexity. The reduction of the number of components comprising an assembly means less material and part control in production and inventories, as well as reduced assembly costs.

Figure 5.5 shows the reduction in the number of components required for a valve. In this particular case, the reduction was an essential feature of a change

BEFORE: The beryl-lium-copper link for a business machine had to be blanked, pierced, hardened, milled, bored.

AFTER: The part now is cast from Delrin plastic in a single step. Service life is increased, cost reduced 80%.

FIGURE **5.3**   Substitution of material in part design. Reprinted by special permission from the October 1960 issue of *International Management Digest*, copyright McGraw-Hill, Inc.

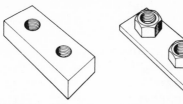

BEFORE: This clamp bar for a diesel-electric locomotive had to be machined from bar stock, then drilled and tapped.

AFTER: Now the clamp is made by welding two standard nuts to a stamping, cutting costs 50%.

FIGURE **5.4**   Uses of standard parts. Reprinted by special permission from the October 1960 issue of *International Management Digest*, copyright McGraw-Hill, Inc.

from conventional to automated manufacturing of the valve. Of course, as we have noted in previous cases, the principle of reducing the number of components does not always hold, and manufacturing costs may be reduced by choosing a design that requires fractionization of the product into a number of components.

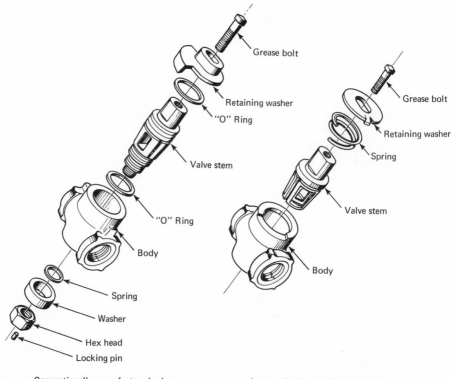

Conventionally manufactured valve

Automatically manufactured valve

FIGURE **5.5**   Valve re-design for automation. Courtesy of Charles Hautau.

DESIGN FOR ECONOMICAL ASSEMBLY: When assembly costs are a significant fraction of total manufacturing costs, then there may be an emphasis on product design to minimize assembly costs. This can be accomplished in a number of ways besides simplifying the design. The following factors are related to making the actual assembly operation simpler or more reliable:

1. Design the parts to eliminate the possibility of incorrect assembly. Two components may be designed so they can be mated in only the correct orientation. Not only is the possibility of incorrect orientation eliminated, but the time spent by the operator in inspecting the parts for correct orientation is reduced.
2. Parts may be color coded to eliminate the need for searching for and selecting the correct part.
3. Tolerances and allowances may be relaxed for easier fitting.
4. Parts may be designed for ease in handling by the assembly operator.
5. Special screws and fastening devices may be designed for rapid assembly.

These factors simply point out the amount of detail that can be considered in product design.

DESIGN FOR ECONOMICAL MAINTENANCE: A product or piece of equipment is an input to a maintenance operation. We are probably all familiar with the problems of maintaining a consumer product or piece of equipment in our own homes. In many cases, the matter of maintenance seems to have been ignored or perhaps is to be considered in the additive design process. Maintenance considerations include the ease with which a piece of equipment can be routinely inspected and lubricated, be cleaned, or have its parts replaced. The problem of designing for maintenance requires an analysis of the operations that must be performed on the equipment with a consideration of who will conduct the maintenance. Frequently, an awareness of the maintenance requirements is left to experience after the design stages, much to the detriment of maintenance costs. This merely suggests that from the systems point of view, maintenance or plant engineering personnel should be an integral part of the design evaluation program.

VALUE ANALYSIS: The formal, concerted effort to reduce costs through the analysis of existing products (or those in the design stages) is known as "value analysis" or "value engineering." Both the term and the formalized approach are attributable to the General Electric Company.

The approach involves the detailed examination of a product by a value analysis team or committee. The procedure may commence with setting a value on the product, a comparison of the present cost with the "par" value, followed by a systematic search for ways of improving the design relative to function, performance, maintenance, or manufacturing cost. This approach is in contrast to the search for cost reduction directly in the manufacturing processes, without direct concern for product design.

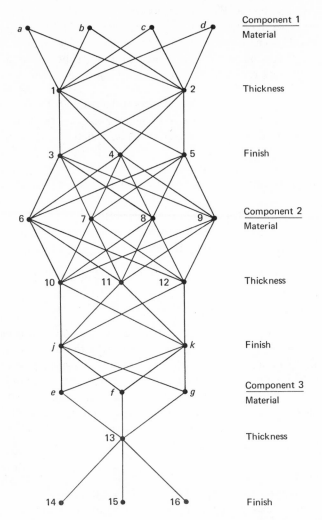

FIGURE **5.6**   A design tree with three components, three characteristics, and 5,184
branches. From Martin K. Starr, *Product Design and Decision Theory*.
© 1963.   Reprinted by permission of Prentice-Hall, Inc., Englewood
Cliffs, N.J.

Design Trees

In the design of a multicomponent product, the designer may be confronted
with a bewildering array of alternative courses of action with respect to materials,
processes, fastening devices, surface finishes, and other design variants. Our previous examples point out some of the things the designer can consider in designing
for economical production. The range of alternatives depends on the designer's

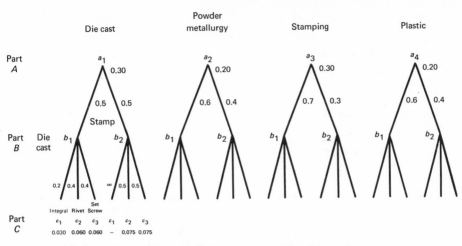

Die cast

FIGURE **5.7**   Design tree for pencil sharpener—weighted branches.

knowledge of existing technology, as well as on his ability to create new and different possibilities.

The theoretical magnitude of the job of evaluating alternative product designs is suggested in the form of a design tree. Starr[1] provides the example shown in Figure 5.6, where three components, each having alternative thicknesses and finishes, are interrelated in a design tree. There are a total of 5,184 unique paths or design configurations in the tree ($1 \times 4 \times 2 \times 3 \times 1 \times 4 \times 3 \times 2 \times 1 \times 3 \times 1 \times 3 = 5,184$). Each possibility has a unique cost if there is dependence between the nodes of the tree. That is, the cost of the alternative finish (4) for component 1 depends on the choice of both thickness and material. At the other extreme, if there is no interdependence between any of the components, then there are only nine possibilities. First, the choice of material is made for component 1. Given this, the choice of thickness is made, then the choice of finish, etc. This corresponds more to the type of decisions we have reviewed so far.

If there is some independence between components, the interdependence must be weighted in the design choice. A different kind of a design tree is shown in Figure 5.7, where we have the following situation. There are three design decisions to make for a pencil sharpener. These include the choice of design for two components and the method of joining them together. Part A is a cutter housing, which can be made by four alternative processes. Part B is the handle arm, which can be made in two different ways. Part C is a choice to be made among three alternative fastening methods.

[1] Martin K. Starr, *Product Design and Decision Theory*. Englewood Cliffs, N.J.: Prentice-Hall, Inc., 1963, p. 9.

Alternative *A*—cutter housing

a_1 die casting
a_2 powder metallurgy
a_3 brazed stamping
a_4 molded plastic

Alternative *B*—handle arm

b_1 die casting
b_2 stamped part

Alternative *C*—fastening and assembly

c_1 integral part (*a* and
      b are a single unit)
c_2 rivet
c_3 set screw

Each of the four alternatives for *A* are listed at the top of the design tree. Next to each is a number representing the relative desirability of the alternative. For example, the numbers might represent a rank number (1, 2, 3, or 4) divided by 10. Assume that the numbers shown represent the designer's rough estimate of the costs converted to a weight scale of 10. Similarly, weights are assigned to the *B* alternatives. Note that these weights vary slightly, depending on or conditioned by the *A* alternative. For example, for the alternative $a_1 - b_1$, the two parts might be integrated into a single-die-cast part, thus reducing the cost of b_1 compared to its production as a single part. Finally, each set of three fastening methods is weighted. The relative values of the 24 paths are obtained by multiplying the weights along each path. Thus, the choice $a_1 - b_1 - c_1$ is weighted $0.3 \times 0.5 \times 0.2 = 0.030$.

This method is a first approach to the design decision problem. In this case, we would look for low values (since we are interested in minimizing the cost). Obviously, where preference is proportional to weight value, the weighting system could be reversed. However, we can note that some paths are impossible and are assigned values of infinity or zero, depending on the weighting system. This leads to the problem of evaluating the remaining alternatives in the particular stage of the tree. The method seems to be best suited to the case where each stage has equal numbers of permissible branches or links at each stage. Otherwise, the weighting system is disproportionate.

This method of signaling those design alternatives that appear to deserve more analysis is valid if the differences between alternatives in terms of the weights is significant at one or more of the tree branches.

Analytical Process Selection

A systematic procedure for selecting economical processing methods for parts has been investigated by Niebel.[2] His system is predicated on considering five principal design parameters that apply to the selection of a primary process for manufacturing a part. These are 1) size of part, 2) geometry or configuration of part,

---

[2] Benjamin W. Niebel, "An Analytical Technique for the Selection of Manufacturing Operations," *J. Ind. Eng.*, vol. XVII, no. 11, November 1966, pp. 598–603.

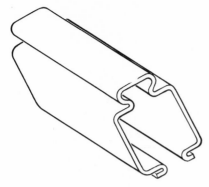

FIGURE **5.8**   Hollow or partly hollow solids involving one or more cross-sectional areas along one axis. The depth of hollow is more than two-thirds the major diameter of the hollow. Taken from the November 1966 issue of *The Journal of Industrial Engineering*.

3) material being utilized, 4) quantity requirements, and 5) cost of manufacture. Each of the first four parameters has been subjected to a classification scheme. The classification of geometry was done so as to facilitate the relationship of geometry to process capabilities. A decision table is used to relate geometry to process, where the processes are the alternative decisions, A_i; geometries are states of nature, S_j; and the outcome is

$$O_{ij} = \begin{cases} 1 & \text{if process } i \text{ can be used to make geometry } j \\ 0 & \text{otherwise} \end{cases}$$

The geometry classification was most difficult to make. Figure 5.8 shows an example of geometry classification N_{04}.

Cost equations were derived in linear form

$$D_t = (A_{ijk})(N) + B_{ij}$$

where

i = index of process
j = index of part size
k = index of material
A_{ijk} = cost coefficient
N = number of units to be produced
B_{ij} = fixed cost element of the process
D_t = total cost through primary process

The method is adapted to the computer, where the input is the part size, quantity, geometry, and material. The output is a listing of alternative feasible processes in descending order of desirability (or ascending cost). A typical computer output is shown in Table 5.2.

Niebel's approach is an important step in the design of integrated information systems to be discussed in Chapter 17. While he has derived specific cost functions, his general approach may be tailored to fit a particular company's experience.

TABLE **5.2**   Typical computer output.[2]

| Part No.   5 | Quantity on Order   200 | Name   C R Moss   Trial 1 |
| Size of Part   4 | Geometry   3 | Material Nonferrous |

| The recommended processes in ascending order of costs | Total costs of order through first operation | Scheduling data—times to completion in hours | | |
		Minimum time	Maximum time	Average time
Shell mold	2,334.00	5.71	8.00	6.86
Plaster mold	2,342.00	10.00	20.00	15.00
Sand casting	2,356.00	8.00	10.00	9.00
Investment casting	2,510.00	20.00	40.00	30.00
Electroformed	3,136.00	50.00	100.00	75.00
Weldments and joint assemblies	3,185.00	4.00	13.33	8.67
Rough machine from mill stock	3,351.00	16.67	66.67	41.67

7 processes possible.

PROCESS CAPABILITY

The capability of a production operation or process refers to the ability of the process to satisfy its output specifications. The quantifiable output of the process is usually some dimension of the part of service being produced. Obvious ones are the diameter of a shaft turned out by a lathe, the hardness of parts from a heat-treating operation, and the gauge of a batch of wire. Less obvious ones are the number of errors in typewritten insurance policies, the proportion of monthly orders shipped late to customers, and the percentage of times a group of machines is down for repair. Each of these measures reflects the output of a production or service system.

Process Variability

In the first chapter, we noted that a production process or operation has the characteristic of repetitiveness. Over time, the system generates a stream of parts or services consisting of similar units of output. Also, the system demands a stream of similar units of input.

This repetitive characteristic of a production system permits the system to be described as a random or stochastic process. A stochastic process is a random phenomenon that changes with time. In the case of the production system, successive units of input or output vary randomly with respect to some dimension of the unit of input or output. For a given dimension, no two units of output are exactly identical except by chance. In many cases, this between-unit variation may be microscopic, and we may need very precise measuring instruments to detect it.

For example, in Figure 5.9, a machine for producing steel shafts generates a

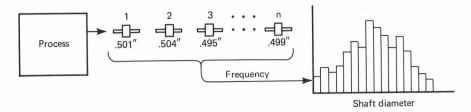

<small>FIGURE</small> **5.9**   Random variation in shaft diameter.

stream of n shafts. The desired middle diameter is 0.500 inches. The actual diameter is a random variable displayed by the frequency distribution of the shaft diameters. Other examples of random production processes are:

1. A cast pump housing is milled on a horizontal milling machine. The Rockwell hardness number of the incoming castings is a random variable.
2. A refuse truck and crew collect refuse from approximately 300 houses per day. The time it takes to service an individual house is a random variable.
3. A process produces 4 × 8 foot sheets of plywood paneling. The number of defects per panel is statistically distributed.
4. An automatic textile machine must be periodically serviced by an attendant. The number of times the machine demands service per hour is a random variable.
5. A part is held in finished goods inventory to meet future customer demand. The time between successive customer demands on inventory is a random variable.

<small>CAUSES OF VARIABILITY</small>: The random properties of production processes are an important consideration in design and control functions. The contributions to variability are both causal and random. If we can assign causes for variation, then these causes may be remedied if we wish to reduce the amount of variation, to a tolerable limit. However, an attempt to remove all the causes of variation would be uneconomical and probably technologically impossible. Therefore, there is always some residual variation in the process, which we refer to as random or chance variation, the causes for which are numerous, unassigned, and not economically worth removing.

A set of parts produced by a process is considered to be homogeneous if the items in the set were produced by a common set of production inputs. Lack of homogeneity is contributed by assignable causes of variation, such as production of the same product by different machines, from different raw material batches, by or different work shifts.

Statistical theory can be used to determine the homogeneity of production output and to detect and remove undesirable causes of variation. A process is statistically stable when the statistical parameters (e.g., mean and variance) of the process variability are constant over time. The process is statistically dynamic when these parameters are changing significantly over time.

Tolerance and Allowance

The product design engineer recognizes the fact that no process can produce successive units of output with exactly the same dimension. He therefore specifies a *tolerance* in the dimension of the part. The tolerance is the range of variation in the dimension of the part that the engineer is willing to accept when he considers the part's function or reliability. Consider the two parts shown in Figure 5.10. Part *A* is a shaft that is to fit into a sleeve, Part *B*. The two parts are to be mated in an assembly operation. The permissible range of the diameter of *A* is 0.7440″ to 0.7428″, and for Part *B* the range is 0.7461″ to 0.7450″.

If the process adheres to these specifications, then there will always be a *clearance* between any two mating parts. The *allowance* is the minimum clearance we would expect to find if the tolerances are adhered to. In this case, the *allowance* is the smallest diameter of *B* less the largest diameter of *A*, or 0.7450 − 0.7440 = 0.0010″. An *interference* between Parts *A* and *B* occurs when the diameter of *A* is larger than the diameter of *B*. In some cases, mating parts such as these might be designed for interference so that the parts would be force fitted.

If Part *A* is mass produced in large quantities on a lathe, then we expect its diameter to be statistically distributed. Such a distribution could be empirically derived by examining a sample of the part diameters. If the process is under statis-

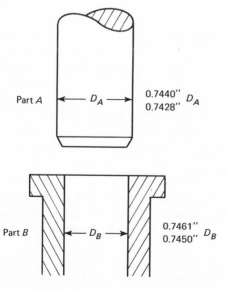

FIGURE **5.10** Tolerance in part dimensions.

tical control, that is, is statistically stable, then the resulting variation is random, and we may assume it is due to a large number of independent unassignable minor causes, such as microscopic variation in material, machine linkages, etc. Then, we can argue that the distribution of the shaft diameter would be normal on the basis of the central limit theorem.

The central limit theorem states that if a number of random variables X_1, X_2, . . . are identically distributed and independent, then the sum

$$S_n = X_1 + X_2 + , \ldots, X_n$$

is normally distributed.

Suppose we assume that the distribution of the shaft diameter is as follows. The mean is equal to the median of the tolerance range, and the standard deviation is equal to $\frac{1}{6}$ the tolerance range, such that there is a very small likelihood that a diameter will fall outside this range.

The range, 6σ, is called the natural tolerance range. (See Figure 5.11.) Of course, the exact mean and variance of the distribution will depend on how the lathe is set up and controlled.

When two or more different parts are brought together in an assembly, the statistical variation in the dimensions of the individual parts results in a statistical variation in the dimensions of the assembly. As we have noted, when two parts are joined together, we are interested in the clearance of the mated parts. Clearance (or interference), then, is the dimension of the assembly that often determines the effectiveness of the assembly function.

THE NONSTATISTICAL ADDITION OF TOLERANCES: The clearance between two mating parts is determined by the arithmetic addition of tolerances. Consider the three parts shown in Figure 5.12. Parts X and Y are placed side by side and inserted in the slot in the Yoke Z.

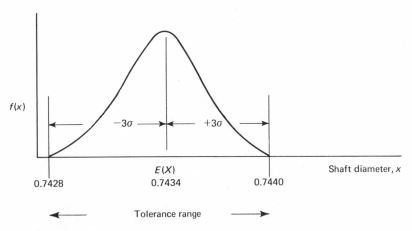

FIGURE **5.11**   Natural tolerance range equals 6σ.

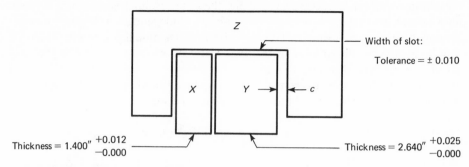

FIGURE **5.12**   Assembly of three parts.

The clearance, designated as C, is the difference between the sum of the widths of X and Y and the dimension of the slot Z. If we let X, Y, and Z stand for the dimensions in question, then $C = Z - (X + Y)$.

Suppose that the parts are to be mass produced and assembled in a random fashion. The dimensions and tolerances of X and Y are specified, as well as the tolerance of Z. Furthermore, the minimum clearance between the parts, or the allowance, is specified to be 0.007″. The problem now is to fully specify the dimensions of Z.

If we ignore the statistical variation in the part dimensions, the dimensions of Z will be determined by finding the extreme conditions of fit. The lower dimension for Z will be determined by simply adding the maximum allowable dimensions of X and Y and the allowance:

$$\text{Lower limit of } Z = \text{maximum width of } X + \text{maximum width of } Y + \text{allowance}$$
$$= 1.412 + 2.665 + 0.007 = 4.084$$

The maximum limiting dimension for Z will simply be the lower limit plus the tolerance range:

$$\text{Maximum limit of } Z = 4.084 + 0.020 = 4.104$$

The maximum clearance is now easy to calculate and is simply

$$\text{Maximum clearance} = \text{maximum width of } Z - \text{minimum width}$$
$$\text{of } X - \text{minimum width of } Y$$
$$= 4.104 - 1.400 - 2.640 = 0.064$$

We can now expect that when the parts are assembled at random, the range of clearances will be from 0.007 to 0.064 or 0.057 inches, which is also equal to the sum of the part tolerances, $0.012 + 0.025 + 0.020 = 0.057$.

Such a system of dimensioning ignores the fact the dimensions of the parts are statistical variables. It assumes that there is an equal likelihood of obtaining clearances throughout the range from 0.007 to 0.064. If we assume that each of the dimensions is normally distributed and that the tolerance range is equal to six standard deviations (or plus or minus three standard deviations from the distribution mean), then the likelihood of obtaining the extreme clearances is very small. For example, the probability of obtaining simultaneously an X and a Y, whose widths exceed the natural tolerance limit, and a Z, whose width is less than the natural tolerance limit, is $(1/740)^3 = 1/405{,}000{,}000$. This is in contrast to the assumption of an equal likelihood for all combinations of widths for the three parts.

The simple arithmetic addition of tolerances and ignoring of the statistical distribution of part dimensions lead to undesirable consequences. Most important is the fact that the parts will fit more loosely than expected. The minimum clearance of 0.007 will not likely be obtained. If tight fits are desirable, which is often the case with mechanical parts, that goal will not be obtained. When this is apparent to the engineer, then the consequence may be the reduction of the tolerance of one or more of the parts, thus increasing production costs in finer machine adjustments, added inspection, rejection of out-of-tolerance parts that could actually be used, etc.

THE STATISTICAL ADDITION OF TOLERANCES: The statistical addition of tolerances recognizes that the variability of an assembly dimension is contributed by the sum, product, or quotient of other random variables. The following relationships are useful and set forth without proof.

Let X and Y be two independent and identically distributed random variables. Let there be a third random variable Z that has the following relationship to X and Y:

1. $Z = X \pm Y$

Then,

$$\text{Expected Value of } Z = E(Z) = E(X) \pm E(Y)$$
$$\text{Variance of } Z = V(Z) = V(X) + V(Y)$$

2. $Z = XY$

Then,

$$E(Z) = E(X) \cdot E(Y)$$
$$V(Z) = [E(X)]^2 V(Y) + [E(Y)]^2 V(X)$$

3. $Z = X/Y$

Then,

$$E(Z) = E(X)/E(Y)$$

$$V(Z) = \frac{V(X \cdot Y)}{[E(Y)]^4}$$

Using the addition relationship, we have a basis for analyzing the characteristics of the clearance generated by the random assembly of the three parts, X, Y, and Z.

Let us assume that the natural tolerance ranges correspond to the tolerances specified in the example. If the processes for generating the three dimensions are under control, then the dimensions will be normally distributed with the means equal to the midpoints of the tolerance ranges and the standard deviation equal to $\frac{1}{6}$ of the tolerance range. That is,

$\overline{X}$ = mean width of dimension X = 1.406
$\overline{Y}$ = mean width of dimension Y = 2.652
$\overline{Z}$ = mean width of dimension Z = 4.094
σ_x = standard deviation of X = 0.012/6 = 0.002
σ_y = standard deviation of Y = 0.025/6 = 0.004
σ_z = standard deviation of Z = 0.020/6 = 0.0035

Now, under the condition of random assembly, the clearance will be a random variable. We are interested in the distribution of the clearance and its parameters. If we let $\overline{C}$ equal the mean of this distribution and σ_c its standard deviation, then

$$\overline{C} = \overline{Z} - (\overline{X} + \overline{Y}) = 4.094 - (1.406 + 2.652) = 0.036$$

$$\sigma_c = \sqrt{\sigma_x^2 + \sigma_y^2 + \sigma_z^2} = \sqrt{0.002^2 + 0.004^2 + 0.0035^2} = 0.0057$$

If we assume that the natural tolerance range of the clearances covers a 6-σ range, then the limits on the clearance will be 0.036 ± 3(0.0057) = 0.019 − 0.053. Note, then, that the minimum clearance is now 0.019, as compared with 0.007 specified by the product designer.

The question now is, how can we alter the product specifications to conform with the characteristics of the variability of dimensions and natural tolerances? If we are willing to accept the design engineer's allowance in a given specification, then we may alter one of the remaining dimension parameters of the system of parts. Suppose, for example, that we leave the limiting dimensions of the slot as the dimension to be determined so as to give us some tolerable limit on the number of assemblies having an allowance less than 0.007. Suppose we specify that no more than 1% of the assemblies should have allowances less than 0.007. This is depicted in the distribution shown in Figure 5.13. Each of the processes will turn out parts with the same natural tolerance range. The mean clearance is to be determined from the distribution in which the variance is known. From a table of areas under the normal

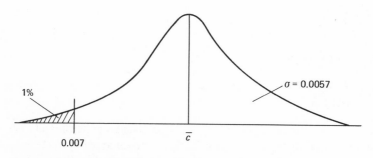

FIGURE **5.13**   Distribution of clearance.

curve, we can determine $\overline{C}$ to be $0.007 + 2.326 \times 0.0057 = 0.020$. Given this, we can obtain the mean dimension for Z.

$$\overline{C} = \overline{Z} - \overline{X} - \overline{Y}; \quad 0.02 = \overline{Z} - 1.406 - 2.652; \quad \overline{Z} = 4.078$$

Now the mean dimension of Z is $0.016''$ less then the previous mean of $4.094''$, and the fits are tighter by this amount.

NONLINEAR RESPONSES: So far we have considered only the statistical response of a linear combination of random variables. The functional relationship between component inputs and the output system dimension can be nonlinear. For example, we might have a chemical process in which the output dimension is the product of two independent variables such that $Y = X_1 \cdot X_2$.

Monte Carlo simulation can be used to estimate nonlinear responses and cases where the inputs have theoretical or empirical distributions. For example, suppose that we know the response function to be $Y = X_1^2 + 2X_2^2$. Then, for each replication of the simulation, values for X_1 and X_2 are generated from their distributions, and a value of Y is determined from the function. After a sample of n replications, the Y values can be arranged in a histogram to indicate the response distribution and its mean and variance estimated from the sample values.

REQUIREMENTS FOR VALID APPLICATION: The preceding discussion has indicated the general conditions required for the valid use of the statistical method. However, it may be well for emphasis to summarize these points.

1. Individual parts produced by controlled machines or processes. Stable machines or processes must be employed that produce part dimensions that form stable frequency distributions. The nature (mean, standard deviation, form) of these frequency distributions must be known. These conditions are generally met in plants employing statistical control charts and other modern quality control techniques.
2. Normal distributions. For the probability values computed by the above methods to correspond exactly to the values that will result under production, the frequency distributions must be normal. However, even a considerable departure from normality will seldom lead to errors of practical consequence.
3. Use of "natural tolerances" for the parts as the drawing tolerances and the maintenance of machine or process operations at these limits.
4. Random selection of pieceparts at the assembly station.
5. Independence of variables. This means that the measurement for a particular piecepart selected for an assembly must not depend in any way on the specific measurements for the other pieceparts that happen to be selected for the same assembly. This is not a difficult requirement to meet in industrial practice. Even when two identical parts from the same machine form part of an assembly, independence is achieved through random selection by the assembly operator, through the normal mixing of parts that occurs in materials handling, and through the random variation of measurements typically found as parts come in succession from production machines.

Practical Considerations

In the preceding section, the theoretical concepts of statistical addition of tolerances and variability assumed that the natural tolerance range ($\pm 3\sigma$) would be equal to the design tolerance range. While the product engineer may specify tolerances that will provide a high probability of good functional performance, the production engineer is likely to control the process such that there is a small likelihood that parts will fall outside the specified tolerance range. That is, both engineers are likely to build into their designs a conservative bias.

The conservatism of the production engineer would be reflected in an output that has a variation much less than the tolerance range. Over time we would expect a process to deteriorate in its ability to produce precise dimensions. Tool wear is the one likely cause of this. Consider Figure 5.14. The design tolerance limits are L and U. The process may be set up to produce dimensions having a distribution with mean $\overline{X}_1$ and variance σ_1^2. As time goes on and due to tool wear, both the mean and variance deteriorate so that eventually the distribution of output has a mean $\overline{X}_2$ and variance σ_2^2. To avoid frequent tool sharpenings or machine adjustments, there will be a tendency to set up for the condition 1.

We might be safe to say that, in general, there is a technical bias in both the product and production design. This is to give a high probability to success as far as the quality of the output is concerned.

THE ECONOMICS OF SETTING TOLERANCES: If we know exactly what kind of a response we want from the output of a system, we can design some combination of the inputs (means and variances) to give this response. Determination of optimal tolerances (i.e., tolerable variance of inputs and response) in monetary terms is more difficult. Of course, to begin with, it may not be well understood just how critical the issue is in a given shop. While the relative gains in examining this question with respect to a given operation may be small, the aggregate benefits as applied across a large number of operations may be significant.

The economics involve a tradeoff between relaxing component tolerances, and therefore using less costly processes, against the added cost of encountering defec-

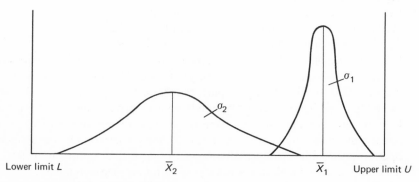

FIGURE **5.14**   Loss of capability.

tive assemblies. In mass assembly operations, when two randomly selected parts do not mate, the operator can try matching another part to the assembly so that no assembly becomes defective. As the lot of parts diminishes, this opportunity decreases so that there may be a residual number of components that do not match in any combination. Sometimes the defect in the assembly may not be discovered until subsequent testing as with an electronic part. In any event, the opportunity for immediately remedying mismatches has a subtle effect on the economics of tolerance setting.

This kind of monetary tradeoff has been examined by several researchers.[3,4] The best that we can do is to convey the idea by a simple example. Suppose that we assemble a shaft into a hole in a mass-produced part. We may assume that the quality of the assembly is not known until subsequent measurements are taken.

Let:

S = shaft diameter; a random variable with mean $\bar{S}$ and variance σ_S^2

H = hole diameter; a random variable with mean $\bar{H}$ and variance σ_H^2

C = $H - S$; a random variable normally distributed with mean $\bar{C} = \bar{H} - \bar{S}$ and variance σ_C^2

p = percent of assemblies defective in a lot size of N

Z_S = cost of producing a lot of S

Z_H = cost of producing a lot of H

Z_C = unit cost of a defective assembly

We now assume that the unit cost of the input components is a function of their process variances, which are determined by the processing method.

$$Z_S = f_1(\sigma_S^2) \qquad Z_H = f_2(\sigma_H^2)$$

There are upper and lower tolerance limits on C, which are k_1 and k_2, respectively. Now the total cost TC is

$$TC = pNZ_C + f_1(\sigma_S^2) + f_2(\sigma_H^2)$$

But

$$p = f_3(\sigma_C^2, k_1, k_2, \bar{C}) \quad \text{and} \quad \sigma_C^2 = f_4(\sigma_S^2, \sigma_H^2)$$

Therefore

$$TC = f(\sigma_S^2, \sigma_H^2, k_1, k_2, \bar{C}).$$

Since k_1, k_2, and $\bar{C}$ are assumed to be constants, we find the optimum input tolerances (or variances) by setting

$$\frac{\delta TC}{\delta \sigma_S^2} = 0 \qquad \frac{\delta TC}{\delta \sigma_H^2} = 0$$

and solving for σ_S^2 and σ_H^2.

---

[3] D. H. Evans, "Optimum Tolerance Assignment to Yield Minimum Manufacturing Cost," *Bell Sys. Tech. J.*, vol. XXXVII, March 1958, pp. 461–84.

[4] Norihiro Yamakawa, "On the Economical Assignment of Component Tolerances," *J. Operations Research Soc. (Japan)*, July 1962.

Problems

5.1   The Delta Mower Company produces a variety of hand and power tools for home, lawn, and garden maintenance. One line of power hedge clippers has been declining in sales, in spite of a general industry-wide sustained demand for this kind of item. An analysis indicates that the price is too high. A value analysis group is given the item to study.
(a) What things might the value analysis group consider in its analysis of the product, assuming that the objective is to reduce the manufacturing cost?
(b) What other factors besides manufacturing cost might the group consider?

5.2   A general campaign has been introduced in the executive branch of the Federal Government to reduce the volume and cost of paperwork. As a staff assistant in the Bureau of the Budget, you are asked to prepare a checklist for the design of paper forms. This checklist is to be used as a means of critically analyzing the design of paper forms in terms of the efficiency of adding or removing information to and from the form, as well as its physical handling.

5.3   Select an industrial or consumer product, and make a critical analysis of its design in terms of
(a) its use in a consumer or user's operating system
(b) its manufacturability
(c) its ease of maintenance

5.4   The Eastern Electronics Company makes a small electronic part consisting of a ring (Part 2) which slips over a shaft (Part 1). The nominal dimension of Part 2 is $0.100 \pm 0.005''$, and the nominal diameter of Part 1 is $0.095 \pm 0.006''$. The assembly department has experienced a good deal of trouble in assembling these two parts. About 30% of the parts failed to mate (the diameter of Part 2 was less than Part 1). The blame was placed on the design engineering department for an incorrect specification of the tolerances.

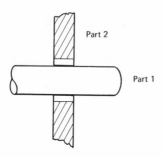

A young engineer attacked the problem in this way. He assumed that the tolerances covered a 6-σ range of dimensions and that the processes producing Parts 1 and 2 were under control. That is, his hypothesis was that the process for Part 1 was turning out parts with a normal distribution having a mean dimension of $0.095''$ and a standard deviation of $0.002''$. Similarly, for Part 2, the mean diameter was $0.100''$ and the standard deviation was $0.001667''$. Using a table of random normal deviates, he simulated the process for a sample of 200 hypothetical parts, each from its particular distribution.

He found that in none of the 200 trials was there interference in the assembly. His conclusion was that the difficulty experienced in assembly was due to lack of process control rather than improper design specifications. As his superior, comment on his methods and conclusions.

5.5   We have laid out a route for a refuse collection truck in a large city. The route consists of 130 stops (individual residences). The number N of cans at each stop is a random variable with the following distribution:

N	0	1	2	3	4	5	6	7	8
$f(n)$	0.02	0.08	0.10	0.15	0.25	0.17	0.10	0.08	0.05

At each stop, there are N refuse cans at the curb ready to be dumped in the truck. The time to load a can into the truck is uniformly distributed with a range of 0.07 to 0.27 minutes. The time to drive between two successive stops is a constant 0.09 minutes. How long will it take to complete 130 stops, and what tolerance would you place on this estimate?

5.6   An electronic company manufactures color television picture tubes. A critical part of this process involves putting three different layers of phosphorus (one on top of the other) upon the face of the glass tube. The process can be controlled only to the extent that the thickness of each layer is 0.020″, subject to a normal distribution with a standard deviation of 0.004″. The combined thickness of the three layers is critical and should not exceed 0.072″ or the focusing and mixing of colors will be inadequate. What is the probability of this latter problem occurring?

5.7   A two-ply metal cylinder is to be manufactured by forcing, by means of a press, an outer metal sleeve, Part A, over an inner metal cylinder, Part B. The process that produces Part A will maintain in production a mean or average diameter of 4.1274 inches and a standard deviation σ_A of 0.0009 inches. The inner cylinder, Part B, will

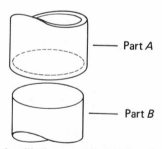

— Part A

— Part B

Sleeve, Part A, will slip over cylinder, Part B

be produced by a process giving a mean outer diameter of 4.1304 inches and a standard deviation of 0.0018 inches. For both parts, controlled processes producing normal distributions can be assumed. Use the following symbols:

$\overline{A}$ = mean diameter of Part A = 4.1274
$\overline{B}$ = mean diameter of Part B = 4.1304
σ_A = standard deviation of process producing A = 0.0009
σ_B = standard deviation of process producing B = 0.0018

Answer the following questions, showing all computations:

(a) In the random assembly of these parts under mass production, can forced fits be expected in all cases? Why? A forced fit occurs when the diameter of the selected cylinder is *equal to or greater than* the diameter of the selected sleeve.

(b) If the answer to (a) is no, what proportion of assemblies can be expected to have free fits? (A free fit is one that is not forced.)

(c) An interference of more than 0.010 inches may cause cracking of the outer sleeve, Part *A*, during the press assembly. With the parts produced as indicated above, would you expect this form of difficulty to develop? Why?

(d) As a matter of practical procedure, what would you instruct the assembler to do in cases for which a free fit is found?

5.8   A certain plastic molding process involves adding together two chemicals, *A* and *B*. The specifications call for 5 lb of *A* and 0.20 lb of *B*. The amount of *B* is added by a pellet. A study of the pellets yields an average weight of 0.20 lb with a population tolerance of ± 0.06 lb ($6\text{-}\sigma$ limits of a population distribution). Material *A* is a powder to be added from a bin by an automatic opening. What must the tolerances be on the bin process if the total batch added $(A + B)$ should have a probability of not over 1 % of being less than 5 lb?

5.9   The Gobelin Tapestry Company produces a certain model rug in a given weaving process. The process can generate a defect at any point in the rug surface. The probability of a defect occurring is equally likely at any point in the weaving process. The rug design department has specified a nominal number of defects to be 10 for every 16 square yards with a tolerance range of from 0 to 15. Is this a reasonable tolerance range?

5.10   The Acerbidity Candy Company produces a jar of sourballs consisting of four flavors. In the present method, the jar passes down a line, where it is filled exactly $\frac{1}{4}$ full with each of the flavors by hand. An engineer proposes an automatic process in which the four varieties of candies are mixed randomly and fed into a large hopper. The hopper then feeds each jar with 40 sourballs. Every time a jar is filled, exactly ten of each flavor are added to the hopper and mixed. The hopper holds 1,000 balls. Management does not want a jar to have less than 20 % of any one variety. What do you think of the ability of the proposed method to meet this tolerance limit?

5.11   A certain chemical process produces at the end of each production run two byproducts, *X* and *Y*. The expected volumes of *X* and *Y*, at the end of a run, are 5 and 10 cubic yards, respectively. However, the variances of *X* and *Y* are 0.09 and 0.25 cubic yards, respectively. *X* and *Y* are then combined to make a third product *Z*. The volume of *Z* is the product of the volumes of *X* and *Y*. The distributions of the volumes of *X* and *Y* are normal and independent. What tolerance limits would you place on the volume of *Z*?

5.12   The square shaft *A* fits into the square hole in Part *B*. The mean clearance on both sides (*L*) is 0.050 inches, and the standard deviation of the clearance is 0.0304 inches. What is an approximate probability that the operator will not be able to fit a shaft to a hole if random selection is made from a large population of Parts *A* and *B*?

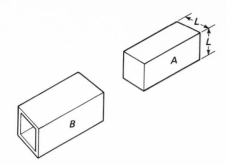

Bibliography

DUNCAN, A. J., *Quality Control and Industrial Statistics*, 3rd ed. Homewood, Ill.: Richard D. Irwin, Inc., 1965.

EARY, D. F., and G. E. JOHNSON, *Process Engineering for Manufacturing*. Englewood Cliffs, N.J.: Prentice-Hall, Inc., 1962.

HINES, WILLIAM W., "Monte Carlo Methods for Statistical Tolerances of Non-Linear Combinations," *J. Ind. Eng.*, March 1966.

JOHNSON, R. H., "How to Evaluate Assembly Tolerances," *Prod. Eng.*, January 1963.

6

Flow Processes: Material Flow

CHARACTERISTICS OF FLOW PROCESSES

The movement or flow of materials and work through a system of production resources is a pervasive characteristic of production systems. The flow of gaseous, liquid, or granular materials in a chemical process, either in batches or in a continuous stream, is obvious. Discrete products made of structural materials also flow through a series of operations or material processing stations. Interruptions in the flow are caused by delays such as waiting for the availability of a machine, temporary storages, or inspections. In certain kinds of processes, the production facilities "flow" to a fixed geographical location of materials that are to be processed. Examples are utility crews repairing power lines, spacecraft assembly, and fire fighting.

We tend to think of "flow" as either the continuous or interrupted geographical movement of material. However, we can represent flow in another manner: as a *sequence* of events or activities that take place in space and/or time. For example, in a project type of production system, jobs and tasks are performed in some time-sequenced relationship, which can be structured as a "network flow" system. A part is processed in a sequence of operations performed on different machines. A school bus is routed through a sequence of "pickup" or "delivery" points.

This characteristic flow can be the focal point for improving, designing, and controlling production processes. A production system can be described and analyzed in terms of the flow of some basic material or object in the system. This might be a raw material (iron, wood, gas), a machine (snow plow, utility truck, bean picker, river dredge), a human being (nurse, hospital patient, janitor), a paper form (invoice, bill, production order, blueprint), or transportation equipment (conveyor, boat, hand cart). In these cases, the materials that flow are either those to which properties are imparted or those which impart the properties. The distinction is not so important because the matter is relative. Material properties are imparted either continuously or in discrete units or batches.

In the design and improvement of flow systems, we will consider these topics:

1. *Routing*   The ways in which requirements for producing a product or service are translated into an operational sequence.
2. *Methods improvement*   The analysis and improvement of an existing flow process.
3. *Materials handling*   The choice of the method for transmitting materials between various locations.

THE ROUTING FUNCTION

The sequence of operations or events that take place in the flow of materials or activities is prescribed by the *routing function*. Given a unit of raw material to which a set of properties is to be imparted, routing specifies the production *method* that will be used to impart each property and the *sequence* in which the material processing operations will be executed. Similarly, routing specifies the activities and their sequence, which are necessary to carry out a service.

The points in the route where material is processed are called *operations*. A route is a sequence of operations.[1] An operation consists of a physical concentration of production resources, such as a machine, tools, material-handling equipment, and a human operator or monitor.

Routing is basically a technical function with important economic overtones. The specification of the basic process to be used to manufacture a part obviously involves the economics of the alternative processes considering both annual operating costs and capital expenditures. At the more detailed level, the specification of kinds of machines to be used, tools, detailed work methods, etc., requires economic judgments. While a multitude of detailed decisions may not be based on formal economic analyses, the engineer will consider cost-oriented criteria. The validity of his decisions will depend very much on his experience with and knowledge of material processing technology and principles of design.

There are other economic considerations in routing besides the selection of process, machine, and method. These relate to the operation of the production system. The choice of the most economical process and method and the designation of a specific operation sequence is made prior to the actual execution of the methods and sequence. In the operation of the shop, a flexible route, in terms of both alternative processes and sequences, allows the shop manager to consider these alternatives in terms of operating criteria. These would include such things as the utilization of facilities, work-in-process inventories, or job lateness. For example, it might be more desirable to assign a job to a less economical process or machine, depending on the shop load at any given time. Similarly, the order in which operations are performed has some bearing on facilities utilization. The fact that

---

[1] The sequencing of operations in routing should not be confused with the sequencing of *jobs* in a shop. The sequencing of jobs is concerned with the order in which a set of jobs competing for the services of a machine will be assigned to that machine.

a relationship exists between routing on the one hand and scheduling and dispatching on the other is generally recognized. But this relationship is not usually understood in detail nor analyzed to determine the economics involved. For the moment, we can only note that a specification of *alternative routings* offers a more suitable base for carrying out the scheduling and dispatching functions when the part is actually made.

In summary, the routing function consists of:

1. The determination of the possible methods for processing a part and the selection of a given method based upon both technical and economic criteria.
2. The analysis of the capability and capacity of available machines and equipment to carry out a given operation.
3. A determination of the need for special or new equipment to perform some operation.
4. The specification of the sequence (or optional sequences) of operations comprising a part routing.
5. The specification of machine feeds and speeds.
6. The determination of operation times, including setups, processing times, handling times, and various allowances.
7. The preparation of route sheets, which summarize the necessary information for operating management.

The results of the routing decisions are summarized on a route sheet, which is the basic technical production document. The modern trend is to store and process routing information by computer. Figure 6.1 shows a computer card printout of such information.

The idea of automating the routing function was discussed in the previous chapter (pages 150–52), in which the engineer's routing logic together with basic technical data are computerized. Chapter 17 provides further discussion of this idea, especially as it is related to integrated shop controls.

					RITTER ROUTING FILE			155426
DATE 05-12-67								
OPERATION NUMBER	SET UP	TIME PER PIECE	NO. PIECES PER HOUR	FILE LOCATION	MACHINE CENTER	DELIVER TO		
110	0.00	0.01960	00051.0	EC	028-0-B	013	1	
120	1.25	0.01510	00066.3	EC	013-8-5	013	1	
125	0.55	0.00910	00110.0	EC	013-2-0	013	1	
130	1.55	0.02090	00048.0	EC	013-8-7	013	1	
140	1.55	0.01290	00077.0	EC	013-8-7	006	1	
150	2.00	0.06350	00015.7	EC	006-3-7	006	1	
160	2.00	0.03510	00028.5	EC	006-3-7	009	1	
170	1.25	0.14300	00007.0	EC	009-2-5	039	1	
175	0.00	0.00000	00000.0	EC	039-0-0	028	1	
185	0.00	0.04460	00021.4	EC	028-0-B	056	1	
190	0.00	0.00000	00000.0	EC	056-0-B	42B	1	

FIGURE **6.1**   Route sheet in form of computer listing. Courtesy of the Ritter Equipment Company.

The Routing Sequence

The routing sequence is the specified order in which a series of operations or activities must be performed. Very often the sequence is rigidly fixed by technical constraints. It often happens that certain operations cannot be performed until they are preceded by others. However, sometimes a subset and rarely a full set of operations can be permuted to permit alternative sequences.

PRECEDENCE RELATIONSHIPS: The order in which operations must be performed can be displayed by a precedence chart and precedence matrix. For example, suppose that a metal part has eight operations performed on it. These include:

- A issue material to the first operation
- 1   cut off
- 2   mill bottom surface
- 3   face-mill pads
- 4   drill two holes $\frac{1}{4}''$ dia.
- 5   thread $\frac{1}{4}''$ holes
- 6   drill $\frac{7}{8}''$ holes
- 7   heat treat for hardness
- 8   grind
- B issue part to stock room

The order in which these operations must be performed is summarized in the precedence matrix $R = (r_{ij})$, where r_{ij} prescribes the precedence relation between operations i and j (Figure 6.2). The element r_{ij} assumes the following values:

$$r_{ij} = \begin{cases} + & \text{if operation } i \text{ must precede operation } j \\ - & \text{if operation } i \text{ must follow operation } j \\ 0 & \text{if no precedence relationship exists} \end{cases}$$

The precedence relationships are also shown in the form of a precedence chart in Figure 6.3. Each node in the chart represents an operation, and the lines connecting the nodes indicate the *direct* precedence relation between the nodes. The indirect relationships are implied. In other words, operation 7 must follow operation 5, which, in turn, must follow operation 4; therefore, operation 7 must follow operation 4.

0	A	1	2	3	4	5	6	7	8	B
A	0	+	+	+	+	+	+	+	+	+
1	−	0	+	+	+	+	+	+	+	+
2	−	−	0	+	+	+	+	+	+	+
3	−	−	−	0	0	0	0	+	+	+
4	−	−	−	0	0	+	0	+	+	+
5	−	−	−	0	−	0	0	+	+	+
6	−	−	−	0	0	0	0	+	+	+
7	−	−	−	−	−	−	−	0	+	+
8	−	−	−	−	−	−	−	−	0	+
B	−	−	−	−	−	−	−	−	−	0

FIGURE **6.2**   Precedence matrix for eight operations.

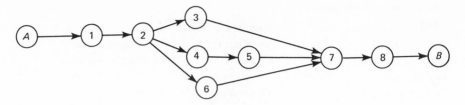

FIGURE **6.3** Precedence chart for eight operations.

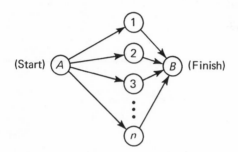

FIGURE **6.4** Flexible routing.

FIGURE **6.5** Fixed routing.

The precedence relationships are specified for both technical and economic reasons. For example, operation 2 must precede 3, 4, and 6, because the results of operation 2 permit the part to be located properly in the fixtures used in the subsequent operations. Operation 7 must follow in the designated order, because it is uneconomical to perform the previous operations on a hardened part.

If there are no precedence relationships in a routing, then the flow chart appears as in Figure 6.4, where only the start and ending are precedent oriented. The case for a fully specified order is shown in Figure 6.5.

Typical routings probably are combinations of constrained and unconstrained subsets of operation sequences.

ROUTING SEQUENCING CRITERIA: If alternative operation sequences are feasible for the whole or partial subset of operations, then the choice of sequence depends on a number of criteria. The choice might be made either at the time the route sheet is made up or at the time the job enters the shop, preferably the latter.

1. *Minimize material handling costs* This could be accomplished by sequencing operations that are performed on the same or like machines in succession. For

instance, if a part has three separate milling operations, then an attempt would be made to have these operations performed in sequence, perhaps on the same machine. If the sequence is completely unconstrained, then operations would be ordered in such a way that the total distance traveled by the part is minimized. However, this situation would be highly unlikely; and even if it were not, we might expect other criteria to dominate.

2. *Maximize facilities utilization*   The influence of routing on facilities utilization is probably most noticeable at the time the job is assigned to the shop. Alternative operation sequences permit the shop dispatcher to assign jobs to machines on the basis of current machine loads. In our previous example, if operation 2 were just completed, the choice of the next operation would depend on the status of the machines required for operations 3, 4, and 6.

3. *Minimize work-in-process inventory*   The investment in work-in-process inventory is influenced by the operation sequence. The choice of a sequence that minimizes inventory can be made either as part of the routing function or as part of the job dispatching function after the job is issued to the shop. We will consider here only the former situation.

SEQUENCING TO MINIMIZE W/P INVENTORY: Suppose that a part is routed through n operations in a job shop. The part will be processed on a given machine, be transported to the next operation, and possibly wait in line until the next machine is ready. Let

p_i = the time to process the part at the ith operation; $i = 1, 2, \ldots, n$
p_i' = the time the part is in transit and wait time between the ith operation and the next operation in sequence
c_i = cost of processing the part at the ith operation
c_i' = cost incurred in transporting and storing the part during the time p_i'

As the part is moved from one operation to the next in the route, the rate at which inventory investment accumulates over time is shown in Figure 6.6. The total investment is represented by the area under the curve. The shaded areas represent the investment generated at each operation, including the processing, transportation, and storage costs. Part of these shaded areas are sequence independent, namely the areas $c_i p_i$. The transportation costs, however, are a function of the sequence. Also, the time spent by the part waiting to be processed is a function of the status of the shop at the time the part is actually produced. Since this time is known only when the part is produced, we might consider it to be independent of the operation sequence.

Gapp *et al.*[2] investigated this situation and developed decision rules for minimizing the area under the curve while considering the shaded areas to be fully sequence independent.

Nonconstrained routing   If the operations can be performed in any order, then the optimal sequencing rule to minimize work-in-process investment is as follows.

---

[2] William Gapp, P. S. Mankekar, and L. G. Mitten, "Sequencing Operations to Minimize In-Process Inventory Costs," *Management Science*, vol. 11, no. 3, January 1965, pp. 476–88.

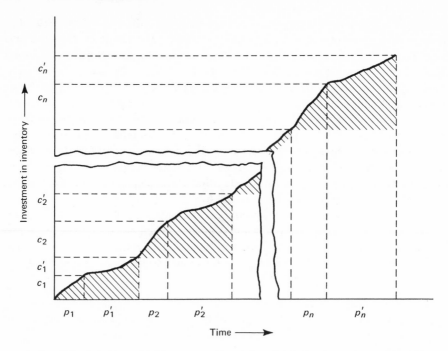

FIGURE **6.6** Inventory investment versus time of job in shop. From W. Gapp, P. S. Mankekar, and L. G. Mitten, *Management Science*, vol. 11, no. 3, January 1965, p. 478.

Let

S_k = a given permutation of operations; $k = 1, 2, \ldots, n!$

$C(k)$ = the work-in-process inventory investment for the sequence S_k, but not including the shaded areas

P_i = $p_i + p_i'$

C_i = $c_i + c_i'$

For any given permutation S_k, the investment cost is

$$C(k) = \sum_{i=1}^{n} C_i \sum_{i<j} P_j$$

The sequencing rule is

$$C(k) = \text{minimum for the order } i = 1, 2, \ldots, n$$
$$\text{if } C_1/P_1 \leq C_2/P_2 \leq \cdots \leq C_n/P_n \qquad (1)$$

Proof: Suppose we consider two operations, i and j, in a sequence $1, 2, \ldots, i, j, \ldots, n$. Assume that $C_i/P_i < C_j/P_j$. Let the total inventory investment up to operation i equal H. Then the total inventory investment including i and j is

$$T = H + C_i(P_i + P_j) + C_j(P_j)$$

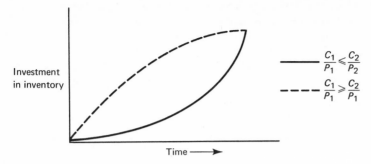

FIGURE **6.7**   Inventory investment for two rules.

Now suppose we interchange the position of i and j. The inventory investment is

$$T' = H + C_j(P_i + P_j) + C_i(P_i)$$

Then,

$$T - T' = C_i P_j - C_j P_i$$

But

$$C_i P_j < C_j P_i$$

Therefore,

$$T - T' < 0 \quad \text{and} \quad T < T'$$

This is intuitively reasonable, for it tends to place the lower cost processes first in the sequence and the higher cost processes plus transport and storage times last in the sequence. This makes the inventory curve assume the shape of the solid line in Figure 6.7. If we reversed the rule, we would obtain the dotted line.

Precedence constraints   When some precedence relations exist in the routing, the development of the optimum sequence is more involved, and we will not reproduce Gapp's method here. They propose an algorithm that employs the ratio rule in a certain manner to find the optimum routing.

Aggregative Effect of Product Routings

When more than a single product is produced, then the aggregation of product routings is a major factor in determining the shop format, that is, the arrangement of the facilities. When the routing sequence for a single product is independent of all other products, then we might expect a job shop format. Carried to its logical conclusion, if all product routings were independent (in terms of sequence and number of operations), then the arrangement of the machines might not be important. That is, if we are interested in minimizing the total material-handling costs between machines, then presumably any relative location of machines would suffice as long as we kept the group of machines in a confined space.

On the other hand, if all product routings are the same or very similar, then, of course, we encounter the flow shop format. Obviously the facilities are arranged in the sequence of the commonly routed operations in order to minimize handling costs. We will examine the matter of assignment of machines to locations in the following two chapters.

Projects involve very complex routing problems. A project such as constructing a building or space ship may consist of hundreds or thousands of individual tasks and jobs that must be executed within some framework of precedence constraints. The economics of routing and scheduling of project tasks and jobs is an important subject to be discussed in Chapter 16.

IMPROVEMENT OF FLOW PROCESSES

For an existing and operating production or service system, the improvement of the system may center on material flow. Among the early developments in industrial engineering was the technique of flow-process analysis. Through the use of diagrammatic devices, the sequence of steps comprising the flow of an object in a process is analyzed to suggest steps that can be taken to improve the process. While these techniques do not involve intellectual sophistication, they nevertheless have contributed significantly to the continued improvement in the economics of production systems.

Improvement Criteria

The improvement of a process through the analysis of its flow characteristics is predicated on a generally accepted set of value criteria. In the typical manufacturing flow process, various local measures of performance are used to guide the steps in improving the process and for judging process efficiency. These include such things as delay times, travel distances, work-in-process inventories, space requirements, physical handling of parts, scrap or material spoilage, and man and facility idleness. Each step of a process is analyzed to determine ways in which these measures of performance can be improved by making either major or minor changes in the process.

In the following pages, we will investigate diagrammatic methods and techniques of analysis. While we emphasize their use in existing processes, it must be noted that they apply equally well to a *proposed* process. That is, diagraming and analyzing a proposed process can lead to further improvements before it is implemented.

Diagrammatic Methods

In order to make a process flow analysis, it is frequently necessary to diagram the nature of the flow in one or more different ways. A few of the more common and useful diagrammatic or schematic methods are outlined below.

PROCESS FLOW SYMBOLS: In representing flow, the first problem is to decide on the object that represents the flow (i.e., raw material, a paper form, equipment).

At any given point in the flow process, the object may be in any one or more of a number of states. These states are represented or symbolized in standard form as follows:

Symbol	State	Description
◯	Operation[3]	The occurrence of an operation means that the material or object is changed in one or more of its physical characteristics. Examples are the machining of a part, addition of information to a paper form, assembly of two parts, and adding oil to a machine in a maintenance process. An operation implies the expenditure of resources, which adds value to the object.
⇨	Transportation	This symbolizes the movement of the material or object from one location to another, for which no value is added directly to the object, even though the movement prepares the object for the next step.
☐	Inspection	An inspection occurs when the object is verified in any one or more of its characteristics or examined for identification.
◗	Delay	A delay occurs when conditions do not permit or require immediate performance of the next step in the process. A part in work-in-process inventory is in the state of delay.
▽	Storage	Storage occurs when the object is kept and protected against unauthorized removal.
⊖	Combined activity	A combined activity takes place when two or more of the above activities take place simultaneously. Examples are the combination of storage and operation on a bottle of wine that is fermenting while in storage, or the combination of transportation and operation on a part that is assembled as it moves along a conveyor.

THE OPERATION PROCESS CHART: The operation process chart summarizes in a concise manner the basic routing information for a *set* of parts that will comprise a final or subassembly. Figure 6.8 shows a simple operation process chart for the components making up a common pencil sharpener. The parts to be made and their raw materials are listed across the top of the chart. The vertical lines show the operations to be performed on each part, the operational sequence, and the point where the part is added to a subassembly or final assembly.

The chart's principal use is in summarizing vital information that is contained in a multitude of documents, such as route sheets and operation sheets, that would otherwise be difficult to grasp in total. It is essentially a communications device between production engineering, production control, and persons who might not be familiar with the details of producing a certain part.

FLOW DIAGRAM AND PROCESS CHART: The flow diagram is a line diagram imposed on a drawing, blueprint, or layout of production facilities showing the geographic flow of the object through the process. The flow-process chart is simply a list of the steps or activities in the process in their proper sequence, together with relevant information about each step.

---

[3] The symbolic operation is more specific than our general definition of an operation as a step in a process. In the general definition, we are not interested in the function of the operation, whereas the symbol ◯ implies material processing.

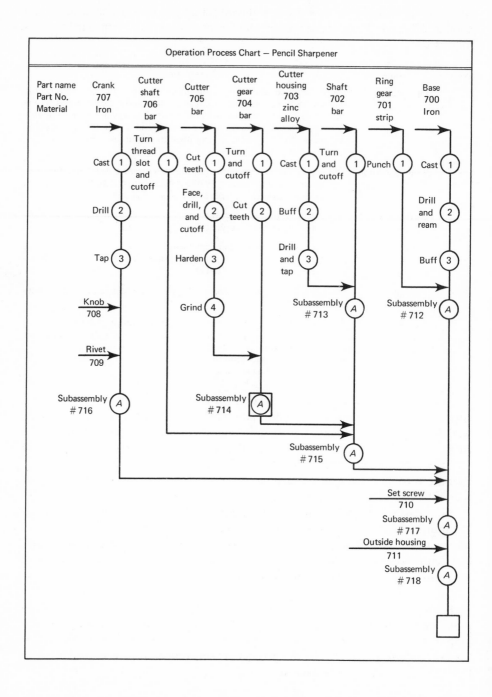

FIGURE **6.8** Operational process chart summarizing the manufacturing process required to produce a pencil sharpener. From E. V. Krick, *Methods Engineering*. New York: John Wiley & Sons, 1962, p. 96.

Zone No.		1	1	1	4	1	3	3	3	3	4	3	2	2	2
	Build-ing	1	2	5*	6	12	14	18	23	24	29	33	36	42	57
1	1		.30 / 1.06 / 1.36 / 71	.64 / 205		.28 / 3.88 / 4.16 / 39	3.55 / .89 / 4.24 / 15		3.67 / 4.00 / 7.67 / 14	1.25 / 3.26 / 4.51 / 18	1.91 / 1.25 / 3.16 / 8	2.39 / 2.51 / 13		1.86 / 1.39 / 3.25 / 25	3.65 / 4.00 / 7.65 / 7
1	2	.21 / 1.33 / 1.54 / 81		.67 / 105		.67 / 3.88 / 4.55 / 50	3.50 / .89 / 4.39 / 9	4.30 / 3.05 / 7.35 / 3	4.07 / 4.00 / 8.07 / 28	1.84 / 3.26 / 5.10 / 8	2.20 / 1.25 / 3.45 / 3	2.60 / .12 / 2.72 / 12	2.55 / .47 / 3.02 / 1	2.00 / 1.39 / 3.39 / 12	3.50 / 4.00 / 7.50 / 1
1	5*	.76 / 1.33 / 2.09 / 64	.67 / 1.06 / 1.73 / 257		4.14 / 1.20 / 5.34 / 6	1.43 / 3.88 / 5.31 / 50	3.31 / 4.20 / 9	3.35 / 3.05 / 6.40 / 2	3.02 / 4.00 / 7.02 / 15	1.75 / 3.26 / 5.01 / 20	2.39 / 1.25 / 3.64 / 12	1.75 / 1.87 / 2	1.78 / 2.25 / 11	1.27 / 1.39 / 2.66 / 43	3.05 / 4.00 / 7.05 / 20
4	6		3.80 / 1.06 / 4.86 / 2	4.13 / 11			6.93 / .89 / 7.82 / 6								
1	12	.20 / 1.33 / 1.53 / 14	.67 / 1.06 / 1.73 / 12	1.43 / 46	3.79 / 1.20 / 4.99 / 2		4.07 / .89 / 4.96 / 26			1.62 / 3.26 / 4.88 / 8	2.13 / 1.25 / 3.38 / 10			1.14 / 1.39 / 2.53 / 2	
3	14	3.35 / 1.33 / 4.68 / 30	3.50 / 1.06 / 4.56 / 9	3.31 / 71		4.07 / 3.88 / 7.95 / 4			1.40 / 4.00 / 5.40 / 1	3.05 / 3.26 / 6.31 / 9					
3	18	4.14 / 1.33 / 5.47 / 5	4.30 / 1.06 / 5.36 / 3	3.35 / 4					.61 / 4.00 / 4.61 / 11						
3	23	3.67 / 1.33 / 5.00 / 20	4.07 / 1.06 / 5.13 / 4	3.02 / 40			1.40 / .89 / 2.29 / 6	.61 / 3.05 / 3.66 / 9				1.37 / .12 / 1.49 / 2			
3	24	1.25 / 1.33 / 2.58 / 6	1.84 / 1.06 / 2.90 / 3	1.75 / 24		1.62 / 3.88 / 5.50 / 4	3.05 / .89 / 3.94 / 24		3.67 / 4.00 / 7.67 / 14						
4	29	1.91 / 1.33 / 3.24 / 1	2.19 / 1.06 / 3.25 / 3	2.39 / 11	1.27 / 1.20 / 2.47 / 3										
3	33	2.39 / 1.33 / 3.72 / 2		1.75 / 14			1.75 / .89 / 2.64 / 1	1.72 / 3.05 / 4.77 / 1	1.37 / 4.00 / 5.37 / 13	2.45 / 3.26 / 5.71 / 1					
2	36			1.78 / 4										0.00 / 1.39 / 1.39 / 9	1.32 / 4.00 / 5.32 / 16
2	42	1.80 / 1.33 / 3.13 / 7	2.00 / 1.06 / 3.06 / 5	1.27 / 28									0.00 / 4.70 / 4.70 / 15		1.32 / 4.00 / 5.32 / 23
2	57	3.65 / 1.33 / 4.98 / 17	3.50 / 1.06 / 4.56 / 4	3.05 / 42									1.34 / .47 / 1.81 / 5	1.32 / 1.39 / 2.71 / 11	

* Messenger office

FIGURE **6.9** Travel chart with frequency-time data.

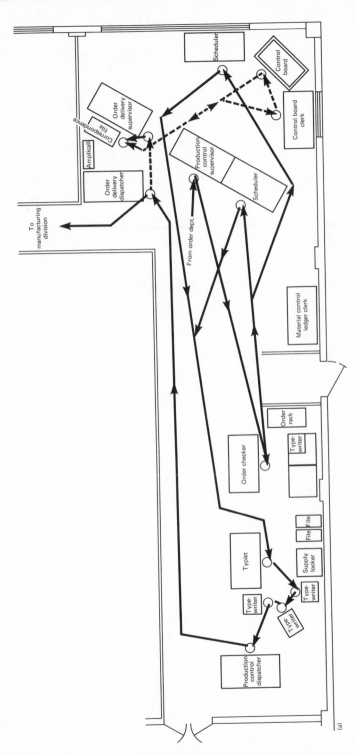

(a)

Examples of these two schematic models are shown in Figures 1.3 and 1.4 on pages 21 and 22 for the process of producing feed pellets.

THE TRAVEL CHART: The travel chart is a simple and convenient way of summarizing the quantities of flow between various points or facilities in a production system.

Figure 6.9 shows a travel chart that indicates the travel time of messengers and mailmen between various buildings of a large company. The chart compiles the frequency of trips between each pair of buildings in a two-week study (figure in lower left-hand corner of element) and the standard time to walk the distance between the buildings plus the travel time within the building traveled to, based on a geographical zoning system. These results were used to determine standard times for a wage incentive plan.

Analysis of Flow Charts

The flow diagram and flow-process charts are particularly useful as aids for the systematic conception of process improvements through the analysis of a present or proposed method. While such analysis can often lead to important improvements in an existing or proposed process, there is a danger in using these charts prematurely because they force the analyst to become immersed in the details of the present method. This can, as we have noted earlier, inhibit the process of creating unique solutions or methods.

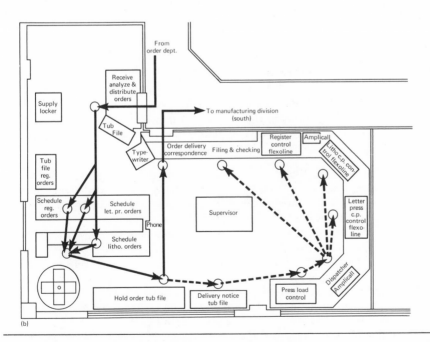

FIGURE **6.10**   Results of applying flow-chart analysis to a paperwork system. (a) Original office layout. (b) New office layout. Courtesy of The Standard Register Company.

On the other hand, it is tempting to want to avoid the detailed work required to construct these charts and trust one's own mental retention and analysis of the detailed facts. This may lead to improvements, but they are less desirable than the kinds of solutions that can be revealed by systematic and skillful use of flow diagrams and charts.

THE QUESTIONING ATTITUDE: The substance of the technique of using flow charts is the critical questioning of each step in the process. There are four basic questions that are asked for each process step (symbol).

Can the step be eliminated?
Can the step be *combined* with one or more other steps?
Can the step be changed in the *sequence?*
Can the step be *improved?*

These questions, as well as such questions as *Who? Where? Why? When?* and *How?*, at each step in the process, can lead often to changes resulting in substantial cost reductions. Both the flow diagram and flow-process chart are work sheets on which the analyst may record information about the process and ideas for its possible improvement.

Figure 6.10a and b shows the "before" and "after" results of applying flow-chart analysis to a paperwork system. The result of the analysis was a new layout of the office space with a reduction in the distance that the paper forms moved and a reduction in the total office space.

The flow-process chart also provides the basis for a tenuous evaluation of improvements. Perfunctory criteria of improvement include the degree to which operational symbols are reduced in number, the reduction in distance traveled, and the number of times the material is handled. It should be noted that only the operations ($\bigcirc$) contribute to the consumer utility of the product or service, while all other symbols represent the expenditure of resources for which no such utility is added. While the reductions in these "nonproductive" elements of the process are not expressed in monetary terms, they are nevertheless "local" criteria and indicators of cost.

CASE PROBLEM 6.1   The White Engine Company manufactures gasoline engines for a variety of uses. The engines range from 1 to 3 hp in size and are used in such items as small power plants, lawn mowers, pumps, etc. They are produced in large batches and assembled on a straight-line conveyor before testing and shipping.

After an engine is completely assembled, it is inspected for noise of operation in an electrically driven test stand. The engine is located in the test stand, coupled to a drive shaft, and electrically run at different speeds. Abnormal noise is detected using a stethoscope. If the unit appears to operate with a certain degree of noise, it is checked for burred parts, and the parts are lapped in a repair operation.

The sequence of operations performed on the unit is carried out in the test room. The present layout of the test room is shown in Figure 6.11.

The following is a description of the operations that take place between the last operation in assembly and shipping.

1. *Operation 21*   The unit is removed from a fixture on the assembly power con-

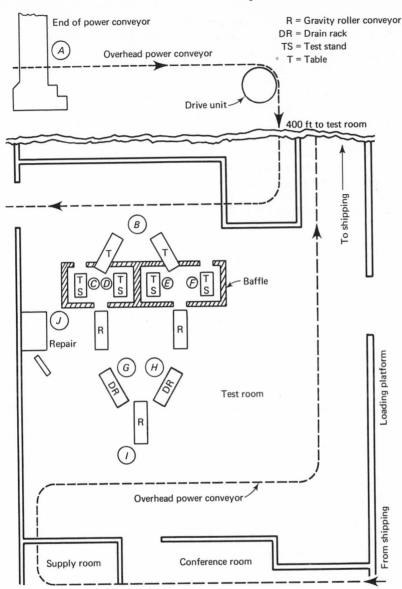

FIGURE **6.11**   Layout of test rooms.

veyor and placed on an overhead conveyor by operator *A*. Note that the assembly power conveyor travels at a rate of 120 units per hour. The overhead conveyor travels at waist level at work stations and at ceiling level at other locations. The maximum angle of ascent or descent of the conveyor is 45 degrees.

2. *Operation 22*   The unit is removed from the overhead conveyor and placed on a metal-lined table by operator *B*. The unit is then lubricated prior to testing. The table represents a work-in-process inventory.

3. *Operation 23*   The unit is placed in the test stand and "run in" for the noise test. Note that there are presently four identical test stands operated by inspectors C, D, E, and F. If the unit fails to pass the test, it is set aside for work to be done at the repair operation by repairman J. After testing, the unit is placed on the gravity roller conveyor, which conveys it to the next operation.

4. *Operation 24*   The unit is taken off the roller conveyor and placed on a drain rack. The drain plug is removed. The oil drains from the unit for three minutes. A spark plug is assembled to the unit. The drain plug is assembled to the unit and tightened with a wrench. The unit is carried to the roller conveyor for transportation to the next operation. Operators G and H carry out this operation.

5. *Operation 25*   Operator I hand punches a code number in the base of the engine, places a small cardboard dust seal over the shaft opening, and places the unit on the overhead conveyor, which carries it to the shipping department.

The detailed elements and times for each operation are summarized below.

Operation Description

Operation number	Element description	Standard time		Hourly production (units)
		min	hr	
21	Remove unit from fixture on assembly power conveyor	0.100		
	Carry to overhead conveyor and return	0.080		
		0.180	0.0030	333
22	Remove unit from overhead conveyor and place on table	0.080		
	Remove oil fill cap and spray oil through cap and spark plug hole	0.150		
	Replace oil cap and push unit down table	0.096		
		0.326	0.0054	184
23	Pick up unit and place on test stand	0.100		
	Couple unit to drive shaft of test machine	0.300		
	Test run at various speeds and listen for noise with stethoscope	1.380		
	Remove unit from test machine	0.100		
	Place on roller conveyor	0.120		
		2.000	0.0333	30
24	Pick up unit and place on drain rack	0.100		
	Remove drain plug	0.085		
	Assemble spark plug and tighten	0.300		
	Assemble drain plug and tighten	0.250		
	Place unit on roller conveyor	0.100		
		0.835	0.0140	72
25	Hand punch code number in base	0.250		
	Place dust seal over shaft opening	0.100		
	Hang on overhead conveyor	0.100		
		0.450	0.0075	133
26	Repair	8.600	0.143	7

Additional information about the process is as follows:

1. The overhead power conveyor can operate at a maximum speed of 140 stations per hour by changing drive speed.
2. The distance between individual stations on the overhead conveyor is five feet.
3. The speed of the assembly power conveyor is 120 units per hour.
4. A sound baffle is used in the test area to minimize noise between test stations. A closed booth for test purposes is not necessary.
5. The distance between the assembly department and the test room is 400 feet.
6. While the product size varies somewhat, the times and rates of output are representative of all sizes.

In the continual search for ways of reducing costs, a young methods engineer has been assigned to investigate this process. Suppose that you, as a department superintendent, are to meet with the engineer in a week to discuss the project. In order to make an intelligent evaluation of any proposal that the engineer might make, you decide to tackle the problem yourself. Therefore, you should be prepared in one week to make your own suggestions of how costs may be reduced for this operation. We will assume that the following are valid restrictions on the problem.

1. The engines must be tested by the noise method, using the present machines.
2. The company uses a payoff criterion of three years on capital investments.
3. The maximum anticipated rate of production will be 140 units per hour.
4. Oil must be drained from the unit prior to shipping.

MATERIAL HANDLING

Much of the economy of American production can be traced to the efficient handling of materials both in the transportation of materials between operations and in the handling of objects at individual work stations. The transportation symbol dominates most process charts, and the rigorous analysis of this process element can result in reduction of both process time and cost. The material handling industry produces a great variety of equipment designed to handle material of widely varying forms and weights for manufacturing, construction, and service industries.

The choice of handling methods and equipment is an integral part of the design and improvement of processes and their locations in a plant. In the original design of a production system, the location of facilities and material-handling methods are joint problems. In a given plant, major cost reductions can be effected by improvement or replacement of handling methods and equipment.

Handling Methods

The problem of choosing a material-handling method is basically one of equipment selection after the handling requirements have been carefully analyzed and specified. The choice of the basic kind of equipment, such as conveyors, fork-lift trucks, and cranes, depends generally on a number of factors, including

1. The nature of the material to be moved, its unit bulk, weight, sensitivity to damage in transit, configuration, etc.
2. The volume of material in the number of units or batches.
3. The rate of flow required and inputs and outputs of the system.
4. The availability and kind of space in which the equipment will operate.
5. The purpose of the handling system, for example, whether it is to transport, act as work-in-process storage capacity, hold the material while it is being processed, or combinations of these.

Once these functional objectives and constraints are known, the choice can be made. The alternatives depend on the designer's knowledge of available equipment, supported, perhaps, by an information retrieval system that brings to his attention innovations that have occurred in the equipment market.

Guides to Material Handling Design

The analysis of flow diagrams, flow-process charts, and travel charts, and the use of work-sampling techniques, can provide information about inadequacies in present material handling methods. Goode suggests certain "principles" that are useful in designing material-handling methods.[4]

1. *Reduce the number of moves and handling required to a minimum*   Obviously, the best solution for a proposed handling or move is to eliminate the need for it. This can be done in a number of ways: 1) combining two or more separate operations into one, 2) moving successive operations in the production of a product adjacent to each other on the plant floor, 3) using skids and pallets to facilitate the use of fork lift, 4) changing routing or scheduling procedures to eliminate the need for delays or temporary storage, etc.

2. *Coordinate handlings and moves between operations with handling at the operations*   Much of the cost in an industrial plant is incurred in handling at work stations—in moving objects from some supply point to the point of use and then disposing of them when the work elements of the operation are completed. Two principal points to consider in meeting this objective are 1) where possible, employ transporting equipment (conveyors) between activities or operations that pick up or discharge objects as near the point of use as possible, and 2) when work in process is moved in batches (in stock boxes or on pallets or skids), use containers, bases, or other holding devices that place the objects at the most convenient point for the operator at the work station.

3. *Reduce the distance of movement to a minimum*   In almost every case, the shorter the distance traveled, the greater the economy of handling. Less labor time and equipment—whether conveyors or trucks—will be required, operation and maintenance costs will be reduced, less aisle space will be needed for transportation, and other savings will accrue.

4. *Use mechanical handling equipment of simple design*   There has sometimes

---

[4] H. P. Goode, "Some Practical Points in the Design of Material Handling Systems," Dept. of Ind. Eng. and Operations Research, Cornell Univ., Ithaca, N. Y., paper 3264, no. 144–1, 1960.

been a temptation in the design of handling equipment, particularly of individually designed pieces for special application, to provide overly complicated designs. Study will often disclose that more simple equipment will be adequate.

5. *Use standard commercial equipment whenever it will serve*   Such equipment is generally relatively low in first cost, is most dependable, and is more flexible as conditions change. Repair parts, replacement or extension units, and repair and maintenance service are relatively easy to secure.

6. *Use handling equipment that depends on gravity if possible*   Gravity roller conveyors, spiral chutes, slides, and similar equipment are widely employed. Gravity devices are almost always quite low in first cost, are quite dependable, require little or no maintenance, and, of course, require no (or little) power for their operation.

7. *Use handling equipment that is sturdy, dependable, and easily maintained*   There are variations in this respect, even among standard forms of equipment. In many cases, a breakdown in materials handling will shut down an entire line or a department; reliability is important.

8. *If possible, use handling equipment or methods that allow for alternatives in the event of breakdown*   Most forms of equipment will fail at times. As mentioned above, materials movement is frequently critical. Hence, free or independent devices, such as fork-lift trucks, may, if other costs or advantages are equal, be preferable to some fixed handling device, such as an overhead monorail powered conveyor.

9. *Use handling equipment that is flexible in application*   Flexibility in the kinds of material that can be handled, in speed or hourly capacity, in path of movement, or in operating conditions required varies considerably from one kind of equipment to another. Demands can be expected to change, often radically, in most plants. Among other things, product design changes or new products may be added, the plant layout may be revised, the process may be revised, or the rate of production may change.

10. *Keep the variety of handling equipment used in the plant at a minimum*   It is good practice to keep the kinds of equipment, the makes, and the models employed at a minimum. Equipment will be better used and maintained.

The personnel will be more experienced with fewer devices; therefore, a larger supply of repair parts for a single type can be more easily justified.

11. *If total costs for alternatives are equal, use handling equipment of lowest first cost*   From an engineering economy viewpoint, the prudent choice, other things being equal, is usually the one requiring the least investment in equipment or other fixed assets. The loss will be smaller if the need for the equipment ceases or if conditions change such that a different type of equipment will be preferable.

12. *Choose equipment and handling methods that promote operator safety*   A large proportion of industrial accidents and operator injuries occurs in connection with material handling. The lifting of heavy objects and containers is hazardous; material and equipment, while traveling through the plant, present many forms of danger.

13. *Choose equipment and methods that do not unduly damage the product*

handled   The product may be dropped, or work pieces may be rubbed against each other or be subject to movements of other forms at the start of, during, or at the end of transport or handling. For obvious reasons, the extent of possible product damage must be a factor in handling system design.

14. *Use equipment that makes efficient use of factory floor space*   Space is costly to provide and to maintain. It separates storage areas and operations and so adds to movement distances. Many forms of handling equipment may operate overhead in unused space; equipment such as monorail conveyors or powered belt conveyors may require no added space at all. Equipment that require no fixed path or space, such as trucks, often make most efficient use of floor area. Handling methods that enable goods to be stacked high at storage points—such as a pallet and fork-lift truck system—minimize storeroom and warehouse space needs.

15. *Coordinate handling methods at different points in the plant into a unified system*   As in other forms of design, suboptimization must be avoided as much as possible. The design objective is clearly to minimize handling costs in the long run and to do so for the plant as a whole. Subsystems interact with each other through the transfer of goods from one subsystem to another, through the way goods are put in storage and then taken out, and in many other ways. Many requirements of unification are obvious—pallet sizes should be standardized, types and sizes of stock boxes should be standardized, and trucks should be chosen such that they can be used freely throughout the plant.

16. *Integrate planning for materials handling with planning of plant layout*   It is impossible to effectively design these two elements of an over-all production system entirely independently of each other. There are too many interactions between these aspects of the plant. The nature of the layout depends in many ways on the handling methods to be employed. Certain forms of mechanical handling equipment will allow the separation (economically) of sequential operations or departments when this is desirable to meet other layout objectives, for example. Also, the selection of floors for each activity will depend on whether or not gravity handling devices will be employed. Likewise, many details of the handling system will depend on the respective locations of work and storage areas.

Evaluation of Variable Path Systems

One way of classifying methods of evaluating handling systems is to consider the flow characteristics induced by the handling method. We might expect job shops to require *variable* path handling methods. In this case, handling equipment is usually mobile and adaptable to a variety of loads and distances and directions traveled. These include fork-lift trucks, hand trucks, overhead cranes, mobile hoists, etc. On the other hand, both gravity and power conveyors provide *fixed* flow patterns. First, we will consider the evaluation of variable flow handling systems and then look at the fixed path situation. Then, in the subsequent two chapters, we will focus our attention on locating facilities in the context of variable and fixed flow patterns.

Before considering the variable path handling case, we should note the following about evaluating material handling. Because material handling decisions are often a matter of equipment selection, the ultimate decision may be supported by a capital expenditure analysis using a minimum annual cost, rate of return, or other criteria. The validity of a choice based upon a capital investment model depends on the proper evaluation of the relevant costs and the performance of the handling system using a given handling method. Therefore, the subject of evaluation is directed particularly to models for analyzing the handling system. Then, based upon such analyses, a capital investment model may be used to determine the choice of equipment. After such a study, the numbers, sizes, and capacities of equipment may be the subject of more detailed analysis.

QUEUING ANALYSIS: The number of a standard type of mobile equipment to be used in a plant can be determined through a queuing theory. For example, suppose we wish to know the number of fork-lift trucks to use in a plant, where the trucks are dispatched from a central dispatching point to service a wide variety of operations. The chart in Figure 6.12 indicates the optimum truck fleet size for different ratios of customer delay cost C_2, and truck idle costs C_1 as a function of the product of mean arrival rate times mean service time. This chart is developed from a basic multiple-channel queuing model, where arrival rates are Poisson distributed and service times are exponential. The optimum fleet size m is that which minimizes the sum of the two costs $(C_1 + C_2)$. The sensitivity of the total cost to the fleet size is shown in Figure 6.13 for various arrival-service ratios and cost ratios.

SIMULATION: Simulation is a useful method of analyzing flow process and material-handling systems, particularly where there is a complex interaction of stochastic variables. For example, consider the following variable path case. The Seldon Company manufactures large glass-lined tanks for the food and chemical industries. One of the main fabrication shops, Shop 2, had been operating at maximum capacity for almost half a year, and the backlog of work was increasing at a rate that alarmed the plant manager, George Develon.

It was conceded that part of the problem was the handling of the material in the shop. The shop was presently serviced by three large battery-driven crane trucks, which moved plates and tanks between various operations. Two of the trucks were old and in need of replacement, and there was a question of whether more than three were needed. There was no question in anyone's mind that there were too many delays and too much machine idle time due to the inefficiency in the present method of handling the materials.

In response to Develon's request, the chief industrial engineer, Harry Cole, made an analysis of the present methods to determine the general shop idle time due to waiting for handling service. In a report submitted to Develon, Cole reported that a preliminary investigation indicated that an overhead crane should be installed as a replacement for the crane trucks. A major advantage of the crane would be that it could traverse the shop much faster than the trucks, which were often impeded by work-in-process congestion. Furthermore, the crane would per-

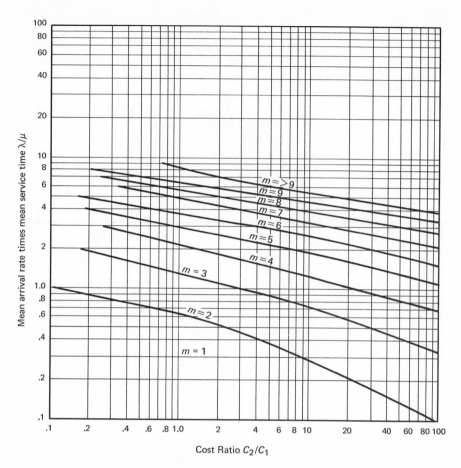

FIGURE **6.12** Optimum number of service channels or optimum fleet size. From William T. Morris, *Analysis for Materials Handling Management.* Homewood, Ill.: Richard D. Irwin, Inc., 1962, p. 97, Fig. 6-2.

mit relocation of equipment in the shop and a better utilization of floor space. The two older crane trucks should be retired and the third one retained to supplement the overhead crane operation if necessary in periods of heavy shop loads.

A second report by Cole pointed out that one of the more detailed decisions related to an overhead crane was the speed at which it would traverse a linear distance. For example, one of the models being considered varied in speed capacity and price for a given load capacity. There were three types, as follows:

Type	Price	Nominal speed (ft/hr)
I	$100,000	3,600
II	200,000	5,000
III	250,000	7,200

The actual linear speed of the conveyor would, of course, depend on the kind of load it carried, as well as on the speed capacity of the crane.

Develon found that the decision of speed capacity was not easy to make. He was inclined to purchase Type I, which had been the standard for comparison in Cole's preliminary report. However, Cole had convinced him that the added speed might be an important variable in further reducing idle capacity. He decided to assign the problem to Ed McGuinness, a young industrial engineer with a background in operations research techniques. McGuinness said he could "simulate

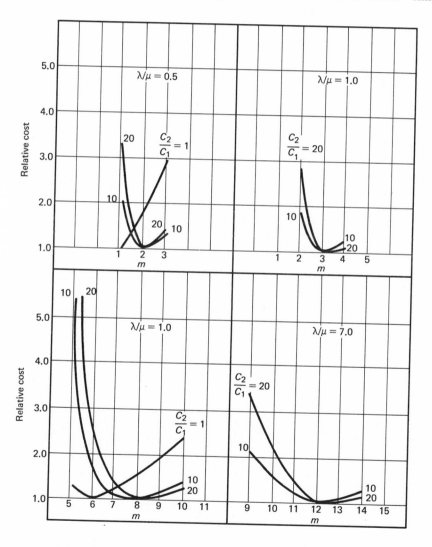

FIGURE **6.13**   Relative cost of various numbers of service channels or fleet sizes. From William T. Morris, *Analysis for Materials Handling Management*. Homewood, Ill.: Richard D. Irwin, Inc., 1962, p. 99, Fig 6-3.

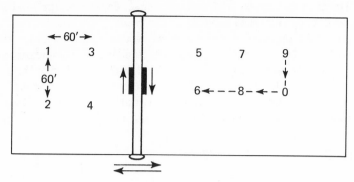

FIGURE **6.14**   Shop partition.

the system on a computer without too much trouble." It might take him two weeks to get the desired information.

McGuinness's study was conducted along the following lines. Demands for service were approximated with a Poisson arrival rate with a mean of 2.9 per hour. The time to service an operation exclusive of travel time was normally distributed with a mean of 15 minutes and a standard deviation of 4.2 minutes. System variables were defined in the following way.

1. *DIST* (I, J): The shop size is 360 feet by 180 feet. The shop is partitioned into ten equal areas numbered 0 to 9 as in Figure 6.14. This variable is an element of a matrix and is the number of 60-foot spaces the crane must travel between a pair of areas, I to J.

2. *TARV:* This event is the time of the next arrival (service call) to the system. Interarrival times are generated from an exponential distribution.

3. *TDPR:* This event is the time in which service to a customer is completed.

4. *CLOCK:* This is a master timer.

5. *QUE:* Number of customers waiting for service.

6. *QHRS:* Total hours spent in waiting per day.

7. *CRANE:* The state of the crane at any point in time. CRANE = 1 if crane is in use, and 0 otherwise.

8. *RATE:* The speed of the crane in feet per hour, which is a random variable. Mean speed is nominal and standard deviation equals 1,000 ft/hr.

9. *FEET:* The number of feet the crane must travel between areas I and J.

10. *TASK:* The time to service a customer after the crane has arrived to the location. TASK is a normally distributed random variable.

11. *BUSY:* The total hours the crane is busy.

12. *TOTHR:* The total hours spent waiting per month.

13. *USE:* The total hours the crane is used per month.

LOGIC DIAGRAM: The logic diagram of the simulator is shown in Figure 6.15. Note that the system is simulated for about eight hours, after which time it is returned to the start of a new eight-hour day. In total, 20 days are simulated to

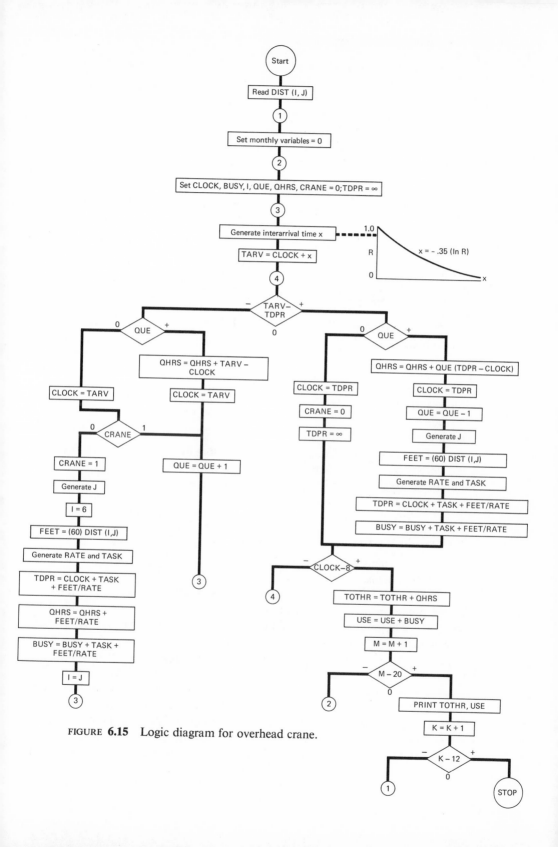

FIGURE **6.15** Logic diagram for overhead crane.

TABLE **6.1** Hours waiting in queue.

Month	Crane I (speed 3,600 ft/hr)	Crane II (speed 5,000 ft/hr)	Crane III (speed 7,200 ft/hr)
January	166.23	148.69	191.08
February	300.24	207.47	181.17
March	174.33	160.65	117.02
April	181.03	159.36	177.09
May	169.06	273.97	99.55
June	282.49	205.24	151.10
July	278.78	177.16	147.40
August	307.58	202.17	153.15
September	232.88	192.02	140.75
October	199.13	166.21	229.29
November	217.56	164.79	177.49
December	184.70	119.26	144.77
Annual totals	2,694.01	2,176.99	1,909.86
Total hours crane is in use per year	1,529.60	1,487.95	1,466.32
Crane utilization	0.795	0.775	0.765

compile a month's data on the waiting time and crane use. Thus, finally, a 12-month period is simulated.

RESULTS: Table 6.1 compiles the information for a 12-month simulation period for each of three crane speeds. The number of hours the crane is waiting in queue should be compared with its total potential working hours per month, which is 160 hours per section or 1,600 hours total. The annual utilization of the crane is based on 1,920 hours available per year.

Fixed Path Systems

Fixed path systems vary from simple gravity conveyors to sophisticated mechanical handling systems.

The purpose of conveyors is to form permanent links between geographically separated points in production or storage systems. Such a link permits the continuous or discontinuous transfer of materials and/or the facility for temporary storage of materials between the points.

There is a wide variety of conveyor methods and equipment. These include the simple roller gravity conveyor, power belt or slat conveyors, overhead power conveyors, gravity chutes, pneumatic systems, pipelines, towlines, etc. Within each of these classes there are many variations in form, capacity, and capabilities.

Just as with the case of variable path handling equipment, the choice of a conveyor system depends on two kinds of investigation. The first, and perhaps more important, is the specification of input-output parameters of the handling system. When it is known how much and what rate materials are to be transferred in, then the second issue is the choice of a system among competing methods and equipment suppliers. The first question requires a good deal of operations analysis and research, while the second is mainly an engineering problem involving, ultimately, equipment replacement or acquisition economics.

The Closed-Loop Irreversible Conveyor

Many high volume production plants use the overhead conveyor as a major material mover. System flexibility can be introduced by using switching devices, by permitting the conveyor speed and direction to be variable and manually controlled during operations, and by specifying conveyor dimensions that permit part of the conveyor to be used as inventory.

The use of switching methods and variable controls adds to the cost of the equipment, and to its maintenance and operation. The least expensive type of overhead conveyor, given certain capacity requirements, is the closed-loop irreversible conveyor, such as the type used by the White Engine Company for feeding the inspection process. While this kind of conveyor is relatively inexpensive, the major problem of its use resides in the selection of the conveyor design parameters that will permit uninterrupted service at both the loading and unloading stations. This matter poses both a practical and a theoretically interesting problem. The behavior of a production system including the loading and unloading stations, as well as the conveyor itself, has become the general subject of "conveyor theory." The subject seems first to have been exposed as a theoretical matter of general interest by T. T. Kwo.[5]

We will investigate the matter of designing the irreversible closed-loop conveyor system in its simplest form. The notation and working of principles follows generally those used and stated by Kwo.

CASE PROBLEM 6.2   One year ago, the White Engine Company designed and installed an automatic process for producing small gasoline engine blocks. This process performs the machining operations on the cast block and then prepares it for transfer to the assembly power conveyor, which is located about 1,600 feet from the automatic process. Figure 6.16 shows the location of the two processes and the intervening distances.

The present method of handling the blocks between the processes is by pallets and fork-lift trucks. The blocks are placed by hand on pallets at the end of the automated process. Four pallets, each containing nine blocks, are stacked as a fork-lift truck unit load. These are then deposited at the head of the assembly power conveyor, at point A, from where the blocks are loaded on the conveyor by hand.

The rate of output of the automated block process is 240 units per hour, which is twice the rate of the assembly power conveyor. The time for a fork-lift truck to pick up a unit load, transport it some 1,600 feet, deposit it, and return to the loading point

---

[5] T. T. Kwo, "A Theory of Conveyors," *Management Science*, vol. 5, no. 1, October 1958.

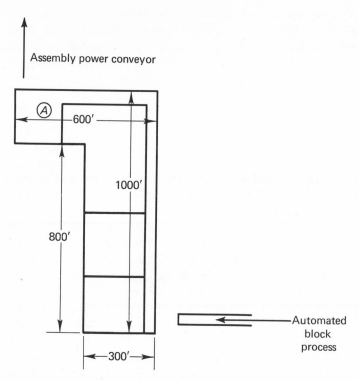

Assembly power conveyor

FIGURE **6.16** Layout between block process and assembly power conveyor.

is about 12 minutes. This is somewhat longer than the time to load four pallets. Usually one fork-lift truck is used, and, therefore, inventory space is needed at both ends of the handling system because of the different rates of production and because of the handling rate itself.

In early 1968, one year after the automated process was started, the general production manager, George Elman, requested a study of the handling system. The foreman of the block process was not satisfied with the present handling method. The accumulation of inventory at the end of the block process contributed to congestion and unsafe operating conditions due to limited space. At the other end of the line, the stored pallet loads had to be manipulated to bring them close to the assembly line when they were needed. Since the block line operated at twice the assembly line rate, the former would operate for a four-hour period during an eight-hour day and then shut down. While this appears inefficient, the company anticipated increased production in the future with the probable addition of assembly lines. When this would occur, the block line would start operating for a greater portion of the eight-hour day.

At a meeting in January 1966, Elman, the foreman of the assembly and block departments, and Robert McKay, the plant engineer, considered alternative handling methods. Shifting the block line closer to the assembly department was out of the question. One standard alternative was to link the two processes with a closed-loop overhead conveyor. The purpose of this conveyor would be to transport the parts between the processes and act as a storage capacity for the inventory caused by the

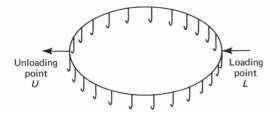

FIGURE **6.17**   Irreversible loop conveyor.

unequal production rates and any reserve stock required. Such a system would eliminate the storage problems now encountered. An overhead conveyor could be adapted to almost any shape of the area shown in Figure 6.16. Before considering available equipment, it would be necessary to specify the parameters of the system, including the length of the conveyor, speed, space between carriers, and number of carriers.

DESIGN PROBLEMS: A simple diagram of the closed-loop irreversible conveyor is shown in Figure 6.17. At the loading point L, a unit of material is added to a carrier. The carriers are equally spaced along the length of the conveyor. The loading rate is r_L units per hour. At the unloading point U, the material is removed at some rate r_U units per hour. If both rates are constant and equal, the design problem is relatively easy. Problems arise when the rates are unequal. Under this condition, it is very possible to arrive at a situation where the conveyor is non-uniformly loaded, giving rise to two conditions. These are, first, when empty carriers (or hooks) are required at the loading stations, none are available, and second, when full carriers are required at the unloading station, none are available. This lack of uniform loading means that material is concentrated on some segment of the total length of the conveyor. Therefore, both empty and full hooks do not arrive uniformly to the point where they are needed.

As an example, let us consider the hypothetical case shown in Figure 6.18. In this example, loading proceeds at a rate of 200 units per hour for a period of two hours and then ceases until the start of the next eight-hour period. The unload-

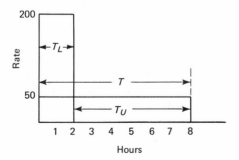

FIGURE **6.18**   Load and unload rates.

ing takes place continuously over the eight-hour period at a rate of 50 units per hour. The daily requirements are therefore 400 units. The conveyor is loaded during the period T_L, and T_U is the period in which the conveyor is unloaded without any loading taking place. The loading function might take place in two cycles of 200 units each at the first and fourth hours of the day. What we are interested in, however, is what happens in a given period T, which is that period during which a complete cycle of loading and unloading takes place. Also, whether the loading or unloading proceeds at a faster rate does not alter the way in which we approach the problem and define the operating characteristics of the conveyor.

SYSTEM PARAMETERS: We will designate the parameters of the system as follows:

W = revolution time of the conveyor
L = length of the conveyor
s = space between carriers
m = number of carriers on the conveyor
v = speed of the conveyor
t_L = average time to load a part on the conveyor
t_U = average time to unload a part off the conveyor
v_c = technologically feasible maximum speed of the conveyor

Then,

$$W = L/v \quad \text{and} \quad s = L/m$$

There are three basic constraints on these parameters.

1. *Uniformity constraint*   The first requirement is that the units must be loaded and unloaded uniformly over the entire length of the conveyor. Uniformity is determined by the number of times the conveyor passes the loading point (or unloading point) during the time that the conveyor is being loaded (or unloaded). It can be seen that if the loading rate is constant, units will be distributed uniformly over the conveyor length if, during the loading period, the entire length of the conveyor passes the loading point an integral number of times. If the loading and unloading are irregular or random, achieving uniformity may be a difficult matter. However, where the rates are as shown in Figure 6.18, the following conditions must be met:

$$T/W = H, \text{ a positive integer not equal to one} \tag{1}$$

$$T_L/W = \text{a positive integer, or } T_U/W = \text{a positive integer} \tag{2}$$

According to this rule, the largest rotation period will be equal to T_L. However, it can also be shown that larger rotation times are possible if the loading and unloading are equalized over several cycles for the conveyor length. For example, in the case of Figure 6.18, a rotation time of six hours will result in a uniform distribution after three cycles of eight hours each.

2. *Capacity constraint*   The number of carriers arriving per unit of time must

at least equal the number required. Capacity is therefore designated as a rate of carriers per unit of time. That is,

$$mv/L = m/W = v/s \geq K \tag{3}$$

where K = carriers required per unit time; K is a constant determined by the revolution time of the conveyor, the operating capacity, and the total reserve capacity desired.

We will see how this works later on. So far we have assumed that each carrier (or hook) carries only one unit. A carrier may be designed to carry more than one unit, thereby increasing the capacity of the conveyor. This complicates the problem only slightly, and later we will consider this case also.

3. *Speed constraint*   The speed of the conveyor is limited at the slow end of the scale by the rate of loading or unloading, whichever is higher. At the other end of the scale, the speed is limited either by technological constraints or by the speed at which the parts can be manually handled. Therefore,

$$\max{(r_L, r_U)} \leq v/s \leq \min{(1/t_L, 1/t_U, v_c/s)}$$

Now suppose that we consider the case of $r_L = 200$ units per hour and $r_U = 50$ units per hour. The distance between loading and unloading points is 1,000 feet, and, therefore, the conveyor length L is 2,000 feet. The cycle time T is eight hours, T_L is two hours, and T_U is six hours.

Possible values of W, according to the uniformity constraint, are 2, 1, $\frac{2}{3}$, $\frac{1}{2}$, $\frac{2}{5}$, $\frac{1}{3}$, ... If we consider 60 feet per minute to be a maximum speed limit, then we can eliminate any rotational time less than $\frac{2}{3}$ hour. As an arbitrary constraint, we will also not consider any rotational time greater than 2 hours.

Now the problem is to designate a rotation time, the number of carriers, and therefore the space between carriers. Several possibilities are summarized in Table 6.4. In trial 1, a rotation time of two hours is selected, and the distance between carriers is set at two feet. This violates the speed constraint since $\max{(3.3, 0.83)} \leq 8.3 > \min{(5, 5, 12)}$, which says that the rate at which a carrier moves past the stations is faster than the manual loading rates, $1/t_L$, $1/t_U$.

In trial 2, we increase the space between carriers to five feet and arrive at a reasonable preliminary solution. A carrier will pass the loading station every

TABLE **6.4**   Design trials.

Trial	W	v ft/min	s ft	m	$\dfrac{s}{v}$	Units per minute				
						$\dfrac{v}{s}$	r_L	r_U	$\dfrac{1}{t_L}$	$\dfrac{1}{t_U}$
1	2	16.6	2	1,000	0.12	8.3	3.33	0.83	5	5
2	2	16.6	5	400	0.30	3.3	3.33	0.83	5	5
3	1	33.3	5	400	0.15	6.6	3.33	0.83	5	5

0.30 minutes, which corresponds to the inverse of the loading rate. If we assume that the loading and unloading stations are located at opposite ends of the conveyor, we can visualize what will happen by the following simple simulation.

Hour	Revolution	Units loaded	Units unloaded	Number of units on delivery half of the conveyor, end of hour	Number of units on return half of conveyor, end of hour
0	0	0	0	0	0
1	$\frac{1}{2}$	200	0	200	0
2	1	200	50	200	150
3	$1\frac{1}{2}$	50	50	150	150
4	2	0	50	150	100
5	$2\frac{1}{2}$	0	50	100	100
6	3	0	50	50	100
7	$3\frac{1}{2}$	0	50	50	50
8	4	0	50	50	0

Note that while the unloading operation had to wait one hour before it could start on the first eight-hour cycle, on the second eight-hour cycle there are 50 units on the delivery half ready to be unloaded.

CAPACITY CONSIDERATIONS: In the previous example, the choice of $W = 2$, $s = 5$, and $L = 2,000$ seems to be a perfect arrangement. However, we must consider capacity in terms of the number of accommodations per unit of time. Recall from Equation (3) that the capacity constraint is expressed as a number K. This number must account for the maximum rate at which parts are added to the conveyor plus a rate that will account for reserve stock.

1. *Working capacity requirements*   In the simulation, we noted that the maximum load on the delivery portion of the conveyor is 200 units. This occurs over a half revolution of the conveyor or in 60 minutes. The corresponding rate is 3.33 units per minute, which, as we noted, corresponds exactly with the loading rate.

2. *Adjustment for distance between load and unload points*   The assumption that the load and unload points are diametrically opposite seems reasonable in most cases. However, the assumption that the end of the cycle accumulation of 50 units is distributed evenly over the delivery section of the conveyor is probably not justified. As the system actually operates, we might expect this inventory to be eventually distributed randomly over the entire length of the conveyor. However, we would still like to have the system able to provide the unload station with 50 units in the first hour regardless of its location. The only way we can do this is to have 100 units distributed evenly over the conveyor. This can be done by producing an extra 50 units during the first 15 minutes of the third hour. An alternative is to provide for the extra fifty as an increase in the rate capacity of the conveyor. Thus, we would increase the capacity requirements by $\frac{50}{120} = 0.42$ unit per minute.

3. *Reserve capacity*   No system such as we have discussed will operate exactly

in the assumed synchronized fashion. Also, it is unreasonable to assume that loading will take place exactly on each carrier, or every other carrier, depending on the rotation period. Therefore, an arbitrary reserve stock may be added. The conversion of this amount to a rate basis is done by dividing the units required by the rotation time. For example, assume that we wish to have a 60-unit reserve stock, which corresponds to a rate of 0.50 units per hour ($\frac{60}{120}$).

The value of K is the sum of these various rates, which, in our case, is

3.33   working stock including one hour's unloading requirement of 50 units
0.42   adjustment for uniform starting quantity for unloading
<u>0.50</u>   reserve stock
4.25

This rate is significantly greater than the decided upon rate of 3.33.

Now the question is: How do we obtain the additional capacity and still have the system operate in synchronization with the loading and unloading tasks? Let us investigate this issue in terms of the capacity relationship: $K = mqv/L$. Here we have added the parameter q, which is the number of units that one carrier can accommodate. Clearly, this is one way of adding capacity to the system. If we wish to synchronize the conveyor with the loading and unloading rates, then we must change the system by a factor of 2 such as by 1) doubling the speed and, therefore, halving the rotational time, or 2) permitting two units to be carried by each carrier, or 3) doubling the number of carriers and, therefore, halving the distance between carriers, or 4) reducing the length of the conveyor by one-half. Clearly, the last alternative is usually not possible. Each of these above alternatives would yield a rate capacity of 6.66 units/min and thus be synchronized with the load-unload rates. However, the synchronization need not be a predominant requirement, particularly if the load-unload unit times are highly variable. Therefore, we might make adjustments in the system to yield a capacity equal to the desired 4.66. The advantage of this would probably be reflected in lower equipment costs.

The fact that the system design depends on capacity requirements over and above the working capacity may defeat some of the advantages of the uniformity principle and that parts may be ultimately randomly distributed over the length of the conveyor, thus introducing unavailability of full or empty carriers at the time they are needed. It must be remembered that a given unit on the conveyor is not tagged for a specific purpose, whether it be for working requirements, reserve stock, or starting quantities. What we have done is to try to specify basic speeds, lengths, and carrier spacing that will tend to provide uniform distribution of parts on the conveyor. The ultimate and detailed understanding of the system performance within these general specifications can be gained only from simulation or empirical knowledge.

Once these general performance parameters are specified, the problem assumes engineering proportions. It is then a question of selecting the equipment in terms of physical dimensions, power capacities, strength capacity, drive units, etc. Prior to this, however, a cost analysis may be made to determine if the closed-loop conveyor is justified compared with other alternative methods of material handling.

Problems

6.1   Suppose you take your car to a large garage for a 40,000 mile checkup. This will include such things as motor tuneup, wheels inspection, brake relining, wheel alignment, tire changes, etc. The shop foreman will set up a route sheet for your car. Discuss the implications of this routing function with the problems of actually getting the jobs done on your car and the other cars in the system. How are routing and actual shop operation interrelated?

6.2   Prepare a precedence flow chart for the process of getting dressed. The articles of clothing to wear are shoes, socks, underpants and shirt, trousers, belt, shirt, tie, tie clasp.

6.3   The following is a routing for a side plate for a fork-lift carriage assembly.

Operation	Machines and equipment	Setup man-hours per operation	Man-hours per operation
1. Burn out to template (3 torches)	No. 665, Oxygraph, gas cutter	1.0	0.1000
2. Rough clean	Rough grinder	—	0.0323
3. Straighten, if required	Lake Erie press	—	0.0666
4. Drill and ream (2), 1.500″ holes	Cincinnati-Bickford radial drill	1.0	0.1956
5. Burr (2) holes	Baker drill press	0.5	0.0137
6. Drill (4), $\frac{21}{64}$″ holes	Baker drill	1.0	0.0537
7. Chamfer (4) holes for tap	Avey drill and tap press	0.3	0.0139
8. Tap (4), $\frac{3}{8}$″-16	Baker drill	0.3	0.0250
9. Inspect	—	—	—

A study of precedence relationships shows the following:

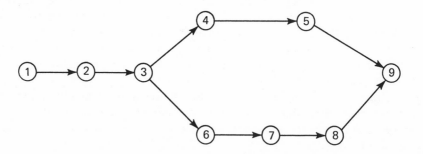

How many different distinct ways can the part be routed? Discuss some of the reasons why one route might be the best. Should the choice of the route actually used be left up to specification by the production engineer or the shop foreman and why?

6.4   Discuss the possibilities and ramifications of using the electronic computer to store routing information and to execute some of the logic in the routing function. Use a logic flow diagram to explain basic ideas.

6.5   One of the arguments for not using an Operations Process Chart is that it takes too much time to compile and draw. Suppose a plant makes 500 assemblies and sub-assemblies. How can one reconcile the usefulness of such a chart with the task of making them?

6.6   Select a process that you are familiar with involving the flow of some object. Make a flow diagram and flow-process chart of this process, and use these charts to suggest areas for improving the process.

6.7   The Monroe County Memorial Hospital faces the problem of many hospitals today—that of improving its operations in view of increased demand for its service. Suppose you are asked to "improve the hospital laundry operation." What approaches would you take? Where in the course of your work would the use of flow-process analysis be useful (if at all)?

6.8   Consider the data related to the Seldon Company Case, page 187. Suppose that the downtime of any section costs the company approximately $100 per hour. Assuming a capital cost of 10% and that the investment in Crane I will be recovered in three years by savings over the present method, what Crane speed would you recommend?

6.9   Suppose you are concerned with improving the process of pelletizing feeds by the process outlined on page 20. Assume the manager has decided to investigate more fully the possibility of making an investment in additional unloading dock space and an additional processing capacity. The truck service times for the additional processing capacity are shown below. There are five load sizes arriving at the mill. The proportions of these sizes are indicated in the table. Also, there are four kinds of raw feed, and their proportions are also shown. Show the logic diagram for a simulator that will determine the characteristics of the waiting line system for the trucks under different arrival rates and unloading capacity.

Size load ⟶	1	2	3	4	5
Proportion ⟶	0.10	0.20	0.40	0.10	0.20
Type grain					
A 0.20	10	12	15	17	20
B 0.25	10	12	17	20	25
C 0.35	12	15	20	25	30
D 0.20	15	20	25	35	40

Time to service trucks (min)

Bibliography

BARNES, RALPH M., *Motion and Time Study*, 5th ed. New York: John Wiley & Sons, 1963.

BOLZ, HAROLD A., Ed., *Materials Handling Handbook*. New York: Ronald Press, 1958.

KRICK, EDWARD V., *Methods Engineering*. New York: John Wiley & Sons, 1962.

KWO, T. T., "A Method for Designing Irreversible Overhead Loop Conveyors," *J. Ind. Eng.*, November–December 1960.

MAYER, HUGO E., "An Introduction to Conveyor Theory," *The Western Electric Engineer*, January 1960.

MODER, JOSEPH J., and HERBERT M. THORNTON, "Quantitative Analysis of the Factors Affecting Floor Space Utilization of Palletized Storage," *J. Ind. Eng.*, January–February 1965.

MORRIS, W. T., *Analysis for Materials Handling Management*. Homewood, Ill.: Richard D. Irwin, Inc., 1962.

NADLER, GERALD, *Work Design*. Homewood, Ill.: Richard D. Irwin, Inc., 1963.

NIEBEL, BENJAMIN W., *Motion and Time Study*. Homewood, Ill.: Richard D. Irwin, Inc., 1958.

PRITSKER, A. A. B., "Application of Multichannel Queuing Results to the Analysis of Conveyor Systems," *J. Ind. Eng.*, January 1966.

7

Flow Processes:
Location of Facilities

INTRODUCTION

Many of the elements of a production system are stationary over relatively long periods of time. In this chapter, we will analyze the spatial arrangement of these elements in terms of a set of objectives. In so doing we could consider microscopic systems such as the arrangement of tools and materials at a work station, the assignment of items to inventory shelves, or the arrangement of components of a man-machine system. However, we will consider only larger systems, the elements of which are machines, pieces of equipment, working spaces, work-in-process inventories, storage areas, or complete plants and buildings.

It should be noted that we are interested in assigning facilities whose aggregate space requirement is equal to or less than the total space available. This is in contrast to the problem of allocating a restricted amount of space to facilities that are competing for the space. We might expect the latter kind of problem to precede the issue of assigning facilities to locations.

The classical terms used to designate the problem are plant layout and plant location, where the former term implies the spatial arrangement of facilities within a plant or building and the latter the geographic location of economic activities. In plant layout, the arrangement of facilities is made within the context of a basic format, the flow shop, or the job shop. In this chapter, we will examine the issue of deciding on the basic format of flow, then concentrate on the assignment of facilities within the job shop format, and conclude with the geographic assignment of economic activities.

The problem of facility location is closely related to the design of methods for handling materials between the facilities in a layout. The problems of layout and material handling are therefore often considered jointly. In the following discussion, we will pay some attention to this relationship but without dwelling on alternative handling methods and equipment.

Layout is the integrative function in the design of a production system, and the cost of operating the system depends to a significant degree on the layout. The relative permanency of facility locations suggests that considerable attention should be paid to the derivation of "good" layouts. Once a layout is fixed, the reduction in costs must come through adjustments of the elements in the system. We may expect, however, that the time will come when facility locations may be altered with relative ease to meet changes in production requirements. This will depend on the design of modular production facilities, which can be rearranged in various spatial combinations, and on economical methods for transferring these facilities between locations.

Obviously, plant layout is limited to the extent that physical facilities can be arranged in alternative spatial combinations or formats. From the historical standpoint, layout has been a major discipline within industrial engineering since the turn of the century. Prior to that time, the layout of machinery and workplaces was dictated to a large extent by the location of power-generating and transmission facilities. Before the steam engine, the water wheel was the primary source of power. Operations requiring such power had to be located near the wheel itself. Minor variations in location within a limited distance of the wheel were restricted by the mechanisms transferring the power from the wheel to the work station.

With the advent of steam engines, the power was transmitted over a much greater distance by metal gears and shafts. In a typical nineteenth-century plant layout the machine arrangement was dictated by the methods of power transmission. All machines were belt driven from main drive shafts overhead and were therefore arranged in a line under the main shaft or close to it.

In this century, four major factors led to the development of plant layout as a major design problem. The first was the use of individual electric power units on machines. This permitted the location of the machine to become independent of the source of power. The second was the realization that heavy machines do not necessarily have to be bolted to the shop floor. A minor shift in the location of a machine that would formerly affect the belt-drive tension no longer mattered. Today, the change in the position of a machine no longer requires uncoupling the machine from the floor. The third factor was the development of a wide variety of material-handling equipment, which permits material to be economically moved in many different types of layouts. The fourth factor was the recognition that plant layout should assume a priority in design over the building that contains the system. The building is now often considered a final covering for a layout, rather than a predesigned constraint on the layout itself. This permits the system designer greater latitude in devising alternative layout configurations.

BASIC LAYOUT FORMATS

A preliminary decision in layout problems is the determination of the basic arrangement of facilities. There are three basic types of layouts. They are the product layout, process layout, and combined layout. The first two correspond to the flow shop and job shop rationale of production, respectively.

1. *Product layout* Product layout is virtually synonymous with product-line design. This format consists in a specific ordering of a set of machines and work stations in accordance with the processing requirements for a given product or

product line. As we already know, the relative location of facilities is partially dictated by the position of the operation in the routing sequence.

2. *Process layout*   The second basic scheme for arranging machines, work centers, and other components of a facility is to group like operations, machines, or processes together in a common area. The location of a specific facility is dictated by the basic process with which it is identified. Thus, all machines of the same generic type, such as lathes, or milling machines, or grinders, are grouped together.

Within this format, a particular part is processed in a batch, as a job, and the batch is routed through the plant from operation to operation, as designated by the route sheet. At any given time, the entire plant or system will contain a number of batches in various stages of completion, each batch having its own distinctive sequence of operations. A department is used to designate a particular machine or facility grouping.

The process-type layout is typically associated with the manufacture of a large product mix in which the facilities must be jointly shared by many different parts and products. The production batch sizes are relatively small, and often a part may be made directly for a given consumer to his set of specifications. Until the twentieth century, this type of layout predominated in almost all manufacturing situations. Figure 7.1 shows a typical arrangement of machines in a process layout.

3. *Combined layout*   Each of the above layout schemes is present in most shops

FIGURE **7.1**   Process layout. Courtesy of Pratt & Whitney Company.

in varying degrees. The departments of a process layout may be arranged in such a way that there is a basic one-directional flow of materials from department to department for the majority of parts made. Within each department, the machines in a process layout are jointly used by the parts being produced. In some cases, certain parts may be standard components of most products and of such volume as to justify their manufacture on a product-line basis within a shop that is basically a process layout. Assembly operations are often designed for a product-type layout where fabrication operations are process laid out.

The Format Decision

The decision as to which type of basic format will be used is sometimes relatively easy to make. When the product mix is large, production batch sizes small, and product redesign frequent, then the product layout is precluded at least for fabricating operations. A product layout can be justified only by a sufficient volume of standard parts or in manual assembly operations where flexibility is possible.

The advantages and disadvantages of each type of layout are proverbial. Obviously, the choice should be based on the total costs of operating the production system for some period. If the decision is not straightforward, then the costing of each alternative may be extremely difficult, owing to the many elements of cost that must be estimated and the problem of relating the estimates to some cost model. Therefore, only first-order cost estimates may be made if the model handles only the critical cost factors. In the future, we may expect that the problem will be submitted to computerized simulation, where a wide variety of layout formats may be evaluated in terms of many cost elements. We shall refer to computerized models later.

When it is impossible to translate everything into monetary terms, the layout format is usually evaluated in terms of various cost indices. Of all the possible criteria, there may be only a few that are considered to be critical. However, since the layout problem is intrinsically complex, it is often necessary to consider the effect of alternative formats on as many cost factors as possible and then to choose on the basis of a judicial weighting of the criteria.

The criteria used to make the choice of format include material-handling costs, direct labor costs, work-in-process inventory, space requirements, ease of supervision, quality and production control, flexibility in meeting changes in product design, changes in production rate, machine and equipment utilization, system reliability, maintenance, cost of supplying utilities, etc. It is easy to generalize the advantages of one format over the other with respect to each of these criteria. For example, material-handling costs are often considered to be less in a product layout due to such things as the use of conveyors, which shunt parts directly between successive operations, shorter travel distances, and reduced handling at each operation.

SHIFTING FROM PROCESS TO PRODUCT LAYOUT: In many situations, a product layout may emerge or evolve from a predominantly process layout. Initially, the decision may be made to leave certain machines set up continually over time to produce a given part with high volume. When this occurs, and if these machines represent an unbroken sequence of operations on the part, they may be segregated and formed into a special product line for the part. Gradually all operations in the routing sequence may be moved into the line with or without complete utilization of the machines. The volume may then be gradually built up through the adaptation of the line to similar parts.

The chances are, however, that in a process layout the operations that represent fully utilized machines are not sequential and, therefore, must remain as isolated but fully utilized machines in the process layout.

When a sequential arrangement of machines is extracted from the process layout, the major saving in cost is due to the reduction of intermachine handling costs and some reduction in scheduling problems inherent in the process layout. Unless the machines are redesigned for specialized production, the direct labor costs would presumably be the same. If the volume of demand for the part increases to exceed the capacity of any machine in the line, then certain adjustments are necessary. These include overtime, extra shifts, redesign of the machine to improve the rate of output, or the purchase of additional machine capacity. With increased volume the routing may be reviewed to determine if other machines in the routing can be added to the line, thus approaching a complete product line process for the part. Then the situation becomes one of machine grouping in the line. This topic will be covered in the following chapter.

PROCESS LAYOUT

Given the basic decision to use a process-type layout, the problem is the assignment of a set of facilities to various available locations in some constrained space. It is important to note that in this discussion we assume that the space requirement for the facilities must be equal to or less than the total space resource. That is, we are not now interested in the problem of allocating a limited space resource to competing facility or departmental demands.

The choice among alternative location assignments is often based on a number of criteria. These include such things as the volume or costs of material handling between facilities, provision for future expansion, flexibility for change, safety factors, ease of supervision, proximity to utility services, etc. In the final analysis, no one criterion may necessarily dominate the decision.

As any design problem, plant layout has the morphological characteristic of evolving in design stages. In the preliminary stage, the predominant criterion is often the cost of handling materials between the facilities. A first-order assignment is made on the basis of minimizing the cost of handling materials, which is a function of the distance and intensity of material traffic flow between facilities. Once a first-order assignment has been made, the problem progresses to the detailed stage where the other factors are considered. This final detailed analysis may involve the judgments and experience of many people concerned with the actual operation of the production system.

In the initial stages of process layout, the predominant criterion again is often the minimization of material handling or traffic costs in the system. In the following pages, we will dwell primarily on this criterion.

The problem can be handled theoretically in a number of ways. First we make these basic assumptions in order to simplify the ensuing discussion.

1. An assignment consists of assigning each of n facilities uniquely to one of m locations.

2. The number of facilities is equal to the number of available locations; that is, $m = n$. If the total available space, or number of locations, exceeds the number of facilities, then we may introduce "dummy" facilities and relate them to the remaining facilities with an arbitrary excessive cost relationship.

3. The facilities have equal space requirements, and the geometric configurations of these space requirements are the same. While this assumption is untenable in practice, the central problem is the relative location of facilities. Once the relative relationships are known, the exact allocation of the existing space can be made in accordance with both the relative locations and space configurations.

4. There are two kinds of situations that we will consider. The first is the case in which the cost resulting from assigning a facility to a location is independent of the remaining assignments. This is formulated as a *linear assignment problem*. If the cost of a facility-location pair is dependent on the remaining assignments, then the problem is formulated as a *quadratic assignment problem*.

LINEAR ASSIGNMENT CASE

Some facility-location problems can be structured as a linear assignment problem. We have a set of n fixed location, and we wish to assign to each element of this set a single facility or resource from a second set of n facilities. Let

$C = [c(i, j)]$ be a cost matrix, where $c(i, j)$ is the cost associated with assigning the ith location to the jth facility: $i, j = 1, 2, \ldots, n$

$X_t = [x(i, j)]$ be a solution matrix such that $x(i, j) = \begin{cases} 1 & \text{if } i \text{ is assigned to } j \\ 0 & \text{otherwise} \end{cases}$

$t = 1, 2, \ldots, n!; \quad \sum_i x(i, j) = 1; \quad \sum_j x(i, j) = 1$

The objective is to minimize the function W_t, where[1]

$W_t = \sum_i \sum_j x(i, j) \cdot c(i, j)$

---

[1] This is also the dot product of two matrices $(C \cdot X_t)$. A dot product is of the following form. Given a matrix X and a matrix Y, the dot product $X \cdot Y$ is

$\sum_i \sum_j x_{ij} \cdot y_{ij}$

Location i \ Facility j	1	2	3	4	5
1	10	8	12	15	9
2	6	6	5	3	8
3	15	16	15	12	10
4	20	25	16	15	25
5	6	5	4	10	8

FIGURE **7.2**   Cost matrix for five materials and locations.

EXAMPLE **7.1**   The Delta Power and Light Company has five acres of land located next to its new operations center. This land is to be used as a "yard storage area" for storing large coils of power line, various construction materials, and other miscellaneous items that can be stored outdoors. The company wishes to determine the location of each of these items in the yard. The yard is partitioned into locations. The cost of assigning an object or material to a location is a function of the volume of movement of the material from and to its location, the ease of moving the material with existing handling equipment, the proximity to unloading and loading areas, the ease of protection from fire, etc. Therefore, the cost of assigning a material to a location is independent of the assignment of the other materials to remaining locations, and a linear assignment model is used to determine a first-order assignment. The cost matrix for five materials and locations is shown in Figure 7.2.

The minimum cost assignment can be found by submitting it to branch and bound (see page 73, Chapter 3).

QUADRATIC ASSIGNMENT CASE

Since material flow or traffic is often between facilities, the cost of assigning a given facility to a given location depends on the assignment of the remaining facilities to remaining locations. That is, the traffic cost is a function of the relative location of the facilities.

This problem was originally formulated as a quadratic assignment problem by Koopmans and Beckmann in the following manner.[2] In general notation, we have n locations to which n facilities are to be assigned. Let there be two $n \times n$ matrices $A = [a(i, j)]$ and $B = [b(k, l)]$ where

$a(i, j)$ = the "distance" between location i and j in the direction $i \rightarrow j$

$b(k, l)$ = the volume of material to be transported between facilities k and l in the direction $k \rightarrow l$

[2] T. C. Koopmans and M. J. Beckmann, "Assignment Problems and the Location of Economic Activities," *Econometrica*, vol. 25, 1957, pp. 52–76.

There is a permutation or solution matrix $X_t = [x(i, k)]$, where

$$x(i, k) = \begin{cases} 1 & \text{if facility } k \text{ is assigned to location } i \\ 0 & \text{otherwise} \end{cases}$$

$$\sum_i x(i, k) = 1; \quad \sum_k x(i, k) = 1; \quad \text{and } t = 1, 2, \ldots, n!$$

The objective then is to minimize $B \cdot (X'AX)$, which is the total system transportation cost.

In this case, where costs depend on relative locations, the determination of an optimum assignment appears to be quite difficult. We will now examine various facets of the problem and consider some approaches to solving it.

Redundancy and Restrictions

The theoretical number of possible assignments is reduced by both redundancy in alternative assignments and restrictions on certain subsets of assignments.

Redundancy arises in the following manner. Suppose we are given the following format of nine locations in which an initial assignment I of nine facilities (1–9) has been made.

1	2	3
4	5	6
7	8	9

Certain other assignments are symmetrical to the initial one. A symmetrical assignment is one in which the distances between the facilities in I are preserved. There are seven such symmetrical arrangements of I. For example, the square can be rotated clockwise about its center 90°, 180°, or 270°. Each of these three rotations produces an assignment that is equivalent to I.

Restrictions are imposed by technological or economic factors. For example, shipping must be located next to a fixed railroad spur. Heavy plate welding must be located in an area serviced by an overhead crane. Unless the entire system is initially designed, the assignment of facilities may be severely restricted to certain locations.

In the following pages, we will consider the problem in its most general form, assuming nonsymmetrical formats and assuming no restrictions in locations. In the methods described, redundancy does not appear to contribute any economies of solution. A constraint in the location of a given facility k to a given location i can be accounted for by imposing a linear cost c_{ik} on the problem. Such linear costs can be handled with relative ease in the quadratic problem, although we will not consider them specifically in the following numerical examples.

Basic Data

The cost of transporting materials between facilities in a layout is a function of the distance between the potential locations for facilities and of the intensity of the traffic between facilities. Each of these measures is independent of any assignment, and it must be determined prior to the actual job of assigning facilities to the locations.

DISTANCE MATRIX: If there are n locations, then there are $n(n-1)/2$ different possible pairs of locations, each pair having a measure of distance between them. The distances between all location pairs are contained in a distance matrix. Let

$$A = [a(i,j)] = \text{distance matrix}$$

where $a(i,j)$ is the distance between location i and location j, $i = 1, \ldots, n$; $j = 1, \ldots, n$. We will assume that $a(i,j) = a(j,i)$ or that the A matrix is symmetrical. While this may appear to be a reasonable assumption, there are cases where, for example, two types of material-handling equipment service the flow, each in a different direction between two departments, thus over two different distances.

Figure 7.3 shows a distance matrix for four locations A, B, C, and D.

In general, the elements of the distance matrix are literally measures of linear distance between locations, assuming some format of aisles and average starting and ending points of travel. However, if the mode of handling material between the locations is *fixed* and *independent* of the kind of facility assigned to the location, then "distance" can represent a unit cost of handling material between the locations. But, in many cases involving manufacturing processes, the material-handling method is a function of the kinds of materials transported and consequently dependent upon the facilities. We then incorporate the unit handling cost in the traffic intensity measure described below.

TRAFFIC INTENSITY MATRIX: There are also $n(n-1)/2$ pairs of facilities, each pair having a measure or cost of material flow between them in both directions.

i \ j	A	B	C	D
A	0	6	7	2
B	6	0	5	6
C	7	5	0	1
D	2	6	1	0

FIGURE **7.3** $A = [a(i,j)]$ distance between locations i and j. Figures 7.3 through 7.8 are taken from J. W. Gavett and N. V. Plyter, *Operations Research*, vol. 14, no. 2, March–April 1966.

k \ l	1	2	3	4
1	0	10	20	5
2	18	0	9	4
3	5	6	0	8
4	8	0	15	0

FIGURE 7.4 $B = [b(k, l)]$ rate of traffic flow between facilities k and l.

Therefore, there is a matrix that contains the indexes of traffic intensity between facility pairs. Let

$$B = [b(k, l)] = \text{traffic intensity matrix}$$

where $b(k, l)$ is the rate at which material is transferred between facilities k and l, $k = 1, \ldots, n$; $l = 1, \ldots, n$. This matrix is usually asymmetrical, because the flow rates in each direction between the two facilities are likely to differ. Figure 7.4 shows such a matrix for four facilities, 1, 2, 3, and 4.

Again we need to consider the meaning of the elements of the matrix. These can represent such things as pounds per year, number of trips per month, unit loads per month, or annual cost of transporting a unit load per unit distance. In the last case, and for a given facility pair, we can take the product of the annual volume of material flow between the pair times the cost of handling a unit of volume per unit distance. For example, the "traffic intensity" between facilities 1 and 2 consists of 1,000 fork-lift truck loads of material times $0.01 per unit load per 100 feet of travel. In this sense, the B matrix can allow for a unique material-handling method to be used between a pair of facilities.

The determination of the elements of the traffic intensity matrix is not likely to be a trivial task. For example, in the case of a job shop in which hundreds or thousands of parts are made, the traffic intensity consists of the aggregate movements of these parts. This information must be gleaned from routing sheets and forecasts of volume requirements. If such data are not readily available in computer files, then some kind of sampling procedure will be required.

The Cost Matrix

The cost of assigning a pair of facilities to a pair of locations is the product of the distance between the location pair and the total traffic intensity between the facility pairs in both directions. Let C be a cost matrix:

$$C = [c(ij, kl)]$$

where $c(ij, kl) = $ cost of assigning facilities k and l to locations i and j: $i, j, k, l = 1, 2, \ldots, n$. Then

$$c(ij, kl) = a(i, j) \times b'(k, l)$$

where

$$b'(k, l) = b(k, l) + b(l, k).$$

For example, the cost of assigning facilities 1 and 2 to locations A and B is the distance between A and B (6) times the total traffic between 1 and 2 $(10 + 18)$, or $6 \times 28 = 168$.

The cost matrix C is shown in Figure 7.5. The row headings consist of a vector L of location pair values $a(i, j)$. The column headings are a vector T of facility pair values $b'(k, l)$. The values $c(ij, kl)$ are the multiplication of the vectors $L \times T$. The dimension of C is $N \times N$, where $N = \dfrac{n(n - 1)}{2}$.

COST OF AN ASSIGNMENT: A single assignment consists in accommodating each location with a facility. Since there are n locations and n facilities, there are $n!$ feasible assignments. Let an assignment be denoted by t, $t = 1, 2, \ldots, n!$. Each t will denote a unique permutation from the $n!$ set of permutations on the numbers $(1, 2, 3, \ldots, n)$.

An assignment t will then select N elements from the cost matrix C, one from each row and column.

For example, using the matrix in Figure 7.6, the assignment t, $\begin{bmatrix} A & B & C & D \\ 3 & 1 & 2 & 4 \end{bmatrix}$, selects the circled elements from C. Note that A–B assigned 3–1 selects the element from the column labeled 1–3 since $b'(k, l) = b'(l, k)$ in constructing the second element of T.

Locations L	Facilities T	28	25	13	15	4	23
		1–2	1–3	1–4	2–3	2–4	3–4
6	A–B	168	150	78	90	24	138
7	A–C	196	175	91	105	28	161
2	A–D	56	50	26	30	8	46
5	B–C	140	125	65	75	20	115
6	B–D	168	150	78	90	24	138
1	C–D	28	25	13	15	4	23

FIGURE **7.5** C matrix $C_{N \times N} = L_{N \times 1} \times T_{1 \times N}$. Costs for assigning each pair of facilities to each pair of locations.

Facilities / Locations	1–2	1–3	1–4	2–3	2–4	3–4
A–B	168	(150)	78	90	24	138
A–C	196	175	91	(105)	28	161
A–D	56	50	26	30	8	(46)
B–C	(140)	125	65	75	20	115
B–D	168	150	(78)	90	24	138
C–D	28	25	13	15	(4)	23

FIGURE **7.6** The assignment t, $\begin{bmatrix} A & B & C & D \\ 3 & 1 & 2 & 4 \end{bmatrix}$, selects the six circled elements.

The total cost of an assignment is the sum of the N elements of C selected by the assignment t and is denoted

$$W(t) = \sum c(ij, kl)$$

where ij and kl are selected by t. For example, the cost of the assignment shown in Figure 7.6 is 523.

L	Location	T	4	13	15	23	25	28
	Facility		2–4	1–4	2–3	3–4	1–3	1–2
7	A–C		28	91	105	161	175	196
6	A–B		24	78	90	138	150	168
6	B–D		24	78	90	138	150	168
5	B–C		20	65	75	115	125	140
2	A–D		8	26	30	46	50	56
1	C–D		4	13	15	23	25	28

FIGURE **7.7** Construction of $C = L \times T$ with ranked L and T.

RANKING THE COST MATRIX: Suppose the components of the vector L and T are rearranged, along with their corresponding labels, so that L is in descending order and T is in ascending order. Then, when C is constructed, it will have the format of Figure 7.7.

ACCEPTABLE ASSIGNMENTS: An assignment consists in selecting elements from the C matrix, one from each row and column. There are, therefore, $N!$ possible assignments. But there are only $n!$ acceptable assignments because of the restrictions on the labels. Therefore, the set of acceptable assignments is less than the set of possible assignments. Let

R = set of possible assignments
S = set of acceptable assignments

Then $S \subset R$ for all n. There will be a minimum assignment cost W_t in each set. Let

W_R = the minimum assignment cost in the set R
W_S = minimum assignment cost in the set S

Then

$$W_R \leq W_S$$

It is an algebraic property of the ranked C matrix that the minimum assignment cost W_R consists of the sum of the elements lying on the diagonal.[3] Therefore, if $W_R = W_S$, the assignment is on the diagonal of C. Most likely this will not be the case so that the problem then is to determine W_R by some method.

Optimal Assignments

An optimal assignment is one for which W_S is a minimum, providing the single criterion of minimizing traffic costs. We cover three possible methods of obtaining the optimum.

COMPLETE ENUMERATION: The first method is to enumerate all $n!$ acceptable assignments, evaluate the cost of each, and select the minimum. Presumably this would be done efficiently on a computer for values of n, say up to 10. The size of n, of course, depends on the progressive developments of computers in speed and capacity.

For our previous example, we have 24 acceptable assignments with their costs as follows:

---

[3] A sum of the pairwise product of two sequences of numbers will be minimized if one sequence is arranged in increasing order and the other in decreasing order.

A	B	C	D	Cost (W_S)	A	B	C	D	Cost (W_S)
1	2	3	4	491	3	1	2	4	523
1	2	4	3	442	3	1	4	2	578
1	3	2	4	589 maximum	3	2	1	4	488
1	3	4	2	506	3	2	4	1	502
1	4	2	3	497	3	4	1	2	460
1	4	3	2	463	3	4	2	1	419
2	1	3	4	507	4	1	2	3	457
2	1	4	3	464	4	1	3	2	555
2	3	1	4	570	4	2	1	3	416
2	3	4	1	452	4	2	3	1	479
2	4	1	3	478	4	3	1	2	480
2	4	3	1	403 minimum	4	3	2	1	445

BRANCH AND BOUND: Gavett and Plyter propose the use of the branch and bound method to solve the quadratic assignment problem.[4] The operations are performed on the ranked cost matrix in a manner basically similar to a linear assignment problem. However, certain variations are necessary. The major steps in the process are:

1. The lower bound for all $n!$ assignments is equal to the sum of the diagonal of the ranked cost matrix.
2. The ranked cost matrix must be reduced to give zeros in at least all elements of the diagonal. This involves a provision for taking care of negative values that appear in the matrix.
3. At each point where a partial assignment is made, the corresponding cost matrix must be adjusted by placing infinity in the elements representing non-permissible partial assignments. That is, the partial assignment $\begin{matrix} A & B & C & D \\ 1 & 2 & — & — \end{matrix}$ precludes the consideration of elements labeled on the row and columns by the following pairs:

AC	BD	BC	AD	CD
24	14	14	24	24
23	34	34	23	14
				23
34	13	13	34	13

Figure 7.8 shows the steps leading to the optimum assignment for our problem.

REDUCTION TO LINEAR ASSIGNMENTS: A method of partitioning the problem into linear assignment subproblems, together with the use of branch and bound, is proposed by Gilmore[5] and Lawler.[6] The method is less direct than the previous use of branch and bound; however, it is somewhat more flexible and computationally

[4] J. W. Gavett and Norman V. Plyter, "The Optimal Assignment of Facilities to Locations by Branch and Bound," *Operations Research*, vol. 14, no. 2, March–April 1966, pp. 210–32.
[5] P. C. Gilmore, "Optimal and Suboptimal Algorithms for the Quadratic Assignment Problem," *J. Soc. for Ind. and Appl. Math.*, vol. 10, June 1962, pp. 305–13.
[6] Eugene L. Lawler, "The Quadratic Assignment Problem," *Management Science*, vol. 9, no. 4, July 1963, pp. 586–99.

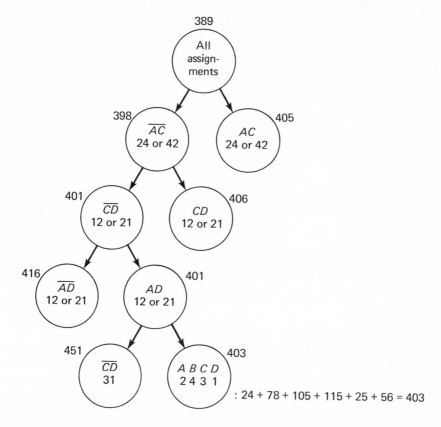

FIGURE **7.8**   Solution tree to branch and bound method using ranked C matrix.

more feasible in complicated problems. We will outline the method as follows.

We are given n facilities to be assigned to n locations, a distance matrix $A = [a(i, j)]$, and a traffic intensity matrix $B = [b(k, l)]$. The method of obtaining an optimum solution involves the following steps.

Step 1. Choose at random a partial assignment of one facility to one location, say facility $k = q$ to location $i = p$. In terms of a permutation solution matrix, we have $x(p, q) = 1$.

Step 2. Select row p of the distance matrix A. Arrange the elements of this row vector $a(p, j)$ in ascending order but starting with the element $a(p, p)$.

Step 3. Select row q of the traffic intensity matrix B. Arrange the element of the row vector $b(q, l)$ in descending order but starting with element $b(q, q)$.

Step 4. Determine the value $f(p, q) = \sum a(p, j) \cdot b(q, l)$. This dot product will result in the minimum sum for all possible cross products of the location and facility vectors if q is assigned to p. This corresponds to an assignment solution X^{pq}, where the facilities labeling the elements of one vector are assigned to the locations labeling the other vector. For example, suppose for the case $n = 4$ that the descending order of facilities is q 2 4 3 and the ascending order of locations is p b c d. Then the solution matrix is

$$X^{pq} =$$

k / i	q	2	3	4
p	1	0	0	0
b	0	1	0	0
c	0	0	0	1
d	0	0	1	0

Step 5. Repeat Steps 1 through 4 until all partial assignments of a single facility to location have been examined. That is, for all $x(i, k)$, $i = 1, 2, \ldots, n$ and $k = 1, 2, \ldots, n$. For each of the n^2 cases, an $f(i, k)$ value is determined. Now construct a matrix $F^\circ = [f(i, k)]$.

Step 6. Solve the F matrix as a linear assignment problem. Let the optimum assignment permutation solution matrix be $Z^\circ = [z(i, k)]$, $\sum_i z(i, k) = 1$, and $\sum_k z(i, k) = 1$. But now Z° corresponds to the selection of specific $f(i, k)$ values from the F° matrix. *Each* of these $f(i, k)$ values was predicated on a given assignment X^{ik} found by the minimum dot product of the facility location vectors. In order to have a feasible (acceptable) assignment, then $Z = X^{ik}$ for i, k in which $z(i, k) = 1$. If this is the case, the problem is solved according to the solution Z°. If it is not, then we continue, starting with Step 7.

Step 7. Consider structuring the problem in branch and bound. Let the initial node consist of all possible feasible assignments. The lower bound for this node is $W^\circ = Z^\circ \cdot F^\circ$. Now we branch from the initial node to each of n nodes. Each of the second stage nodes represents the commitment to a partial assignment of a single facility to a single location, such as $x(p, 1) = 1$, $x(p, 2) = 1, \ldots, x(p, n) = 1$.

Step 8. For each of the n nodes formulated in Step 7, repeat Steps 1 through 6. Assume that we select a node pq, representing the assignment of facility q to location p. Steps 1 through 6 will yield a solution matrix $Z^{pq} = z(i, k)$ for $i = 1, 2, \ldots, p - 1, p + 1, \ldots, n$ and $k = 1, 2, \ldots, q - 1, q + 1, \ldots, n$. Again, if $Z^{pq} = X^{ik}$ for i, k in which $z(i, k) = 1$, then the solution is feasible, and its lower bound can be checked with those of the other n nodes. If none of the n nodes yields a feasible solution, then further branching is required.

The calculation of the lower bound for a node pq involves the following. Suppose that we are at some stage or node where previous partial assignments have been made in the branching process. Let M be the set of locations to which assignments have been made including p. Let $\bar{M}$ be the set of unassigned locations. Then in the construction of each X^{ik} matrix at the pq node we arrange the ith row of the

A matrix in ascending order and the kth row of the B matrix in descending order *but fix* the assignments of i to k for all i in the set M. Then f^{ik} will be equal to the dot product of the two rows i and k, *plus* $\sum a(j, i) \cdot b(l, k)$; $j, l \in M$. And the lower bound on node pq is

$$W^{pq} = Z^{pq} \cdot F^{pq} + \sum a(i, j) \cdot b(k, l); \ i, j, k, l \in M$$

Again, if $Z^{pq} = X^{ik}$, then the problem is solved; otherwise, further branching will take place in the node pq for which W^{pq} is a minimum. At each subsequent level of branching, a partial assignment will be fixed and the remaining assignment determined by solving a reduced F matrix until a feasible solution is determined for which lower bound on the node is a minimum.

To demonstrate the method, we assume the following $n = 3$ problem for simplicity. The A and B matrices are

$$A = \begin{array}{c|ccc} & a & b & c \\ \hline a & x & 6 & 8 \\ b & 10 & x & 5 \\ c & 2 & 9 & x \end{array} \qquad B = \begin{array}{c|ccc} & 1 & 2 & 3 \\ \hline 1 & x & 10 & 20 \\ 2 & 5 & x & 15 \\ 3 & 8 & 5 & x \end{array}$$

where for A the rows are indexed by i and columns by j, and for B the rows are indexed by k and columns by l.

Step 1. Choose the partial assignment $x(a, 1) = 1$.

Step 2. Arrange the elements of row a in ascending order such that we have x–6–8.

Step 3. Arrange the elements in row 1 in descending order such that we have x–20–10.

Step 4. $f(a, 1) = (6)(20) + (8)(10) = 200$. This corresponds to a permutation matrix

$$X^{a1} = \begin{array}{c|ccc} & 1 & 2 & 3 \\ a & 1 & 0 & 0 \\ b & 0 & 0 & 1 \\ c & 0 & 1 & 0 \end{array}$$

Step 5. Repeating steps 1–4 for all i, k and summarizing, we have

i, k	Assignment to			$f(i, k)$
	a	b	c	
$a1$	1	3	2	200
$b1$	2	1	3	200
$c1$	3	2	1	130
$a2$	2	3	1	130
$b2$	1	2	3	125
$c2$	3	1	2	75
$a3$	3	1	2	88
$b3$	2	3	1	90
$c3$	1	2	3	61

$$F° = \begin{array}{ccc} 200 & 130 & 88 \\ 200 & 125 & 90 \\ 130 & 75 & 61 \end{array}$$

Step 6. Solving the $F°$ matrix as a linear assignment problem, we have the permutation solution matrix

$$Z° = \begin{array}{c} \\ a \\ b \\ c \end{array} \begin{array}{ccc} 1 & 2 & 3 \\ 0 & 0 & 1 \\ 0 & 1 & 0 \\ 1 & 0 & 0 \end{array} \quad \text{corresponding to a value of 343}$$

But the X^{ik} matrices corresponding to the $z(i, k) = 1$ are

$$X^{a3} = \begin{array}{ccc} 0 & 0 & 1 \\ 1 & 0 & 0 \\ 0 & 1 & 0 \end{array}; \quad X^{b2} = \begin{array}{ccc} 1 & 0 & 0 \\ 0 & 1 & 0 \\ 0 & 0 & 1 \end{array}; \quad X^{c1} = \begin{array}{ccc} 0 & 0 & 1 \\ 0 & 1 & 0 \\ 1 & 0 & 0 \end{array}$$

and, therefore, since $Z° \neq X^{a3} \neq X^{b2}$, we have not obtained a feasible solution.

Step 7. The initial node of the branch and bound is assigned a lower bound $W° = 343$. Now branch to three nodes as follows:

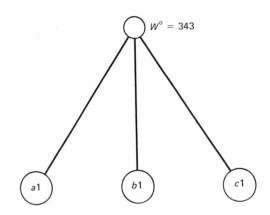

Step 8. Summarizing the remaining steps in which a lower bound is calculated for each of the n nodes, we have the following:

Node	ik	Assignment to a b c			$f(ik)$
$a1$	$b2$	1	2	3	125
	$c2$	1	3	2	145
	$b3$	1	3	2	105
	$c3$	1	2	3	61

$$F^{a1} = \begin{array}{c} \\ b \\ \\ c \end{array} \begin{array}{|c|c|} \hline \begin{array}{cc} 2 & 3 \end{array} & \\ \hline 125 & 105 \\ 60 & 120 \\ \hline 145 & 61 \\ 80 & 160 \\ \hline \end{array} \quad Z^{a1} = \begin{array}{cc} 1 & 0 \\ 0 & 1 \end{array} \text{ (feasible)}$$

$$W^{a1} = (125 + 60) + (61 + 160) = 406$$

(Note: 60 is cost of 1 in a to 2 in b, and 160 is cost of 1 in a to 3 in c)

$b1$ $a2$ 2 1 3   150

     $c2$ 3 1 2   75

     $a3$ 3 1 2   88

     $c3$ 2 1 3   82

$c1$ $a2$ 2 3 1   130

     $b2$ 3 2 1   175

     $a3$ 3 2 1   94

     $b3$ 2 3 1   90

$$F^{b1} = \begin{array}{c} \\ a \\ \\ c \\ \end{array} \begin{array}{|c|c|} \multicolumn{1}{c}{2} & \multicolumn{1}{c}{3} \\ \hline 150 & 88 \\ 100 & 200 \\ \hline 75 & 82 \\ 50 & 100 \\ \hline \end{array} \qquad Z^{b1} = \begin{array}{cc} 0 & 1 \\ 1 & 0 \end{array} \text{ (feasible)}$$

$$W^{b1} = (88 + 200) + (75 + 50) = 413$$

$$F^{c1} = \begin{array}{c} \\ a \\ \\ b \\ \end{array} \begin{array}{|c|c|} \multicolumn{1}{c}{2} & \multicolumn{1}{c}{3} \\ \hline 130 & 94 \\ 180 & 40 \\ \hline 175 & 90 \\ 90 & 20 \\ \hline \end{array} \qquad Z^{c1} = \begin{array}{cc} 0 & 1 \\ 1 & 0 \end{array} \text{ (feasible)}$$

$$W^{c1} = (94 + 40) + (175 + 90) = 399$$

Therefore, the optimal assignment is

$$Z = \begin{array}{c} \\ a \\ b \\ c \end{array} \begin{array}{ccc} 1 & 2 & 3 \\ 0 & 0 & 1 \\ 0 & 1 & 0 \\ 1 & 0 & 0 \end{array}$$

at a cost of 399. The student may try the method by referring to Problem 7.7 at the end of this chapter.

Heuristic Approaches

In some senses, the search for an optimal assignment boils down to an academic pursuit. Remember that optimal is relative only to a single criterion, namely, the minimization of handling costs, and the subsequent application of other criteria can result in changes to what was an optimal assignment, in terms of traffic costs. Then, of course, the data input, especially traffic intensities, are subject to error as estimators of future performance. In systems consisting of a large number of machines and traffic composed of a large product mix, a certain aggregation of the data is necessary to accommodate the computational requirements, or sampling may be required to efficiently collect the raw data. Finally, one might question the wisdom of seeking optimal solutions for a problem of this kind when the conditions contributing to the optimum will most likely change to some degree as time passes. New equipment, changes in product mix, alterations in method, etc., contribute to a gradual obsolescence of layouts. One can hypothesize that the rate of obsolescence is not necessarily correlated positively with the degree to which the original layout was optimal.

In any event, there may well be a payoff in using nonoptimal or heuristic problem-solving devices in the tradeoff of reduced solution costs versus the gain foregone by not obtaining an optimum solution. Suppose that we listed all 10! solution costs of a problem of size $n = 10$. We might expect a frequency distribution of the kind shown in Figure 7.9, where the costs W_S are arranged in some finite

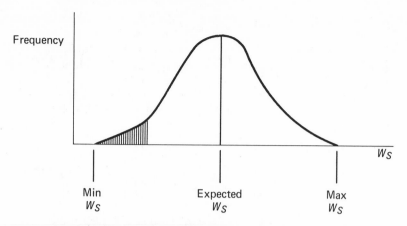

FIGURE **7.9**   Distribution of $n!$ assignment costs W_S.

set of classes. We might hope that nonoptimal methods would yield solutions lying in the shaded region of the distribution. Then the cost of applying an optimal seeking method must be weighed against the advantages gained by shifting from some solution in the shaded area to the minimum.

PAIRED TRADEOFFS: One method is to make an arbitrary initial assignment and then proceed systematically to exchange the location of one facility with every other facility. If an improvement results, the improved assignment will be used for a similar tradeoff and the process continued until no further improvement takes place. For example, suppose in our case that we start out with the assignment $\begin{bmatrix} A & B & C & D \\ 2 & 3 & 4 & 1 \end{bmatrix}$.

Tradeoff 2

$\begin{bmatrix} A & B & C & D \\ 2 & 3 & 4 & 1 \end{bmatrix}$ 452

3	2	4	1	502
4	3	2	1	445
1	3	4	2	506

Tradeoff 4

$\begin{bmatrix} A & B & C & D \\ 4 & 3 & 2 & 1 \end{bmatrix}$ 445

3	4	2	1	419
2	3	4	1	452
1	3	2	4	589

Tradeoff 3

$\begin{bmatrix} A & B & C & D \\ 3 & 4 & 2 & 1 \end{bmatrix}$ 419

4	3	2	1	445
2	4	3	1	403
1	4	2	3	497

Tradeoff 2

$\begin{bmatrix} A & B & C & D \\ 2 & 4 & 3 & 1 \end{bmatrix}$ 403

4	2	3	1	479
3	4	2	1	419
1	4	3	2	463

In this case, we arrive at the optimum, but there is no guarantee that this would happen with larger problems.

CRAFT: An ambitious computer program to deal with the plant layout problems was proposed by Armour and Buffa in 1963.[7] This program has been labeled

---

[7] Gordon C. Armour and Elwood S. Buffa, "A Heuristic Algorithm and Simulation Approach to Relative Location of Facilities," *Management Science*, vol. 9, no. 2, January 1963, pp. 294–309.

CRAFT (Computerized Relative Allocation of Facilities Technique). Their method is based on minimizing material-handling costs using a variation of the paired tradeoff heuristic method. The program accepts variable area requirements for the facilities and prints out an actual format of the layout for alternative assignments. The method has been applied to several situations in both manufacturing and service systems with claims for significant savings over actual or proposed layouts. We may expect that the CRAFT program will be the precursor to a variety of computer programs, which will find increasing use in industry for assisting in layout decisions.

Multiple Criteria

The numerical methods we have discussed are useful in providing a first-order approximation for the relative location of facilities. But this does not necessarily constitute the major portion of the layout function. Furthermore, these methods are based solely on the single criterion of minimizing material flow costs for either one or a variety of handling methods.

FIXED COSTS: In the quadratic case, we have considered only the traffic costs between facilities. We may add to the problem a fixed cost of locating the kth facility to the ith location. Thus, a linear cost $c(i, k)$ represents the undesirability of locating facility k in location i. Such a cost can represent one or more factors, such as cost of accommodating the facility with utilities, imputed costs of potential hazards, etc. A given facility may be "forced" into a given location by attaching a high fixed cost to all other location possibilities.

This fixed cost can be integrated into the methods of solving the quadratic problem, and the quadratic problem becomes

$$\text{minimize } W_t = \sum_{ij} \sum_{kl} c(ij, kl) + \sum_{ik} c(i, k)$$

WEIGHTED FACTORS: Reis and Andersen[8] express concern over the possible neglect of important factors that would not normally be included in the measures of distance and traffic intensity. For example, a product that has a relatively long expected sales life should be given more weight than one that may be obsolete within the near future in the calculation of traffic intensity. Or, short travel distances should be required for a part because of its properties after leaving a given operation (e.g., it assumes a fragile state, is radioactive, is eminently needed at the next operation, etc.). They propose that each product be evaluated in terms of such criteria and assigned an importance factor, which is a multiplier equal to or greater than 1, to be applied to the normal traffic intensity measure. Thus, for example, if product x constitutes a move of material between facilities 4 and 5 and this move should be short, for one of the reasons cited, then it might be assigned an importance factor of 1.5 by which its normal volume of flow is multiplied.

---

[8] Irvin L. Reis and Glenn E. Andersen, "Relative Importance Factors in Layout Analysis," *J. Ind. Eng.*, vol. XI, no. 4, July–August 1960, pp. 312–16.

Distances between locations can be similarly adjusted. For example, we might consider a general flow shop pattern and then weight or magnify any distance running counter to this flow with a multiplier. This would require an asymmetrical distance matrix. In cases of large product mixes, the use of multiple criteria expands the data collection problem, and it would appear to be most efficient to apply in cases where importance factors are applied to a limited number of the products.

FLEXIBILITY: Since the variables affecting the efficiency of assignments are constantly changing over time, a given layout must be evaluated in terms of the ease with which it can be altered to accommodate changes.

One of the values of computerized quantitative methods is to evaluate alternative uses of a given assignment and to determine the potential savings that can be gained at any point in time by making changes in the layout. Such savings can be compared with the investments required to redesign the system or to make new assignments.

FIGURE **7.10** Template layout for a given shop. Courtesy of the Halliburton Company.

DETAILED LAYOUT: The final stage in layout design involves the exact location of each machine, piece of equipment, work and storage area, service or utility system, and aisle space. This is usually facilitated with the use of either two- or three-dimensional, scaled models or templates to represent each facility.

Figure 7.10 shows a template layout for a given shop. The models are three-dimensional and permit the analyst to verify the areas needed for aisle space, work-in-process storage, and manipulation and handling of materials between and at the workplaces, as well as the format of the facilities. This model also permits the many persons in the organization who are concerned with the layout to evaluate the system personally and make suggestions for improvements in its various details. This applies particularly to the line-operating personnel, such as foremen and supervisors, whose intimate knowledge of the operating areas is important in the evaluation of the detailed layout.

LOCATION OF ECONOMIC ACTIVITIES

In the assignment of facilities to locations, we confined the discussion to locating facilities within a given plant. Now we extend the discussion to the location of plants or other activities within some geographically constrained area, such as a city, county, or other region. In this case, the location problem has a more strategic character with long-term implications. The subject has classically been labeled "plant location," but we wish to generalize it to any type of economic activity that is to be fixed in location.

The treatment of the problem involves the examination of alternative locations within a region in terms of total and long-range costs of construction and operations. Since the commitment to a regional location is an initial design problem, most of the construction and operating costs can be influenced by location. Therefore, a major part of the analysis of the problem includes compiling an exhaustive list of these costs and their valuation for each alternative location.

Sometimes there are certain critical costs or factors that imply or define the kind of location desired. Thus, a cheap source of power is required for aluminum production, low labor costs for textile manufacture, a regional market for paper box production, or a pure water source for a brewery. First-order location choice is sometimes governed, therefore, by the availability of a critical input resource or market. On the other hand, where there is no single critical factor, the initial choice is less obvious, and a more exhaustive preliminary examination of all costs is necessary.

Regional Factors

Location criteria can be broadly classified into regional costs and distance-oriented costs. Regional costs are those which are peculiar to the regional location without explicit regard for costs generated by the transportation of inputs and outputs of the activity. Regional costs include wage levels, the kinds and stability of labor sources, regional taxes, construction costs, the availability of land and space for expansion, employee living conditions, etc.

The analysis of regional factors is a major portion of activity location studies, particularly where a location in a state- or country-wide region is to be chosen. Information is readily available from a variety of sources, such as chambers of commerce, railroads, and government agencies. Survey methods that spell out in detail the factors to be considered are well documented.[9] However, wherever possible, each factor must be evaluated in monetary terms or otherwise weighted.

Minimizing Transportation Costs

In some cases, the costs of transporting raw materials or other inputs to an activity and shipping its outputs are a substantial portion of the set of relevant location costs. Either they are the determining factor in locating an activity, or, if a region has otherwise been chosen, they subsequently determine the more exact location within a given region.

In transportation-oriented location problems, there is usually a discrete set of *destinations*, which are serviced by a second set of *sources*, and both sets are fixed in location. Either set, but not both, may be a null set. We then wish to add to either set (or possibly both) one or more additional elements (facilities or activities). There can be flow of material from sources to destinations, or vice versa, or in both directions. In the following discussion, we will use the term *source* to imply the subset of activities to be located and the term *destinations* to imply the recipients of flow from the source or originators of flow to the source.

While we assume that both the sources and destinations ultimately have fixed locations, we might note that certain location problems involve probabilistic locations for destinations, such as in a problem of locating fire stations or a dairy processing plant. In these cases, we may make statements about the general locale of destinations (fires) or temporary locations (customers).

Various quantitative approaches have been suggested for optimizing the location of an activity in terms of minimizing the total costs of transporting materials in the source-destination system. Just as in the case of plant layout, a model will provide a first-order location choice. But the final and exact location choice can depend on criteria other than transport costs. For example, suppose that we find an optimum location for a municipal refuse disposal incinerator, which minimizes the costs of transporting refuse from the collection points (destinations) to the incinerator (source). The exact location may subsequently be influenced by objections from neighborhood residents, proximity to main travel arteries, availability of space for ash disposal, etc.

The kinds of models considered in plant layout are applicable to locating economic activities. However, in the case of the activity location problem, we usually deal with the problem of locating a small number of facilities in a system of pre-

---

[9] For example, see Leonard C. Yassen, *Plant Location.* New York: American Research Council, 1958.

determined locations for a larger number of remaining facilities. Also, the traffic between facilities depends on their location, rather than being independent of it, as in the case of the previous assignment problems. Therefore, the following methods dwell on the joint issue of allocating flow between sources and destinations and locating a limited number of activities in the system.

LINEAR DISTANCE COSTS: In the following discussion, we will make the initial assumption that transportation costs are a linear function of the distance between points and the volume to be moved. While this is not so in many practical cases, it permits an easier entry into the subject.

CASE PROBLEM 7.1   The Delta County Power and Light Company services a three-county area. The company wishes to determine the *number* and *location* of service centers, which will house trucks, maintenance shops, parts inventories, and supervision. For each service center, trucks will be dispatched at the beginning of the day to serve some area of the county and return at the end of the day to the center. The main volume of their work is concentrated in six towns. The initial problem is to choose between having one or two centers and their approximate locations. The major criterion for location will be the minimization of transportation costs.

To begin, we might note that there are two problems in attempting to locate one or more sources. The first is to *allocate* destinations to sources, in our case the communities to the service centers, assuming that a destination will be serviced by one and only one source. Allocation specifies which source will serve each destination. Once the allocation has been specified, the problem is to determine the location of each source relative to its allocated destinations. The total transportation cost is a function of both the allocation and location decisions.

ALLOCATIONS: The problem of allocation is, of course, relevant only when there is more than one source. Suppose in our case that there are to be two service centers (1 and 2) and six communities (a, b, c, d, e, f). There are a total of 31 possible allocations to a source. That is, for n destinations and m sources, the number of possible allocations to a given source is

$$A(n, m) = \frac{1}{m!} \sum_{k=0}^{k=m} \frac{m!}{k!(m-k)!} (-1)^k (m-k)^n$$

For example, one possible allocation is communities a, b, and c to center 1 and the remaining to center 2. For each possible allocation there is an optimum location for the source. A global optimum is the allocation giving the least cost location for the sources.

We will assume that the capacity of the sources will be designed to meet the demands of the allocated destinations. Therefore, each destination will be served by only one source.

Continuum of Locations

Within some constrained geographic region, sources can be assigned positions in a continuum of locations, or they can be assigned positions in a set of discrete alternative locations. We will consider the continuum case first.

CARTESIAN COORDINATES: One approach is to bound the region of destinations by orthogonal axes and assign positions in terms of cartesian coordinates as proposed by Cooper.[10] Let

$x_i, y_i =$ location of the ith destination (community) in terms of cartesian coordinates; $i = 1, 2, \ldots, n$

$x_j, y_j =$ location of the jth source (service center) in terms of cartesian coordinates; $j = 1, 2, \ldots, m$

$a_{ij} =$ an allocation index; $a_{ij} = \begin{cases} 1 & \text{if destination } i \text{ is served by source } j \\ 0 & \text{otherwise} \end{cases}$

$w_{ij} =$ a measure of traffic intensity between destination i and source j (e.g., number of trips per year, weighted cost per mile, etc.).

For a given set of a_{ij}'s (i.e., for a given allocation), the objective is to minimize the total transportation costs Z_t for some time period t. The first issue is to decide how distance is to be measured. One way is to consider the Euclidean distance so that we have

$$Z_t = \sum_{j=1}^{m} \sum_{i=1}^{n} a_{ij} w_{ij} \left(\sqrt{(x_i - x_j)^2 + (y_i - y_j)^2} \right) \tag{1}$$

We differentiate this function and set it equal to zero to find the minimum Z_t. Thus,

$$\frac{\partial Z_t}{\partial x_j} = 0 = \sum_{i=1}^{n} a_{ij} w_{ij} (x_i - x_j) / [(x_i - x_j)^2 + (y_i - y_j)^2]^{1/2}$$

$$\frac{\partial Z_t}{\partial y_j} = 0 = \sum_{i=1}^{n} a_{ij} w_{ij} (y_i - y_j) / [(x_i - x_j)^2 + (y_i - y_j)^2]^{1/2} \tag{2}$$

$$j = 1, 2, \ldots, m$$

These two equations are solved simultaneously m times to find the x_j, y_j values.

Cooper shows that the conditions for a minimum are satisfied for these equations and proposes a method of iteration for their solution on a digital computer, which is feasible for values of $n \leq 10$.

A QUADRATIC APPROXIMATION: McHose[11] suggests that the computational difficulties of the linear model can be overcome by a quadratic approximation of the linear case. He formulates a second-degree cost function as follows for $m = 1$:

$$Z'_t = \sum_{i=1}^{n} w_i^2 \left[\sqrt{(x_i - x_j)^2 + (y_i - y_j)^2} \right]^2$$

Taking the partial derivative with respect to x, we obtain

$$\frac{\partial Z'_t}{\partial x_j} = \sum_{i=1}^{n} w_i^2 2(x_i - x_j) = 0$$

$$2x_j \sum_{i=1}^{n} w_i^2 = 2 \sum w_i^2 x_i$$

[10] Leon Cooper, "Location–Allocation Problems," *Operations Research*, vol. 11, no. 3, May–June 1963.
[11] Andre H. McHose, "A Quadratic Formulation of the Activity Location Problem," *J. Ind. Eng.*, vol. XII, no. 5, September–October 1961, pp. 334–37.

Therefore,

$$x_j = \frac{\sum\limits_{i=1}^{n} w_i^2 x_i}{\sum\limits_{i=1}^{n} w_i^2} \qquad (3)$$

and, similarly,

$$y_j = \frac{\sum\limits_{i=1}^{n} w_i^2 y_i}{\sum\limits_{i=1}^{n} w_i^2} \qquad (4)$$

McHose tested the method in three trials in which he generated a random set of fixed locations (x_i, y_i values) and random weights (w_i). In all three cases, he compared the Z_t value using the quadratic generated cartesian points with the Z_t value using the cartesian points found by the Cooper formula. The latter points were found by graphical exploration of cartesian points in the area of the quadratic solution. In all three trials, the percentage difference between the two values of Z_t was less than one percent, and his conclusion was that the second-degree function is a good first approximation to the first-degree function.

EXAMPLE 7.2   Figure 7.11 shows the locations of the six communities for the Delta County Power Company. Two points, namely, p_2 and p_6, are dummy locations for which there is no traffic flow. We can assume that they represent intersections of major highways in the area. To the right are the coordinates of each destination and the index of traffic flow to and from the destination. The question is, where should two

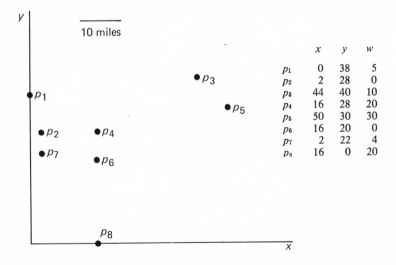

	x	y	w
p_1	0	38	5
p_2	2	28	0
p_3	44	40	10
p_4	16	28	20
p_5	50	30	30
p_6	16	20	0
p_7	2	22	4
p_8	16	0	20

FIGURE **7.11**   Location of destinations.

service centers be located? First, we will make the arbitrary allocation of destinations p_1, p_6, p_7, p_8 to service center 1 and p_3 and p_5 to service center 2. Using Equations (3) and (4), we find that service center 1 should be located at $x = 15.3$, $y = 14.9$ and center 2 at $x = 49.4$, $y = 31.0$.

Discrete Locations

A second approach is to represent destinations as nodes in a network of transportation links, such as highways, railroads, or air routes. Figure 7.12 represents the major highways linking the six communities to be serviced by Delta County Power and Light. There are eight nodes, six representing the communities (dark) and two representing major highway intersections, which are potential locations for the service centers. The distance for a link connecting two nodes is also indicated.

In this case, we are given a set P of n nodes, $p_1, \ldots, p_n$. Each pair of nodes has an associated shortest route d_{ij} between nodes i and j. These can be summarized in a non-negative n-dimensional symmetric distance matrix $\mathbf{D} = (D_{ij})$. For m sources, $p_{x_1}, \ldots, p_{x_m}$, we wish to find an associated partition of P into m subsets of nodes (allocations), $P_{x_1}, \ldots, P_{x_m}$ served respectively by the m sources such that

$$Z = \sum_{i=1}^{m} \sum_{p_i \in P_{xi}} D_{x_{i,i}} w_j = \text{minimum}$$

where w_j is the traffic intensity to (or from) node j.

Three problems must be dealt with. The first is the determination of the shortest route between node pairs. The second and third are the allocation of nodes to the

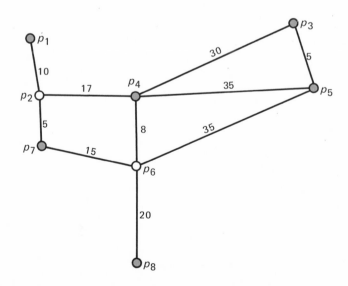

FIGURE **7.12** Highway network and nodes.

m sources and the optimum location of the sources, respectively. Note that a source p_{x_i} will be located at one of the discrete location nodes of the set P_{x_i}.

The first problem is a matter of determining the shortest route through a network of links connecting node pairs. For example, in Figure 7.12, there are two possible routes between nodes p_6 and p_1, namely, through nodes 6–4–2–1 or 6–7–2–1. An algorithm for determining the shortest route between two nodes in a network has been developed by Bellman,[12] and the method is discussed on page 90, Chapter 3.

Maranzana[13] introduces an algorithm for solving this kind of problem. The basic idea is as follows. An arbitrary selection of source nodes is made. The set of all nodes is then partitioned into subsets to be served by the sources. This is done by assigning each node to its nearest source. Then the "center of gravity" of each partitioned set is determined, and the original sources are replaced by these points. The process is repeated until the source points do not change. More specifically, the steps of the algorithm are as follows:

Step 1. Arbitrarily select m distinct points in P and assign them to the array p_{x_i}.

Step 2. Determine a partition of P into the subsets $P_{x_1}, \ldots, P_{x_m}$ by putting $P_{x_i} = (p_k; D_{k,x_i} < D_{k,x_j} \text{ for all } j)$. That is, each point is assigned to the nearest node.

Step 3. Determine the center of gravity for each P_{x_i}. The center of gravity is a point p_j if

$$\sum_{p_k \in Px_i} D_{j,k} w_k \leq \sum_{p_k \in Px_i} D_{i,k} w_k \qquad \text{for all } i$$

This is to say that the sum of the weighted distances between a point j and all other points in the subset is a minimum.

Step 4. If the center of gravity p_j is equal to p_{x_i} for all i, then the problem is solved, and the current values of the sources p_{x_i} and the allocations P_{x_i} constitute the desired solution. Otherwise, the centers of gravity represent the new source locations, and the steps are repeated, starting with Step 2. Note that if a point is equidistant from two sources, we will assign it arbitrarily to the source with the lower subscript i.

We can test the method using the information shown in Figure 7.12 for the Delta Company. A distance matrix is constructed and shown in Figure 7.13 along with a vector of weights, which are a measure of the intensity of the annual travel to each node. Suppose we wish to determine the location and allocations for two service centers.

Trial

1. Arbitrarily assign the two sources to points 4 and 6.
2. Partition the eight nodes into two sets such that each node is allocated to the nearest source. This will give

$$P_{x_4} = \{1, 2, 3, 4, 5\}$$
$$P_{x_6} = \{6, 7, 8\}$$

---

[12] R. Bellman, "On a Routing Problem," *Quart. Appl. Math.*, vol. XVI, no. 1, 1958.
[13] F. E. Maranzana, "On the Location of Supply Points to Minimize Transport Costs," *Operational Research Quart.*, vol. 15, 1964, pp. 261–70.

p_i \ p_j	1	2	3	4	5	6	7	8	w_i
1	0	10	57	27	62	30	15	50	5
2	10	0	47	17	52	20	5	40	0
3	57	47	0	30	5	38	52	58	10
4	27	17	30	0	35	8	22	28	20
5	62	52	5	35	0	35	50	55	30
6	30	20	38	8	35	0	15	20	0
7	15	5	52	22	50	15	0	35	4
8	50	40	58	28	55	20	35	0	20

FIGURE **7.13** Distance matrix D and weights w_1.

3. Find the center of gravity for each of the two sets. The calculations are

$$\text{Set } P_{x_4} \begin{cases} p_j \\ 1 & 0 \times 5 + 10 \times 0 + 57 \times 10 + 27 \times 20 + 62 \times 30 = 2{,}970 \\ 2 & 10 \times 5 + 0 \times 0 + 47 \times 10 + 17 \times 20 + 52 \times 30 = 2{,}420 \\ 3 & 57 \times 5 + 47 \times 0 + 0 \times 10 + 30 \times 20 + 5 \times 30 = 1{,}035 \text{ minimum} \\ 4 & 27 \times 5 + 17 \times 0 + 30 \times 10 + 0 \times 20 + 35 \times 30 = 1{,}485 \\ 5 & 62 \times 5 + 52 \times 0 + 5 \times 10 + 35 \times 20 + 0 \times 30 = 1{,}060 \end{cases}$$

$$P_{x_6} \begin{cases} 6 & 0 \times 0 + 15 \times 4 + 20 \times 20 = 460 \\ 7 & 15 \times 0 + 0 \times 4 + 35 \times 20 = 700 \\ 8 & 20 \times 0 + 35 \times 4 + 0 \times 20 = 140 \text{ minimum} \end{cases}$$

4. Reassign the two sources to points 3 and 8. The reallocation of nodes will now be

$$P_{x_3} = \{3, 5\}$$
$$P_{x_8} = \{1, 2, 4, 6, 7, 8\}$$

5. The centers of gravity of the sets P_{x_3} and P_{x_8} will be points 5 and 6, respectively.
6. Reassign the two sources to points 5 and 6. The reallocation of nodes will now be

$$P_{x_5} = \{3, 5\}$$
$$P_{x_6} = \{1, 2, 4, 6, 7, 8\}$$

Since this is the same allocation as (4), the method has converged to a solution which is to locate the service centers at nodes 5 and 6 with the allocations as shown above.

Maranzana conducted several tests, including a problem involving 40 nodes and three sources. The computational time using an IBM 704 computer was approximately one minute for that case.

We might briefly compare the continuous and discrete methods. From the point of view of raw data collection, the continuous method appears to be simpler. While a map needs to be translated into a grid for establishing cartesian points, the distances are implicit in the solution as straight lines with some loss of accuracy. In the discrete method, the formulation of the more exact distances between nodes in the network requires a good deal of preliminary map analysis, especially if the number of nodes is large. However, this results in more accurate transportation values. The distances may be expressed in terms of cost or time and related directly to transportation methods and route characteristics. We might expect the discrete method to be particularly useful for locating sources in a local region of destinations, such as a city or county where the local route conditions are familiar. Finally, the method must be related to the reasons for wanting to reduce transportation in the system. Presumably, a reduction in transportation can lead to 1) lower direct costs of travel (shipping charges, vehicle operating costs); 2) reduced investment in equipment (number of trucks); 3) faster service (fire stations, utility service centers); 4) increased capacity for fixed investment in equipment (retail delivery fleets in an expanding market); 5) reduction in direct labor (truck drivers).

Distribution Systems

Location problems are classically exemplified in the problem of planning factory-warehouse-consumer distribution systems. For companies producing a line of consumer goods in more than one factory and serving a nation-wide market, the kinds of questions that must be answered are:

How many warehouses of specific capacity are needed, and where should they be located?

If additional producing capacity is needed, where should it be located to augment existing capacity?

How should the output of factories be allocated to warehouses to minimize total cost?

These questions can be answered in a number of ways, including by the methods previously described. The techniques depend on the assumptions made, the complexity of the problem, and particularly the degree of detail and refinement desired in the answers.

A major consideration in these problems is the constraints on the capacities of both warehouses and factories. Therefore, the allocation of factory outputs to warehouses and then to customers must be considered in a model. Also, there is a multileveled distribution system, rather than simply one set of sources and destinations.

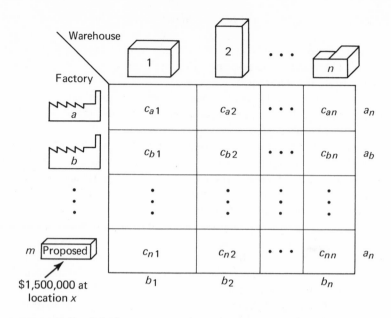

FIGURE **7.14**   Trial investment and location for factory distribution linear program.

LINEAR PROGRAMING: The distribution method of linear programing is a logical means for structuring and solving location problems. The method generally assumes a fixed number of sources of limited capacity from which the output is to be distributed to a fixed number of destinations, each with known input requirements. However, we can envision a problem in which it is desired to locate one or more new factories in an existing distribution system of factories and warehouses. The model would be used in a reiterative manner. Each reiteration would represent trial locations for the new factories. Also, different factory capacities can be tested in terms of a tradeoff between investment costs and transportation costs (Figure 7.14).

A somewhat more direct method is adding a fixed cost component to the linear cost in each cell of the distribution matrix. This fixed cost is incurred only if there is a shipment between the source and destination labeling the cell. A number of optimal and nonoptimal methods have been suggested for handling this situation.[14]

The use of the distribution linear programing model provides an optimum allocation of factory output for each location-investment trial. A global solution depends on the number of trials made for various investment-location alternatives. Presumably, each set of trials is for one class of product. Therefore, the final results for the product classes must be aggregated and checked to see that total factory warehouse capacities are not violated.

---

[14] See footnotes 3 and 4, page 73.

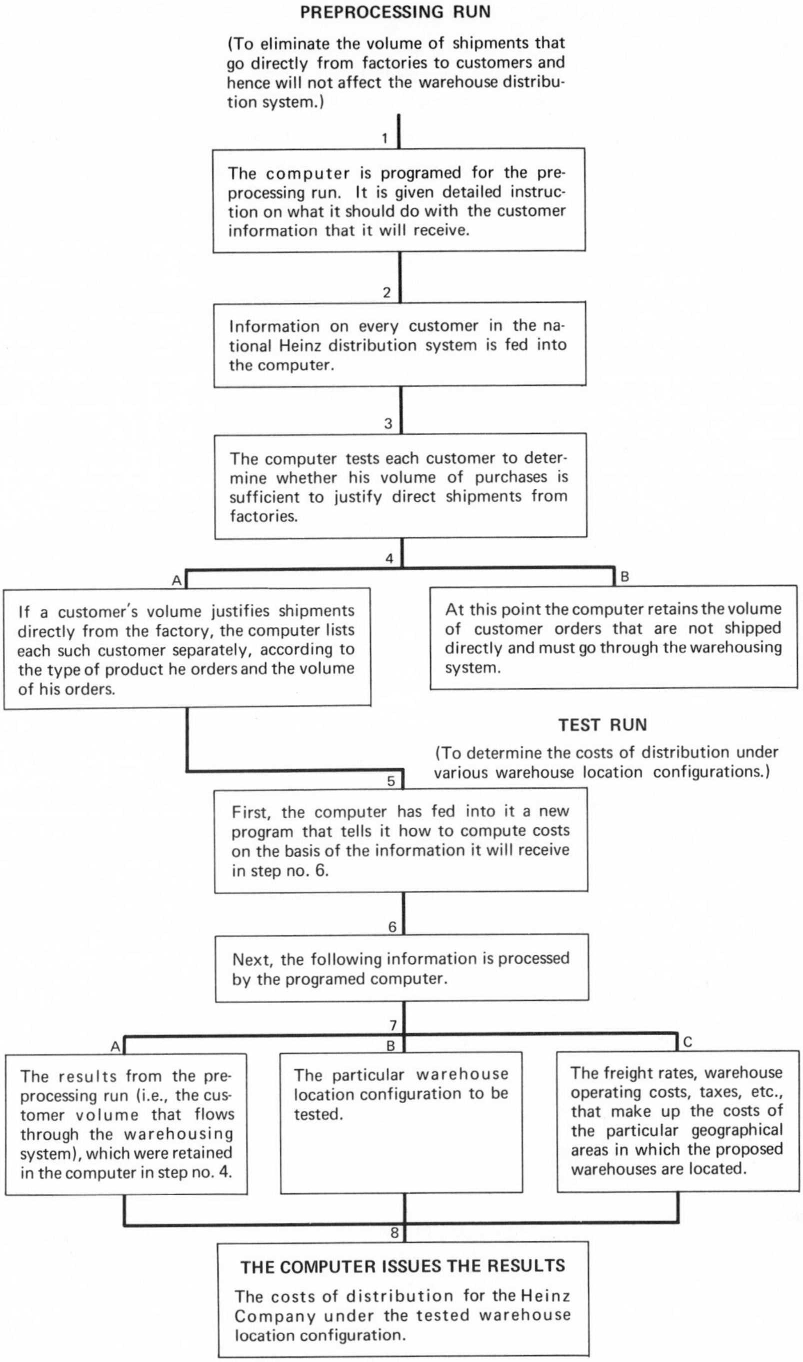

PREPROCESSING RUN

(To eliminate the volume of shipments that go directly from factories to customers and hence will not affect the warehouse distribution system.)

1

The computer is programed for the preprocessing run. It is given detailed instruction on what it should do with the customer information that it will receive.

2

Information on every customer in the national Heinz distribution system is fed into the computer.

3

The computer tests each customer to determine whether his volume of purchases is sufficient to justify direct shipments from factories.

4

A If a customer's volume justifies shipments directly from the factory, the computer lists each such customer separately, according to the type of product he orders and the volume of his orders.

B At this point the computer retains the volume of customer orders that are not shipped directly and must go through the warehousing system.

TEST RUN

(To determine the costs of distribution under various warehouse location configurations.)

5

First, the computer has fed into it a new program that tells it how to compute costs on the basis of the information it will receive in step no. 6.

6

Next, the following information is processed by the programed computer.

7

A The results from the preprocessing run (i.e., the customer volume that flows through the warehousing system), which were retained in the computer in step no. 4.

B The particular warehouse location configuration to be tested.

C The freight rates, warehouse operating costs, taxes, etc., that make up the costs of the particular geographical areas in which the proposed warehouses are located.

8

THE COMPUTER ISSUES THE RESULTS

The costs of distribution for the Heinz Company under the tested warehouse location configuration.

FIGURE **7.15** How the simulation tests a particular warehouse configuration. From H. N. Shycon and R. B. Maffei, *Harvard Business Rev.*, November–December 1960. Adaption of Exhibit IV.

SIMULATION: A variety of computerized approaches have been taken to solve the warehouse location problem.[15,16] Both optimal and heuristic methods are useful to the extent that they do not mask important or critical detail. For example, product variety, differences in consumer demand patterns, detail in transportation method, and costs can be obscured by using gross demand and transportation figures.

In order to accommodate the detailed variety existing in a distribution system, a computer simulator has been used by Shycon and Maffei in locating warehouses for a food processor.[17] The function of the simulator is to determine the economical allocation of customers to warehouses and to determine the costs of operating the entire factory-warehouse-consumer system, providing enough detail by product, by area, by warehouse, and by customer-type to evaluate cost and profitability. Figure 7.15 shows the basic features of the program for testing a particular warehouse configuration.

Problems

7.1   The city of Deerfield has been hit by a severe snowstorm. The problem is to get the city plowed out as soon as possible. The city is divided into five areas. Each area received a different amount of snow due to the differences in exposure to wind, kinds of streets, street congestion, etc. There are five pieces of snow removal equipment—two truck plows, a road grader plow, a large bulldozer with a V-plow, and a large payloader with a special plow blade. The matrix below is an assessment of the time (hours) it would take each type of equipment to service each area. Make an initial assignment of vehicles to areas, assuming each vehicle can serve only one area and each area can be served by only one vehicle. After your first assignment, consider how you would reschedule the vehicles when they are through with their tasks, assuming other areas are not yet plowed out.

Vehicles	I	II	Area III	IV	V
Truck A	8	32	24	17	50
Truck B	12	42	32	23	60
Grader C	10	30	15	9	30
Dozer D	50	60	10	11	15
Payload E	24	40	50	16	17

7.2   The city of Fanwood has just purchased two new pumpers for the fire department. The engines are assigned to two of the downtown stations. This has necessitated a reassignment of six remaining engines to six remaining stations. The engines are:

---

[15] S. Eilon and D. P. Deziel, "Setting a Distribution Centre, An Analogue Computer Application," *Management Science*, vol. 12, no. 6, February 1966, B245–54.

[16] A. A. Kuehn and M. J. Hamburger, "A Heuristic Program for Locating Warehouses," *Management Science*, vol. 9, no. 4, July 1963, pp. 643–66.

[17] H. N. Shycon and R. B. Maffei, "Simulation—Tool for Better Distribution," *Harvard Business Rev.*, vol. 38, no. 6, November–December 1960, pp. 65–75.

Year purchased	Capacity (gals per min)
(1) 1948	1,500
(2) 1966	1,250
(3) 1960	1,000
(4) 1956	750
(5) 1940	750
(6) 1961	500

The fire chief and three commissioners prepare a rating scale for the assignment of the six engines to the six stations. Each assignment is rated on a scale of 0 to 10, and the priority is in proportion to the rating. Factors considered are the age of the engine, speed, capacity, appearance for political reasons, etc. The stations are located in six areas described as follows:

Location	Description
A	mid-downtown, commercial area
B	inner city, low-rent housing, small commercial and industrial
C	same as B
D	high-rent suburban, where most of the influential politicians live
E	low-rent suburban and small commercial, large territory
F	low-rent suburban housing and large industrial concentration

The rating has been converted into an assignment "cost" matrix as follows.

Engine	Station					
	A	B	C	D	E	F
1	2	3	3	1	0	10
2	8	1	2	7	0	5
3	5	8	8	2	0	8
4	4	7	5	1	5	4
5	2	9	10	0	3	5
6	0	2	1	7	5	0

Choose an assignment that maximizes the value of the assignment.

7.3   The Ahrens Air Tool Company is moving its shop operations to a new location. The company uses a job shop format to make thousands of parts for a large line of powered hand tools. Since a completely new layout is to be made, traffic-intensity data are required. Discuss alternative methods and potential problems of obtaining the data necessary for such a matrix.

7.4   In this chapter, we have emphasized the use of quantitative techniques for minimizing traffic costs in a process layout. How can we integrate into these methods a qualitative consideration of nontraffic factors, such as desirability or undesirability of locating a pair of facilities next to each other for reasons of supervision, economics of utility servicing, replacement of equipment, etc.?

7.5   The following is a traffic intensity matrix for seven facilities. Traffic intensity in this case is an index of the number of trips between facility pairs. Suppose that the general format of locations is as follows:

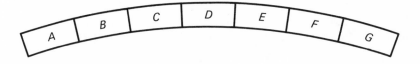

Use the linear assignment technique to determine the relative location of the facilities. (Hint: Convert the matrix into a symmetrical matrix.)

To From	1	2	3	4	5	6	7
1	0	9	54	42	1	80	6
2		0	0	0	0	58	45
3			0	6	33	56	7
4				0	9	69	1
5					0	0	0
6						0	10
7							0

7.6   Let $X = [x(i, k)]$ be a permutation solution matrix to a facilities assignment problem:

i/k	1	2	3	4
1	0	0	0	1
X = 2	1	0	0	0
3	0	1	0	0
4	0	0	1	0

Show that the assignment cost Z for this permutation is $Z = B \cdot (X^1AX)$, where A and B are the location and traffic intensity matrices, respectively.

7.7   A chemical company has four interrelated processes that it wishes to locate. There are four possible locations. To each location will be assigned only one process. The problem is to minimize the cost of piping between the processes. Let $a(i, j)$ = index of distance between location i and j.

$$A = [a(i, j)] =$$

i \ j	A	B	C	D
A	2	1	3	4
B	1	3	6	2
C	3	6	5	4
D	4	2	4	8

Let $b(k, l)$ = index of pipe cost per foot between facilities k and l.

k \ l	1	2	3	4
1	0	20	30	40
2	10	0	40	50
3	30	10	0	40
4	50	30	5	0

Minimize the cost of piping by using the methods of reduction to linear assignment and branch and bound.

7.8   The following are cartesian coordinates for fifteen communities in a three-county area. Certain of the communities are reception centers for farm produce in the area. We wish to determine the location of a food-processing factory that will minimize the costs of transporting the produce from reception centers to the factory.

Community	Index of quantity to be shipped	Coordinates (miles)	
		x	y
1	20	0.0	10.0
2	9	13.0	0.0
3	10	20.0	1.0
4	5	10.0	44.0
5	8	28.0	27.0
6	18	35.0	52.0
7	3	42.0	39.0
8	15	40.0	21.0
9	20	51.0	2.0
10	10	65.0	25.0
11	7	60.0	60.0
12	15	90.0	32.0
13	0	10.0	20.0
14	0	45.0	45.0
15	2	80.0	10.0

The direct distances between community pairs is indicated in the following matrix. These are actual mileages.

	1	2	3	4	5	6	7	8	9	10	11	12	13	14	15
1	1														
2	15	2													
3	—	10	3												
4	41	—	—	4											
5	—	—	39	28	5										
6	—	—	—	31	29	6									
7	—	—	—	—	16	15	7								
8	—	—	40	—	15	—	25	8							
9	—	—	31	—	—	—	—	31	9						
10	—	—	—	—	—	—	35	24	39	10					
11	—	—	—	—	—	—	28	—	—	26	11				
12	—	—	—	—	—	—	—	—	—	30	40	12			
13	13	25	—	—	17	—	—	—	—	—	—	—	13		
14	—	—	—	—	—	17	11	—	—	—	16	—	—	14	
15	—	—	—	—	—	—	—	—	32	30	—	36	—	—	15

Bibliography

Assignment Locations:

APPLE, JAMES M., *Plant Layout and Materials Handling*, 2nd ed. New York: Ronald Press, 1963.

BUFFA, E. S., G. C. ARMOUR, and T. E. VOLLMANN, "Allocating Facilities with CRAFT," *Harvard Business Rev.*, March–April 1964.

CONWAY, R. W., and W. L. MAXWELL, "A Note on the Assignment of Facility Location," *J. Ind. Eng.*, January–February 1961.

HILLIER, FREDERICK S., "Quantitative Tools for Plant Layout," *J. Ind. Eng.*, January–February 1963.

HILLIER, FREDERICK S., and MICHAEL M. CONNORS, "Quadratic Assignment Problem Algorithms and the Location of Indivisible Facilities," *Management Science*, September 1966.

IRESON, WILLIAM G., *Factory Planning and Plant Layout*. Englewood Cliffs, N.J.: Prentice-Hall, Inc., 1951.

LAND, A. H., and A. G. DOIG, "An Automatic Method of Solving Discrete Programming Problems," *Econometrica*, vol. 28, 1960.

LEE, ROBERT C., and JAMES M. MOORE, "CORELAP—COmputerized RElationship LAyout Planning," *J. Ind. Eng.*, March 1967.

LITTLE, J. D. C., K. G. MURTY, D. W. SWEENEY, and C. KAREL, "An Algorithm for Traveling Salesman Problem," *Operations Research*, November–December 1963.

MOORE, JAMES M., *Plant Layout and Design*. New York: The Macmillan Company, 1962.

MUTHER, RICHARD, *Systematic Layout Planning*. Boston, Mass.: Industrial Education Institute, 1961.

SCHNEIDER, MARSHALL, "Cross Charting Technique as a Basis for Plant Layout," *J. Ind. Eng.*, November–December 1960.

STEINBERG, L., "The Backboard Wiring Problem: A Placement Algorithm," *Soc. Ind. and Appl. Math. Rev.*, January 1961.

SUGANAMI, SABURA, "Schedule of Rooming Assignment," *J. Operations Research Soc. (Japan)*, vol. 8, no. 2, February 1966.

VOLLMANN, T. E., and E. S. BUFFA, "The Facilities Layout Problem in Prospective," *Management Science*, June 1966.

Location of Economic Activities:

BAUMOL, W. M., and P. WOLFE, "A Warehouse Location Problem," *Operations Research*, March–April 1958.

CHUANG, Y. H., and W. G. SMITH, "A Dynamic Programming Model for Combined Production, Distribution, and Storage," *J. Ind. Eng.*, January 1966.

COOPER, L., "Location-Allocation Problems," *Operations Research*, May–June 1963.

DILLON, J. D., "The Geographic Distribution of Production in Multiple Plant Operations," *Management Science*, July 1956.

EILON, S., and D. P. DEZIEL, "Setting a Distribution Centre, An Analogue Computer Application," *Management Science*, Series B, February 1966.

FELDMAN, E., F. A. LEHRER, and T. L. RAY, "Warehouse Location Under Continuous Economies of Scale," *Management Science*, May 1966.

GERSON, M. L., and R. B. MAFFEI, "Technical Characteristics of Distribution Simulators," *Management Science*, October 1963.

GREENHUT, MELVIN L., *Plant Location in Theory and in Practice*. North Carolina: Univ. of North Carolina Press, 1956.

HOOVER, EDGAR M., *The Location of Economic Activity*. New York: McGraw-Hill Book Co., 1948.

KUEHN, A. A., and M. J. HAMBURGER, "A Heuristic Program for Locating Warehouses," *Management Science*, July 1963.

LEFEBER, LOUIS, *Allocation in Space*. Amsterdam, Netherlands: North-Holland Publishing Co., 1958.

MANNE, A. S., "Plant Location Under Economies-of-Scale-Decentralization and Computation," *Management Science*, November 1964.

National Industrial Conference Board, *Techniques of Plant Location, Studies in Business Policy No. 61*, 1953.

Other:

BINDSCHEDLER, ANDRE E., and JAMES M. MOORE, "Optimal Location of New Machines in Existing Plant Layouts," *J. Ind. Eng.*, January–February 1961.

FRANCIS, RICHARD L., "A Note on the Optimal Location of a New Machine in an Existing Plant Layout," *J. Ind. Eng.*, January–February 1963.

——, "On the Location of Multiple New Facilities with Respect to Existing Facilities," *J. Ind. Eng.*, March–April 1964.

8
Flow Processes:
Product-Line Design

FLOW SHOP FORMAT

In the previous chapter, we differentiated the general format of a production system into three basic types, the job shop, the flow shop, and the project. In this chapter, we will consider some specific design problems related to the flow shop format. This format, or arrangement of facilities, is variously called product-layout, product-line, continuous-line, or continuous-flow design.

In the product-line format, the spatial arrangement of a facility is governed mainly by the processing requirements of the product or by the sequence of operations comprising a service. Machines, equipment, and work stations are arranged in a given order to conform to a specific sequence of operations, as prescribed by the routing function. Since the product line is product oriented, we might expect the facilities to be used to make products that have identical or very similar routings.

One way of categorizing product lines is by the degree of independence of the operations comprising the line. At one extreme is a line in which each operation has a potential rate of output that is independent of that of each of the other operations in the line. This independence of output rates is made possible by maintaining inventories between successive operations. If the whole system is to maintain a given rate of output, then each operation must produce the product in batches with subsequent inventories and idleness of those facilities which produce faster than the system rate. At the other extreme is the *paced* line in which each operation has the same production rate. The material or product moves continuously and at a uniform rate through the series of operations.

The standard rate of output is the normal rate that could be expected for an operation if it were performed independently. For example, in the White Engine Company inspection process, the standard times for some of the operations were considerably different from the actual rate. The *balance* of a product line is the degree of similarity between the standard times for the operations in the line. An unbalanced line implies a lack of full utilization of the facilities in those operations having standard rates in excess of the actual rates. Therefore, a major problem in product-line design is to gain a balanced line in order to minimize idle facilities.

MACHINE GROUPING

Fabricating or material-processing operations that are arranged in a product-line format often reflect the unpaced situation with independent output rates, batch production, and work-in-process inventories. This is the case where machines are general purpose and manually or semi-automatically controlled, as compared to a fully automated system, which would represent a paced line. The issue of balancing the system and reducing idle labor centers around the problem of *machine grouping*.

The product line is usually designed for some desired rate of line output. Each operation required on the part or material demands sufficient resources to guarantee this rate of output. However, such resources can be added only in discrete units, which introduces the condition of excess capacity at some operations. For example, assume that a product line is to turn out a part at the rate of 50 units per hour. One of the operations in the line drills two holes in the part. The standard output rate for this operation is 100 units per hour. This means that the operation will be idle 50% of the time. In contrast, a second operation mills two surfaces at a rate of 30 units per hour. This means that two machines will be required whose over-all capacity will exceed the desired rate, or the desired capacity may be gained by overtime or extra shift operations.

Given that each machine's standard output rate is fixed, the problem of machine grouping is to assign men to machines in such a way that utilization of manpower is maximized. For example, if there are two machines in the line and both are 50% idle, they may be arranged so that they can be run by a single operator. He will produce a batch of parts on the first machine and then shift to the second machine and produce a similar batch size. The batch size may vary between one unit and the hourly system requirement. Another problem in machine grouping is the design of a material-handling system, as well as the necessary inventory capacity between successive operations in the line.

PACED ASSEMBLY LINES

In contrast to the fabrication line, most product lines consist of a series of manual tasks or jobs. The term "assembly line" connotes a predominant use of this form of production.

A paced line consists of a moving conveyor, or another piece of material-handling equipment, which moves the material or part through a series of work stations. At each station, the operator performs some task on the material, such

FIGURE **8.1**   Paced assembly line. Courtesy of Western Electric Company, Inc.

as adding a component, fastening parts, inspecting, packaging, etc. The operator may be located at a fixed position or, conversely, he may move along a stationary line. A fully paced line is shown in Figure 8.1.

There are basic questions that must be considered before the design of an assembly line. These include such things as the design of the part to facilitate assembly operations, the number and composition of subassemblies, as well as the exact method of assembly. For our discussion of assembly-line design, we will assume that product design, subassembly composition, and general methods have been fixed and only minor changes can be made to improve assembly-line performance.

Design Considerations

Just as with the machine grouping in a fabrication problem, the balancing of the work among stations in the paced line is an important part of the design. We will cover this problem in subsequent pages and will assume for the moment that balancing has taken place.

One might assume that if the operations in a production line are balanced and *designed* to produce at equal rates, then the output of the line will equal this rate. Actual operating conditions, however, may prove this to be otherwise.

PACING EFFECTS ON OUTPUT RATE: In the fully paced line, each operator must perform his task within both time and space constraints. These constraints can be severe in a situation where an operation time has significant variance, assuming that time is a random variable. Since human performance times are usually random, the operator must consciously vary his output rate such that his performance time is always equal to or less than the time the part is available to him. This suggests that the average time must be less than the designed cycle time, or available time. Otherwise, the random occurrence of a long performance time may result in a part being unfinished or possibly of inferior quality when it leaves the work station.

Research has indicated that the time the part is available to the operator at a given work station on the line is a critical determinant of output rate. For product lines in which the part is rigidly attached to the conveyor, the time the part is available to the worker is a function of line speed, distance between successive parts, and length of the work station.

Let

L = length of the workplace station in feet (this is the length of the conveyor available to the operator)

S = speed of the conveyor in units per hour

D = distance between successive units of product on the conveyor in feet

T = time that part is available to the operator in minutes

Then,

$$T = (60 \times L)/(D \times S)$$

Given a certain line rate of output, some design features can be incorporated to accommodate the inherent variability in worker performance. The purpose is to maximize the time that a part is available to the operator. An obvious one is to permit the operator to perform his task independently of the conveyor by having work-in-process inventories between stations in the line. If the part must be attached to the line, the length of the work station (L) can be increased such that two or more parts are in the domain of the work station at any one time. Or, the space between successive parts on the line (D) and the belt speed (S) can both be decreased proportionally. In each case, the operator can take more than the allotted cycle time on one part, if necessary, and then compensate by speeding up on successive parts.

IN-LINE INVENTORIES: In the semi-paced assembly line, the matter of design for between-station, work-in-process inventories assumes importance to the degree that there is variation in between-station and within-station production rates. We have already dealt with the situation of differences in the average rates of production between stations in the fabrication of a part. If the production line is reasonably well balanced, then we are mainly interested in the within-station variance in production times.

For example, assume that we have a number of work stations in tandem with some predetermined space between each station for work-in-process inventories.

If the rate of output at each station is independent of every other station and is a random variable, then we are interested in the behavior of the inventories between stations. The design problem is to determine the space required between operations, given some conflicting objectives, such as minimizing station delays and inventory space.

If the stations are designed to have the same average rate of output, through line balancing, then theoretically the amount of space between each station should be infinite. This follows from basic queuing theory. Without going into the details, the argument proceeds as follows:

1. We assume that the supply of parts to the first station is infinite, or that the operator always has sufficient parts.
2. The average rate of output of the first operation is equal to the average of the distribution of output rates for the first operation. This output will also have a variance. Let the rate of output of station 1 be equal to μ.
3. The rate of input to the second operation (average) is therefore μ. But the rate of output of the second operation is also equal to μ, since we assumed that all stations have the same rate of output.
4. The service intensity of each operation is the ratio of the average rate of input to the average rate of output, which equals 1.

If the arrivals per unit time are Poisson distributed and the service times at each station are negatively exponentially distributed, then the required inventory is infinite, since, in theory, the waiting line of parts will approach infinity over time.

The usual case is that there is some limited storage space between successive operations. This limit in space will force the system to operate at a lower rate of output than is possible in terms of the capacity of the operations. Barten[1] has subjected this problem to a computer simulation. The output rate of any operation except the first and last is a function of the capacity rate and the state of the inventories leading and following the operation. Barten's simulator considers three design variables:

1. The number of operations in the line.
2. The mean and variance of the operation times.
3. The storage capacities between operations.

Table 8.1 shows the results in terms of the actual mean output rate for various combinations of the design variables. Figure 8.2 shows a graph of the output rate in excess of the mean versus the storage capacity in items for the case of six operations.

As we might expect, the storage capacity at each station is the important variable, and the results indicate that only a small storage capacity is needed to permit the effects of inventorying to take place.

---

[1] Kenneth Barten, "A Queueing Simulator for Determining Optimum Inventory Levels in a Sequential Process," *J. Ind. Eng.*, vol. XIII, no. 4, July–August 1962, pp. 245–52.

TABLE **8.1**   Mean total time (output production rate), minutes per piece.[1]

Number of operations	Mean operation time R	Standard deviation s	Storage capacity						Sample size
			0	1	2	3	4	6	
2	3.0	1.0	NA	3.377	3.176	3.047	3.058	3.030	2,000
4	3.0	1.0	4.208	3.603	3.284	3.259	3.248	3.251	1,000
4	10.0	3.0	NA	11.840	11.029	10.761	10.533	10.659	500
6	3.0	1.0	4.430	3.651	3.374	3.312	3.263	3.239	500
6	5.0	1.5	NA	5.921	5.591	5.465	5.404	5.329	500
6	10.0	3.0	NA	12.044	11.016	10.785	10.610	10.619	500
10	3.0	1.0	4.605	3.768	3.479	3.328	3.299	3.274	500
10	5.0	1.5	NA	6.029	5.671	5.470	5.519	5.431	500
10	10.0	3.0	NA	12.234	11.253	10.984	11.003	10.850	500

NA—NOT AVAILABLE

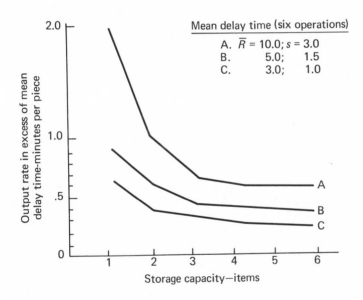

FIGURE **8.2**   Mean delay time for various distributions at various storage capacities. From K. Barten, *J. Ind. Eng.*, July–August, 1962, p. 249.

EFFECT OF IMBALANCE: Hillier and Boling arrived at very interesting conclusions as a result of using queuing theory to study a production-line phenomenon.[2]

---

[2] Frederick S. Hillier and Ronald W. Boling, "The Effect of Some Design Factors on the Efficiency of Production Lines with Variable Operation Times," *J. Ind. Eng.*, vol. XVII, no. 12, December 1966, pp. 651–58.

TABLE **8.2** System production rates for three-station systems with buffer storage.[2] (*C* = buffer storage size)

Average operation times		*C* = 0		*C* = 1		*C* = 2		*C* = 3		*C* = 4	
Station											
1 and 3	2	Rate	Per-cent base	Rate	Per-cent base	Rate	Per-cent base	Rate	Per-cent base	Rate	Per-cent base
1.00	1.00	0.5641	100.0	0.6705	100.0	0.7340	100.0	0.7767	100.0	0.8075	100.0
1.01	0.98	0.5648	100.1	0.6715	100.2	0.7352	100.2	0.7779	100.2	0.8087	100.2
1.02	0.96	0.5654	100.2	0.6723	100.3	0.7361	100.3	0.7788	100.3	0.8095	100.2
1.03	0.94	0.5659	100.3	0.6730	100.4	0.7366	100.4	0.7792	100.3	0.8096	100.3
1.04	0.92	0.5663	100.4	0.6734	100.4	0.7369	100.4	0.7792	100.3	0.8093	100.2
1.05	0.90	0.5667	100.5	0.6737	100.5	0.7369	100.4	0.7787	100.3	0.8085	100.1
1.06	0.88	0.5669	100.5	0.6738	100.5	0.7366	100.4	0.7779	100.2	0.8071	100.0
1.07	0.86	0.5671	100.5	0.6737	100.5	0.7360	100.3	0.7767	100.0	0.8053	99.7
1.08	0.84	0.5672	100.5	0.6734	100.4	0.7351	100.1	0.7752	99.8	0.8031	99.5
1.09	0.82	0.5672	100.5	0.6729	100.4	0.7339	100.0	0.7733	99.6	0.8005	99.1
1.10	0.80	0.5671	100.5	0.6722	100.3	0.7325	99.8	0.7711	99.3	0.7975	98.8
1.11	0.78	0.5669	100.5	0.6714	100.1	0.7308	99.6	0.7685	98.9	0.7942	98.4
1.12	0.76	0.5667	100.5	0.6703	100.0	0.7288	99.3	0.7657	98.6	0.7905	97.9
1.13	0.74	0.5663	100.4	0.6691	99.8	0.7266	99.0	0.7626	98.2	0.7866	97.4
1.14	0.72	0.5659	100.3	0.6678	99.6	0.7242	98.7	0.7592	97.7	0.7824	96.9
1.15	0.70	0.5654	100.2	0.6662	99.4	0.7216	98.3	0.7556	97.3	0.7781	96.4

They studied hypothetical three- and four-station production lines to test the conjecture that production lines might operate more efficiently, in terms of line rate, if some imbalance were permitted in operation times. Their model assumed infinite supply at the start of the line, equal (or no) storage space between lines, and variable station times. The standard for comparison was the production rate of a line in which the operation times were exponentially distributed with equal averages. In the case of the three- and four-station lines, with or without buffer inventories between stations, an improvement in the line production rate was gained by introducing imbalance in the station times. By lowering the average rate of the middle-of-line operations and raising the average rates of the end-of-line operations, a gain in the line rate was realized, although only of an order of magnitude of 1%. Table 8.2 shows his results for a three-station trial. Perhaps more important was the fact that the desired production rate (i.e., the standard) was maintained in spite of a significant imbalance in the direction indicated above.

It is therefore evident that, contrary to popular belief, in the design of paced production lines maximum production may not be gained by adhering to the fully paced line if the part is rigidly fixed to a conveyor going at some fixed speed.

Simulation of a Product Line

The random characteristics of a product line can be studied by simulation. A convenient example is the case of the White Engine Company inspection process explained on pages 180–83.

EXAMPLE 8.1   As a result of analyzing the flow-process chart and flow diagram of the engine inspection process, an industrial engineer proposes two alternative improvements.

Alternative A   Operator *B* is eliminated from the process. His task of lubricating the part is assigned to Operator *A*. The engines are removed from the incoming overhead conveyor by the inspectors. After testing the engine, the inspector places it on an outgoing roller conveyor, which transports it to the series of remaining operations. This arrangement is shown in Figure 8.3a.

Alternative B   This is the same as alternative *A* except that, after testing the engine, the inspector removes the drain plug and places the engine on a hook of an outgoing overhead conveyor. The engine drains while on the conveyor. Subsequent operations are performed directly on this outgoing overhead conveyor. Figure 8.3b shows the test stand layout for this alternative. In both cases *A* and *B*, the overhead conveyors are located at waist-high level.

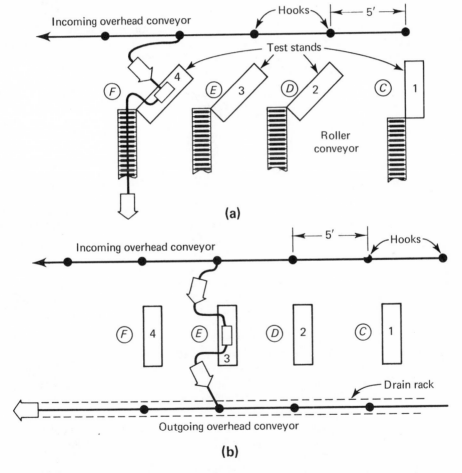

FIGURE **8.3**   (a) Part taken from incoming overhead conveyor and disposed of on roller conveyor. (b) Part taken from incoming overhead conveyor and disposed of on outgoing overhead conveyor leading to shipping room.

Each of these alternatives suggests a basic question related to the random nature of the inspection operations. We may expect the inspection time to be a random variable, in which case the inspectors will be out of phase with the constant speed of the conveyors. For instance, with respect to the more flexible design A it is possible that, after completing a unit, the inspector will find that the incoming conveyor hook in the 5-foot domain of his station is empty, thereby introducing waiting time. Or, the inspector may take longer than the standard of 2.00 min to inspect a unit. Therefore, a unit on the conveyor may pass his station and similarly pass all remaining stations in the line. In the case of alternative B, the matter is more critical, since two power conveyors are involved.

We wish to know the percentage of units that will pass through the system unattended and the amount of idle time that is experienced by the inspectors. We may note that if a part is not picked off the incoming conveyor, it will simply ride the conveyor circuit and come back to the inspection process. However, the desired rate of 120 units per hour will not be attained.

DESIGN VARIABLES: We wish to determine not only the effect of the two alternatives on the measures of performance, but also the design variations that might improve the situation. In constructing a simulator, we can consider the following design variables besides the two basic alternatives A and B:

1. The length of the work stations, or distance between inspection stands, can be increased to 10 feet. This will permit two conveyor hooks to be in the domain of each station at all times.
2. The direction of the outgoing conveyor in alternative B can be reversed. That is, we might expect that station 4 will incur the most idle time, since it is at the mercy of the performance of the other three stations. By reversing the outgoing conveyor direction, we permit station 4 to be guaranteed an empty hook on this conveyor.
3. Changes in the average and variance of the inspection time can be studied. If the measures of performance are sensitive to these parameters, we might institute methods changes in the jobs to reduce either one or both.

A SIMULATOR: Figure 8.4 shows the logic diagram for simulating alternatives A and B. We will assume that the conveyor speed is 120 units per hour, the distance between hooks is 5 ft, and the length of the inspection station domain is 5 ft. The time T that a hook is available to an inspector is therefore

$$T = (60 \times 5)/(5 \times 120) = 0.5 \text{ min}$$

The inspection times are normally distributed with a designated mean and variance. The simulated period will be equivalent to the passage of 1,000 hooks through the system, which corresponds to about an eight-hour work day. The simulator will start at time zero by assuming that each of the four inspectors has just taken a part off the hook of the incoming conveyor.

We will use a "master clock" method of simulation. We will advance the time in units of 0.10 min, which corresponds to 1.0 ft of conveyor travel. At the end of each increment of time advancement, the simulator will examine the status of each of the four inspection stations, as well as the hooks in each station domain. If an inspector has completed a unit, he will be assigned a new unit or placed in an idle status if he cannot dispose of the finished unit or obtain a new unit. The simulator will keep track

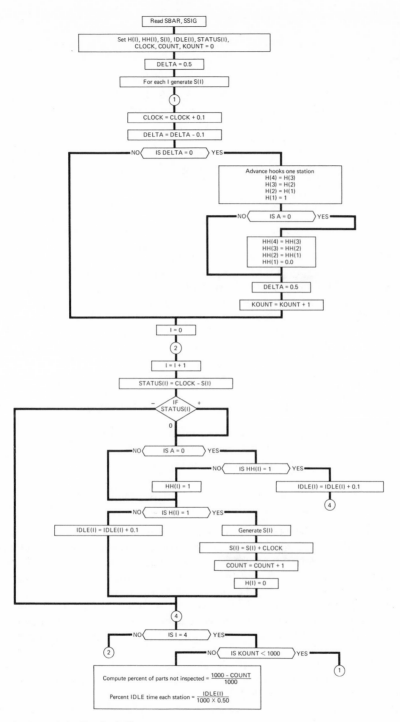

FIGURE **8.4** Logical diagram.

of the cumulative number of parts inspected and the cumulative idle time for each station.

The following are variables and parameters of the system:

I = Ith inspection station, I = 1, 2, 3, 4

$H(I)$ = status of the incoming conveyor hook in the domain of the Ith station

$$= \begin{cases} 1 \text{ if the hook contains a unit} \\ 0 \text{ if the hook is empty} \end{cases}$$

$HH(I)$ = status of the outgoing conveyor hook in the domain of the Ith station

$$= \begin{cases} 1 \text{ if the hook is full} \\ 0 \text{ if the hook is empty} \end{cases}$$

$S(I)$ = current inspection time for the Ith station, a random variable

$IDLE(I)$ = cumulative idle time for the Ith station

$STATUS(I)$ = status of the Ith station at any time. $STATUS(I)$ is less than 0 if the station is busy inspecting a unit and is equal to or greater than 0 if the inspector is waiting for an empty hook to dispose of a part or for a full hook if he is waiting for a new unit

SBAR = mean inspection time

SSIG = standard deviation of inspection time

CLOCK = cumulative clock time

DELTA = time counter to signal when conveyor hooks have shifted position from one station to the next station in the line

COUNT = cumulative number of units inspected by all stations

KOUNT = number of incoming conveyor hooks that have passed through the system

A = a switch to indicate if design alternative A or B is being used

$$= \begin{cases} 1 \text{ if the outgoing conveyor is roller} \\ 0 \text{ if the outgoing conveyor is overhead} \end{cases}$$

RESULTS: Table 8.3 shows the results of 11 trials, each simulating a particular combination of design variables on a computer.

1. *Trials 1 and 2*   These two trials represent the 5-ft distance between the stations. They compare designs A and B using a mean service or inspection time of 2.00 min and a standard deviation of 0.3 for a normal distribution. The number of units un-inspected increases in design B, and the idle time is due to waiting at the outgoing conveyor. It is also clear that the idle time increases with distance from station 1.

It must be remembered that the inspection times are strictly random from a normal distribution. There is no relationship between successive times, such as the pairing of a long cycle with a short cycle time, which we stated is an advisable characteristic of a line operation.

2. *Trial 3*   In trial 3, for design B, the standard deviation was doubled to a value of 0.6. This caused the number of passed parts to increase to over 10% and the idle time to increase by roughly 33%.

3. *Trials 4 and 5*   In these trials, the distance between stations is increased to 10 ft. This permits each hook to be available to an inspector for 1.00 rather than 0.50 min. Of the two hooks, the inspector will always first check the hook that arrived first at the station on either conveyor and then, if necessary, go to the other hook.

TABLE **8.3** Results of 11 simulation trials for inspection process.

Trial no.	Design	L (ft)	Mean inspection time SBAR	Inspection time standard deviation SSIG	Uninspected parts — Units	Uninspected parts — Percent of kount	Incoming conveyor 1	Incoming conveyor 2	Incoming conveyor 3	Incoming conveyor 4	Outgoing conveyor 1	Outgoing conveyor 2	Outgoing conveyor 3	Outgoing conveyor 4	Total idle time percent
1	A	5	2.0	0.3	76	7.6	0	3.62	8.10	20.30	0				32.02
2	B	5	2.0	0.3	84	8.4	0	0	.04	0	0	3.44	9.76	19.00	32.28
3	B	5	2.0	0.6	105	10.5	0	0	0	0		3.94	10.68	27.74	42.36
4	A	10	2.0	0.3	57	5.7	0	0	2.44	19.00					21.44
5	B	10	2.0	0.3	57	5.7	0	0	0	0.16			2.40	19.00	21.40
6	B	10	2.1	0.3	79	7.9	0	0	0	0			2.66	10.76	13.58
7	B	10	2.2	0.3	114	11.4	0	0	0	0			1.82	7.76	9.58
8	B	10	2.2	0.5	125	12.5	0	0	0	0			2.24	10.24	12.48
9	B	10	2.0	0.3	180	8.0	0	0	1.72	14.86	11.20	3.00	0	0	30.78
10	B	10	2.0	0.6	107	10.7	0	0	3.42	23.22	14.86	4.22	0.22	0	45.94
11	B	10	2.2	0.3	143	14.3	0	0	2.46	9.36	9.34	1.92	0	0	23.08

Station idle time in percent of total run time

When requiring either an incoming or outgoing hook, the inspector will always first check the hook that had the earliest arrival at the station domain. Then, if necessary, he will use the remaining hook.

In these two cases, the flexibility advantage in design A is not apparent, and both designs appear to perform equally well with the minimum percent of uninspected parts.

4. *Trials 6, 7, and 8* When the stations are 10 ft apart, there is some chance that the inspections time would be increased due to the increased walking distance. These three trials indicate the result of increasing the average service time and the variance. The percentage of passed parts is sensitive to the increase in the mean inspection time. A 10% increase in the mean from 2.00 to 2.20 results in doubling the percentage of passed parts.

5. *Trials 9, 10, and 11* These three trials represent the condition in which the direction of the outgoing conveyor is reversed. This shifts the waiting time on the outgoing conveyor to stations 1 and 2, which is to be expected. However, compared with trial 5, the over-all performance is not improved.

Besides these variations, we could introduce other design or planning variables. The success of the design depends on the character of the inspection time distribution and its parameters. Its determination requires careful time measurement of the inspection job, together with a detailed analysis of the method to determine if the times would conform to a realistic distribution. There is also the additional factor of the inspectors adjusting to the system such that long cycle times are complemented by subsequent short cycle times. This condition could be simulated by using more than one inspection time distribution.

LINE BALANCING

Line balancing is a pervasive problem in all kinds of product-line designs. The problem of line balancing is to distribute the total work content of the line output evenly to the stations in the line, such that idleness of resources at each station is minimized. Usually the case involves the minimization of labor idle time. Line balancing is a problem in both paced and unpaced product lines. However, it assumes special importance in paced-line situations.

Line balancing has been subjected to a good deal of analysis from both a theoretical and a practical viewpoint. The problem has interesting theoretical combinatorial properties. In the production of high-volume consumer goods, techniques of line balancing are a standard item of industrial engineering repertoires.

Basic Steps in Line Balancing

Some of the theoretical work in line balancing is directed toward the development of models that attempt to derive an optimally balanced line. But many of the more practical aspects of line balancing involve the collection and analysis of considerable data and the application of some basic steps. These steps are discussed below.

DEFINITION OF JOB AND TASKS: A job consists of the total work required to complete a unit of line output. This total work content can be described as a set of basic tasks, which are minimal and rational units of work. Usually a basic task is a set of elemental motions.

The criterion for what comprises a task is the loss in economy by a further subdivision of the task. For example, assume that alternative *B* is used in the inspection process of engines in the White Engine Company (see page 180). After inspection, these remaining elements of work must be performed on the outgoing overhead conveyor:

Assemble spark plug and tighten	0.300 min
Assemble drain plug and tighten	0.250
Hand punch code number in base	0.250
Place dust seal over shaft opening	0.100

We could allocate these elements to two workers. However, we might prefer to further subdivide these elements into a set of basic tasks. For example, "assemble and tighten spark plug and drain plug" might be each broken down into two basic tasks, that is,

Assemble spark plug	0.200 min
Tighten spark plug	0.100
Assemble drain plug	0.170
Tighten drain plug	0.080

With this subdivision, we can assign the assembly to one man and the tightening to a second man and thereby possibly get a better balance in the two stations. Any further subdivision of these tasks would result in a loss of economy in their performance.

The unit times for the tasks are usually derived from standard motion-time systems. For a large assembly job, it can be seen that the derivation of the tasks and their times is a substantial engineering job.

CYCLE TIME: The cycle time is the reciprocal of the rate at which assemblies are completed on the line. It is therefore the time that is available to the operator to complete his unit of work at his station. As we have noted before, the cycle time is a function of the paced-line speed. We will symbolize the cycle time as C $[C = (60 \times L)/(D \times S)]$.

The actual time that the operator consumes in performing his set of tasks at his station is a random variable. The standard time is the sum of the elemental task times. If the entire job is made up of N basic tasks, and if

t_i = standard time for the ith task, $i = 1, 2, \ldots, N$

then

$$\sum_{1}^{N} t_i = T = \text{the total work content of the job}$$

The standard work content of an individual station on the line must be equal to or less than the cycle time. The fact that it may be less than the cycle time introduces the matter of idle time at the station. A "limiting" station is one whose standard work content is equal to the cycle time.

NUMBER OF STATIONS: The number of stations is clearly a function of the cycle time and the total work content of the job. If the cycle time is fixed at a value of C, then the number of stations must be equal to or greater than the integer value of the ratio T/C. Or, if M equals the minimum number of stations, then

$$M = \{\text{integer}/j = T/C\}_{j}$$

PRECEDENCE AND ZONING CONSTRAINTS: The assignment of basic tasks to stations is restricted by the product design or the technical character of the processes used in the line. If there are N basic tasks, then there are $N(N \doteq 1)/2$ pairs of tasks that have some relationship between them. The relationship between any pair of tasks can exist in four different ways. We will assume two basic tasks x and y.

1. x must be performed prior to y. For instance, the hole must be drilled before the bolt can be attached. Or the spark plug must be assembled before it can be tightened.
2. The reverse of 1 is true with respect to x and y.
3. A zoning restriction may be assigned to x and y such that they cannot be performed at the same station. Examples are such things as x and y are performed by different labor grades, or the performance of x and y at the same station poses a safety hazard, or x is a dirty job that can't be done at the same station with y. The opposite is to have a zoning constraint where x and y should be performed at the same station. For example, we want to tighten the spark plug and drain plug at the same station to avoid the extra handling of a wrench at two separate stations.
4. There is no restriction between x and y.

	A	B	C	D	E	F	G	H	I
A	0	+	+	+	+	0	+	0	0
B	−	0	+	+	0	0	0	0	+
C	−	−	0	+	0	0	0	0	+
D	−	−	−	0	0	0	0	0	+
E	−	0	0	0	0	+	0	0	0
F	0	0	0	0	−	0	0	+	0
G	−	0	0	0	0	0	0	+	0
H	0	0	0	0	0	−	−	0	0
I	0	−	−	−	0	0	0	0	0

FIGURE 8.5   Precedence matrix.

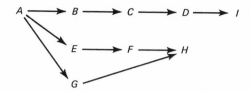

FIGURE **8.6**   Precedence graph.

The relationship between all pairs of tasks is summarized conveniently in the form of a precedence matrix. Figure 8.5 shows such a matrix for a job consisting of nine tasks *A* through *I*. The three possibilities are symbolized using a +, −, or 0. The plus sign indicates that the task labeling the row must precede the task labeling the column. The negative sign indicates the reverse case, and the 0 means there are no relations. Thus, for example, task *B* must follow task *A* but must precede tasks *C*, *D*, and *I*. No zoning restrictions are shown.

The task relationships are shown in the form of a *precedence graph* in Figure 8.6. This is more convenient to work with than the matrix when making assignments. We will use the simple case shown in the matrix.

One method of constructing the graph is as follows:

1. First consider task *A*. Place it at the head of a column containing all of the tasks that have no relationship with *A*. Then place in a column to the right all of the tasks that must follow *A*.

A	*B*
F	*C*
H	*D*
I	*E*
	G

2. Now consider Task *B*. Place all tasks that must follow *B* in a column directly to the right of the column in which *B* is now located.

A	*B*	*C*
F	*E*	*D*
H	*G*	*I*

3. Repeat step 2 with task *C*.

A	*B*		*D*
F	*E*	*C*	*I*
H	*G*		

4. Now proceed through all tasks systematically from *A* to *I*. This will result in a graph as shown in Fig. 8.6. Note that direct relationships between tasks are connected by lines, unless the relationship is implied in intervening columns. Tasks in the same column can be sequenced among themselves in any order.

Suppose in our example that each of the tasks has a standard time, as follows:

Task	Standard time	Task	Standard time
A	5	F	3
B	3	G	2
C	1	H	2
D	2	I	4
E	4		—

Total job time = 26

We will assume that the desired cycle time is ten time units, which means that we will need three stations. The problem is to so assign the nine tasks to the three stations as to minimize station idle time, where the idle time is simply the difference between the station standard time and the cycle time summed over all stations.

Two possible assignments are indicated below, with the second obviously in better balance than the first with a smaller cycle time.

Station	1		2		3		
	A	5	E	4	H	2	Cycle time = 10
	B	3	F	3	I	4	Idleness = 4
	G	2	C	1		6	
		10	D	2			
				10			
	A	5	G	2	D	2	Cycle time = 9
	B	3	E	4	H	2	Idleness = 1
	C	1	F	3	I	4	
		9		9		8	

So far we have said nothing about zoning restrictions. The zoning restrictions can be noted by assigning each task to at least one zone and then keeping track of the zone constraints in the assignments of the tasks.

CRITERION OF BALANCE: The criterion used in line balancing is the minimization of total idle time in the line. Let

I = total idle time in the line

$I = (M \times C) - T$

By minimizing I we would expect to minimize the number of man-hours per piece.

The problem may be dealt with by specifying C and permitting the number of stations to vary, or holding M constant and varying C, or by some variable com-

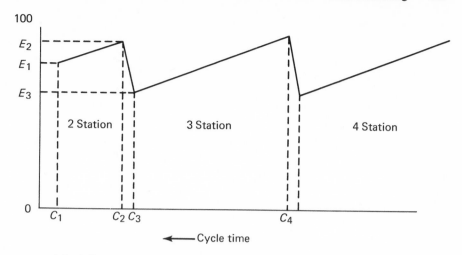

FIGURE **8.7**   Effect of cycle time and number of stations on efficiency.

bination of both parameters. The general methods of line balancing usually consider the cycle time to be a constant and the number of stations to be variable, since the reverse situation is difficult to deal with theoretically.

Figure 8.7 shows the relationship between cycle time and the number of stations and the efficiency of the line. In this case, efficiency is defined as

$$E = 1 - \frac{(M \times C) - T}{M \times C}$$

At a cycle time of C_1 minutes, two stations are necessary, and the best balance yields an efficiency of E_1. If the cycle time is lowered to C_2, a redistribution of the elements among the two stations results in greater efficiency E_2. At this point, any decrease in cycle time necessitates the addition of a station and, therefore, a reduction in efficiency to E_3. A redistribution of the tasks after reducing the cycle time to C_4 brings the efficiency back up again. Thus, the process may be repeated, and a final choice of stations and cycle time can be made.

If the cycle time is the design variable, then we might expect the rate of output to differ from the rate of demand for the part. This will incur additional costs, such as inventory holding costs, if the rate is faster than demand, or overtime or added lines, if the rate is slower than demand. It seems reasonable to assume that the problem is one of finding the best balanced line within a reasonable range of cycle times.

If the entire job could be continuously subdivided into smaller and smaller tasks, and the tasks could be assigned without restriction to any station, then the problem of line balancing would disappear. The problem exists because of the discrete but unequal size of the basic tasks. Furthermore, the freedom with which tasks can be assigned to stations is limited by the technological and zoning constraints.

Methods of Line Balancing

For large values of N, the number of basic tasks, the job of line balancing is one of considerable magnitude. The possible order in which N tasks can be performed provides the basic structure to the problem. Of the $N!$ possible ways of ordering N tasks, some are not feasible because of precedence restrictions, and there are approximately $N!/2^k$ feasible sequences, where k is the number of precedence relations or number of precedence arrows in the precedence graph.

A distinct balance for a line of M stations means that all tasks are assigned to the stations such that for each station the sum of the task times is equal to or less than a desired cycle time C. We may note that the number of distinct balances is less than the number of feasible sequences. Thus, for our previous example, the following sequences yield the same distinct balance.

Station 1	Station 2	Station 3
$A–B–C$	$G–E–F$	$D–H–I$
$A–B–C$	$E–G–F$	$H–D–I$

Within-station rearrangement of tasks results in no change in balance, while between-station shifting of tasks may result in a new balance.

A variety of methods have been proposed for determining either optimal or good line balances. Considering the practical complexities of a large problem, such as estimating task times, deciding on cycle times, and determining constraints on the problem, the goal of attaining an optimal balance is probably academic. However, considering the combinatorial aspects, what is needed are methods of efficiently finding reasonably good balances, which in turn can be refined by the engineer's ability to introduce changes, such as redefining tasks or altering various constraints. We mention a few of the approaches.

LINEAR PROGRAMING: The first published paper on assembly-line balancing, by M. E. Salveson,[3] in 1955, used a linear programing approach. A subsequent article by Bowman[4] also considers a linear programing solution to the problem, which is summarized below.

Suppose the theoretical number of stations, for a fixed cycle time C and a job content T, is $M'' = T/C$. Then, let there be some practical upper limit on the actual number of stations, and call this M. The balanced number of stations is M', where $M'' \leq M' \leq M$. The objective is to minimize M'.

Now let

$i =$ the ith task, $i = 1, 2, \ldots, N$

$j =$ the jth station, $j = 1, 2, \ldots, M$

[3] M. E. Salveson, "The Assembly Line Balancing Problem," *J. Ind. Eng.*, vol. VI, no. 3, May–June 1955, pp. 18–25.
[4] E. H. Bowman, "Assembly Line Balancing by Linear Programming," *Operations Research*, vol. 8, no. 3, May–June 1960, pp. 385–89.

t_i = time to perform the ith task

$$\delta_{ij} = \begin{cases} 1 & \text{if task } i \text{ is assigned to station } j \\ 0 & \text{otherwise} \end{cases}$$

The linear programing formulation of the problem follows.

First, there is a set of restrictions that insure that the sum of the times for the tasks assigned to a station is equal or less than the cycle time.

$$\sum_{i=1}^{N} t_i \delta_{i1} \leq C$$

$$\begin{matrix} \cdot & \cdot & \cdot \\ \cdot & \cdot & \cdot \\ \cdot & \cdot & \cdot \end{matrix}$$

$$\sum_{i=1}^{N} t_i \delta_{iM} \leq C$$

Second, there is a set of restrictions that insure that every task is assigned to only one station.

$$\sum_{j=1}^{M} \delta_{1j} = 1$$

$$\sum_{j=1}^{M} \delta_{2j} = 1$$

$$\begin{matrix} \cdot & \cdot & \cdot \\ \cdot & \cdot & \cdot \end{matrix}$$

$$\sum_{j=1}^{M} \delta_{Nj} = 1$$

Third, there is a set of restrictions that express the precedence constraints between pairs of tasks. In order to present this, we will use our previous example, which had the following precedence graph.

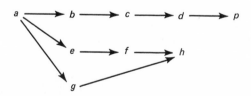

For a given task we need only consider its relation to the preceding task in the chain of constraints.

$$\delta_{b1} \leq \delta_{a1}; \delta_{b2} \leq \delta_{a1} + \delta_{a2}; \ldots ; \delta_{bM} \leq \delta_{a1} + \delta_{a2} + \cdots + \delta_{aM}$$
$$\delta_{pM} \leq \delta_{d1} + \delta_{d2} + \cdots + \delta_{dM}$$

Again, referring to our example, assume that $M'' = 3$ and $M = 5$. The objective is to minimize the number of stations. This is done by moving the last or ending tasks (h and p in the example) as far forward as possible by making assignments

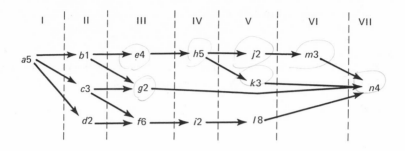

FIGURE **8.8** Precedence graph for 14 tasks.

to the later stations very costly. Since stations 1, 2, and 3 are necessary, they assume no costs. The objective function is

$$z = \min\{1(t_p\delta_{p4} + t_h\delta_{h4}) + (1 + t_p + t_h)(t_p\delta_{p5} + t_h\delta_{h5})\}$$

This makes any assignment to a later station more costly than the sum of all preceding station assignments.

HEURISTIC METHODS: A heuristic method for line balancing has been proposed by Wester and Kilbridge.[5] This method makes systematic use of the precedence graph and appears to be a useful way of arriving at a balanced line by hand computation. In order to explain the method, we will use the following example.

Assume that 14 tasks have the precedence graph in Figure 8.8 with the task times indicated next to each task. The tasks are assigned to columns I through VII, where tasks within a column can be permuted in any way. Also, certain tasks can be moved laterally to the right between columns without affecting the freedom of permuting within the column.

The systematic approach to the problem is facilitated by the use of Table 8.4. Suppose that the cycle time is 10. The minimum number of stations will be 5 or $(\frac{50}{10})$. We now apply the following steps.

1. We try to assign 10 units of work to each station. Therefore, station 1 will be assigned tasks up to and including column II, since the cumulative time for that column is the first number greater than 10. We find that the first station can include tasks *a-c-d* for a station time of 10.

2. Station 2 must now include task *b* plus others from column III, which hopefully sum to a station time of 10 and a cumulative time of 20. This is not possible, so we start moving tasks out of column III and to column IV, where possible. Column IV now contains three tasks from which we take one to combine

---

[5] L. Wester and M. D. Kilbridge, "Heuristic Line Balancing—A Case," *J. Ind. Eng.*, vol. XIII, no. 3, May–June 1962, pp. 139–49.

TABLE **8.4** Table for use in line balancing.

Step 1

Column	Task	Columns task can be moved to	t_i	Cumulative time
I	a		5	5
II	b		1	
	c		3	
	d		2	11
III	e		4	
	f	IV (if i V, l VI)	6	
	g	IV, V, VI	2	23
IV	h		5	
	i	V (if l VI)	2	30
V	j		2	
	k	VI	3	
	l	VI	8	43
VI	m		3	46
VII	n		4	50

Step 2

Column	Task	Columns task can be moved to	t_i	Cumulative time	
I	a		5	5	⎫
II	c		3		⎬ Station 1
	d		2	10	⎭
	b		1	11	
III	e		4	15	
IV	f		6		
	g	V, VI	2		
	h		5	28	
V	i		2		
	j		2		
	k	VI	3	35	
VI	l		8		
	m		3	46	
VII	n		4	50	

TABLE **8.4** Continued.

Step 3

Column	Task	Columns task can be moved to	t_i	Cumulative time	
I	a		5	5	Station 1
II	c		3		
	d		2	10	
	b		1	11	
III	e		4	15	Station 2
IV	h		5	20	
	f		6	26	
V	i		2		
	j		2		
	g	VI	2		
	k	VI	3	35	
VI	l		8		
	m		3	46	
VII	n		4	50	

Step 4

Column	Task	Columns task can be moved to	t_i	Cumulative time	
I	f		6		
V	i		2		
	j		2	30 30	
VI	g		2		
	k		3		
	l		8		
	m		3	46	
VII	n		4	50	

with tasks b and e to construct a station. Tasks b-e-h will make up the second station with a station time of 10. Note that f has been shifted to column IV and i and l to columns V and VI, respectively (Table 8.4, Step 2). Also, by shifting the tasks to columns to the right we force the relevant cumulative time to later columns, thus permitting a larger selection of tasks to form a station.

3. In order to get the composition of the third station, we shift task g from column IV to V and then choose f-i-j as the task assignments for station 3 with a cumulative time of 30 (Step 3).

4. Finally, we shift g and k to column VI, thus permitting us to clearly see that

station 4 will consist of tasks g and l and station 5 will then include k-m-n (Step 4).

It may be seen that this method works rather well for the case where the tasks for each station overlap several columns. For cases where the cycle time is small and number of stations large, such that each station has a small number of tasks, the method may not work as well.

Helgeson and Birnie[6] propose a Ranked Positional Weight Method. Each task is assigned a positional weight, which is the sum of times for all tasks that must follow it. The tasks are then ranked in order of descending values of the positional weights. For the immediately preceding example, the positional weights and rankings are shown below.

Task	a	b	c	d	e	f	h	i	j	g	k	l	m	n
t_i	5	1	3	2	4	6	5	2	2	2	3	8	3	4
Positional weight	45	23	22	20	17	14	12	12	7	4	4	4	4	0
Immediate Predecessors	—	a	a	a	b	c,d	e	f	h	b,c	h	i	j	g,k,l,m

The method consists in assigning tasks to stations in order of positional weight, assuming some given cycle time. If a task time is greater than the remaining time for the station, then it is passed over in favor of another task farther down the scale, provided that precedence or zoning constraints are not violated. Once a station is filled, the next station is assigned tasks starting with the first unassigned task in the ranked order. Using this approach, we arrive at a six-station assignment as follows:

Station 1		Station 2		Station 3		Station 4		Station 5		Station 6	
a	5	d	2	f	6	h	5	l	8	m	3
b	1	e	4	i	2	j	2			n	4
c	3	g	2			k	3				
	9		8		8		10		8		7

An approach taken by Arcus[7] employs a sampling procedure. His method is to generate randomly a number of feasible assignments from which a best, but not necessarily optimum, assignment is selected.

The steps in Arcus' method applied to Figure 8.8 on page 262 are outlined below. We wish to have a cycle time of 10 or less.

Step 1   The tasks are listed. Next to each task is a list of tasks that imme-

[6] W. P. Helgeson and D. P. Birnie, "Assembly Line Balancing Using the Ranked Positional Weight Technique," *J. Ind. Eng.*, vol. XII, no. 6, November–December 1961, pp. 394–98.

[7] A. L. Arcus, "Comsoal: A Computer Method of Sequencing Operations for Assembly Lines," in Elwood S. Buffa, *Readings in Production and Operations Management*. New York: John Wiley & Sons, 1966, pp. 336–60.

diately follow it. Then, in a third column, the number of tasks immediately preceding are indicated.

Tasks	Tasks immediately following	Number of tasks immediately preceding
a	b, c, d	0
b	e, g	1
c	g, f	1
d	f	1
e	h	1
f	i	2
g	n	2
h	j, k	1
i	l	1
j	m	1
k	n	1
l	n	1
m	n	1
n		4

Step 2   Make a list of tasks having 0 for the number of immediately preceding tasks. In the first cycle, this would include only task a. Call this List X.

Step 3   From List X, select a task randomly. The probabilities assigned to each task may be equal or weighted according to some rule. We will assume equal weight. Assign the selected task to the station in question. If this results in exceeding the station time limit, the task is assigned to a new station.

Step 4   For each of the tasks immediately following the selected task, subtract 1 from their number of immediately preceding tasks. Add to List X those tasks which now have 0 for the number of immediately preceding tasks. Remove from List X the task just selected.

Steps 3 and 4 are then repeated until all tasks have been assigned, resulting in a randomly selected feasible assignment. The following is such a randomly selected assignment with task times and station times shown.

Station 1	Station 2	Station 3	Station 4	Station 5	Station 6
a 5	c 3	e 4	h 5	l 8	m 3
b 1	f 6	g 2	k 3	— 8	n 4
d 2	— 9	i 2	j 2		— 7
— 8		— 8	— 10		

The partial sequence of the steps leading to the assignment is as follows:

Task a is assigned to station 1, since it is the only task on List X at the start. The number of immediately preceding tasks for b, c, and d are reduced by 1. They then become zero and are added to List X, and task a is removed.

The remaining station time is 5. List X is surveyed to determine which tasks have times equal to or less than 5. If a task time is greater than the remaining station time, then it is assigned a probability 0 of being selected, unless it is the only task in the list. Now b, c, and d are given equal probabilities of being selected. Task b is selected by a random mechanism.

Tasks e and g have their numbers reduced by 1. Task e is now a candidate for selection and is added to List X, while b is removed. The list now contains c, d, and e, all of which have times equal to or less than the remaining station time of 4. Task d is randomly selected.

The process is thus repeated until all tasks have been assigned.

Arcus proposes a number of methods for weighting the selection of admissible tasks at each stage of the process. The reader can refer to the reference for this method.

SUMMARY

Product lines exist in both paced and unpaced forms. Nonautomated fabrication lines involve the grouping of semi-automatic machines to effect labor economies by having one operator run more than one machine. This kind of product line is quite specialized and is one step removed from a fully automated process.

In the context of the assembly line, where operations are manually controlled, evidence indicates that an unpaced line may result in higher production rates than a paced line for a given desired rate of line output. Where lines are designed to be paced, certain design features should be incorporated to maximize the time that a part is available to the operator, thus recognizing the performance variability that is inherent in manual work.

The balancing of paced lines has developed into a highly formalized function. A variety of quantitative techniques have been suggested for line balancing, in which the objective is to minimize line stations for a given rate of output or maximize line output for a given number of stations. The practical problems of paced line design are beyond those of balancing. In sophisticated product-line systems, subassembly lines must be designed and balanced to relate to the final assembly line parameters. Also, in many cases, lines must be designed to adapt to a product mix. This is the case in mass-production industries (TV, automobile, washing machine), in which final product model variations, such as style, size, and subassembly structure, are the order of the day. This lack of standardization imposes new constraints on the economics of the product-line method of production, where the volume of any one model is insufficient to support the full utilization of a line designed especially for its production or assembly. The economics depend on the ability of the product engineer to design standardized intermodel components or modular units and the ability of the production engineer to evaluate combinatorial alternative product-line configurations.

Problems

8.1   The Remsen Machine Company has received a contract to supply the government with approximately 35,000 units of an assembled part each year for the next three years. The process required to manufacture a shaft for one of these assemblies is as follows:

Operation	Description	Man cycle time
1	Turn	0.0625 hours per piece
2	Mill first cut	0.0590
3	Drill	0.0365
4	Mill second cut	0.0325
5	Sand blast	0.1000

In operation 5 the machine is semi-automatic. It takes 2.00 minutes to unload and load the machine with parts. The machine then automatically blasts the part for 4.00 minutes. You are to evaluate a proposed product-line layout for these operations. The proposal is to group the machines as follows:

Group I	Operations 1 and 4
Group II	Operations 2 and 3
Group III	Operation 5

More specifically:
  1. The required production rate is about 17 pieces per hour assuming an eight-hour day. However, the line utilization is set at 85% due to interruptions.
  2. The problem is to determine the number of machines and operators in each group, the maximum expected number of parts in work-in-process inventory between successive operations assuming a one-hour production cycle and the relative location of the machines. Assume that the parts are transferred between operations on a gravity conveyor.

8.2   Suppose that, due to specialization, positive economies can be gained by assembling a product on an assembly line. The desired rate of output indicated that 10 stations will be required.
(a) Discuss the various ways of maximizing production on the line.
(b) Would there be any advantage in splitting up the 10-station line into two 5-station lines with a large inventory separating them?

8.3   Consider the simulator for the White Engine Company inspection process explained on pages 249–52. Make a list of other possible design variables that could be introduced into the simulator. Make the necessary changes in the logic diagram to accommodate these new variables. Construct a simulator using a compiler language for the White Engine Company inspection problem. Verify the results in the text, and study other design features.

8.4   Assume that design B is to be used in the White Engine Company problem, page 249. Assign the remaining tasks after the inspection operation to two operators who will perform them directly on the overhead conveyor. Make a precedence chart of the tasks, and assume that both the assembly and the tighten tasks for the spark plug and the drain plug can be separated.

8.5 Apply the line balancing method proposed by Arcus to the problem shown on page 262.

8.6 A student is given a methods project at a toy manufacturing plant. He is shown the design for a 16″ plastic model of the B-58 "Hustler" intercontinental bomber. The plane is now being assembled by individual workers doing the entire job, but the company wants it turned out on a small assembly line capable of assembling at least 12 planes per hour. The student analyzes the job carefully and finds that it can be broken down into nine distinct operations as follows:

Element	Time-min	He also finds that the relationships among these operations are as follows:
A	0.80	
B	1.30	A must precede B and C
C	3.40	B must precede E
D	1.50	C must precede F
E	1.80	D must precede F
F	1.50	E must precede G and H
G	1.00	F must precede H and I
H	2.10	G must precede I
I	1.10	
	14.50	

(a) Draw a precedence chart and set up a balanced assembly line to turn out this toy at the desired product level.
(b) Name and briefly discuss three factors that should be considered in determining whether an assembly line should be used to assemble a given product.

8.7 The Cole Stove Company makes a line of space heaters. Currently there is a revived market (international) for wood and coal space heaters. The company currently produces a magazine type of heater that is an assembly of cast-iron and sheet-metal parts. The heater is not assembled at an individual work station. The manager considers setting up the assembly on a product-line basis. The following is a list of the jobs constituting the assembly of the product.

Estimated job time (min)	Job	Description
1.50	1	Support channels are bolted inside the sheet-metal circular body. These channels support the ceramic lining.
3.60	2	The ashpit door hinge, the ashpit door frame, the ashpit door draft slide, the ashpit door handle, and the ashpit door are bolted together.
2.00	3	The fuel door, the fuel door wire drop handle, the fuel door frame, and the fuel door hinge are bolted together.
0.30	4	The grate slide and the grate are tied together with a cotter pin.
0.80	5	The two-part collar is bolted together.
0.60	6	The two halves of the down draft tube are bolted together. This tube conducts air from the surface of the fuel door to the combustion chamber.

2.00	7	The ashpit door subassembly (2) is bolted to the body.
0.50	8	The body as assembled in (1) is placed manually on a crate bottom on top of the conveyor.
2.00	9	The fuel door subassembly (3) is bolted to the top.
0.30	10	The grate ring is placed inside the body resting on the three support channels.
0.20	11	The grate subassembly (4) is placed inside the body on top of the grate ring.
1.50	12	The nine ceramic whole shapes are placed inside the body atop the circumference of the grate ring.
1.50	13	The ceramic half shapes are added.
4.20	14	A top ring for the ceramic shapes and ceramic shape support ring, front and left, are bolted together atop the ceramic shapes in conformity with the contour of the door opening.
2.00	15	The top is placed over the top ring and bolted to the body.
1.00	16	The collar section subassembly (5) is bolted to the top.
1.00	17	The top draft is bolted to the top.
2.00	18	The heater is sprayed on the outside surface.
0.50	19	The grate shaker, down draft tube, ashpan, and legs are packed inside the body in excelsior.
0.20	20	Bolts, nuts, and washers required for final assembly by the user are placed in a paper bag inside the heater.
5.00	21	The heater is crated with precut pieces of lumber.
32.70		

A precedence diagram for the product is shown below.

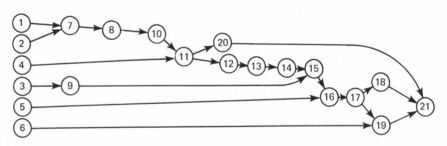

Assuming that the desired rate of output is around 12 units per hour, design the assembly line in terms of number of stations and work content at each station. On which jobs would you emphasize the methods analysis?

Bibliography

ARCUS, A. L., *Assembly Line Balancing by Computer*, Graduate School of Business, University of California, Berkeley, July 1962.

BUFFA, ELWOOD S., "Pacing Effects in Production Lines," *J. Ind. Eng.*, November–December 1961.

CONRAD, R., "Setting the Pace," Medical Research Council, APU 232-55, Applied Research Units, London, 1955.

FREEMAN, MICHAEL C., "The Effects of Breakdowns and Interstage Storage on Production Line Capacity," *J. Ind. Eng.*, July–August 1964.

GOODE, HENRY P., and S. SALTZMAN, "Estimating Inventory Limits in a Station Grouped Production Line," *J. Ind. Eng.*, November–December 1962.

HELD, M., R. M. KARP, and R. SHARESHIAN, "Assembly Line Balancing—Dynamic Programming with Precedence Constraints," *Operations Research*, vol. 11, no. 3, May–June 1963, pp. 442–59.

HUNT, G. C., "Sequential Arrays of Waiting Lines," *Operations Research*, vol. 4, 1956.

IGNALL, EDWARD J., "A Review of Assembly Line Balancing," *J. Ind. Eng.*, July–August 1965.

KILBRIDGE, M. D., and L. WESTER, "A Heuristic Method of Assembly Line Balancing," *J. Ind. Eng.*, vol. 12, no. 4, July–August 1961, pp. 292–98.

——, "A Review of Analytical Systems of Line Balancing," *Operations Research*, vol. 10, no. 5, September–October 1962, pp. 626–38.

REIS, IRVIN L., LLOYD L. DUNLAP, and MORRIS H. SCHNEIDER, "Conveyor Theory: The Individual Station," *J. Ind. Eng.*, July–August 1963.

TONGE, F. M., *A Heuristic Program for Assembly Line Balancing*. Englewood Cliffs, N.J.: Prentice-Hall, Inc., 1961, or "Summary of a Heuristic Line Balancing Procedure," *Management Science*, vol. 7, no. 1, October 1960, pp. 21–42.

9

Microproduction Systems: Man and Machine

Read to 286

INTRODUCTION

Plant layouts, flow processes, and product lines are aggregations of individual micro-man-machine systems. These microsystems are identified as jobs or operations, which are collections of resources at some geographic point to perform a very specific kind of work. The resources may include a machine, a piece of equipment, a human operator, various minor tools, and materials or objects to which certain properties are to be imparted. The basis for differentiation is the specificity of the output. Usually, however, the job or operation is physically identified by a machine, piece of equipment, or work station.

In this chapter, we are concerned with the design and improvement of these systems, particularly where the human being is present as an operator. If the operations were completely automated, we might be tempted to leave the matter to the engineer as a technical design problem, tempered by the economics of capital equipment investment. But even if the machine surplants the human as the source of productive work, man must act as the system installer, monitor, and maintainer in work situations. And, of course, it will be some time before the impact of automation is felt in many service operations.

The formalization of the design and improvement of work situations as a specific management responsibility is a twentieth-century phenomenon. Prior to the industrial revolution, work methods were a legacy handed down from one generation to the next and ensconced as trade secrets by the craft guilds. As the factory system matured in the nineteenth century, the more mechanically oriented job methods were jointly determined by the worker and the foreman. After scientific management assumed the responsibility for methods design, much of the content of twentieth-century industrial engineering involved specifying the material processing requirements for parts, improving methods of work, and setting time standards.

The more enlightened industrial engineering practice has always recognized that the prerogative of job design and improvement should not belong exclusively to management. One of the major tenets of *work simplification* has been to encourage worker participation in job improvement and to promote the simplification of work by the line organization. This is in contrast to the analysis and design of jobs by engineers with little or no participation by those who must either do the work or supervise it. Obviously, when the work is highly technical, then the latter approach may be justified. However, many jobs can be improved with substantial savings by making nontechnical changes. The aggregate effect of literally hundreds of changes to manual jobs through a program of work simplification can be substantial enough to warrant management's making the formal effort to train the line organization in methods of and attitudes toward work improvement.

The approaches taken to the design and improvement of operations and jobs vary from those which are "common sense" to those which require some engineering skill. Jobs that are mainly the application of manual power and control may be submitted to analysis and improvement by "principles" reflecting more common sense and experience than scientific tenets. On the other hand, jobs of monitoring complex equipment and systems demand the use of scientifically derived data for their design. Such data relate human physiological and psychological systems with hardware systems. Thus, "human engineering" is the term applied to the science of integrating the human being into a hardware system that he must control and monitor.

The approaches also involve different design criteria. The improvement of operations and processes is often based on economic criteria such as increased rate of output, reduced labor costs, elimination of scrap, or material spoilage, reduction in space, elimination of unnecessary material handling, and higher quality of work. The design of man-machine interfaces uses criteria such as system reliability, human fatigue, or elimination of human error. Job design criteria include mainly worker job satisfaction, reduction of monotony, and, in general, the effect of work assignments on psychological and social factors.

METHODS IMPROVEMENT

In the improvement of an operation, the design variables are related to the use of the human body, the arrangement of the workplace, and the design of tools and equipment. The depth of analysis and the kinds of techniques used in each of these areas depend on the nature of the job. A highly repetitive job that is expected to function for a long time and turn out a high volume may be subjected to intensive analysis, including a detailed study of the motions used by the operator. In a simple manual task, such as cleaning offices, the focal point of study might be in the design of tools and equipment.

The Operator Chart

One step in the improvement of a process is the analysis of symbolized steps shown in process charts. Similarly, operations can be analyzed in detail by the symbolic representation of the elements of the operation in chart form.

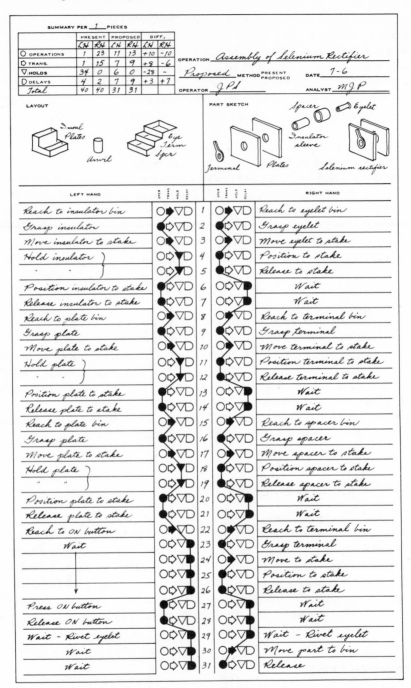

The operator chart shows the elements of work performed by a human in carrying out a repetitive task at a work station. Sometimes known as a "left hand–right hand" chart, it shows the sequence of elemental tasks performed by the left and right hands. The steps may vary in detail from a simple written list of the tasks on down to a detailed symbolic representation of the motions of each hand. For example, Figure 9.1 shows an operator chart for carrying out a simple task using the process chart symbols.

Each of the symbolic elements performed by the hands is examined in search for improvement of the method. The motions include, at the microscopic level, reaching for a part, moving a part, grasping, turning the hand, holding a part, etc. The criteria of improvement include such things as the elimination of unnecessary motions, the reduction of the distance that hands must reach or move, and the selection of a sequence of motions that result in a smooth and rhythmic motion pattern. While the detail in this kind of analysis may appear to be excessive, it must be realized that a 10% reduction in the cycle time is meaningful in the aggregate when one considers the number of cycles repeated over the life of the operation.

Principles of Motion Economy

Repetitive manual operations have many similar characteristics. As a result of empirical investigations and experience, certain "principles" have been derived for use in the design and improvement of operations. Twenty-two of these principles, which have become standard guides for methods improvement, are listed below.[1]

Use of the Human Body
1. The two hands should begin as well as complete their motions at the same instant.
2. The two hands should not be idle at the same instant except during rest periods.
3. Motions of the arms should be in opposite and symmetrical directions, instead of in the same direction, and should be made simultaneously.
4. Hand motions should be confined to the lowest classification with which it is possible to perform the work satisfactorily.
5. Momentum should be employed to assist the worker wherever possible, and it should be reduced to a minimum if it must be overcome by muscular effort.
6. Continuous curved motions are preferable to straight-line motions involving sudden and sharp changes in direction.
7. Ballistic movements are faster, easier, and more accurate than restricted (fixation) or "controlled" movements.
8. Rhythm is essential to the smooth and automatic performance of an operation, and the work should be arranged to permit easy and natural rhythm wherever possible.

Arrangement of the Work Place
9. Definite and fixed stations should be provided for all tools and materials.

---

[1] A more detailed explanation of these principles, their derivation, and examples is available in an early and comprehensive text in this area: R. M. Barnes, *Motion and Time Study*, 5th ed. New York: John Wiley & Sons, 1963.

10. Tools, materials, and controls should be located around the work place and as close in front of the worker as possible.
11. Gravity feed bins and containers should be used to deliver the material as close to the point of assembly or use as possible.
12. "Drop deliveries" should be used wherever possible.
13. Materials and tools should be located to permit the best sequence of motions.
14. Provisions should be made for adequate conditions for seeing. Good illumination is the first requirement for satisfactory visual perception.
15. The height of the work place and the chair should preferably be so arranged that alternate sitting and standing at work are easily possible.
16. A chair of the type and height to permit good posture should be provided for every worker.

Design of Tools and Equipment

17. The hands should be relieved of all work that can be performed more advantageously by the feet.
18. Two or more tools should be combined wherever possible.
19. Tools and materials should be pre-positioned wherever possible.
20. Where each finger performs some specific movement, such as in typewriting, the load should be distributed in accordance with the inherent capacities of the fingers.
21. Handles such as those used on cranks and large screwdrivers should be designed to permit as much of the surface of the hand to come in contact with the handle as possible. This is particularly true when considerable force is exerted in using the handle. For light assembly work, the screwdriver handle should be so shaped that it is smaller at the bottom than at the top.
22. Levers, crossbars, and handwheels should be located in such positions that the operator can manipulate them with the least change in body position and with the greatest mechanical advantage.

Each new or existing operation poses a unique problem in methods design or improvement. The principles of motion economy, checklists of predetermined questions directed to various facets of a job, or other guides are useful, but the analyst must still use his own creative ability to derive good alternative solutions. Each job, no matter how simple it appears, very often has the potential of improvement. The following are examples of improvements made in relatively simple operations.

EXAMPLE 9.1   Figure 9.2 shows the use of the lazy Susan concept of locating materials close to the operator. The rotating table permits one operator to locate about 200 file spaces directly in front of her.

EXAMPLE 9.2   Figure 9.3 shows a simple improved method of locating materials at a machine operation. The operator selects a part from the top half of the handtruck, machines the part, and disposes of it through the chute leading to the bottom half of the truck. The joint location of the disposal and pickup points eliminates unnecessary movement from one side of the machine to the other.

EXAMPLE 9.3   Figures 9.4a and b show desirable design features of manual assembly operations. In Figure 9.4a, parts used in assembling Stromberg-Carlson switches are readily accessible to the operator. The longest distance the operator must reach for parts and tools does not exceed 12 inches. Figure 9.4b shows an assembly operation

FIGURE **9.2**   Clerical filing operations used to process more than three-and-a-half million items per year. Courtesy of Con Edision of New York.

for switches used in Stromberg-Carlson telephone switching systems. This improvement resulted in an annual savings of $55,000. The changes incorporated a new bench fixture for holding the switch, the location of wires at the operator's fingertips, and the design of a plier with a pistol handle.

EXAMPLE 9.4   In the wiring and construction of telephone bays, ladders were previously used. Using improved methods, the operator wires the bay from a mounted platform that moves back and forth on tracks, as shown in Figure 9.5. In addition, the platform moves up and down to provide safer and faster wiring.

EXAMPLE 9.5   It previously took four men to move the telephone bays. As a result of a change in the structure of a four wheeled dolly, as shown in Figure 9.6, it now takes two men to perform the operation with increased safety.

These examples emphasize the application of methods improvement where relatively little or no technological complexity is involved. Again we note that while these improvements represent micro adjustments to production systems, the broadest application of this kind of approach has an important aggregate effect on production costs. The major management problem underlying the concepts of method improvement is not so much the actual application of the techniques per se, but rather their development. This means the recognition of the importance of

FIGURE **9.3** Improved location of materials at machine operation. From *Factory*, vol. 116, no. 2, February 1958, p. 84.

such work, a system of formal or informal rewards for accomplishment, provision for training in attitude and skills, and encouragement of participation in the simplification or improvement of jobs on every level of the organization.

CASE PROBLEM 9.1 Just after graduating from a master's program in business administration, Bruce Farnum was recently hired by the Goliath Tractor Company. For the first six months, he was assigned to the superintendent of the Accessory Manufacturing Department to work in an informal on-the-job training program. During part of this period, he worked jointly with the Industrial Engineering Department in trying to find areas where work simplification could be applied. This provided Farnum with a chance to become acquainted with the operations in accessory manufacturing while at the same time making a contribution to his job.

The company had recently decided to manufacture brake rings, which they had bought previously from a subcontractor. The last operation on the rings was to dip them in oil prior to packaging and shipment to assembly plants or dealers.

The oiling operation came to Farnum's attention because the operator had requested that the barrel in which the rings were dipped be placed on a raised platform to reduce the amount of bending necessary when dipping the rings. Farnum described the present operation on a standard LH-RH chart used by the Industrial Engineering Department, Figure 9.7. The chart shows the steps in the operation, the layout, and other pertinent information.

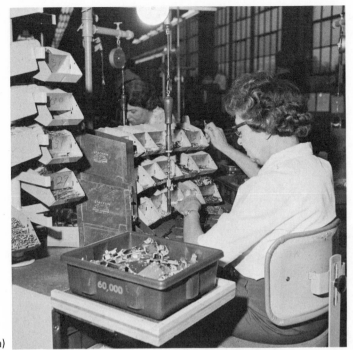

(a)

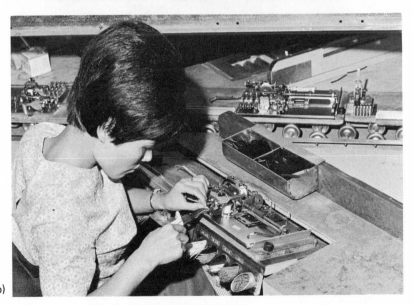

(b)

FIGURE **9.4**   (a) Location of parts close to operator in manual assembly operation. Courtesy of Stromberg Carlson Company. (b) Improved assembly operation incorporating certain principles of motion economy. Courtesy of Stromberg Carlson Company.

FIGURE **9.5** New method of assembling telephone bays. Courtesy of Stromberg
Carlson Company.

Because this was a simple manual operation, Farnum felt that he should be able
to come up with good ideas for its improvement. He wondered if spending the time
in making the LH-RH chart was worthwhile. Also, because of heavy seasonal demand,
the company had started working the job on the second shift, and Farnum was anxious
to get an improvement soon in the hope of possibly being able to eliminate that shift.

CASE PROBLEM 9.2 In October 1965, David Highland, president of Highland Green-
house Company, made a difficult decision to continue his operations in a city in upper
New York State. A major part of the business consisted in growing and selling cut
flowers mainly to wholesalers in a five-state area around his location. In the past five
years, the business had become extremely competitive due to the rise of southern
growers who enjoyed a more favorable environment and also due to the availability
of artificial flowers. In order to stay in New York State and remain competitive,
Highland decided to move from his present old plant to a new location outside the
city limits. The design of the new plant included a careful analysis of the production
methods in a search to find ways of lowering labor costs in both the design of the
buildings and the job methods.

One of the major operations, however, had not been given sufficient thought. This

FIGURE **9.6**   Improved method of handling telephone bays. Courtesy of Stromberg Carlson Company.

operation consisted in "grading" the cut flowers just prior to the packing operations. The criterion for classifying the flowers into grades is the weight of the flower, which reflects the quality of the stem and the flower itself. The heavier the weight, the higher the quality. Grading had become important in the industry as a whole, and competitive advantages depended partially on the ability to deliver the kind of quality required by the wholesaler.

In the old or present method of grading, the flowers were brought in bundles from the cutting operation in the greenhouses to a large table. Figure 9.8 shows the general layout.

At point B, the flowers are weighed and sorted into boxes at C, each box containing a certain grade of flower. The boxes are then moved to section D, where the flowers are tied in bundles of 13 and the bundles packaged. A second or third weighing station could be added if the demand required.

David Highland considered this present method of grading unsatisfactory. For one thing, he felt that certain flowers were damaged while being placed in and carried by the boxes at C. He decided that a thorough study should be made of this operation; he turned the job over to his son, Larry, who had recently joined the company after graduating from a state agricultural college.

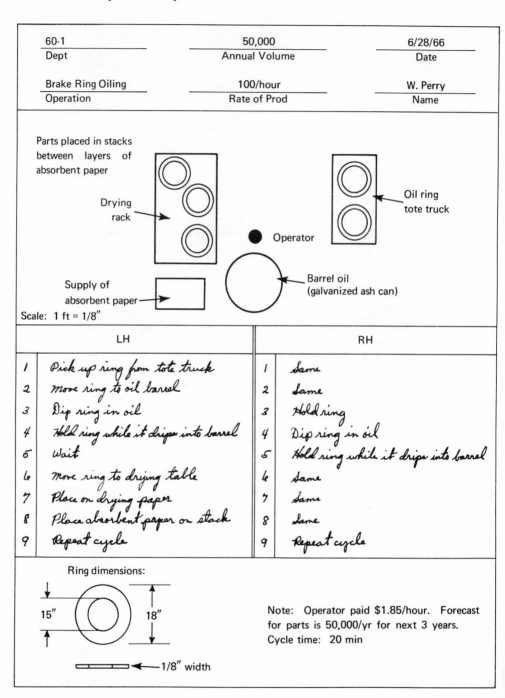

60-1	50,000	6/28/66
Dept	Annual Volume	Date
Brake Ring Oiling	100/hour	W. Perry
Operation	Rate of Prod	Name

Parts placed in stacks between layers of absorbent paper

Drying rack

Oil ring tote truck

Operator

Supply of absorbent paper

Barrel oil (galvanized ash can)

Scale: 1 ft = 1/8"

	LH		RH
1	Pick up ring from tote truck	1	Same
2	Move ring to oil barrel	2	Same
3	Dip ring in oil	3	Hold ring
4	Hold ring while it drips into barrel	4	Dip ring in oil
5	Wait	5	Hold ring while it drips into barrel
6	Move ring to drying table	6	Same
7	Place on drying paper	7	Same
8	Place absorbent paper on stack	8	Same
9	Repeat cycle	9	Repeat cycle

Ring dimensions:

15"   18"

1/8" width

Note: Operator paid $1.85/hour. Forecast for parts is 50,000/yr for next 3 years. Cycle time: 20 min

FIGURE 9.7 Left hand-right hand chart for brake ring oiling operation.

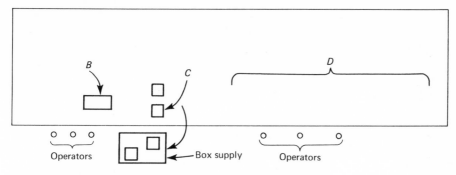

<figure>FIGURE **9.8**   Present layout for flower grading.</figure>

Automation of Methods Design

The design of a method for performing a repetitive or complex manual operation often involves the analysis of the job in terms of elemental hand motions. Examples of typical hand motions are reaching for a part, grasping an object, or orienting two objects. Individually, these motions consume a period of time on the order of $\frac{1}{1000}$ to $\frac{1}{100}$ of a minute. A variety of motion systems are in use today and consist of a standardized description of fundamental hand motions with associated standard motion times.[2] A given job method and time are simultaneously synthesized by a particular sequence or pattern of these standard motions and usually displayed in the form of the left hand–right hand chart.

The translation of the functional requirements of a job into a detailed method as described by a motion pattern requires some logical procedure by the engineer. The possibilities of defining this logic in order to semi-automate the procedure have been investigated. Figure 9.9 presents the features of a computer program proposed by Mason and Towne for analyzing human tasks in electronic maintenance operations (ARMAN or Artificial Methods Analyst). The system input consists of an identification of the body members of the operator, parts to be manipulated, tools, and location of these elements at the start of the job. The output consists of an annotated left hand–right hand chart showing the motion sequence for each hand and the standard times. The actual computer program consists of 1) an executive routine, which directs the synthesis of the required motion pattern, 2) analytical subroutines, which perform the micromotion analyses, and 3) criterion files, which contain the transient location of parts, tools, and human body members, as well as general criteria for sequencing motions.

The authors have evaluated the procedure as applied specifically to electronic maintenance operations with "excellent" results, although the criteria for evaluation are not discussed. They conclude that the application of the concept in a universal environment will require considerable advanced research and develop-

---

[2] See pages 386–88 for a description of a motion system.

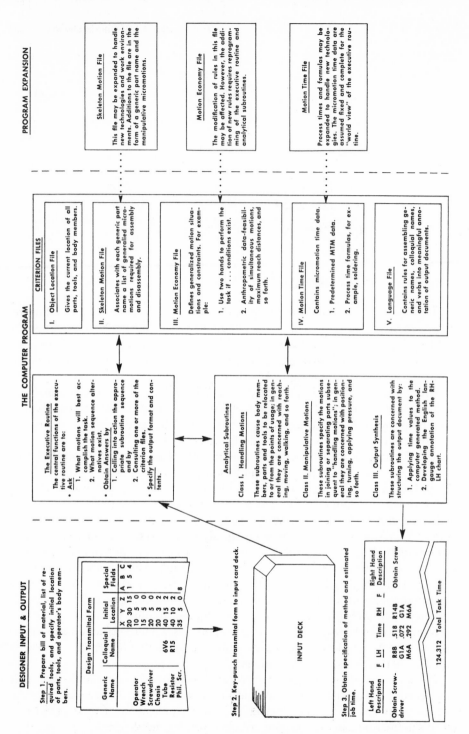

PROGRAM EXPANSION

Skeleton Motion File

This file may be expanded to handle new technologies and work environments. Additions to the file are in the form of a generic part name and the manipulative micromotions.

Motion Economy File

The modification of rules in this file may be affected. However, the addition of new rules requires reprogramming of the executive routine and analytical subroutines.

Motion Time File

Process times and formulas may be expanded to handle new technologies. The micromotion time data are assumed fixed and complete for the "world view" of the executive routine.

THE COMPUTER PROGRAM

CRITERION FILES

I. **Object Location File**

Gives the current location of all parts, tools, and body members.

II. **Skeleton Motion File**

Associates with each generic part name a list of generalized micro-motions required for assembly and disassembly.

III. **Motion Economy File**

Defines generalized motion situations and constraints. For example:

1. Use two hands to perform the task if ... conditions exist.
2. Anthropometric data–feasibility of simultaneous motions, maximum reach distances, and so forth.

IV. **Motion Time File**

Contains micromotion time data.

1. Predetermined MTM data.
2. Process time formulas, for example, soldering.

V. **Language File**

Contains rules for assembling generic names, colloquial names, and verbs into meaningful annotation of output documents.

The Executive Routine

The central functions of the executive routine are to:

- Ask
  1. What motions will best accomplish the task.
  2. What motion sequence alternatives exist.
- Obtain Answers by
  1. Calling into action the appropriate subroutine sequence and by
  2. Consulting one or more of the criterion files.
- Specify the output format and contents.

Analytical Subroutines

Class I. Handling Motions

These subroutines cause body members, parts and tools to be relocated to or from the points of usage; in general they are concerned with reaching, moving, walking, and so forth.

Class II. Manipulative Motions

These subroutines specify the motions in joining or separating parts subsequent to "handling motions"; in general they are concerned with positioning, turning, applying pressure, and so forth.

Class III. Output Synthesis

These subroutines are concerned with structuring the output document by:

1. Applying time values to the computer generated method.
2. Developing the English language annotation of the RH-LH chart.

DESIGNER INPUT & OUTPUT

Step 1. Prepare bill of material, list of required tools, and specify initial location of parts, tools, and operator's body members.

Design Transmittal Form

Generic Name	Colloquial Name	Initial Location			Special Fields		
		X	Y	Z	A	B	C
					1	5	4
Operator		20	30	15	0		
Wrench		10	5	0			
Screwdriver		15	5	0			
Chasis		20	5	0			
Tube	6V6	20	3	2			
Resistor	R15	40	15	2			
Phil. Scr.		35	10	5			
							8

Step 2. Key-punch transmittal form to input card deck.

INPUT DECK

Step 3. Obtain specification of method and estimated job time.

Left Hand Description	F	LH	Time	RH	F	Right Hand Description
Obtain Screw-driver		R8B	.518	R14B		Obtain Screw
		G1A	.072	G1A		
		M6A	.292	M6A		

124.312   Total Task Time

FIGURE **9.9** Relationship between major components of methods analysis system. From Anthony K. Mason and Douglas M. Towne, "Toward Synthetic Methods Analysis," *J. Ind. Eng.*, vol. XVIII, no. 1, January 1967, p. 53, Fig. 1.

ment, particularly in the kind of data needed to support the logical structure of motion sequence determination and in the kind of information required as input to the system.

MAN-MACHINE INTERFACE

The continued evolution of complex operating systems of men and machines has forced the designer to consider in more detail the relationship between the human being and the machine he must control, monitor, or maintain. The emphasis on integrating the human being into these complex systems has led to the profession of human engineering, variously referred to as biomechanics, human factors analysis, engineering psychology, and ergonomics. Human engineering is the application of the techniques and data of psychology, physiology, medicine, and anthropology to the problems of man-machine systems design. The essential problem is the design of machines, equipment, and physical systems for their adaptation to the capabilities of the human as a component of the system. The range of application is both large and important, varying from the design of consumer durable goods to the design of complex military systems, automated industrial processes, and space systems.

The impetus for the concentrated interest in the relationship between man and machine was provided by World War II. The technological developments such as radar, fire control systems, high-speed aircraft, and flight control systems resulted in the awareness that such systems were often poorly designed in terms of the abilities of men to control, monitor, and maintain them. There was insufficient time to gain experience that would lead to an evolutionary change in the systems to reduce the causes contributing to human error and inefficiency. Furthermore, there was no formal body of knowledge that systems designers could draw upon.

Historically, the industrial engineer has relied on the empirically derived principles of motion economy and job design to improve the efficiency of manual tasks. These principles consider the design of workplace, tools, and equipment, and some of them reflect the work that has been done in human engineering. However, much of the historical work has concentrated on fitting the operator to equipment design constraints by worker selection, training, and minor adaptations through the design of fixtures, tools, and workplace equipment. The adjustment of the human operator to the work system was a matter of learning and experience at a possible cost of psychological or physiological worker discomfort. By World War II, the human demands of system control involved less physical effort than psychological and sensory requirements and adaptations to unusual environmental stresses. Economic criteria of design were no longer solely paramount, and such things as worker fatigue, rapidity of response to signals, reduction of error, safety, and reliability of system operation assumed importance.

The requirement for an optimum man-machine interface led to the development of a body of knowledge that has been translated into design rules for adapting machines and equipment to human capabilities. Human factors research has pro-

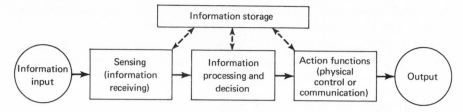

FIGURE **9.10**   Types of functions performed by man or machine components of man-machine systems. From *Human Factors Engineering* by E. J. McCormick. © 1964 by McGraw-Hill, Inc. Used by permission of McGraw-Hill Book Company.

vided extensive scientific data about the sensory and physical aptitudes of the human being and their limitations. These, in turn, have given substance to the profession of human engineering as an applied science.

In designing and improving operations and jobs, we are now interested in the point where the man interacts with the machine. This interaction occurs in so many different ways in our own personal lives that it is not difficult to perceive the problem. We are constantly interacting with consumer goods in our environment, and we have already noted the importance of product design as it relates to the consumer operating system. This is part of human engineering.

In complex man-machine systems, the substance of the design problem involves three fundamental things. First, there is determination of the various functions that are to be performed by the operator, as opposed to those which will be mechanized. Second, there is the selection of the types of information and controls that will be required by the operator to perform the assigned tasks. Finally, there is the design of the controls, information displays, their locations relative to the operator's position, and the design of environmental equipment and their location.

Human versus Machine Capabilities

The hardware components of the system are essentially extensions of human capabilities. Figure 9.10 shows the elements of the man-machine "interface," or the point at which the man interacts with the machine. Each of these elements may be performed to some degree by a human being.

The assignment of functions to the human operator requires knowledge about his relative capabilities, compared to alternative possibilities of mechanizing or automating these functions. Much of human factors research has been directed toward determining both the advantages and the disadvantages of man versus machine.

Schnorr[3] notes the comparative advantages of man and machines as follows:

---

[3] Charles G. Schnorr, "Human Engineering," *J. Ind. Eng.*, vol. IX, no. 6, November–December 1958, p. 508.

Humans are relatively superior to machines, in terms of our present understanding of human and equipment capabilities, with respect to the following:

1. Ability to handle unexpected events—machine must be explicitly programmed.
2. Ability to use perceptual constancies (e.g., to recognize objects and places despite varying conditions of perception).
3. Ability to use sequential dependencies in the real world (i.e., profit from experience).
4. Sensitivity to a wide variety of stimuli (heat, light, sound, pressure, etc.); range of sensitivity, however it is restricted.
5. Originality in putting to use incidental intelligence picked up over a period of time.
6. Detecting signals in an overlapping noise spectrum (e.g., detection of radar signals through jamming).
7. Capability for improvising and adopting flexible procedures (e.g., can reprogram easily and quickly; can vary performance tolerances readily).
8. Capability for acting as a servo with a wide variety of modes (e.g., linear amplifier, integrator, etc.).
9. Capability to perform under some conditions of overload and ability to select own inputs.
10. Ability to reason inductively (i.e., to make generalizations from specific observations).

Humans are inferior to machines with respect to the following:

1. Monitoring other men or machines.
2. Exerting large amounts of force smoothly and precisely.
3. Performing routine, repetitive tasks (human becomes bored, fatigued, careless).
4. Rapid computing and handling large amounts of stored information.
5. Ability to reason deductively (i.e., to use rules for processing information).
6. Responding quickly to control signals.

Man is generally excluded from the performance of certain functions where conditions are likely to result in human errors:

1. Perceptual requirements which are beyond or near physiological limits or which conflict with established habit patterns.
2. Response requirements which are physically difficult, conflict with established habit patterns or which cannot be readily checked or monitored for their adequacy (e.g., the application of extreme physical force).
3. Decisions which require undue reliance on memory must be preceded by extensive organization of information or must be accomplished in too short a time in view of other necessary activities.
4. Communication requirements which interfere with other activities.
5. Tasks which overload the human, which result in inadequate workload distribution with respect to time or do not permit adequate or timely monitoring of the general situation.

Principles Related to Equipment Design

The amount and variety of information related to the design of equipment, controls, and workplace is so voluminous and well documented that we need note only a few examples here to convey the general ideas.

For fixed dials with moving pointers
  Position numerals horizontal to line of sight, not radially.

For moving dials with fixed pointers
  Position numerals radially. Pointer preferably should be in twelve o'clock position.

If space is not limited, it is desirable to place the numerals beyond the scale markers to avoid having numerals obscured by pointer. (if there is any restriction at all on space, however, it is usually desirable to place the numerals inside the markers in order to have the scale as large as possible).

For open-window dials
  Window should show numbered scale markers at either side, to indicate direction of scale.

Numerals should be placed to appear right side up when exposed.

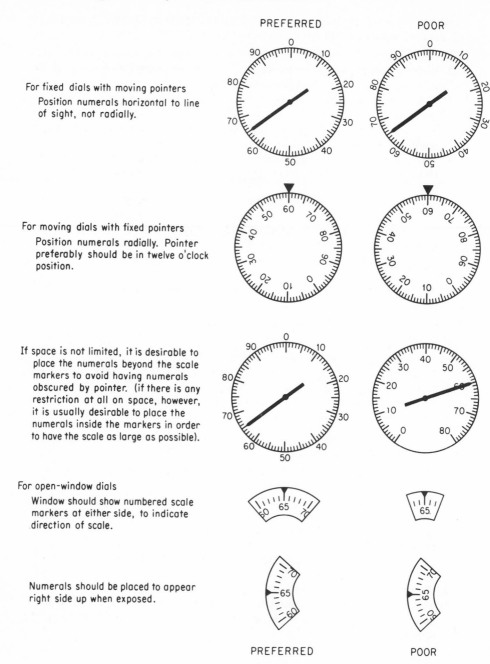

FIGURE **9.11** Preferred practice in the printing of numerals on visual instruments. From *Human Factors Engineering* by E. J. McCormick. © 1964 by McGraw-Hill, Inc. Used by permission of McGraw-Hill Book Company.

The proper design of information displays and control devices has consumed a good deal of attention in applied human engineering. This is obviously reasonable, since in many man-machine systems, the operator is essentially an information processor and control manipulator. Figure 9.11 shows preferred practice in the design of visual instruments and exemplifies the results of concerted research in this area.

Human engineering is very relevant to the design of work stations and equipment to be operated or monitored by human beings. In the design of equipment, the relationship between the operator and the equipment should permit maximum visibility of the work area. Also, tools and controls should be placed so as to maximize speed and ease of handling and to minimize error. Figure 9.12 shows a unique design of an aerial rock drill. The cab can be moved along the boom to permit the operator to be located directly in front of the drilling location. The operator is clear of falling rock, flying chips, and dust. The entire rig is controlled from the cab, where controls are designed for safe and easy reach.

MULTIPLE MACHINE ASSIGNMENTS

There are many situations in industry where a machine or a service operation requires only periodic or random attention by an operator. In the case of machines, they may be semi-automatic, requiring someone to load and unload them at regular or random intervals, or they may be fully automatic, in which case they require service or maintenance at random points in time. As examples of service operations, consider a conveyor that requires periodic loading or unloading, a patient in a hospital ward who requires attention at random times, an automatic vending machine that has to be periodically replenished, etc.

All these situations present the possibility that one operator or attendant can service more than one machine, piece of equipment, or service center. The basic question, therefore, is the number of machines that should be assigned to one man. Hereafter, we will use the terms "machine" and "operator" in a general sense.

Semi-Automatic Machines

The case of tending a set of semi-automatic machines is typified by the following simple example. A part is manually loaded onto a semi-automatic machine, and the machine is started. It processes the part and stops automatically when the task is completed. At this point, the machine is unloaded, and the cycle is repeated. The following data apply to the operation:

(U) = time to unload   (2.0 min)
(L) = time to load   (1.0 min)
(P) = process time   (5.0 min)

We want to know what the output rate will be for a system of one operator and one or more machines. If the times are deterministic (nonrandom), then the Man-Machine Chart (Figure 9.13) shows what will happen if one man runs one, two,

FIGURE **9.12**   Location of operator's cab for maximum vision. Cab moves along crane to any desired position rather than in a fixed position at the crane base. Courtesy of Athey Products Corporation.

or three machines. Note that when the man runs three machines, the idle time has shifted from the man to the machines. The hourly rate of output does not include any allowances for interruptions to the system.

Certain industrial operations can be designed in this fashion. If the process times have little time variability, as is the case with many machines if the raw material is uniform, then the system consisting of man and machine can be synchronized to produce in a uniform cycle. This is true provided that the loading and unloading tasks are simple enough so that the variability in the time to perform them is reduced to a minimum.

The choice of the number of machines may be based either on some required rate of output or on a combination that minimizes the sum of labor and machine costs per unit of output.

In the case of semi-automatic machines, the more general question is what rate of output can be expected if there is significant variability in either the processing

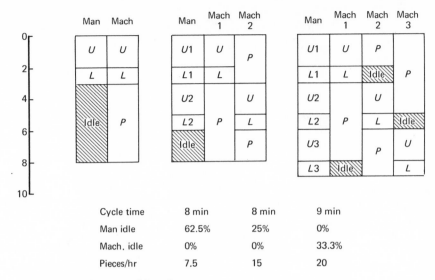

Cycle time	8 min	8 min	9 min
Man idle	62.5%	25%	0%
Mach. idle	0%	0%	33.3%
Pieces/hr	7.5	15	20

FIGURE **9.13**   Man-machine charts.

or handling times or both. Also, we might wish to examine cases where one man operates a set of machines and each machine in the set is different with unique process and handling times.

For example, the Sandra Corporation makes large metal tanks to customer specification. One of the later operations in the shop is to anneal the tanks in a semi-automatic annealing furnace located at the end of the shop. There are three such furnaces located side by side. The tanks are brought to the furnaces by an overhead crane, which deposits them in front of one of the furnaces. A tank is loaded into the furnace by an electric hand-operated hoist and remains in the furnace for a predetermined time, after which it is unloaded onto a large gravity conveyor, which sends it to the next operation. The time that the tank spends in the furnace is set by the operator and depends on the size of the tank and the type of metal. The average time to load the furnace is five minutes and to unload, ten minutes. The average annealing time is 40 minutes. The question is, what will be the expected rate of output if one man tends the three furnaces?

A man-machine chart using the expected times is shown in Figure 9.14. However, the variation in the size of the tanks introduces variability in both the handling and processing times, and the system will not perform exactly as depicted in Figure 9.14. Also, there is no reason to assume that the operator will service the furnaces in exactly the same sequence in each cycle. Therefore, we will examine the arrangement using a model that considers the random nature of the times.

AN ANALYTICAL MODEL: If we assume that the furnaces will be serviced in the same order in every cycle, we can express the system by the following equations.[4]

---

[4] R. W. Conway, W. L. Maxwell, and M. W. Sampson, "On the Cyclic Servicing of Semiautomatic Machines," *J. Ind. Eng.*, vol. XIII, no. 2, March–April 1962, pp. 105–07.

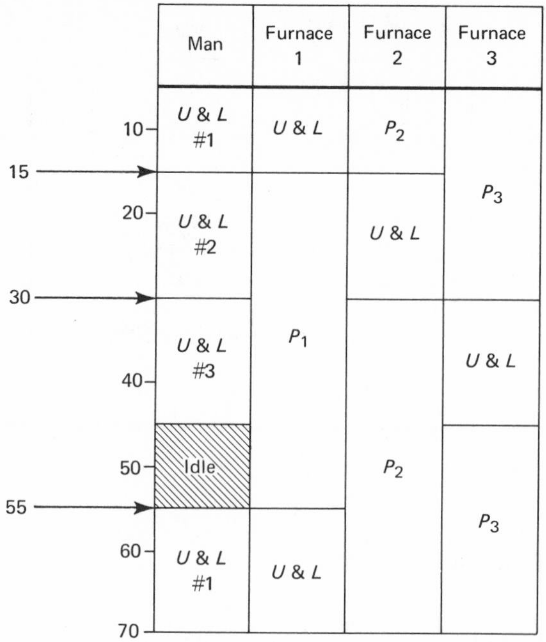

Man	Furnace 1	Furnace 2	Furnace 3
U & L #1 (10)	*U & L*	P_2	
(15 →)			P_3
U & L #2 (20)		*U & L*	
(30 →)	P_1		
U & L #3 (40)			*U & L*
Idle (50)		P_2	
(55 →)			P_3
U & L #1 (60)	*U & L*		
(70)			

Cycle time: 55 min
Man idle time: 10 min
Man idle percent: 18.2
Machine idle time: 0
Machine idle percent: 0
Units produced per hour: 3.27

Average time to load = 5.00 min
Average time to unload = 10.00 min
Average process time = 40.00 min

FIGURE **9.14** Man-machine chart for three-furnace operation.

Let

$P(i,j)$ = the random variable representing the processing time of the ith machine during the jth cycle. In our particular example, $i = 3$, and j can take on any value greater than zero.

$U(i,j)$ = the random variable representing the time to unload and load the ith machine during the jth cycle

$W(i,j)$ = the time that the ith machine must wait to be unloaded and loaded during the jth cycle

$D(i,j)$ = the time that the man must wait during the jth cycle to service the ith machine. The cycle is defined such that $D(i,j)$ will be at the end of the cycle. But for $i \neq 1$, $D(i,j)$ will precede $U(i,j)$.

C_j = the length of the jth cycle. In this case, the cycle is defined for the man and is the time from the start of unloading and loading machine 1 until the exact point of unloading and loading machine 1 is next reached.

Let us now consider the condition on the kth cycle:

$$C_k = U(1, k) + D(2, k) + U(2, k) + D(3, k) + U(3, k) + D(1, k) \tag{1}$$

Also,

$$C_k = U(1, k) + P(1, k) + W(1, k) \tag{2}$$

Now, in any given cycle, $D(1, k)$ and $W(1, k)$ cannot be both positive and nonzero. That is, either the machine waits for the man or the man waits for the machine. If we substitute Equation (2) into Equation (1), we have

$$D(1, k) = P(1, k) + W(1, k) - D(2, k) - U(2, k) - D(3, k) - U(3, k) \tag{3}$$

If $W(1, k)$ is zero, then $D(1, k)$ will be equal to Equation (3) less the term $W(1, k)$. On the other hand, if $D(1, k)$ is zero, then $W(1, k)$ will be the negative of Equation (3). Therefore, if we let

$$X(1, k) = P(1, k) - D(2, k) - U(2, k) - D(3, k) - U(3, k)$$

then $D(1, k)$ will have either its maximum value of zero or $X(1, k)$, and $W(1, k)$ will have either its maximum value of zero or *minus* $X(1, k)$.

We can set up similar expressions for each of the cycles involving the other machines. That is, for the second machine, the first cycle expressions are

$$C'_k = U(2, k) + D(3, k) + U(3, k) + D(1, k) + U(1, k) + D(2, k)$$

and

$$C'_k = U(2, k) + P(2, k) + W(2, k)$$

The expressions for the second machine are the same as for the first machine, except that the subscript i is increased by 1. In the expressions for machine 3, the subscript i is increased by 2, etc.

These equations can then be solved for the unknown D's and W's. However, this is a difficult task if the number of cycles is particularly large.

SIMULATION: If the sequence of servicing is constant, we can construct a computer model of the system using the above equations as the basis for calculation, or, in the more general case, using a Monte Carlo simulation.

Table 9.1 shows the results of simulation assuming a given sequence of furnace tending for each cycle. Each trial constitutes a unique set of unload-load and processing time parameters for a sample size of 50 cycles.

Suppose a study reveals that the system parameters are 40-5-15-2 (average processing time, standard deviation of processing time, average unload-load time, standard deviation of unload-load time, respectively). This corresponds to trial 1. In this case, we would expect an average hourly rate of 3.05 units or a 6.7% reduction over the rate of output determined by using the deterministic times. The remaining trials give some idea of the effect of variability for a range of time parameters.

Obviously, a flexible order of servicing the furnaces would suggest a higher rate of output. If the operator is idle in any cycle, he waits for the first furnace that will demand service and then tends to it, regardless of the order in which it was last served. Using a Monte Carlo simulation and permitting a flexible order of serving, the hourly output rate is 3.14 units for the case of 40-5-15-2. This yields

TABLE **9.1**   Simulation for three furnaces (each sample size = 50 cycles).

Trial No.	Average processing time	Standard dev. processing time	Average unload-load time	Standard dev. unload-load time	Total time for 50 cycles	Average units produced per hour	Average percent man idle	Average percent machine idle
Base	40	0	15	0	2,750	3.27	18.2	0
1	40	5	15	2	2,904	3.05	19.5	12.0
2	40	5	15	4	2,983	3.01	24.9	15.9
3	40	5	15	6	3,067	2.93	24.3	21.6
4	40	7	15	2	3,010	2.98	23.5	18.6
5	40	10	15	2	2,965	3.04	23.3	21.5
6	40	10	15	4	3,025	2.85	25.6	20.9
7	40	15	15	2	3,326	2.70	30.8	42.7
8	50	5	15	2	3,399	2.58	32.5	7.7
9	50	10	15	2	3,568	2.52	35.5	19.6
10	50	10	15	5	3,623	2.48	36.1	23.4

Times are normally distributed.

only about a 3% increase over the fixed sequence. When the processing and handling times are not as well balanced, as the ratio of 40 and 15, we might expect a more favorable performance for the flexible sequencing.

Finally, in all the above cases, the machines were considered to be alike. A general-purpose simulator should permit an examination of a man-machine combination where the unload-load and processing time parameters are unique for each machine. For example, in the case of the furnaces, we might wish to examine the possibility of letting each furnace specialize in a given size or kind of tank.

Grouping Men and Machines

So far we have dealt with a system consisting of one man operating a number of machines, where the primary task was the unloading and loading of the machines. Furthermore, the service times were a significant proportion of the processing times.

More generally, we might be confronted with a situation of a set of machines being serviced by a group of servicemen. The system might be, for example, a bank of automatic machines, each requiring service at random times. The service requirement would include preparing supplies of input materials, minor maintenance, tool replacements, or other machine adjustments. The number of machines assigned to a serviceman might be large and the service times might be a relatively small proportion of the machine running time.

Such a man-machine system may be treated as a "finite" queuing system. The term "finite" refers to the population of machines or "customers," which is fixed and small, at least relative to the more general kinds of queuing systems. The basic problem is to determine the number of men or operators to be assigned to the system. The criteria are such things as desired rate of output or an assignment that minimizes the machine and labor costs of operating the system.

A finite queuing model was originally proposed by Palm in the late 1940's.[5] It permits the calculation of the expected waiting time for a machine, given the number of machines in the system, the number of servicemen, and the parameters of distributions for arrival and service rates. We will examine only the results and leave the matter of derivation to the source indicated.

We will use the following notation:

m = total number of machines (customers) in the system

n = number of machines requiring service at any given time

r = number of servicemen

P_n = probability that n machines require service at any given time $(0 \leq n \leq m - r)$

P_0 = probability that none of the machines requires service at any given time

μ = rate at which machines are serviced

λ = rate at which machines demand service; $1/\lambda$ equals the average machine running time

λ/μ = service factor

$E(R)$ = expected percent of time a machine is running (not waiting or being serviced)

$E(W)$ = expected percent of time a machine must wait for service

$E(S)$ = expected percent of time a machine is being serviced

Then, for any given unit of time,

$$E(R) + E(W) + E(S) = 1$$

Now, each of these three terms can be expressed as follows:

$$E(R) = \frac{\sum_{n=0}^{m} (m - n)P_n}{m}$$

$$E(W) = \sum_{n=r+1}^{m} \frac{(n - r)P_n}{m}$$

$$E(S) = \frac{\lambda}{\mu} \sum_{n=0}^{m} \frac{(m - n)P_n}{m}$$

Since

$$E(S) = \left(\frac{\lambda}{\mu}\right) E(R)$$

then

$$E(R) + \frac{\lambda}{\mu} E(R) + E(W) = 1$$

$$E(R) = \frac{1 - E(W)}{1 + \lambda/\mu} \tag{4}$$

---

[5] Docent C. Palm, "The Assignment of Workers in Servicing Machines," translated by Birger Lovgren, *J. Ind. Eng.*, January–February 1958.

TABLE **9.2**   Table for determining P_n.

(1)	(2)	(3)	(4)	(5)
	Machines being serviced	Machines waiting for service	$\dfrac{P_n}{P_0}$	
n				P_n
0	0	0	1.000	—
1	1	0	—	—
2	2	0	—	—
.				
.				
.				
$r+1$	r	1	—	—
.				
.				
.				
m	r	$m-r$	—	—

$$\sum \frac{P_n}{P_0} = \frac{1}{P_0} \qquad 1.000$$

Equation (4) provides the basis for making an economical analysis of the system. However, we need the method of calculating $E(W)$. For this we require the probability distribution of the system state (the number of machines waiting for service). Palm's method requires the recursive solution of two equations:

$$\frac{P_n}{P_0} = \frac{m!}{n!(m-n)!} \left(\frac{\lambda}{\mu}\right)^n \qquad (0 < n < r) \tag{5}$$

$$\frac{P_n}{P_0} = \frac{m!}{r!r^{n-r}(m-n)!} \left(\frac{\lambda}{\mu}\right)^n \qquad (n \geq r) \tag{6}$$

The method for calculating P_n is as follows: Referring to Table 9.2, for each of the states n, we determine P_n/P_0 using Equations (5) and (6) for a given value of r. The value of P_0 is then determined from the expression

$$\sum \frac{P_n}{P_0} = \frac{1}{P_0} \sum P_n = \frac{1}{P_0} \tag{7}$$

The value of P_n for each particular value of n is now calculated by multiplying each value in column 4 by the value of P_0. Then, the expected number of machines waiting and, in turn, the expected waiting time are easily determined.

Palm's method assumes that both the arrival and service rates are Poisson distributed. Deviations from this assumption may not be important. It is suggested that the method is valid if the distribution of the number of machines waiting, as determined from empirical studies of an existing system, conforms with the theoretical distribution. Just as with general queuing models assuming infinite populations, an exhaustive treatment of variations in assumptions is difficult.

The problem of computation has been eased by the development of tables that

TABLE **9.3** Machine-serviceman table.*

a	r	5m		10m		15m		20m		30m		40m	
		f	i	f	i	f	i	f	i	f	i	f	i
0.025	1	.8784	.0026	.7577	.0065	.6384	.0117	.5213	.0187	.2993	.0424	.1161	.0941
	2	.9390	.0000	.8780	.0003	.8172	.0007	.7564	.0013	.6353	.0033	.5154	.0065
	3	.9593	.0000	.9187	.0000	.8781	.0000	.8374	.0001	.7562	.0003	.6751	.0009
	4	.9695	.0000	.9390	.0000	.9085	.0000	.8780	.0000	.8171	.0000	.7561	.0001
	6	.9797	.0000	.9593	.0000	.9390	.0000	.9187	.0000	.8780	.0000	.8374	.0000
	8	.9848	.0000	.9695	.0000	.9543	.0000	.9390	.0000	.9085	.0000	.8780	.0000
0.05	1	.7644	.0103	.5380	.0297	.3300	.0620	.1589	.1168	.0085	.3059	.0000	.4750
	2	.8810	.0003	.7624	.0020	.6447	.0052	.5288	.0105	.3080	.0312	.1233	.0795
	3	.9206	.0000	.8413	.0001	.7620	.0005	.6830	.0014	.5262	.0050	.3732	.0130
	4	.9405	.0000	.8810	.0000	.8214	.0000	.7619	.0002	.6432	.0009	.5251	.0027
	6	.9603	.0000	.9206	.0000	.8810	.0000	.8413	.0000	.7619	.0000	.6826	.0001
	8	.9702	.0000	.9405	.0000	.9107	.0000	.8810	.0000	.8214	.0000	.7619	.0000
0.10	1	.5640	.0407	.2146	.1360	.0365	.2934	.0019	.4510	.0000	.6333	.0000	.7250
	2	.7732	.0023	.5519	.0143	.3458	.0405	.1726	.0899	.0106	.2745	.0000	.4500
	3	.8485	.0001	.6975	.0016	.5484	.0065	.4092	.0169	.1536	.0689	.0204	.1919
	4	.8864	.0000	.7728	.0002	.6594	.0010	.5470	.0034	.3299	.0172	.1423	.0565
	6	.9242	.0000	.8485	.0000	.7727	.0000	.6970	.0001	.5460	.0011	.3970	.0051
	8	.9432	.0000	.8864	.0000	.8295	.0000	.7727	.0000	.6591	.0000	.5457	.0004
0.15	1	.4045	.0869	.0659	.2838	.0022	.4900	.0000	.6167	.0000	.7444	.0000	.8083
	2	.6751	.0066	.3758	.0429	.1433	.1243	.0274	.2543	.0000	.4889	.0000	.6167
	3	.7827	.0004	.5681	.0065	.3648	.0260	.1897	.0682	.0138	.2439	.0001	.4250
	4	.8370	.0000	.6742	.0009	.5135	.0054	.3592	.0174	.1069	.0871	.0076	.2391
	6	.8913	.0000	.7826	.0000	.6740	.0002	.5656	.0010	.3537	.0090	.1643	.0390
	8	.9185	.0000	.8370	.0000	.7554	.0000	.6739	.0000	.5113	.0008	.3513	.0053
0.20	1	.2849	.1418	.0184	.4110	.0002	.6001	.0000	.7000	.0000	.8000	.0000	.8500
	2	.5891	.0138	.2404	.0884	.0465	.2372	.0028	.4017	.0000	.6000	.0000	.7000
	3	.7225	.0010	.4536	.0165	.2205	.0646	.0665	.1599	.0005	.4003	.0000	.5500
	4	.7917	.0000	.5845	.0027	.3851	.0161	.2088	.0506	.0181	.2144	.0001	.4001
	6	.8611	.0000	.7222	.0000	.5836	.0007	.4468	.0042	.1956	.0347	.0363	.1327
	8	.8958	.0000	.7917	.0000	.6875	.0000	.5834	.0002	.3777	.0044	.1882	.0258

m = number of machines
r = number of servicemen
$$a = \frac{l}{u} = \frac{\text{average servicing time}}{\text{average run time}}$$
i = average machine wait time $\Big\}$ expressed as a decimal fraction
f = average serviceman wait time

* Computed under the direction of Mr. Robert H. Morris by Mr. Charles H. Remilen, both of the Scientific and Industrial Computing Laboratory, Time and Payroll Dept., Kodak Park Works. Reproduced with permission from Ralph Barnes, *Work Sampling*. New York: John Wiley & Sons, 1957.

give the waiting time percentages for various system parameters. Table 9.3 permits the determination of average machine waiting time and average serviceman idle time for various values of m, r, and service factors $\frac{\lambda}{\mu}$, assuming the arrival and service rates are Poisson distributed.

ECONOMIC CRITERIA: The queuing model provides information about the system state. The use of this information in making economic decisions depends on the nature of the problem. For example, we might place some general constraint on the system, such as a desired level of service, and then determine an assignment that satisfies the constraint.

EXAMPLE 9.6 The Monroe County Hospital has a ward containing 30 beds. It is desired to staff the ward with nurses such that the average patient waiting time is less than 0.10 hr. Suppose a sampling study shows that the service factor (a) for the system is 0.20. Using Table 9.3, we find that for $m = 30$, $a = 0.20$, the average patient waiting time for an assignment of four nurses (r) is 0.21 and for six nurses is 0.035. Therefore, we might choose an assignment of five nurses.

EXAMPLE 9.7 The Limpkins Construction Company has a large job of constructing part of a new highway. The operation will require the use of 40 vehicles and pieces of construction equipment. The problem is to determine the number of repairmen to have on hand at the construction site to service the various pieces of equipment at the site. This service involves refueling, lubricating, and making minor repairs and adjustments. The cost of a serviceman is $5.00 per hour. The company imputes a cost of $100 per hour for every hour a piece of equipment is idle and waiting for repairs.

A long-term study showed that requests for service are roughly Poisson distributed and that the service times are exponential. A service factor of 0.05 is chosen. An hourly maintenance cost function is used as follows:

$$C = (\$100)E(W) + (\$5)(r).$$

Using Table 9.3, the optimum number of repairmen is three.

SUMMARY

In conclusion, we make these general comments on the future characteristics of designing and improving microproduction systems.

1. The application of elementary and common-sense principles of job improvement will continue to be important, if not spectacular. There is no reason to believe that automation will swiftly replace the infinite variety of manual production operations. Certainly the human component will be an important part of service jobs for some time. Much of this kind of improvement should be the responsibility of line operating management and personnel. An important production management job is the design of organizational incentives, which explicitly assign this responsibility to the line offering rewards for performance.

2. The human engineering component of job design will continue to grow as mechanization and automation replace the manual effort in operations. In space operations, human engineering will constitute the sole content of job design. One can imagine the vast difference in the training requirements and skills of space operation designers and the historical industrial engineer with his pragmatic guides.

3. As we have noted, part of the job of designing highly repetitive or complex industrial tasks will be relegated in part to the computer. The future will demand a good deal of research in order to understand and express fully the logic now used

by the engineer and then to relate this logic to the requisite human physiological and psychological data.

4. Finally, we should relate the substance of this chapter to the discussion in Chapter 5. We might assume that the astute produce manufacturer will utilize the industrial engineering skills in his organization in evaluating the efficiency of his own product as a component of a man-machine system. It is surprising how many companies have supported job design skills related to their own manufacturing operations while ignoring the use of these skills in the design of their own product. All this suggests that industrial or human engineers logically should be members of product design and marketing groups.

Problems

9.1   Consider one or more of the following positions: 1) manager of operations for a large department store, 2) manager of electrical line maintenance for an electric utility, 3) chief administrator for a large hospital, 4) superintendent of maintenance for a firm making photographic equipment, 5) plant superintendent for a company making power tools. Suppose that you wish to institute a vigorous cost-reduction and improvement program in your operation.
(a) Discuss the advisability of hiring professional staff resources to execute the program, versus relying on the existing line organization to do the job.
(b) Assume that you want the line organization to share a major part of the responsibility for operations improvement. Outline the steps of a program to accomplish this.

9.2   Suppose you are concerned with improving office procedures in a company office. A study reveals that, on the average, three girls are required daily to collate and assemble reports consisting of from 12 to 200 pages each and from 12 to 50 copies each. The job is currently done on a long table where piles of identical copies of a given page are arranged in a row, from which a girl collates a copy or partial copy of the report. Design a method for collating and assembling the reports. Make a left hand–right hand chart of the method.

9.3   The application of principles of motion economy and the application of human engineering are two approaches taken in the design of individual jobs and operations. Briefly explain where they might be applied in the following situations.
(a) The design of a power-driven saw that will cut limbs off trees up to a height of 35 feet and that is controlled at ground level and can be operated off highway areas.
(b) The assembly of a common hand-driven pencil sharpener at a given work station.

9.4   Industrial engineers have often claimed that a careful study can take 20% of the labor out of a job. This depends, of course, on many factors: the amount of control an operator exercises, the complexity or standardization of the job, the amount of thought already given to the way the job is done, etc.

As you think of the following situations, try to decide the answers to the following questions:
(a) What factors would affect the amount of time this job should be studied?
(b) What improvements might reasonably be tried?

(c) What are the job's characteristics, and how might they affect the direction the study would take?

If you are familiar with a manufacturing or service operation, you may, instead, describe it and discuss the types of studies and improvements that you could make in this operation.

Situation I: supermarket checkout counters

Assume your chain has ten stores, each with six checkout counters. From your experience, what improvements might be made in this operation? What tools of analysis, measurement, or design would you like to use (or know more about) to help you analyze this operation? How much time do you think you would need to make a thorough study? How would your study be affected by the number of stores in the chain (e.g., 1 or 100)?

Situation II: television repair business

Assume you own 10 trucks and employ 20 men. The operations have not been studied previously, and no records have been kept. You feel there is a problem, though, since you are not making any money. What sort of records might help? How would you go about analyzing your repair operations? What improvements might be worth investigation? How would your decisions on this study be affected if you had only four men? if you had 100 men?

Situation III: a manufacturing contract

You have landed a contract for making 100,000 souvenir models of a New York World's Fair exhibit. It is to be formed from wood or plastic of a specified color and have specified printing on it. It is to represent an exhibit in the form of a cone on top of a six-sided building. What studies would you make regarding manufacturing methods, materials, work designs, and labor? How would your decisions be affected by the order size (e.g., if the order were for 500, 10,000, or 1,000,000 models)?

Actual size

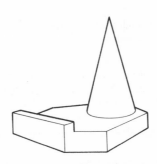

9.5   Do the case problem described on pages 278 and 280.

9.6   Design a general-purpose computer simulator for either one of the following situations.

(a) A man-machine simulator to permit the analysis of a combination of one operator and semi-automatic machines, each having independent and random unload-load and processing times; the machines can be tended in any order.

(b) A system of n machine attendants and m automatic machines, where requirements for different kinds of service are random in time and service times are dependent on the kind of service and random within each kind.

Construct a detailed logic diagram of the method.

9.7   This problem is concerned with the method of collecting refuse in a large city. The present method is as follows:

1. The cans are carried out to the curb by a "carryout man." The carryout man does nothing but carry out cans from the rear of a house to the curb.
2. Sometime later, the cans are emptied into a compactor truck by a "loader."
3. The empty cans are carried back to the house at a later time by a carryback man.

A crew consists of seven laborers, two trucks, and their drivers. The laborers include three carryout men, who serve both trucks, one loader for each truck, and two carryback men.

A day's route consists of the work for two trucks and the crew of seven. There are about 165 routes in the city, and 33 of them are serviced in one day.

We wish to find out what might happen if certain methods changes are instituted. These changes might include:

1. Assigning two men directly to a truck and having them carry out the cans and load at the same time.
2. Assigning two men directly to a truck and having them use a tote barrel. They empty the cans into the tote barrel at the rear of the house and then tote the barrel to the truck, where it is emptied.
3. Having the carryout men use a tote barrel. They place a large plastic bag in the tote barrel, empty the cans into the plastic liner in the barrel, tote the barrel to the curb, and remove the liner and leave it at the curb. The truck then picks up the filled liner.

Design a simulator that will simulate in some detail the collection operation. We might like to know how long it will take to service 250–300 stops, how much waiting time the truck experiences, the total number of cans emptied, etc. The simulator should test different decision variables, including methods of collection, crew sizes, task time distributions, etc.

9.8   The Xorex Company has three main assembly lines on which six models of a small computer are made. Each line is scheduled for a model for one to five days independently of the other lines. A band of roving inspectors service the lines in the following way: Any one of the operations in any line will randomly require an inspector to check some aspect of the assembly that cannot be checked by the assembler. The distribution of the time between successive calls appears to have the following form, where u is the median value, and the times are shown as deviations from u.

Time (min)	−21	−18	−15	−12	−9	−6	−3	u	+3	+6	+9	+12	+15	+18	+21
Probability	0.01	0.03	0.06	0.08	0.04	0.07	0.23	0.20	0.13	0.04	0.02	0.02	0.03	0.03	0.01

A study shows that the mean is a function of the model on the line.

Model	A	B	C	D	E	F
u(min)	21	23	25	30	32	35

A study shows that the service time is normally distributed with a mean of 20 min and variance of 5 min. The chief inspector wants to schedule inspector requirements each day. The cost of an inspector is \$15 per hour. The cost of a delay in inspecting a unit is \$1.00 per minute of delay.

Bibliography

Work Methods:

CARSON, GORDON, Ed., *Production Handbook*, 2nd ed. New York: Ronald Press, 1958.

KRICK, EDWARD V., *Methods Engineering*. New York: John Wiley & Sons, 1962.

LEHRER, ROBERT N., *Work Simplification*. Englewood Cliffs, N.J.: Prentice-Hall, Inc., 1957.

MASON, ANTHONY K., and DOUGLAS M. TOWNE, "Toward Synthetic Methods Analysis," *J. Ind. Eng.*, January 1967.

NADLER, GERALD, *Work Design*. Homewood, Ill.: Richard D. Irwin, Inc., 1963.

Human Engineering:

CHAPANIS, ALPHONSE, *Man-Machine Engineering*. Belmont, Calif.: Wadsworth Publishing Co., 1965.

——, *Research Techniques in Human Engineering*. Baltimore, Md.: Johns Hopkins Press, 1959.

FOGEL, LAWRENCE J., *Biotechnology: Concepts and Applications*. Englewood Cliffs, N.J.: Prentice-Hall, Inc., 1963.

Handbook of Human Engineering Data, 2nd ed., Tufts College, Medford, Mass., 1952.

MC CORMICK, E. J., *Human Factors Engineering*. New York: McGraw-Hill Book Co., 1964.

MORGAN, CLIFFORD T., JAMES S. COOK, ALPHONSE CHAPANIS, and MAX LUND, *Human Engineering Guide to Equipment Design*. New York: McGraw-Hill Book Co., 1963.

MURRELL, K. F. H., *Human Performance in Industry*. New York: Reinhold Publishing Co., 1965.

WOODSON, WESLEY E., *Human Engineering Guide for Equipment Designers*. Berkeley, Calif.: Univ. of California Press, 1954.

Man-Machine Assignment:

ASHCROFT, H., "The Productivity of Several Machines Under the Care of One Operator," *Royal Stat. Soc. J. (B)*, vol. 12, 1950.

BENSON, F., and D. R. COX, "The Productivity of Machines Requiring Attention at Random Intervals," *Royal Stat. Soc. J. (B)*, vol. 13, 1951.

DUVALL, WILLIAM G., "Machine Interference, Part II," *Mech. Eng.*, August 1936.

FELLER, W., *An Introduction to Probability Theory and Its Applications*. New York: John Wiley & Sons, 1950, pp. 379–83.

FETTER, ROBERT N., "The Assignment of Operators to Service Automatic Machines," *J. Ind. Eng.*, September–October 1955.

JONES, DALE, "Machine Interference," *J. Ind. Eng.*, September 1949.

MALCOLM, D. G., "Queuing Theory in Organization Design," *J. Ind. Eng.*, November–December 1955.

WRIGHT, WILMER R., "Machine Interference, Part I," *Mech. Eng.*, August 1936.

10

Facilities Replacement and Maintenance

THE NATURE OF REPLACEMENT

We have defined the design function as a management function concerned with the derivation of the physical production system. This includes both the original design and the acquisition of physical facilities, including machines, equipment, tools, and fixtures, which are either parts of an initially designed system or replacements for existing facilities. In most cases, the problem is one of replacing facilities within the broader context of a cost-reduction or expansion program.

There are two general kinds of replacement. The first is the replacement of relatively long-lived equipment. Such equipment is usually "capitalized" in the books of the company. It deteriorates over time in terms of reduced capability to perform its function, which is reflected in increased maintenance costs. It may also have several stages of service, being relegated from one kind of service to a secondary kind after a number of years. The second kind of replacement is equipment that has a "terminal life" and is subject to sudden failure, after which no further service can be rendered. Maintenance is unnecessary or a negligible factor. This type of equipment includes electronic tubes, bulbs, tires, and batteries. We will first concentrate on the replacement of long-lived equipment and turn to the terminal-life or nondeteriorating equipment at the end of the section.

The replacement of existing production facilities lies in the domain of general capital investment theory. It is difficult to conceive of situations where an existing piece of capital equipment or method of production is superseded by a system involving only a future stream of annual operating costs. The reverse is more likely to be true where predominantly manual methods or an existing process is replaced by a mechanized or automated system requiring an initial outlay of capital. In replacement problems, one alternative is always to continue with the incumbent method, machine, or piece of equipment. Therefore, replacement economics must consider the proper way of evaluating the future performance of the present method.

The Impetus for Replacement

In theory, a given existing and operating facility always stands in competition with alternative facilities that exist in the capital equipment market or internally on the design boards of the company. This includes the possible replacement of the facility by a new but like kind.

In this theoretical vein, there is the suggestion that a periodic review or even continuous assessment of facility performance compared with the state of the art could lead to a systematic replacement policy for the company. This is analogous to a dynamic value analysis program applied to facilities as well as products. Such a program would signal the time when, according to some criterion and on the basis of a rational analysis and evaluation of alternatives, the facility should be replaced.

The requirements for such a program probably exceed practical limitations. It would require that the organization keep informed of the developments in the state of the art with respect to the process and methods employed in the production system. This is not an easy job today with the proliferation of technical innovations. Furthermore, a file of current facility capabilities must be maintained and kept up to date. In order to approach a continuous evaluation program, it is necessary to design an information storage and retrieval system, probably computerized, that will facilitate the continual review of existing and competitive facilities for any area of the business. And this, then, must be supplemented with decision models that indicate the optimum time for changeover. Also, the anticipation of future inadequacies in facility capabilities is important. This is part of the problem of production planning over future time periods, which exceed the lead times necessary to consider alternatives and acquire new facilities.

All of this suggests that facilities replacement is a viable part of a general program of cost reduction and methods improvement and should not necessarily be the spontaneous reaction to suddenly recognized symptoms of incapabilities of existing facilities. At the least, any sort of workable program requires a complete inventory of information on present facilities, their capabilities, locations, current costs of maintenance, and quality performance, as well as operating costs. This could be adapted to computer or peripheral storage systems. The real problem is to design the methods of economically updating the file. This is a matter of minimizing the amount of redundant information that is gathered and piped into the system or, conversely, of limiting the data to the amount that can be effectively used to make replacement decisions. In conjunction with this, the degree of control exerted on investment proposals should reflect the amounts of capital required by proposals. Undoubtedly, the distribution of the size of proposals, that is, amount of capital requested, follows the typical *ABC* classification. In Figure 10.1, we note that a small percentage of the proposals requires a large percentage of the total capital requested. These are Group *A* projects and presumably require the closest control. The largest percentage of the proposals in Group *C* requires the smallest percentage of total capital and therefore needs less control in terms of supporting data and refinement of analysis. Group *B* is intermediate.

In the more practical vein, the impetus to propose a replacement is generated

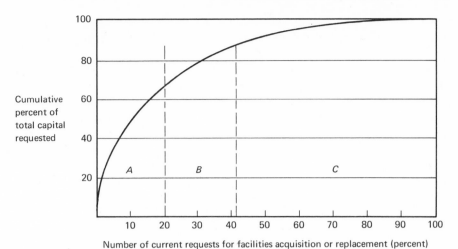

FIGURE **10.1**   *ABC* classification of investment proposals.

by a number of factors. Certainly, at some point in the life of a facility, there is an awareness by management that the facility is incapable of meeting functional objectives or that it appears uneconomical to maintain it in service. Or, an awareness of an innovation may prompt an examination of existing facilities with which the innovation competes. If the company has a continuing cost-reduction program, the question of replacement may arise in some phase of the operations. In any event, the replacement of facilities can often be the result of a number of actions taken by management, some more or less spontaneous than others. This is in contrast to a continuing and highly programed policy of replacement.

The major weakness of relying solely on symptoms of inadequacies to generate proposals for replacement is that perhaps only two alternatives are considered. These include the present method and an alternative that is clearly superior to the incumbent. A thorough evaluation of a set of alternatives may be neglected in order to expedite the retirement of the present facility. If the incumbent is bad enough, any alternative may be superior.

Replacement Criteria

Any proposal for the replacement of a piece of equipment competes with the existing or incumbent facility and any other technologically feasible and economical alternatives. It also competes internally within the firm with other proposals for the use of the firm's capital. The latter is part of capital investment theory. In this section, we are interested more in assessing the merits of replacing a facility relative to alternative methods of production than in finding alternative uses of capital.

We stress the use of monetary criteria to judge replacement alternatives or alternative replacement policies. However, very few replacement proposals are judged solely on the basis of monetary criteria. There are usually too many variables (events or outcomes) that cannot be quantified in monetary terms. In the lexicon of engineering economy, these are often called the "intangibles" of the problem. Their impact on the problem must be weighed by the decision maker. Most managers who are held responsible for the decision would seldom rely solely on formula-based decisions. There are undoubtedly cases where the manager places little reliance on formalized monetary evaluations and relies solely on his own judgment. We have insufficient scientific evidence to strongly suggest that this does not result in good decisions. The fact that we can structure outcomes in monetary economic formulas does not refute the method of human judgment.

It is obvious that, in some situations, replacements are necessary for reasons other than improving the cost or profit position. Some replacements are necessary for legal or safety requirements, such as replacing outdated fire-protection equipment or installing safety devices on machines. Replacements are also necessary to maximize capacity when it is urgently needed in a period of expanding demand. If the situation is urgent enough, cost may be subsidiary to capacity. There are certainly many decisions made to replace or add to existing facilities in order to expedite the remedy of a serious production problem and in cases where economic formulas are redundant.

In the more normal situation, many companies lend some formality to the matter of equipment replacement by requiring the justification of a proposal on the basis of monetary criteria supplemented with an analysis of the intangibles. The methods currently in vogue include the time-tested criteria of payback period, rate of return, comparative annual costs, or present worths (or discounted cash flows).

The replacement policy of the firm usually includes some absolute standard against which the proposal is judged. This is the secondary screening of the project, the first being its choice over alternative methods. The absolute standard judges the merit of the proposal relative to other uses of capital. These standards include a maximum payback period, a minimum rate of return or interest, as well as a limit on the value of the economic life of the asset in the formula.

The Life of a Facility

Economical replacement studies invariably involve the consideration of the life of each alternative. In the classical economic formulas, asset life is reflected in the value assigned to the variable n. From a different point of view, *replacement theory* is the title given to a class of analytical models that determine the optimal life for a piece of equipment, thus focusing attention on the question of *when* facilities should be replaced. We will examine these models later in this section.

Various measures and concepts of equipment life include the following.

SERVICE LIFE: The service life of an asset is the period in which it can remain in service and still perform the function for which it is intended. Service life is synonymous with physical life for terminal life or nondeteriorating equipment.

On the other hand, deteriorating equipment may be perpetuated indefinitely by maintenance and rebuilding. However, the termination of service occurs when further upkeep becomes uneconomical. Such equipment may have several stages of service life. Thus, a fire department may retire a 20-year-old pumper from active service. The pumper may be relegated to a second period of service in a fire-fighting school. The net realizable value of the asset is the avoided cost of having to purchase a training pumper.

The service lives of either deteriorating or terminal life assets may be terminated through obsolescence. Obsolescence occurs either when the function for which the asset serves is no longer required, or when an alternative that is functionally or economically superior replaces the present method.

ECONOMIC LIFE: Certain costs, such as maintenance, increase with the life of a piece of equipment. Other costs, such as capital costs when converted to an annual basis, decline with equipment life. The economic life is that period of service for which the total costs are a discounted minimum. Such an optimal life usually assumes replacement by like kind or superior models at the end of economic life. Economic life studies are used less for determining when replacement is advisable than for obtaining information as inputs to replacement analyses. We will examine this idea later.

STUDY LIFE: The study life is the chosen life of the equipment to be used in the comparative analysis. This life may be specified in a number of ways. It may be the service life of the equipment if this is shorter than the future period over which the service is to be rendered. It may be defined as a period beyond which the operating costs of the alternative cannot be reliably predicted. It may simply be limited by obsolescence, including the point when the service will be terminated or when a superior model will become available. Or, it is possible that the study life is restricted arbitrarily by management to provide a screen for capital investment proposals. That is, the shorter the life of a proposal, the less competitive it is with the present method.

Study life, when interpreted as the period over which alternatives will be compared, can be longer than either economic or service life. The parameter n can represent a period that encompasses a sequence of equipment replacements whose combined service or economic lives equal the study period.

In the case of deteriorating equipment, either where we wish to determine economic life as a decision variable or where study life is set as a parameter, the practical problem is to determine the nature of a future stream of annual operating costs, such as maintenance or decline of function, which reflect the condition of deterioration with increasing age. For example, in the case of a bulldozer, advancing age is reflected in increased fuel consumption, repairs, downtime, rescheduling of equipment and personnel on the job, lost revenue, etc. We must recognize that the prediction of the future behavior of these costs is not necessarily easy, and we should consider the sensitivity of the decision criterion to errors in these forecasts or predictions.

REPLACEMENT METHODS, WHERE ECONOMIC LIFE IS A PARAMETER

Replacement studies are essentially the same as economy studies involving capital expenditures. However, in this case, one alternative is always the possibility of retaining the present method. Therefore, one problem is that of determining the present net realizable value of the existing facility. Also, there is likely to be a difference in the economic lives of the various alternatives under study, particularly between the present method and the proposed replacements.

First, we should realize that the present book value (original cost minus accumulated depreciation) of the present or existing piece of equipment is never the relevant first cost of that alternative. The present book value is a sunk cost that must be written off the books whether or not the present piece of equipment is replaced. The relevant first cost is the net realizable value and includes the possible receipts from selling the equipment (less any out-of-pocket disposal costs) plus the costs that would be necessary to bring the equipment to serviceable condition. That is, if we retain the present piece of equipment, we forego the revenues from selling it on the second-hand market or using it for a secondary service and incur the costs of renovating it.

Both the approximate and exact methods of comparing alternative proposals are applicable. When the lives of the alternatives are short and equal, the approximate methods are appropriate. When the life of one of the proposals is significantly longer than the other, or when the annual operating costs are highly variable over the life of the alternative, the exact methods are more desirable.

Uniform Annual Series

Replacement problems usually compare the continuation of a present method with one or more alternatives, each requiring initial outlays of capital. The comparison of the alternatives on the basis of equivalent uniform annual costs is an appealing method, since many people are more familiar with annual costs than with the notion of present worths or even rate of return.

One major advantage of the exact methods, including the uniform annual cost method, is the facility with which a stream of unequal costs can be converted to an exact equivalent uniform series, present worth, or end-of-period amount. This is in contrast to averaging such costs in the approximate methods.

EXAMPLE 10.1   In a can manufacturing plant, sheets of tin plate are at present being fed by hand into coaters, splitters, and like machines. The installation of automatic feeders has been proposed. The installed cost of a feeder is $12,000. Service life is estimated at ten years with no salvage value remaining at the end of that time. Estimated expenses for power, making adjustments, maintenance, and downtime are $2,000 per year for the first four years of life and $3,000 per year for the remaining six years. The yearly costs for wages, fringe benefits, and related expenses for the workman who will be displaced by an automatic feeder are approximately $5,000. Installations can be made at 15 points in the plant.

Converting the stream of annual disbursements to uniform annual series we have (let AC = uniform annual cost series):

Automatic uniform annual cost:

$$AC = CRF_{0.10}^{10}[12,000 + PWF(u)_{0.10}^6(1,000)(PWF(s)_{0.10}^4)] + 2,000$$
$$= 0.1628[12,000 + (4.355)(1,000)(0.6830)] + 2,000$$
$$= 4440$$

Hand-feed uniform annual cost:

$$AC_2 = 5,000$$

We conclude from this that the automatic system will save $560 per year over the hand-feed method for each station.

Actually, in this type of analysis, we are really interested in the differences between the alternatives. The incremental investment for the automatic feeder is $12,000, resulting in a stream of annual savings. The conversion of this stream of differences into a uniform annual series should give us the same results as comparing the two independent series.

$$\text{Annual uniform savings} = 2,000 + CRF_{0.10}^{10}[PWF(u)_{0.10}^4(1,000)] - CRF_{0.10}^{10}(12,000)$$
$$= 2,000 + 0.1628[(3.170)(1,000)] - 0.1628(12,000)$$
$$= 560$$

EXAMPLE 10.2   Two alternative types of storage batteries are being considered for use in central office standby service at many points in a telephone system. Type X has a first cost of $450 per unit, an estimated life of ten years, and an estimated salvage value of $100 at the end of that time. Type Y has a first cost of $300, an estimated life of six years, and an estimated salvage value of $50 at the end of that time. Little difference in expenses for operation and maintenance is expected between the two types.

Compare the annual costs for the two types, at an interest rate of 10% and using an exact method for your computations.

The uniform annual series for each alternative is based on the independently determined service life for that alternative. We have

$$AC(X) = (450 - 100)CRF_{0.10}^{10} + (100)(0.10) = 67.00$$
$$AC(Y) = (300 - 50)CRF_{0.10}^6 + (50)(0.10) = 62.50$$

We now see that alternative Y is superior to X over the life of Y, which is six years. But what about the remaining four years? If the service is to continue indefinitely, then we may assume that Y will be replaced with like kind indefinitely and would therefore generate the same cost series. The same would be true for X.

There are other ways of looking at the unequal lives problem when the service is assumed to continue indefinitely. What happens after the termination of the life of the shortest lived asset is a matter for a future decision. If the difference between the annual costs of the two alternatives is small, we might favor the shortest lived asset if there are prospects for future technological improvements, price reductions, or changes in the service requirements. Prospects for cost and price increases might favor the longer lived assets. These may be considered either in the data used in the formulas or as intangibles.

Another approach is to consider a future replacement for either X or Y or both.

In this case, we must extend the decision horizon to a point where the replacements terminate at a common date for both alternatives. The practical difficulty of dealing with future replacements is the determination of the prices and operating characteristics of those replacements.

In summary, when the service lives of the assets are different, we may consider the following:

1. If the function or service rendered by the facilities is to terminate at some specific date that is less than the service life of both alternatives, then the uniform annual series for each alternative is based on that period. The difference in potential physical lives may be reflected in the salvage values, which indicate a possible secondary life.
2. If the service is to be continued indefinitely, then the two alternatives are compared over the life of the shortest lived alternative, but the uniform annual series for an alternative is based on its own independently determined service life. The assumption is made that replacements will be in like kind.
3. If there is a significant difference between the lives, then exact methods of determining an equivalent uniform annual series should be used, rather than the approximate method of straight-line depreciation plus average interest.
4. The higher the interest rate, the less favorable the longer lived alternative.
5. Possible future changes in prices, costs, innovations, and service function can be reflected in the estimates of future disbursements and receipts or as intangibles, which favor either the short- or long-lived alternative, depending on the circumstances.

Present Worth

The present worth method reduces the stream of future receipts and disbursements to an equivalent present value. Two alternatives may be compared on the basis of their streams of future costs or the present worth of their differences. In the latter case, the incremental investment in an alternative presumably results in a stream of annual savings. If the present worth of the differences between two alternatives is equal to zero, then the added investment is recovered with a rate of return equal to the interest rate used to discount savings.

EXAMPLE 10.3   A telephone company is to replace a central dispatching office. In one of the design details, two alternatives are proposed. The more costly of the two alternatives will require an additional investment (over and above the other alternative) of $35,000 in construction costs. However, under this alternative it will be easier to bring in additional cables, since service expansion is required later. The estimated savings are $6,000 per year for the fifth to ninth years. What must the minimum savings be from the tenth to twentieth years in order to make the additional investment attractive, if the rate of interest is 10% and the estimated life of the structure is 20 years? No savings are expected for the first four years.

Let X be the annual savings from the tenth to twentieth years. We solve for X such that the present worth of the proposal is equal to zero.

$$0 = 35,000 - [6,000 + PWF(u)^4_{0.10}6,000]PWF(s)^5_{0.10} - [X + X(PWF(u))^{10}_{0.10}]PWF(s)^{10}_{0.10}$$

Solving for X, we get

$$X = \$7,100$$

The future period over which the present worths are calculated *must be the same for each alternative.* This is not to say that their economic lives must be the same. When the economic lives of the assets are unequal, we may, as a present worth period of comparison, choose the study period to be equal to the shortest life.

EXAMPLE 10.4   Machine X has a present value of $4,000 and an expected service life of four years. A possible replacement Y has a purchase and installation cost of $20,000 and a service life of eight years. The operating costs of X are $8,000 per year and those of Y are $5,000 per year. Using interest at 10%,

$$PW(X) = 4,000 + 8,000[PWF(u)^4_{0.10}] = 29,400$$
$$PW(Y) = 2,000 + PWF(u)^4_{0.10}[CRF^8_{0.10}(5,000)] = 22,970$$

Another way of handling unequal lives is to equate the lives of the alternatives to the nearest common period, assuming replacements of like kind.

EXAMPLE 10.5   Machine X is presently used in a certain process. Its present value is $2,000, estimated life two years, and annual operating costs $1,000. It has no estimated salvage value at the end of its life. A replacement alternative Y would have a first cost of $5,000, estimated life of three years, operating costs of $500 per year, and salvage value of $1,000.

Using an interest rate of 10%, we compare the present worths on a common multiple of lives equal to six years as follows:

Alternative	x		y	
First cost		= 2,000		= 5,000
1st replacement	$2,000PWF(s)^2_{0.10}$	= 1,653	$4,000PWF(s)^3_{0.10}$	= 3,005
2nd replacement	$2,000PWF(s)^4_{0.10}$	= 1,366		
Present worth of annual costs	$1,000PWF(u)^6_{0.10}$	= 4,355	$500PWF(u)^6_{0.10}$	= 2,177
Salvage present worth	none	= 0	$-1,000PWF(s)^6_{0.10}$	= −564
Total		9,374		9,618

So far, the prospective lives of each of the alternatives has been the same. Now, the question naturally arises concerning what happens if the lives (or values of n) are different.

First of all, we have already noted that n is some estimate of the life of the alternative, and this is determined in a number of ways short of being the direct decision variable in the problem. We should again refer to the matter of making n arbitrarily small for any proposed alternative involving a capital expenditure. This introduces a note of conservatism into the study. It inflates the uniform annual costs of the proposal, and if the proposal still proves to be advantageous in terms of lower annual cost, then it has passed a rigorous test. This can be deceptive, since it biases the study in favor of the alternatives with lower first costs.

The present worth method is not generally used in replacement studies in deference to the annual cost method. The necessity of equating alternative lives is restrictive. However, there are certain situations where it may be more meaningful than annual costs. The method will shed light on the value or price of a proposal.

EXAMPLE 10.6   A company currently handles packages in a shipping department by the use of hand trucks and some roller conveyors. A vendor X submits a proposal for a mechanized handling system, which will be superior to the present method. The purchase price and installation cost of the system will be $40,000 and the annual operating costs of the system will be $10,000. The management balks at the initial cost of the system and investigates an alternative system proposed by another vendor Y with a first cost of $30,000 and annual operating costs of $14,500. If the study period is set at ten years and interest is 10%, is the price of X's system too high relative to the alternative Y?

$$PW(X) = \$40,000 + PWF(u)_{0.10}^{10}(10,000) = 101,440$$
$$PW(Y) = \$30,000 + 2PWF(u)_{0.10}^{10}(14,500) = 119,000$$

The difference between the two proposals is $17,560. A price of $12,440 would make Y's proposal exactly equivalent to X's.

Rate of Return

In any economy study, the rate of return is the interest that makes the disbursements equal to the receipts. If alternatives are compared by the differences in investments and costs, the incremental investment usually results in a savings of one alternative over the other. In most of our examples, the rate of return was assumed in order to determine equivalencies. However, we may simply let the interest factors be the unknowns in any calculation and then determine their values when costs and incomes or savings are equated in some equivalent terms.

Unfortunately, we must usually determine the rate of interest by trial-and-error methods unless a single factor is involved. But even this may demand the interpolation of values from charts.

EXAMPLE 10.7   The design, construction, and installation of an automatic machine for assembling an electrical component has been proposed. The total cost is estimated at $65,000. It is expected that a savings of $24,000 per year can be achieved. Assume a service life of five years.

If we equate savings to costs on, say, a present-worth basis, we have

$$65,000 = 24,000(PWF(u)_i^5)$$
$$PWF(u)_i^5 = 2.707$$

This corresponds to an interest rate of about 24%.

In problems that deal with more than two levels of investment, the choice may be made from an analysis of the added investment required of each alternative over the next lower investment. Suppose that the problem is to make a choice among five alternative proposals for the use of mechanical materials-handling equipment at a certain point in a factory. For simplicity, we will use the approximate method of analyzing rate of return. The required investment and estimated annual savings (before deducting depreciation) for each proposal are:

Proposal	Investment	Estimated annual savings
I	$11,000	$3,900
II	8,000	3,000
III	9,500	3,300
IV	5,000	2,000
V	13,500	4,500

The current policy of this manufacturing concern is to require all plans for cost reduction to show annual savings (before depreciation charges) of at least 30% on any money invested. Funds are readily available to finance any level of investment, provided this specified rate of return (or more) can be made.

The first step in reaching a decision is to compute the rate of return on total investment for each proposal. Only those that meet the 30% requirement on total investment can be considered at all. The computations are shown below. For convenience in the steps that will follow, the proposals have been listed in order of increasing investment.

			Proposal No.		
	IV	II	III	I	V
Total investment	$5,000	$8,000	$9,500	$11,000	$13,500
Estimated annual savings	$2,000	$3,000	$3,300	$3,900	$4,500
Rate of return on total investment	40.0%	37.5%	34.7%	35.5%	33.3%

The rate of return on total investment is simply the estimated annual savings for a proposal, divided by the total investment required. For Proposal IV, for example, it is $2,000/$5,000, which is 0.400 or 40.0%. Note that all proposals meet the 30% requirement. The next step now is to test each increment of added investment by this criterion. The results are as shown below.

			Proposal No.		
	IV	II	III	I	V
Added investment above next lower investment	—	$3,000	$1,500	$1,500	$2,500
Increase in annual savings	—	$1,000	$300	$600	$600
Rate of return on extra investment	—	33.3%	20.0%	40.0%	24.0%

Note that the increased investment in going from Proposal IV to Proposal II is worthwhile; the added $3,000 of investment results in an increase in annual savings of $1,000, a rate of return on the added investment of 33.3%. However, the added investment required in going from Proposal II to Proposal III is not worthwhile; the rate of return on the extra investment is only 20%. Proposal III must therefore be discarded. As a result, the 40% rate of return on extra investment shown under Proposal I is no longer a valid figure; the comparison was made with an uneconomical proposal. Proposal I must now be compared with Proposal II. The new computations give

		Proposal No.		
	IV	II	I	V
Added investment above next lower investment	—	$3,000	$3,000	$2,500
Increase in annual savings	—	$1,000	$900	$600
Rate of return on extra investment	—	33.3%	30.0%	24.0%

These figures show that the added investment required in going from Proposal II to Proposal I does pay its own way. However, Proposal V does not meet the rate-of-return requirement; the added investment ($2,500) in going from Proposal I to Proposal V yields a return of only 24.0%. It should therefore be used for investment elsewhere, where a return of 30% can presumably be made. The choice of the alternatives should be Proposal I. Each increment of investment in going from one proposal to the next up to the $11,000 total required by Proposal I meets the test for required rate of return. It should be noted that the best choice under the conditions given is not the proposal that yields the greatest rate of return on the total investment (which in this case is Proposal IV). Each added dollar of investment in going from Proposal IV to Proposal I yields a return of 30% or more. Since the concern has ample funds to invest if such a return can be made, the larger investment should be made.

ECONOMIC LIFE STUDIES

Equipment with Deteriorating Lives

In most of the previous examples, we dealt with the comparison of an existing method or facility with alternative, technologically different, methods. We will now concentrate on the determination of the economic life of a piece of equipment assuming its replacement by a new but identical type of equipment. Using any one of the foregoing exact methods, the problem can be one of determining an economic life of a proposal, where n is the unknown.

EXAMPLE 10.8   A maintenance and repair concern has proposed that it be allowed to make a complete renovation and overhaul of a motor-generator converter in regular use by an automobile battery manufacturer for battery forming and charging. The total cost of making the overhaul has been quoted as $8,200. The machine is quite old and has been written off completely on the company's books. The resale value at the present time is approximately $2,000. Unless an overhaul is made, the machine must be replaced very soon. The cost of a new unit will be $20,000. A new machine will provide essentially the same service with the same efficiency and do so over a life of 15 years. With interest at 8%, how many additional years of service life must be provided by the overhaul to make it worthwhile?

The economic life of the renovation will be such that the uniform annual costs of the renovation will equal uniform annual costs of the proposed new device.

$$10,200 CRF_{0.08}^{n} = 20,000 CRF_{0.08}^{15}$$

$$CRF_{0.08}^{n} = \frac{(20,000)(0.1168)}{10,200}$$

$$= 0.2285$$

This corresponds to $5 < n < 6$.

Optimal Life

The disbursements that are traceable to some asset are generally of two types. The first is the initial lump-sum payment made for the asset and its installation. The second is the annual operating costs, which are paid each year over the life of the asset. If salvage value is a factor, then there is also an annual change in this amount as a function of the age of the equipment.

Intuitively, one can recognize that "optimal" life means the age of the equipment when equivalent costs are minimized. As the life of the equipment or asset increases, the first cost is spread out so that it decreases with time as a uniform equivalent annual series. On the other hand, the annual operating costs increase and the salvage value decreases with time. The optimal life of the equipment is that in which the total equivalent uniform annual costs (or equivalent present worths) are minimum.

EXAMPLE 10.9   The following are estimated to be the typical costs for a unit of equipment used in some quantities in a manufacturing plant:

Year	Out-of-pocket expenses for year	End-of-year salvage value
1	$ 600	$2,000
2	800	1,600
3	1,000	1,200
4	1,600	1,000

The first cost per unit is $3,000. Assume that future replacements will typically have the above pattern of costs and will have the same first cost per unit. Ignoring interest costs, what is the average annual cost for expenses and capital recovery over the economic life for a typical machine?

Year	Out-of-pocket expense	Average annual out-of-pocket expense	Capital cost	Average annual capital cost	Total average annual cost
1	$ 600	$ 600	$1,000	$1,000	$1,600
2	800	700	1,400	700	1,400
3	1,000	800	1,800	600	1,400
4	1,600	1,000	2,000	500	1,500

The machine should be replaced at the end of every three years.

There are some cumbersome practical problems involved in trying to determine the theoretical optimal life of an asset. First, it is obvious that one must determine the behavior of annual operating costs as a function of the life of the asset. This might require extrapolating the experience that the company has had with past models or similar types of equipment, assuming that relevant data have been collected. If no such data are available, the analyst must hypothesize the behavior of cost as a function of time. Second, some assumption must be made about the disposition of the asset at the end of its optimal life. The easiest thing to do is to assume that the asset will be replaced with an identical but new unit. And this will continue indefinitely in the form of an infinite chain of like replacements. This assumes that the asset deteriorates but does not become obsolete. Third, one may conclude that the asset can be replaced by a superior model. As we shall see, the problem then becomes one of trying to express obsolescence as a cost function.

A GENERAL MODEL: We will construct a model for the case where a facility is to be replaced by an identical but new unit, and this mode of replacement will continue indefinitely. In most practical cases, we would find this to be an untenable assumption. Some pieces of equipment, however, follow this pattern somewhat, such as sidewalks, transformers, school buses, etc., but even for these cases, we can easily suggest that innovations either improve the function or replace it entirely. But making this assumption starts us into the subject with relative ease, and it also provides us with a model that might be useful under certain conditions.

Suppose that we make the following assumptions with respect to some production facility:

1. The facility deteriorates over time such that the annual costs of operating it increase monotonically over time.
2. There is an indefinite planning horizon, and the facility will be replaced by a new and identical unit at the end of each of an indefinite series of time periods in the future.
3. Annual operating costs are end-of-period payments. Now let

A = the initial cost of the facility

c_j = end-of-period operating cost for jth period

S_j = salvage value of the machine at end of jth period

P_n = discounted value of all future costs for a policy of replacing the machine after each of n periods

i = interest rate

c_1 = first-year annual operating cost

Now we will convert all the disbursements to an equivalent present worth, considering that the facility will be replaced at the end of each of a future series of n years. This can be done easily by converting all the disbursements and salvage values for each year of the n-year period to an equivalent present worth, then converting the present worth to an equivalent uniform annual series, and then converting the equivalent uniform annual series to the present worth of an infinite series. Or,

$$P_n = \left(A - \frac{S_n}{(1+i)^n} + \sum_{j=1}^{n} \frac{c_j}{(1+i)^j} \right) \left(CRF_i^n \right) \left(\frac{1}{i} \right)$$

$$P_n = \left(A - \frac{S_n}{(1+i)^n} + \sum_{j=1}^{n} \frac{c_j}{(1+i)^j} \right) \left(\frac{i(1+i)^n}{(1+i)^n - 1} \right) \left(\frac{1}{i} \right)$$

The first term on the right-hand side of the equation converts all the disbursements (including the salvage value) made during the period n to an equivalent present worth. The second term, which is the capital recovery factor, converts the present worth into equivalent uniform annual series, and the last term then converts the uniform annual series back to the present worth of an equivalent *indefinite* annual series. P_n is therefore an amount in the present that is equivalent to all the future costs with a replacement at the end of every n periods.

Suppose now that we let the optimal renewal period be N. Then it can be shown that the facility should be replaced when

$$P_{N+1} - P_N \geq 0; \qquad P_{N-1} - P_N \geq 0$$

EXAMPLE 10.10   A machine has an initial cost of $15,000. A schedule of annual operating costs and salvage values for each of five years is shown below:

n	c_j	S_n
1	$2,000	$12,000
2	3,000	9,000
3	4,000	6,000
4	6,000	4,000
5	8,000	2,000

The optimal life of the machine is determined to be one year, as follows ($i = 0.10$):

(1)	(2)	(3)	(4)	(5)	(6)	(7)	(8)	(9)
n	$PWF(s)_{0.10}^n$	c_j	$\sum_{}^{n} \dfrac{c_j}{(1+i)^j}$	S_n	$\dfrac{S_n}{(1+i)^n}$	$15,000 + $ (4) $-$ (6)	$\dfrac{CRF}{i}$	(7) $\times$ (8)
1	0.909	2,000	1,818	12,000	10,908	5,910	11.00	65,010
2	0.826	3,000	4,296	9,000	7,435	11,861	5.76	68,319
3	0.751	4,000	7,300	6,000	4,506	17,794	4.02	71,531
4	0.683	6,000	11,398	4,000	2,732	23,666	3.15	74,547
5	0.621	8,000	16,366	2,000	1,242	30,124	2.63	79,226

In view of the above discussion, we could very simply multiply each side of the equation by i. If we let AC_n equal the equivalent uniform annual cost of operating the facility for n years, then

$$AC_n = iP_n = \left(A - \frac{S_n}{(1+i)^n} + \sum_{j=1}^{n} \frac{c_j}{(1+i)^j} \right) \left(\frac{i(1+i)^n}{(1+i)^n - 1} \right)$$

and

$$AC_{N+1} - AC_N \geq 0; \qquad AC_{N-1} - AC_N \geq 0$$

It can also be shown that replacement should occur in the year when the marginal cost of operating the equipment an additional year is greater than the equivalent uniform annual cost of operating the equipment to date. That is,

$$AC_N \leq c_{N+1} - S_{N+1} + S_N(1 + i).$$

AVERAGES VERSUS INDIVIDUALS: Optimal life studies indicate the economic life of a piece of equipment. Now what does this mean in the practical sense? It does not mean that we literally replace the piece of equipment on the date of its optimal life with a like model. It would be absurd to follow a policy like that. Obviously, with each year we know a good deal more about the operating characteristics of a piece of equipment than we did prior to acquiring it. Therefore, the problem is to examine the piece of equipment (the present one) at some point in time and compare it with a new model. The time at which we make the comparison may be either before or after the predicted optimal life of the present equipment.

For example, suppose we had applied our theory to the replacement of a fleet of taxicabs and found the optimal replacement period to be five years. But this is an average. Suppose that at the end of five years, cab number 1551 required less maintenance than predicted using the average calculations. Now the problem becomes one of deciding whether or not to replace cab 1551 at the end of six years with a new model. Our theory now applies to the new model. We calculate the annual equivalent series for the new model, assuming that it will be replaced with like kind in perpetuity. Then we compare the costs of extending the old model for an additional year with the costs of providing the service with the new model. The costs of the new model, in turn, are predicated on its own economic or optimal life. What we are saying is that if the marginal cost of extending the life of the old piece of equipment exceeds the cost of providing the service with the new piece of equipment, then the former should be replaced, otherwise not.

EXAMPLE 10.11   The Atlantic Electric and Gas Company has a large fleet of small passenger cars used by its employees. A study of operating records plus manufacturer's data shows that the maintenance schedule for a new car expressed as a percent of P, the purchase price (first cost) of the car, is:

Life in years	1	2	3	4	5	6	7	8
Annual maintenance cost	3.75	5.05	10.70	11.70	16.30	17.30	23.40	25.40
C_m (average annual maintenance cost)	3.75	4.40	6.50	7.80	9.50	10.80	12.60	14.20

The trade-in allowance as a percent of the first cost of the car is as follows:

Life in years	1	2	3	4	5	6	7	8
S_n (trade-in value percent of first cost)	75.0	50.0	40.0	35.0	32.0	25.0	20.0	18.0

Now the company calculates the equivalent annual cost of capital recovery plus interest. This is done in terms of sinking fund depreciation plus interest on first cost.

Year	Annual cost of depreciation as percent of first cost D_n $SFF_{0.06}^n \times (P - S_n)$	Interest on first cost (at 6%)
1	$(100.00)(1 - 0.75) = 25.00$	6.00
2	$(48.54)(1 - 0.50) = 24.27$	
3	$(31.41)(1 - 0.40) = 18.84$	
4	$(22.86)(1 - 0.35) = 14.86$	
5	$(17.74)(1 - 0.32) = 12.06$	
6	$(14.34)(1 - 0.25) = 10.75$	
7	$(11.91)(1 - 0.20) = 9.52$	
8	$(10.10)(1 - 0.18) = 8.28$	

Ignoring income taxes, and assuming that the operating costs such as gasoline, insurance, tires, antifreeze, etc., are the same for all models, the average annual costs of operation as percent of the first cost are

Years	1	2	3	4	5	6	7	8
C_m	3.75	4.40	6.50	7.80	9.50	10.80	12.60	14.20
D_n	25.00	24.27	18.84	14.86	12.06	10.75	9.52	8.28
i	6.00	6.00	6.00	6.00	6.00	6.00	6.00	6.00
Total	34.75	34.67	31.34	28.66	27.56	27.55	28.12	28.48

Note that we are using an average maintenance cost rather than determining a uniform annual series for these costs based on an exact calculation. The average will suffice for our purposes here.

Now assume that we currently have a five-year-old model, and, in light of information that is now available to us, we wish to know if we should replace it with a new model costing \$2,000. Assume, for instance, that the old model requires at this time a major overhaul costing \$450. The salvage value of the old model is:

Age

5	\$580
6	450
7	360
8	324

Suppose we compare the alternative of replacing the five-year-old car now (at the end of five years) with a new model costing \$2,000 versus the alternative of keeping it in service for one more year.

A. Replace now

Present worth of one year service for the new car

$$= (2,000)(0.2755)(PWF(s))^1_{0.06} = \qquad 520$$

Less credit for the turn-in value of old model   (580)

                                                                    (60)

B. Retain in service for one year

Major repair cost   450

Present worth of salvage value one year hence $= (450)(PWF(s))^1_{0.06} =$ (424)

                                                                     26

This says to make the replacement since A has the lower present worth. However, we may continue the analysis and ask what might happen if we chose to continue the service of the old car for two more years. Assume that during the second year the maintenance cost will be \$300. We now have the following:

A. Replace now

Present worth of two years' service for new car

$$= (2,000)(0.2755)(PWF(u))^2_{0.06} = \qquad 1,010$$

Less credit for salvage value of old model   (580)

                                                                    430

B. Retain in service for two more years

Major repair cost   450

Present worth of second year's maintenance $= (300)(PWF(s))^2_{0.06} =$ 267

Less present worth of salvage value two years hence

$$= (360)(PWF(s))^2_{0.06} = \qquad (320)$$

                                                                    397

This indicates a savings by continuing the service for two more years.

If we used an exact method of comparing these alternatives, we would use an economic life of six years for the new car and compute present worth on the basis of an infinite chain of six-year replacements.

A DETERIORATION GRADIENT: In the previous example, we listed each year's annual operating cost. We may approximate this annual cost as a function of n. A deterioration gradient is a series of annual increments to the operating costs. Suppose we assume a linear gradient as follows: Let

  c_1 = first year's operating cost
  d = constant rate of increase of annual costs

Then,

  $c_j = c_1 + nd$

Given this simple gradient, we might try an approximate method of obtaining the optimal life of a facility. Suppose we use the following approximate formula for calculating a uniform series of annual costs:

$$AC_n = \frac{(A - S_n)}{n} + (A - S_n)\left(\frac{n + 1}{n}\right)\frac{i}{2} + iS_n + c_1 + d\frac{(n - 1)}{2}$$

If we set the derivative of this function, with respect to n, equal to zero and solve for n, we obtain the optimal life N.

$$N = \sqrt{\frac{(A - S_n)(2 + i)}{d}}$$

and if

  $S_n = 0$

then

$$N = \sqrt{\frac{A(2 + i)}{d}}$$

OBSOLESCENCE: As we have noted, many replacement problems deal with obsolescence. If obsolescence occurs due to the termination of the functions served by the facility, then the life of alternatives is equal to the time the service is concluded, unless the economic lives are less. If obsolescence occurs due to the appearance of a superior facility, then the economic life of an existing facility is governed by the degree of superiority of the new challenger.

In determining the optimal life of a facility, where obsolescence is a factor, we must be able to quantify the effect of a future stream of superior replacements. Obviously, this is a demanding task unless we make some simplifying assumptions.

If a new model suddenly appears on the market, we can simply compare the incumbent facility with the challenger in terms of the previous types of analysis. We can either set a restrictive life to each alternative or possibly determine the economic life of the challenger, assuming an infinite chain of like replacements, and compare it with extending the incumbent's service for one or more years into the future.

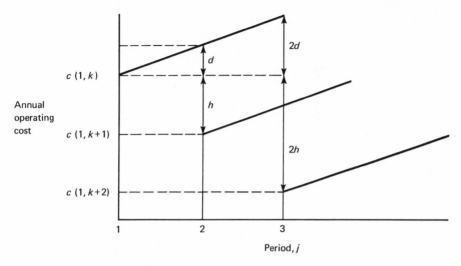

FIGURE **10.2** Effect of deterioration and obsolescence on annual operating cost.

Another approach is to assume that there is a future stream of annual improvements over the incumbent facility. A pattern of improvements, or *obsolescence gradient*, occurs such that at the end of each year, a new challenger appears that is superior to the challenger of the previous year. The superiority is in terms of reduced first cost, greater salvage value, or reduced first year's (and subsequent years') cost of operation.

The difference between an incumbent facility and a challenger consists in the increased deterioration of the incumbent machine plus the opportunity savings that could have accrued by choosing the challenger. We are familiar with the deterioration gradient. An obsolescence gradient could, for instance, consist of continued annual reduction in the first year's operating costs for each successive member of a stream of annual challengers.

Suppose we let $c(1, k)$ be the first year's operating cost of a machine purchased in the first year. Let the annual operating cost of the machine increase yearly with a constant deteriorating gradient d. Let the best available challenger at the beginning of period 2 have a first year's operating cost of $c(1, k) - h$, where h is a constant annual reduction in the first year's operating costs of two successive challengers, or $h = c(1, k) - c(1, k + 1)$. Then, the difference between the cost of any incumbent purchased in period 1 and that of a challenger in year j is shown in Figure 10.2. Then, the total annual operating cost in period j is

$$c_j = c(1, k) + (j - 1)(d + h)$$

EXAMPLE 10.12 A program for school bus replacement is to be planned. Each year the annual costs of operating a bus increase by $200, and the reduction in the first year's operating costs is $25 if a new model is purchased. The first year's operating costs of the present buses, which were purchased this year, are $500. What is their economic life? The purchase cost of a new model is $3,800 ($i = 0.10$).

(1)	(2)	(3)	(4)	(5)	(6)	(7)	(8)	(9)	(10)	(11)
n	A	d	h	c_1	$PWF(s)_{0.10}^{n}$	c_i	$\sum_{1}^{n} (6) \times (7)$	$(2)+(8)$	$\dfrac{(CRF)_{0.10}^{n}}{i}$	$(9) \times (10)$
1	3,800	200	25	500	0.909	500	454	4,254	11.60	49,346
2					0.826	725	1,053	4,853	5.76	27,953
3					0.751	950	1,767	5,567	4.02	22,379
4					0.683	1,175	2,569	6,369	3.15	20,062
5					0.621	1,400	3,439	7,239	2.63	19,039
6					0.565	1,625	4,357	8,157	2.29	18,689
7					0.513	1,850	5,306	9,106	2.05	18,667
8					0.467	2,075	6,275	10,075	1.87	18,840

DEFERRING AN INVESTMENT: In the case where future innovations contribute to the obsolescence of an existing facility, we might wish to examine the following question. Given that we have the opportunity *now* of investing in a new facility to replace an existing one, should we defer the investment one year in order to take advantage of the improvements that will be available at the end of the year? The period of deferment may be longer than a year. The decision to defer depends not only on the relative merits of the future innovation, but also upon the condition of the existing facility, relative to this year's possible investment and the prospects for other uses of the funds.

Suppose we are faced with the following two possibilities. We have the opportunity now of investing in a new machine (A) costing $10,000 to replace an existing facility. We may defer the investment in the new machine in favor of waiting until the start of the next year. At that time, another machine (B), costing $12,000, will be available. The present existing facility has no net realizable value, and it will cost $7,000 to operate it in the coming year. The projected operating costs for each type of new machine are as follows:

	First cost	Operating costs as percent of first cost in year					
		1	2	3	4	5	6
Machine A	$10,000	0.2	0.3	0.4	0.5	0.6	0.8
Machine B	$12,000	0.1	0.2	0.3	0.4	0.5	0.7

Salvage values as a percent of first cost are

	Salvage value as percent of first cost in year					
Year	1	2	3	4	5	6
Machine A	0.75	0.65	0.30	0.20	0.10	0
Machine B	0.80	0.65	0.50	0.30	0.20	0

The alternatives are now:

(a) Purchase $10,000 machine now.
(b) Retain present facility for a year and then invest in $12,000 machine.

First, we might make a straightforward annual cost comparison assuming a service life of four years for each investment after it is made. Using the exact method, we have:

$$\text{Annual cost } (A) = (10,000 - 2,000)CRF_{0.10}^4 + (2,000)(0.10)$$

$$+ CRF_{0.10}^4 \sum_{1}^{4} \frac{c_j}{(1 - 0.10)^i}$$

$$= 6,115$$

In a similar fashion, the annual cost of B is $6,137, indicating a slight advantage in favor of A.

In the above method, we assumed n to be an arbitrary constant equal to four years for each new machine. If we determine the economic life of each investment, the results are as follows:

Determination of Economic Life for Machines A and B (Percent of First Cost)

	(1) n	(2) Operating costs	(3) Salvage	(4) $PWF(s)_{0.10}^n$	(5) $\sum (3)(4)$	(6) $(3)(4)$	(7) $\frac{1.00 +}{(5) - (6)}$	(8) $\frac{CRF}{i}$	(9) $(7)(8)$
	1	0.2	0.75	0.909	0.1818	0.682	0.4998	11.00	5.4980
	2	0.3	0.65	0.826	0.4296	0.537	0.8927	5.76	5.1419
A	3	0.4	0.30	0.751	0.7300	0.225	1.5050	4.02	6.0501
	4	0.5	0.20	0.683	1.0735	0.137	1.9365	3.15	6.0999
	2	0.1	0.80	0.909	0.0900	0.727	0.363	11.00	3.9930
	3	0.2	0.65	0.826	0.2561	0.537	0.719	5.76	4.1455
B	4	0.3	0.50	0.751	0.4814	0.376	1.105	4.02	4.4421
	5	0.4	0.30	0.683	0.7546	0.205	1.550	3.15	4.8825

We now assume that each alternative A and B will involve an infinite series of replacements of A and B, respectively, at the end of their economic lives, which are two years for A and one year for B. Comparing their present worth at time zero, we have

PW_A (time 0) = 51,419
PW_B (time 0) = $PWF_{0.10}^1[(12,000)(3.9930) + 7,000] = 49,919$

showing a slight advantage for B.

CONCEPT OF URGENCY RATING: There is nothing particularly new in the preceding analyses. But they do lead to a discussion of the concept of urgency rating and the MAPI method of comparing alternatives. First, we will generalize the deferment problem as follows:

An investment proposal P_x to replace an existing facility will now result in a stream of operating costs and potential salvage values for each of n years in the future. If this investment is deferred for one year, we can take advantage of another investment proposal P_y, which will provide the same function but with superior economic results in lower operating costs and/or higher salvage values.

Let

P_x = first cost of this year's investment at time zero

P_y = first cost of next year's investment if made at the end of the first year

a_j = operating cost of investment x at end of the jth year, $1 \leq j \leq n$

b_j = operating cost of investment y at end of the jth year, $2 \leq j \leq n+1$

S_j = salvage value of investment x at end of the jth year

Z_j = salvage value of investment y at end of the jth year

i = rate of return

d = annual cost of operating the present facility for one more year

Assume that

1. n is the economic life of both investments x and y.
2. $a_j > b_j$ for all j greater than 1.
3. Future replacements of either investment 1 or 2 are of like kind.
4. The first-year cost of continuing with the present method is equal to d and $d > a_1$.

Symbolically, on a time scale, we have:

(x)

P_x · ———————+———+ · · ·—+———$P_x - S_n$———+———————+ · · ·

　　　a_1　　a_2　　a_{n-1}　　a_n　　a_1　　a_2

(y)

P_y · ———————+———+ · · ·—+———$P_y - Z_{n+1}$———+———————+ · · ·

　　　d　　b_2　　b_{n-1}　　b_n　　b_{n+1}　　b_2

Suppose we subtract the stream of costs associated with proposal y from those of proposal x and then determine the present worth of these differences *at the end of the first year*. We then have

PW = present worth at end of the first year of an infinite series of the differences between proposals 1 and 2.

$$PW = \left[P_x(1 + i) + (a_1 - d) - P_y + \sum_{j=2}^{n} \frac{(a_j - b_j)}{(1 + i)^{j-1}} + \frac{(P_x - S_n)}{(1 + i)^{n-1}} \right.$$

$$\left. - \frac{(P_y - Z_{n+1})}{(1 + i)^n} + \frac{(a_1 - b_{n+1})}{(1 - i)^n} \right] \frac{CRF_i^n}{i}$$

Each of the terms in brackets represents either an advantage or a disadvantage of making investment 1 now. The disadvantages are:

$P_x(1 + i)$ 　　　　　　　First cost of x

$\dfrac{P_x - S_n}{(1 + i)^{n-1}}$ 　　　　　Future replacement of x by like kind

$\sum \dfrac{(a_j - b_j)}{(1 + i)^{j-1}}, \dfrac{(a_1 - b_{n+1})}{(1 + i)^n}$ 　　Opportunity savings in operating costs by using y

The advantages of making the investment P_x now are:

$(a_1 - d)$ — The savings in operating costs during the first year

P_y — The first cost of y avoided

$\dfrac{P_y - Z_{n+1}}{(1 + i)^n}$ — Replacement of y by like kind avoided

We now have to consider the matter of "urgency rating." The urgency rating is a relative measure of the desirability of making the investment now. It is the first-year return on the investment P_x, when compared with deferring the investment one year. It is computed in the following manner.

We first adjust the value of PW to a new value PW',

$$PW' = PW - P_x(1 + i) - (a_1 - d)$$

where PW' represents the present worth, at the end of the first year, of the advantages of investment y over investment x. We can consider PW' to be the salvage value of the investment proposal P_x at the end of the first year. We could, of course, have calculated PW' directly by simply ignoring the inclusion of the two terms, $P_x(1 + i)$ and $(a_1 - d)$, but this might obscure the reasoning behind the method.

Now we have the basis for computing the first-year rate of return on the investment proposal x. The alternatives are 1) make the investment P_x or 2) continue with the present facility for one more year. Diagrammatically we have

The rate of return for the first year is that return which makes the annual costs of each alternative for the first year ($n = 1$) equal to each other. We note here without proof that PW' is likely to be arithmetically negative, and therefore, in the following, we will use its absolute value for purposes of comparing annual costs. Setting the annual costs equal to each other, we have

$$AC_A = AC_B$$

$$(P_x - PW')(1 + i) + (PW')(h) + a_1 = d$$

where h is the rate of return on P_x for the first year and is arbitrarily called the urgency rating. Since h is a function of the absolute value of PW', the urgency rating will increase in proportion to the advantages of investing P_x. Thus, the urgency rating is a relative index of the desirability of making a current investment versus delaying it for another year.

THE MAPI FORMULA: The notion of urgency rating was originally proposed by George Terborgh and the Machinery and Allied Products Institute.[1] The MAPI

---

[1] George Terborgh, *Dynamic Equipment Policy*. New York: McGraw-Hill Book Co., 1949.

formula is a procedure for determining the urgency of making an investment now, compared to deferring the investment for one year and continuing with the present method. Recent developments permit longer than one-year comparisons.[2] The method of calculating the urgency rating is more complicated than our example in the previous section. In our demonstration formula we had

$$h = \text{urgency rating} = \frac{(d - a_1) - (P_x - PW')}{P_x}$$

The term $P_x - PW'$ represents the first year's capital consumption. In the MAPI method, the capital consumption allowance for the project can be determined from charts that reflect a specified normal degree of deterioration and obsolescence and are classified according to methods of depreciation. The method, however, does not require the use of these charts, and individual experience may be substituted.

The MAPI urgency rating is an after-tax rate of return. An example of its determination is indicated below.[3]

A study of packaging methods employed by the ABC Company in shipping certain electronic equipment discloses the fact that the company purchases annually about 600,000 assorted units of fibre containers, representing approximately 200 different sizes. The quantity of each size used varies from 200 to 50,000 units. Fibre containers must be purchased in quantity lots (at least 100 per order) if their purchase price is to be minimized. As a result, the inventory turnover for some sizes is only twice per year. Heavy carrying charges are therefore incurred, and substantial storage space is required, both of which add to production costs.

The study further discloses that a great many electronic items are packed in wooden boxes and crates which are custom made in the carpenter shop. The only reason that many of these items are not packed in less expensive corrugated containers is that they require such a great number of different sizes that their purchase is impractical. These facts lead the analyst to investigate whether it would be more economical for the company to make its own corrugated containers. He finds that to do this the company will have to purchase a large box machine and a box stitcher at a combined cost of $29,800.

The box machine is hydraulically operated, electrically controlled, and is capable of delivering box blanks, scored in both directions and slotted in one operation, at an average rate of 350 blanks per hour. The machine will fabricate from all grades of corrugated fibre, from nontest single flute through 500-lb double wall. One of its unique features is dimensional control capable of a complete box size change in $1\frac{1}{2}$ minutes or less. The maximum size of box it will fabricate is 74'' long with a maximum width and depth of 84''. These will be large enough to meet requirements. The minimum size is 9'' long, with combined width and depth of 10''. Only 15 percent of the containers required are smaller than this minimum.

The second machine, the box stitcher, is required to stitch the seams of the box blanks. The stitcher head operates at speeds from 300 to 400 stitches per minute. It is easily adjusted to accommodate the various thicknesses of corrugated material. The machine is manually operated but power driven.

---

[2] George Terborgh, *Business Investment Management*. Washington, D.C.: Machinery and Allied Products Inst., 1967.
[3] *Ibid.*, pp. 155–56.

PROJECT NO._____

MAPI SUMMARY FORM
(AVERAGING SHORTCUT)

PROJECT _____ Box Machine and Stitcher _____

ALTERNATIVE _____ Continuing as is _____

COMPARISON PERIOD (YEARS)   (P)_____1_____

ASSUMED OPERATING RATE OF PROJECT (HOURS PER YEAR)   _____1,200_____

I. OPERATING ADVANTAGE
(NEXT-YEAR FOR A 1-YEAR COMPARISON PERIOD,* ANNUAL AVERAGES FOR LONGER PERIODS)

A. EFFECT OF PROJECT ON REVENUE

		INCREASE	DECREASE	
1	FROM CHANGE IN QUALITY OF PRODUCTS	$	$	1
2	FROM CHANGE IN VOLUME OF OUTPUT			2
3	TOTAL	$ X	$ Y	3

B. EFFECT ON OPERATING COSTS

		INCREASE	DECREASE	
4	DIRECT LABOR	$ 900	$	4
5	INDIRECT LABOR	150		5
6	FRINGE BENEFITS	190		6
7	MAINTENANCE	200		7
8	TOOLING	80		8
9	MATERIALS AND SUPPLIES		16,800	9
10	INSPECTION			10
11	ASSEMBLY			11
12	SCRAP AND REWORK			12
13	DOWN TIME			13
14	POWER	40		14
15	FLOOR SPACE		1,000	15
16	PROPERTY TAXES AND INSURANCE	320		16
17	SUBCONTRACTING			17
18	INVENTORY		1,100	18
19	SAFETY			19
20	FLEXIBILITY			20
21	OTHER			21
22	TOTAL	$ 1,880 Y	$ 18,900 X	22

C. COMBINED EFFECT

		$	23
23	NET INCREASE IN REVENUE (3X−3Y)	$ 17,020	24
24	NET DECREASE IN OPERATING COSTS (22X−22Y)	$ 17,020	25
25	ANNUAL OPERATING ADVANTAGE (23+24)		

* Next year means the first year of project operation. For projects with a significant break-in period, use performance after break-in.

FIGURE **10.3**   MAPI summary form. Courtesy of Machinery and Allied Products Institute.

It is estimated that direct labor cost will be increased by $900 a year, indirect labor (supervision) by $150, and fringe benefits by $190. Maintenance will be higher by

II. INVESTMENT AND RETURN

A. INITIAL INVESTMENT

26	INSTALLED COST OF PROJECT	$ 29,800		
	MINUS INITIAL TAX BENEFIT OF	$ 2,100	(Net Cost) $ 27,700	26
27	INVESTMENT IN ALTERNATIVE			
	CAPITAL ADDITIONS MINUS INITIAL TAX BENEFIT	$		
	PLUS: DISPOSAL VALUE OF ASSETS RETIRED			
	BY PROJECT *	$ 4,000	$ 4,000	27
28	INITIAL NET INVESTMENT (26−27)		$ 23,700	28

B. TERMINAL INVESTMENT

29 RETENTION VALUE OF PROJECT AT END OF COMPARISON PERIOD
(ESTIMATE FOR ASSETS, IF ANY, THAT CANNOT BE DEPRECIATED OR EXPENSED. FOR OTHERS, ESTIMATE OR USE MAPI CHARTS.)

Item or Group	Installed Cost, Minus Initial Tax Benefit (Net Cost) A	Service Life (Years) B	Disposal Value, End of Life (Percent of Net Cost) C	MAPI Chart Number D	Chart Percentage E	Retention Value $\left(\dfrac{A \times E}{100}\right)$ F
Box Machine and Stitcher	$ 27,700	13	10	1A	89.4	$ 24,760

	ESTIMATED FROM CHARTS (TOTAL OF COL. F)	$		
	PLUS: OTHERWISE ESTIMATED	$	$ 24,760	29
30	DISPOSAL VALUE OF ALTERNATIVE AT END OF PERIOD *		$ 4,000	30
31	TERMINAL NET INVESTMENT (29−30)		$ 20,760	31

C. RETURN

32	AVERAGE NET CAPITAL CONSUMPTION $\left(\dfrac{28-31}{P}\right)$	$ 2,940	32
33	AVERAGE NET INVESTMENT $\left(\dfrac{28+31}{2}\right)$	$ 22,230	33
34	BEFORE-TAX RETURN $\left(\dfrac{25-32}{33} \times 100\right)$	% 63.3	34
35	INCREASE IN DEPRECIATION AND INTEREST DEDUCTIONS	$ 4,190	35
36	TAXABLE OPERATING ADVANTAGE (25−35)	$ 12,830	36
37	INCREASE IN INCOME TAX (36×TAX RATE)	$ 6,415	37
38	AFTER-TAX OPERATING ADVANTAGE (25−37)	$ 10,605	38
39	AVAILABLE FOR RETURN ON INVESTMENT (38−32)	$ 7,665	39
40	AFTER-TAX RETURN $\left(\dfrac{39}{33} \times 100\right)$	% 34.5	40

* After terminal tax adjustments.

FIGURE **10.4** MAPI summary form. Courtesy of Machinery and Allied Products Institute.

$200, tool costs by $80, power consumption by $40, and property taxes and insurance by $320. On the other hand, there will be a saving of $16,800 in the cost of purchased materials, $1,100 in inventory carrying costs (other than floor space), and $1,000 in floor space. The net cost reduction is therefore $17,020.

In addition to this operating advantage, the equipment will permit a reduction of $4,000 in inventory investment.

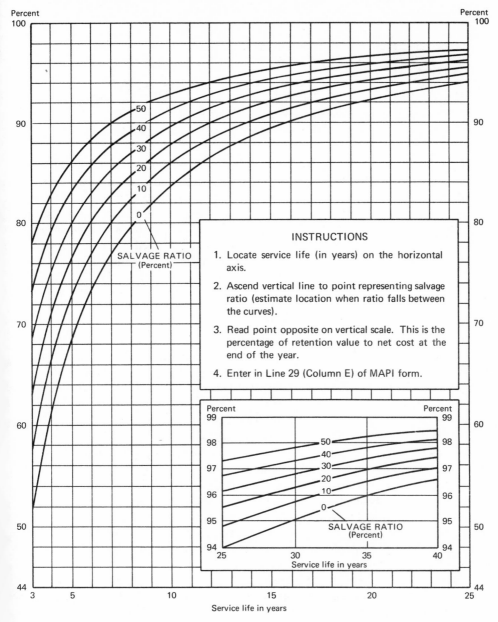

MAPI CHART NO. 1A

(ONE-YEAR COMPARISON PERIOD AND SUM-OF-DIGITS TAX DEPRECIATION)

INSTRUCTIONS

1. Locate service life (in years) on the horizontal axis.

2. Ascend vertical line to point representing salvage ratio (estimate location when ratio falls between the curves).

3. Read point opposite on vertical scale. This is the percentage of retention value to net cost at the end of the year.

4. Enter in Line 29 (Column E) of MAPI form.

SALVAGE RATIO
(Percent)

Service life in years

FIGURE **10.5** MAPI chart 1A. Courtesy of Machinery and Allied Products Institute.

After consulting with operating officials and others, the analyst comes up with the following stipulations:

Comparison period	1 year
Project operating rate	1,200 hours
Service life	13 years
Terminal salvage ratio	10 percent of net cost
Tax depreciation method	Sum-of-digits
Tax rate	50 percent
Debt ratio	30 percent
Debt interest rate	5 percent
Investment credit	7 percent

The results of the foregoing estimates and stipulations are shown on the executed MAPI form, Figures 10.3 and 10.4, and using the chart in Figure 10.5. The after-tax return is 34.5 percent, indicating of course an extremely urgent project.

It can be noted that the sophistication of the MAPI method lies in the procedure for determining the MAPI allowances for a project. The charts represent the equivalent of the computations made in the previous demonstration problem for the value of PW'. The MAPI formulas recognize the influence of taxes and make assumptions concerning the value of i, the interest rate, and the proportion of debt and equity capital used to fund the investment. We need not be concerned with these details here, although they are important in the final analysis.

Some Conclusions About Models
for Deteriorating Equipment Replacement

Review of the various theoretical models proposed for replacement of deteriorating equipment leads one to suspect that the degree of sophistication and refinements of the models may be far outweighed by more practical considerations in making replacements. Certainly, many replacements offer superior product function, quality, or rate of output, as well as reduced costs of operation and better salvage potential. Improvements in equipment design may be hard to predict for later than the near future. And improvements are likely to appear at random times in the future and result in some uneven accumulation of depreciation and obsolescence, rather than in a continuous gradient.

However, the possibility of computerizing replacement models offers the opportunity of a more thorough and constant evaluation of the economics of existing equipment, machines, and facilities. But we repeat that any method must recognize the need for information retrieval relative to the availability of possible replacements on the equipment market. This is the matter of gathering the raw data to be incorporated in whatever model is to be used.

On the theoretical side, more needs to be done to examine the sensitivity of the various models to changes in the variables and parameters constituting the replacement models.[4] Once the analyst is familiar with the critical variables in the models, he is in a more advantageous position to judge their usefulness and to simplify them without sacrificing accuracy.

---

[4] For one such study of sensitivity, see Robert B. Fetter and Thomas Goodman, "An Equipment Investment Analog," *Operations Research*, vol. 5, no. 5, October 1957.

Equipment with Terminal Life

In contrast to equipment that deteriorates over time and must be maintained, there are certain items that terminate their service life through sudden failure and must be replaced with like kind. These include such items as light bulbs, electronic tubes, truck tires, and batteries. Maintenance is a negligible factor, such as for batteries, or unnecessary, such as for light bulbs. Also included are more complex pieces of equipment, which must be replaced in event of failure rather than temporarily ceasing operations while they are maintained. For example, the breakdown of a machine in a highly automated manufacturing process may require the replacement of the machine rather than the cessation of the process while the machine is repaired. Whether or not the machine is subsequently repaired off the line is not the issue.

The central problem in situations involving such failures is to determine a replacement policy that minimizes the cost of replacement and the costs due to the temporary loss of service. For most kinds of equipment, the period between original installation and failure is a random variable, and the number of units to be maintained may be very large. The most that is known is the behavior of the rate of failure of the class of items. If the number of units is large, as is the case with street lights, a group replacement policy may be invoked, resulting in the replacement of some of the units prior to their failure, in contrast to replacing each unit as it fails.

FAILURE OR MORTALITY RATES: The rational approach to the replacement of items that fail depends on the determination of failure or mortality rates for the item. The rate at which an item fails may be either a function of the service life of the item, or independent of it, or some complex combination of the two. Certain electronic tubes, for example, might fail independently of their time in service due to random shocks to the system they serve. In this case, the life expectancy of the item would assume an exponential distribution corresponding to our discussion of queuing models in which arrivals are random. However, in most cases, we might assume that the life of the item is a function of service time, such as with tires or batteries.

The rate at which items fail must be determined either by using specially designed life tests or by observing the behavior of the items in the field. The choice, of course, depends on the hazards of failure; thus, in the case of aircraft components, one would prefer laboratory analysis to field testing.

Table 10.1 shows the results (hypothetical) of life testing 1,000 truck tires. While failures are obviously distributed continuously over time, we must work with discrete time periods and assume that failures occur on the last day of the period in question. From these data, we may construct a probability distribution of failures, as shown in Table 10.2.

INDIVIDUAL REPLACEMENT: Suppose that we replace each tire that fails in the period in which the failure takes place. Also let us assume that the actual number

TABLE **10.1**   Failure rate for 1,000 truck tires.

Period j	Number of units failing in period	Cumulative percent of items failing
0	0	0
1	10	1
2	40	5
3	60	11
4	100	21
5	120	33
6	170	50
7	200	70
8	150	85
9	100	95
10	50	100

TABLE **10.2**   Probability distribution of truck tire failures based on sample of 1,000 tires (mean life = 6.29).

Period j	Probability that a unit installed at time $j = 0$ will fail in period j p_i
0	0
1	0.01
2	0.04
3	0.06
4	0.10
5	0.12
6	0.17
7	0.20
8	0.15
9	0.10
10	0.05

of failures for a group of tires of the same age is the same as the expected number derived from the mortality table. Then, the number of failures in a period behaves in the following manner. If we let n_j be the number of failures (and therefore the number of replacements) in the jth period, the failure rate will have an oscillating characteristic that dampens to a steady value.

Suppose we start out at the beginning of period 0 with an initial installation of 1,000 new tires. The method of calculating the failure rate is as follows:

for period $j = 0, 1, \ldots, 10$

$n_0 = $ initial installation of 1,000 tires   1,000

$n_1 = n_0 p_1$ 10

$n_2 = n_0 p_2 + n_1 p_1$ 40.1

.

$n_j = n_0 p_j + n_1 p_{j-1} + n_2 p_{j-2} + \cdots + n_{j-1} p_1$

for period $j = 11, 12, \ldots, 20$

$$n_{11} = n_1 p_{10} + n_2 p_9 + \cdots + n_{10} p_1 \qquad\qquad 120.2$$

.
.

$$n_j = n_1 p_{j-1} + n_2 p_{j-2} + \cdots + n_{j-1} p_1$$

.
.
.

The rate of failures per period for 30 periods is shown in Table 10.3 and plotted in Figure 10.6. Note that the rate oscillates about the reciprocal of the mean tire life ($1,000/6.29 = 159$ failures per period). This is the steady-state failure rate.

GROUP REPLACEMENT: Group replacement consists in replacing an entire set of units, or some proportion of the total, at a given point in time. The advantages of group replacement are the possible reduction in the cost of making the replacement, due to economies of scale, plus the avoidance of the costs directly traceable to the failure itself. This occurs at the expense of retiring equipment while it still has serviceable life.

In the kind of situation previously discussed, the total cost of a group replacement policy, as a function of the period of time between group replacements, has both a transient and a steady-state behavior. Suppose we wish to determine a

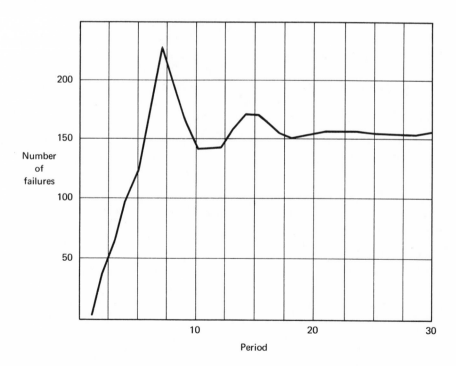

FIGURE **10.6**   Rate of failures for individual replacement of 1,000 tires.

TABLE **10.3**   Rate of failures for individual replacement of 1,000 tires.

Period	Failure rate	Period	Failure rate	Period	Failure rate
1	10.0	11	120.2	21	160.7
2	40.1	12	143.3	22	162.8
3	60.8	13	162.3	23	161.8
4	102.8	14	172.4	24	159.5
5	126.9	15	171.7	25	157.6
6	184.2	16	165.6	26	157.1
7	225.7	17	157.0	27	157.7
8	193.6	18	151.5	28	158.8
9	166.9	19	152.5	29	159.7
10	143.3	20	156.6	30	159.8

policy for replacing tires on a fleet of heavy construction equipment. Let the tire life data previously shown apply to this problem. The life of a tire will be expressed in terms of mileage, and we will assume that one period corresponds to 2,000 miles of vehicle travel. The policy will be to send the vehicle to the garage at the end of some period of usage and replace all its tires. Tires failing in the field are replaced at the time of failure. The problem is to determine the optimum number of miles (or periods) between group replacements. Assuming ten tires to a vehicle, let

C_f = cost of replacing a tire in the field when it fails

C_r = cost of replacing ten tires at group replacement

J = the period by which steady-state rate of failures has been reached

K = cumulative number of tires failed in the field up to period J. No group replacement takes place up to and including period J.

m = number of periods after J before group replacement takes place

R = steady-state rate of failures per period

Then, the total cost of replacement per a vehicle mile is

$$TC = \frac{C_r}{2,000(J + m)} + \frac{C_f(K + Rm)}{2,000(J + m)}$$

Setting the derivative of total cost with respect to m equal to zero, we have

$$\frac{dTC}{dm} = 0 = \frac{-C_r}{2,000(J + m)^2} + \frac{C_f(RJ - k)}{2,000(J + m)^2}$$

Then, the derivative approaches zero as m approaches infinity. The rate of change of the total cost is either negative or positive, depending on the parameters.

Assuming C_r = \$600, C_f = \$150, J = 40, K = 4,403, and R = 159, the student may determine a group replacement policy and plot the total cost per vehicle mile, but removing the constraint that group replacement cannot take place before the period $J + 1$.

PARTIAL GROUP REPLACEMENT: In the preceding example, and at the time of group replacement, some of the tires would have been replaced relatively recently in the field. Therefore, it would seem desirable to refrain from replacing tires that had minimum service time or minimum amount of wear. Suppose, for instance, that it was possible to know how many miles each tire had been in service at the time the vehicle was scheduled for group replacement. We might then have a policy that says: Replace all tires except those which have had L or less periods (or miles) of service. It might be better to state the rule in terms of tire wear (tread measurements), but then the mortality data would have to be in terms of tire wear.

A model that considers only partial group replacement would designate the optimum replacement interval and also the minimum service life above which the tire would be replaced. Such a model is presented as follows:

Let

n_j = failure rate (in percent) in the jth period, assuming that all tires are new, starting at n_0. Let one period equal 2,000 miles.

T = number of tires on the vehicle

K = group replacement interval or number of periods between group replacements

L = maximum life of a tire in periods, which will exclude it from being replaced at the time the group replacement is scheduled. If a tire has L or less periods of service at the time of group replacement, it will be left on the vehicle.

m = number of group replacement *intervals* that have occurred since the start of the program. We may assume that the life of a vehicle is 40,000 miles. Therefore, $m = 1, 2, \ldots, M$, where $M = 40,000/K$.

p_K = percent of failures (replacements) occurring during the interval K

$$= \sum_{j=1}^{K} n_j$$

$F(m)$ = expected number of tire failures occurring in the mth replacement interval

$G(m)$ = expected number of tires replaced in the group replacement at the end of the mth replacement interval

$H(m)$ = expected number of tires that are not replaced in the group replacement at the end of the mth replacement interval

C_1 = cost of changing one tire in the field

C_2 = cost of changing a tire in the group replacement

C_3 = fixed group replacement cost

$C(m)$ = total tire replacement cost for the mth replacement interval

$$= C_1 \times F(m) + C_2 \times G(m) + C_3$$

Cost = total tire replacement cost per mile of travel per truck

$$= \frac{\sum_{m=1}^{M} C(m)}{K \times m \times 2{,}000}$$

We now select a given value of K and L. That is, we will schedule the vehicle for group replacement every K periods (or miles). We will replace all tires except those that have had L miles (or periods) of service or less. If the life of the vehicle is

TABLE **10.4**   Partial tire group replacement costs per mile
for various values of K and L.

K	$L = 1$	$L = 2$	Miles
1	—	—	2,000
2	0.1645	—	4,000
3	0.1215	0.1237	6,000
4	0.1068	0.1115	8,000
5	0.1025	0.1097	10,000
6	0.1064	0.1130	12,000
7	0.1113	0.1177	14,000
8	0.1153	0.1195	16,000

40,000 miles, then it will be scheduled $40,000/K$ times for tire group replacement.
At the end of the first replacement interval and for a given value of K and L,

$$m = 1$$
$$F(1) = Tp_K$$
$$H(1) = T(p_K - p_{K-L})$$
$$G(1) = T - H(1)$$
$$C(1) = C_1 \times F(1) + C_2 \times G(1) + C_3$$

$$\text{Cost} = \frac{C(1)}{K \times 1 \times 2,000}$$

At the end of the second replacement interval, the vehicle has traveled a total
of $4,000K$ miles and

$$m = 2$$
$$F(2) = p_K \times G(1) + p_{K+L} \times H(1)$$
$$H(2) = G(1) \times (p_K - p_{K-L}) + H(1) \times (p_{K+L} - p_K)$$
$$G(2) = T - H(2)$$
$$C(2) = C_1 \times F(2) + C_2 \times G(2) + C_3$$

$$\text{Cost} = \frac{C(1) + C(2)}{K \times 2 \times 2,000}$$

We can continue the computations until M replacement intervals have been
examined.

Table 10.4 shows the results for different values of K and two values of L. In
this case, $C_1 = \$150$, $C_2 = \$50$, and $C_3 = \$100$. By deferring the replacement of
a certain number of tires at the time of scheduled group replacement, the rule is to
schedule the vehicle for group replacement every 10,000 miles ($K = 5$) and to
replace only those tires which have more than 2,000 miles of service ($L = 1$).

THE MAINTENANCE FUNCTION

Maintenance is a highly organized and complex function, the purpose of which is
to return a failed or deteriorating system to a satisfactory operating state. The pro-

gressive development of highly automated production systems, the advent of complex space systems, and continued mechanization have contributed to a growing interest in the management of maintenance programs.

In the context of a large industrial organization, the maintenance function is itself a production system having many of the characteristics of a large job shop. In certain service industries, such as airlines and trucking, maintenance does represent the production function. Therefore, many of the subjects in this text apply to the management of maintenance operations. These include the organization of operating units, the establishment of maintenance methods and time standards, determination of manpower levels, scheduling of maintenance operations, control of spare part inventories, and location of maintenance facilities.

While all these subjects are of particular interest and may involve certain specific principles related to maintenance, we prefer in this section to examine briefly certain kinds of decisions that are quite peculiar to facilities maintenance and to discuss several approaches to their quantitative treatment.

CORRECTIVE REPAIR
AND PREVENTIVE MAINTENANCE

In broad terms, there are two extreme maintenance policies that can be applied to a piece of equipment that is subject to deterioration as a function of operating time. The first is to subject the equipment to repair only at the time one or more of its components fail to operate, when it can no longer satisfy its functional objectives, or when its costs of operation become exorbitantly high. This is referred to as a policy of corrective maintenance or emergency repair. The second policy is to periodically subject the equipment or its components to inspection and then to repair or replace, depending on the state of deterioration. This is a policy of preventive maintenance.

As might be expected, the usual maintenance program involves the joint application of these two policies to varying degrees. Intuitively, one can visualize the behavior of relevant maintenance costs for varying degrees of these two policies. Each level of preventive maintenance implies a corresponding level of corrective action necessary. The relevant costs of maintaining a specific piece of equipment include maintenance labor, spare parts, supplies, lost production, interruptions to normal production schedules, scrapped production, and supervision, as well as maintenance planning and scheduling. An optimum policy would be one that minimizes the sum of these relevant costs. Then, the aggregate measure of maintenance effectiveness would be the sum of individual equipment policies, assuming an independence of individual policy actions.

The complexity of equipment maintenance precludes the easy derivation of an optimum policy. Maintenance is usually performed on equipment components, and, in many cases, the number of components for which data, such as failure and deterioration rates, must be collected and applied to individual component policies can be large. Also, aggregative maintenance costs and policies are usually not the simple summation of policies independently determined and applied to each piece of equipment. That is, the maintenance program for one component of a given machine or for one machine of a set will depend on the availability of maintenance resources as determined by many factors.

PREVENTIVE MAINTENANCE POLICIES

The prevalence of complex and automated systems has intensified interest in preventive maintenance programs as a logical condition for avoiding the high costs of system failure. The major decisions concern the times when preventive measures should be taken in the life of the equipment and the intensity of the action taken, such as inspection, repair, or complete replacement, as well as crew size.

Empirical Considerations

For a given piece of equipment, a preventive maintenance program can involve varying intensities of maintenance at different times. Preventive maintenance on an automobile is a function of the use of the car, with various kinds of maintenance being applied for different mileage increments. Maintenance may also be recommended depending on current operating information, regardless of the life of the equipment.

In general, many of the decisions to institute a preventive maintenance job are based upon trial-and-error methods or empirical information. A piece of equipment may be maintained according to a schedule set forth by the equipment manufacturer, or by the industry, or possibly by insurance companies. Preventive maintenance may also be a response to the status of both the equipment and the availability of maintenance personnel. In periods of low demand, line personnel may be retained in order to carry out various preventive maintenance operations. Similarly, if the demand for corrective repair is momentarily low, maintenance personnel may be scheduled for preventive maintenance functions.

System States

The boundary states of a system subjected to preventive maintenance are on the one hand a new or newly repaired piece of equipment, which is in a ready state, and on the other hand a complete failure. In between lie intermediate states of deterioration of the equipment, which, at any time, may be fully or partially restored to the original ready state or new condition.

Equipment inspection is a normal part of a preventive maintenance program. Either continuously or periodically, the equipment may be inspected to determine its operating state. At this time, repairs (adjustment, cleaning, part replacement, lubrication) may be instituted or deferred until a later date. Furthermore, the amount of repair may depend on various states of the machine at the time of inspec-

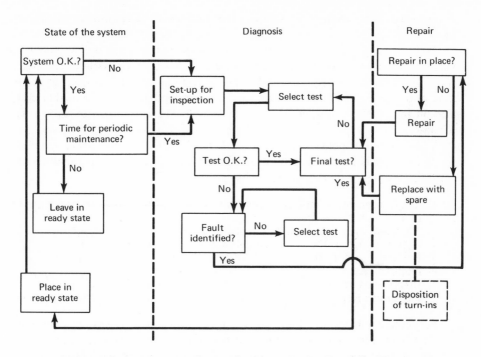

FIGURE **10.7**   Maintenance operating cycle. From R. L. Bovaird, *Management Science*, April 1961, p. 239.

tion. The shutdown of a machine to replace a component may lead to a decision to extend the repairs to other nonfailed components.

Figure 10.7 shows the short-term maintenance operating cycle in which decisions are categorized as the state of the system, diagnosis, and repair.

Diagnostic procedures involve the design of tests and the preparation of the necessary inspection equipment, tools, and spare parts. An important part of the test is the sequence of tests to minimize their cost and to maximize the opportunity to find the exact areas of repair.

Once these are located, the decision involves the choice of making repairs on the spot, or removing the component for repair elsewhere, after replacing it with a spare. Furthermore, the disposition of failed parts may be left to choice, including disposal or refurbishing.

Cost Models

The decision of when inspection, repair, or component replacement should be made has been subjected to considerable analytical treatment under a wide variety of assumptions. The problem has been of most interest in situations of stochastically or randomly failing equipment. This random characteristic is exhibited in terms of the distribution of failure rate, distributions of failure times, or by regular Markov chains.

McCall[5] suggests two broad classifications of maintenance policy models involving random failure: 1) preparedness models, in which the state of the system is unknown until it is inspected and 2) preventive maintenance models, where the state of the system is known for certainty. Each of these includes the further classification into cases where the failure distributions are known or not known with certainty.

Several kinds of policies can be studied. These include period policies, where a single decision is made, namely, the determination of a preventive maintenance period T. Examples of alternative period policies are:

1. The equipment is replaced upon failure or upon reaching an operating life of T, whichever is first.
2. The equipment is replaced or repaired at times T, $2T$, ..., regardless of the operating age of the equipment. Failures are taken care of when occurring.
3. Failures are not taken care of until the next regularly scheduled preventive maintenance.
4. Inspections are made at times T, $2T$, ..., and the state of the equipment is measured. Replacement or repair will depend on the state of the equipment.

Sequential policies are those for which the decision variables are determined not just once, but after each maintenance action. Opportunistic policies consider the interdependence between components of a system. The decision to maintain a component depends on the state of the rest of the equipment. The choice then takes into consideration economies of scale.

Because the variety of situations for which models exist is large, we will present only two approaches under simplified assumptions.

A Basic Periodic Policy

Suppose we have a single piece of equipment subject to a certain random failure rate that is increasing with time. The equipment is continuously inspected. A preventive maintenance program is: Perform a preventive maintenance repair after T hours of continuing operation, and if the equipment fails before T hours have elapsed, perform the repair when it fails, and reschedule the next preventive maintenance action for T hours in the future. The assumption is made that the system is returned to its original state after repair.

Solutions to this problem can be found in the literature, and the policy set forth is for an infinite time span. We assume that the equipment has a time-to-failure distribution function $F(T)$, which is the probability that a failure will occur after T hours of continuous operations. Then, the failure rate $g(t)$ is defined as the conditional probability that the equipment will fail in the interval $(t, t + \Delta t)$, given that it has not failed by time t.

---

[5] John J. McCall, "Maintenance Policies for Stochastically Failing Equipment: A Survey," *Management Science*, vol. 11, no. 5, March 1965, pp. 493–524.

$$g(t) = f(t)/[1 - F(t)]$$

Now we let C_1 and C_2 be the costs of repair before and after failure, respectively. Then, the limiting cost per unit time of operating the equipment when it is repaired at failure or time T, whichever is first, is

$$C'(T) = \frac{C_1[1 - F(T)] + C_2 F(T)}{\int_0^T [1 - F(t)]\, dt}$$

The optimal preventive maintenance period T^* is obtained by setting the derivative of $C'(T)$ equal to zero. The optimum value of T satisfies

$$g(T) \int_0^T [1 - F(t)]\, dt - F(T) = \frac{C_1}{C_2 - C_1} \qquad C_2 > C_1$$

For example, we have a piece of equipment for which the failure data for a sample of 100 units are as follows.

t (months)	$f(t)$	$F(t)$	$1 - F(t)$	$g(t)$	$g(T) \int_0^T [1 - F(t)]\, dt - F(T)$	$\dfrac{C_2}{C_1}$
1	0.05	0.05	0.95	0.0526	0	∞
2	0.15	0.20	0.80	0.1875	0.128	8.75
3	0.20	0.40	0.60	0.3333	0.380	3.63
4	0.25	0.65	0.35	0.7150	1.280	1.78
5	0.20	0.85	0.15	1.333	2.950	1.34
6	0.10	0.95	0.05	2.000	4.850	1.20
7	0.05	1.00	0	∞	∞	1.00

In Figure 10.8 we have plotted the optimum T^* for values of C_2/C_1. Obviously, for a failure rate of infinity, the policy would be to execute only repair maintenance and $T^* \to \infty$ as $C_2/C_1 \to 1$.

Multicomponent Cost Model

Suppose we have a multicomponent system and we wish to set a preventive maintenance policy that results in minimum total costs. Periodically, the system is to be subjected to inspection. Each time the system is inspected, one or more of the components may be subjected to its own inspection and repair if necessary. Each component has its own deterioration probability function, which is independent of other components. The problem is twofold: 1) determine the time interval (period) between system inspections, and 2) determine the set of components that will be inspected in each succeeding period.

The set of relevant costs includes the cost of inspecting the system, the individual component inspection and repair costs, and the costs associated with the

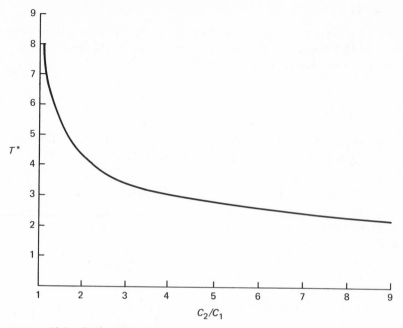

FIGURE **10.8**   Optimum preventive maintenance period (T^*) as a function of C_2/C_1.

failure of a component prior to its scheduled inspection. We wish to minimize the sum of these costs.[6]

MARKOV DETERIORATION PROCESS: The deterioration process for a given component can be described as a Markov chain. We can consider a given component to be in one of three states at the end of some time interval t. The maintenance action taken at the end of the interval t depends on the state, as follows:

Component state at end of t	Maintenance action
1. Good	None
2. Deteriorated	Make a repair at the next scheduled inspection
3. Failed	Repair immediately

Suppose we let the time interval t be short enough that not more than one change of state will take place, but long enough to permit the repair of a failed item. Then, there is a transition matrix of probabilities p_{mn} which is the probability

─────────
[6] This approach with additional variables and considerations is presented by Robert L. Bovaird, "Characteristics of Optimal Maintenance Policies," *Management Science*, vol. 8, no. 2, April 1961.

that the component will change from state m to state n in the interval t. These probabilities are

$$
\begin{array}{c}
\text{final state} \\
n \\
\begin{array}{c}
\quad\;\; 1 \quad 2 \quad 3 \\
\begin{array}{cc}
\text{initial} & 1 \\
\text{state} & 2 \\
m & 3
\end{array}
\left(
\begin{array}{ccc}
p_{11} & p_{12} & p_{13} \\
0 & p_{22} & p_{23} \\
1 & 0 & 0
\end{array}
\right)
\end{array}
\end{array}
$$

Now we will want to know the probability that the component will be in any one of the three states at the end of $r + 1$ time periods of length t. Let $P_m^{(r+1)}$ be the probability that the component will be in the mth state at the end of $r + 1$ time periods. Then,

$$
[P_1^{(r)}, P_2^{(r)}, P_3^{(r)}]
\begin{pmatrix}
p_{11} & p_{12} & p_{13} \\
0 & p_{22} & p_{23} \\
1 & 0 & 0
\end{pmatrix}
= [P_1^{(r+1)}, P_2^{(r+1)}, P_3^{(r+1)}]
$$

or

$$
\sum_{i=1}^{3} P_i^{(r)} p_{im} = P_m^{(r+1)}
$$

Letting the initial state be $m = 1$ and $P_m^0 = (1, 0, 0)$, then we have, for the start,

$$
[P_m^{(r)}] = [P_m^0]
\begin{pmatrix}
p_{11} & p_{12} & p_{13} \\
0 & p_{22} & p_{23} \\
1 & 0 & 0
\end{pmatrix}^r
$$

Let

i = index number of components in system, $i = 1, 2, \ldots, I$

T = period in years between successive system inspections

k_i = number of periods between successive inspections of the ith component; therefore, $k_i T$ will be the time between component inspections

C_{1i} = cost of making a preventive inspection of the ith component; therefore, the expected annual cost will be $C_{1i}/(k_i T)$

$P_{2,i}$ = probability of making a preventive repair of the ith component at the time of a preventive inspection

C_{2i} = cost of making a preventive repair of the ith component at the time of a preventive inspection. Its expected annual cost will be $(C_{2i})(P_{2,i})/(k_i T)$.

E_i = expected number of failures of the ith component between preventive inspections

$$
= \sum_{r=1}^{r=k_i T/t} P_{3,i}^r
$$

C_{3i} = cost of making a corrective repair to the ith component when it fails. The expected annual cost is, therefore,

$$
\frac{(C_{3i})(E_i)}{k_i T}
$$

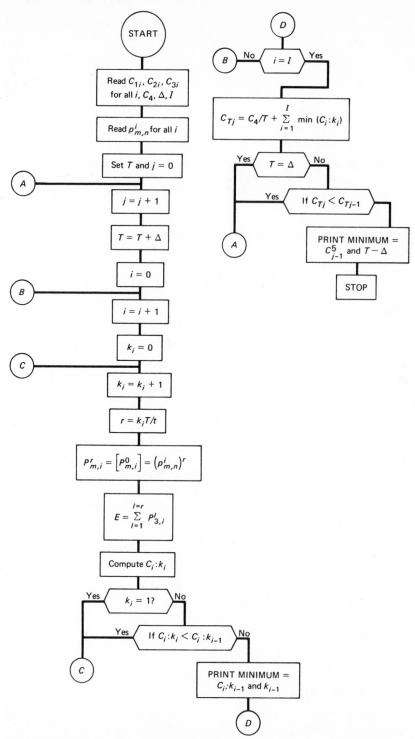

FIGURE **10.9** Logic diagram for determining optimum inspection periods.

C_i = total annual costs of failure and maintenance for the ith component

$\quad = C_{1i} + C_{2i} + C_{3i}$

C_4 = cost of inspecting the system. Its annual cost = C_4/T.

C_T = total annual cost of a policy of system inspection every period of length T

$$= \frac{C_4}{T} + \sum_{i=1}^{I} C_i$$

We should note that the relevant costs include the downtime of the system, as well as the direct marginal costs of making the inspections and repairs.

The problem now is to find the values for all i of k_i for a given value of T that will minimize $\sum C_i$. Then we wish to find a value of T that minimizes C_T. The problem-solving procedure is shown in Figure 10.9, in the form of a logic diagram. The general procedure is to advance T in increments until the total cost C_T is minimized, or beyond that point if we wish, to plot the behavior of C_T as T is varied.

EXAMPLE 10.13   Figure 10.10 shows the behavior of C_T for systems of three components and for a range of cost values. Two probability transition matrices were used:

$$\text{Matrix I} \quad \begin{pmatrix} 0.90 & 0.09 & 0.01 \\ 0.00 & 0.90 & 0.10 \\ 1.00 & 0.00 & 0.00 \end{pmatrix}$$

$$\text{Matrix II} \quad \begin{pmatrix} 0.80 & 0.15 & 0.05 \\ 0.00 & 0.85 & 0.15 \\ 1.00 & 0.00 & 0.00 \end{pmatrix}$$

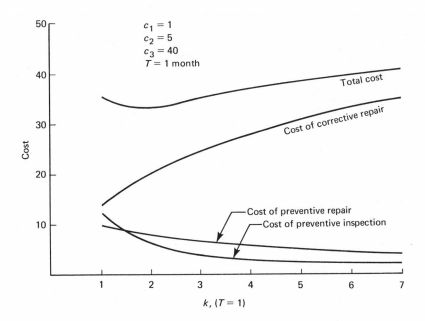

FIGURE **10.10**   Change in cost for component 1 as k is varied.

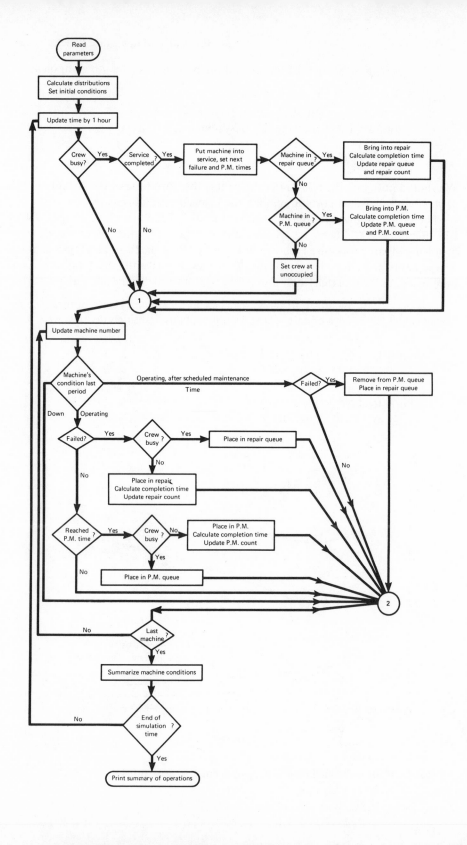

The conditions for each of six trials are indicated below:

Trial	Component 1				Component 2				Component 3			
	C_1	C_2	C_3	P_{mn}	C_1	C_2	C_3	P_{mn}	C_1	C_2	C_3	P_{mn}
1	1	5	40	I	1	5	20	I	1	5	100	II
2	5	25	200	I	5	25	200	I	5	25	200	I
3	10	50	400	I	10	50	400	I	10	50	400	I
4	5	25	100	I	5	50	200	I	5	100	500	II
5	5	25	500	I	5	25	500	I	5	25	500	I
6	2.5	12.5	250	I	2.5	12.5	250	I	2.5	12.5	250	II

In all trials, C_4 was equal to 40.

When the cost of repairs is high relative to the other costs, the total cost curve tends to have a sharply defined optimum, such as in Trial 5. In Trial 4, the relatively high cost of a preventive repair balances the corrective repair costs, such that the total cost curve is relatively flat.

MULTIMACHINE MAINTENANCE SYSTEMS

Many of the purely analytical methods of determining optimal maintenance policies can be trivial compared to the actual problems of managing the maintenance of a system of machines. For example, consider a system of M unlike machines, which are to be serviced by a maintenance crew. If the machines are subject to random breakdowns as well as to deterioration, then the system operates as a complex finite queuing multichannel maintenance system. Some of the questions are:

1. How large a crew size is desirable, and can economies of scale be realized by assigning unlike machines to the same crew?
2. For a stated crew size, when should preventive maintenance be performed on each kind of machine?
3. If more than one machine is waiting in queue for service, and the kinds of service (i.e., repair or preventive) differ, what priorities should be used for machine selection?
4. What effect will changes in the machine failure distributions have on the system economics?

FIGURE **10.11**   Simulation model for determining operating characteristics of multi-machine maintenance system. This flow chart illustrates the system operating under the assumption that repair has priority over maintenance. Only very slight changes are required to operate with preventive maintenance priority or to allow machine stoppage before failure. From R. C. Vergin, *Management Science*, vol. 13, no. 2, October 1966, pp. 352–65.

Vergin has subjected this kind of a situation to simulation.[7] The logic is set forth in Figure 10.11. The purpose of the simulator was to test very specific hypotheses about the operation of a multimachine situation with random failure. Design variables included

1. Time to failure distributions.
2. Preventive maintenance periods.
3. Preventive maintenance and repair service time-distribution parameters.
4. Priority rules for choosing between repair and preventive maintenance demands.
5. Time beyond the preventive maintenance periodic when a machine should be shut down to avoid a repair situation.

We will not pursue the results of Vergin's studies. We wish rather to point out his general approach and to concur with him that the simulation model will have a valid place in the investigation and solution of maintenance problems.

Problems

10.1   A small screw machine plant uses a chip disposal method that will now require replacement. Two possible methods are proposed. Method I is to rebuild the present system with an initial investment of $35,000. Estimated costs for the operation and maintenance are $3,000 per year for the first five years, $4,000 a year for the next five years, and $5,000 a year for the remaining life. The alternative is a method requiring a new piece of equipment initially costing $60,000, but the disbursements for the operation and maintenance are expected to be $1,500 a year for the first ten years and $2,000 a year thereafter.

Using an interest rate of 10% and a service life of 15 years for each method, compare the alternatives on the annual cost basis using exact methods.

10.2   A transistor manufacturer is considering the replacement of a testing machine currently in use. The machine was purchased three years ago at an installed cost of $7,000. At that time, its service life was estimated at six years with a salvage value of $1,000 at the end of that time. It has been depreciated in the company's books on these terms, using the straight-line method. Its present book value is thus $4,000. Its present salvage or resale value, however, is apparently only $1,000.

The installed cost of the proposed replacement will be $12,000. However, considerable savings in labor costs can be expected if it is used. The service life for this machine is also estimated at six years, but, due to contemplated changes in basic product design three years hence, it appears that neither this machine nor the one currently in use will likely be of any value to the company (or anyone else) after that time.

Determine what the annual savings in labor must be to justify the proposed replacement. Use interest at 10%.

10.3   Two years ago, a special oven was purchased and installed for drying paint on sheets of paper coming from a coater in a decal manufacturing plant. The installed

[7] R. C. Vergin, "Scheduling Maintenance and Determining Crew Size for Stochastically Failing Equipment," *Management Science*, vol. 13, no. 2, October 1966, pp. B 52–65.

cost was $10,000. Service life was estimated at eight years with no salvage value at the end of that time. Annual disbursements for fuel and other variable operating expenses have averaged $4,000 per year. Since the machine is now two years old, its book value is $7,500. However, its market value at the present time is approximately $2,000.

A much better oven has been developed in the meantime and is now available. Its first cost is also $10,000 with an estimated salvage value of $1,000 at the end of an estimated service life of eight years. Annual disbursements for fuel and other variable operating expenses are estimated at only $2,500 per year. Furthermore, if this new oven is purchased at this time, a trade-in allowance of $3,000 will be made for the old machine.

With interest at 10%, determine whether or not a replacement can be justified by the yearly savings that will be realized in operating costs.

10.4   A manufacturing concern is considering the investment of $15,000 in a cost-reduction project. Of this amount, $10,000 will be invested in a machine, which must be depreciated on the accounting records over a 20-year period (using the straight-line method). The remaining $5,000 will be invested in special tools, which will be written off over a two-year period.

A cost study has been made using an arbitrary study period of five years. It indicates that the gross savings will amount to $5,000 per year for the first three years and $6,000 per year for the remaining two years of the five-year study period. The "gross savings" amount represents the expected reduction in cash outlays for direct labor, direct material, and other direct costs.

(a) Determine the net savings each year over this five-year study period after the effects of the Federal corporation income tax have been taken into account. For simplicity in computations, assume the tax rate is 50%.

(b) With interest at 10%, determine whether or not the net savings over this study period will justify the proposed investment.

10.5   A production engineer faces the decision of whether to buy a certain part for a new product that is to be manufactured or whether to produce it in the plant. It can be purchased (subcontracted) for $2.25 per unit. Approximately 3,600 units will be required each year for the next three years.

If the part is to be manufactured, a new machine will have to be purchased—a special one, needed only for this part. In addition, part of the production time of one of the company's general-purpose machine tools will be required. The capacity of such a machine is available, however, for use on this part during the coming three years. Some cost and production figures are given below. Determine which will be the most economical—to manufacture or to buy. Use interest at 10%. State any assumptions that you have to make, and assume some value for any additional cost figures that you may need. Show all computations you make in determining your answer.

Cost of new machine, including installation	$6,000
Estimated resale value three years hence	$1,000
Original cost of general-purpose machine (four years ago)	$10,000
Estimated life	10 years
Estimated salvage value (when ten years old)	$2,000
Present book value	$3,000
Maintenance costs per year—new machine	$900
Maintenance costs per year—existing machine	$500
Total labor hours per unit	0.20

Total labor costs per unit	$0.50
Total materials costs per unit	$0.60
Power and miscellaneous variable costs per unit	$0.15
Present fixed factory costs per hour of direct labor	$2.00

10.6   The design, construction, and installation of an automatic machine for assembling an electrical component has been proposed. The total cost is estimated at $65,000. It is expected that a savings of $17,000 per year can be achieved.

Assuming a service life of five years for this machine with no salvage value remaining at the end of that time, determine the rate of return on the investment by interpolation in interest tables.

10.7   Two alternative machines for the provision of a certain service in an industrial plant are being compared. Either one will have a service life of eight years.

Machine P will cost $9,000 to be installed. Estimated annual disbursements are $4,000 for labor and $1,600 for maintenance, power, and like items. The salvage value at the end of eight years is estimated at $2,000.

Machine Q will cost $13,000 to be installed. Estimated annual disbursements are $3,000 for labor and $1,800 for maintenance, power, and like items. The salvage value at the end of eight years is estimated at $3,000.

Estimate the prospective rate of return on the extra investment by an "exact" method.

10.8   The use of mechanical material-handling equipment has been proposed for the finished product warehouse for a large manufacturer of automobile storage batteries. Five different systems have been suggested. The investment cost for each, together with estimated yearly costs (including depreciation but not interest or expected profit on the investment) are tabulated below. Comparable annual costs under the present method for materials handling are $11,000.

	Method A	Method B	Method C	Method D	Method E
Investment	$22,000	$17,000	$30,000	$36,000	$25,000
Annual costs	7,400	9,100	5,900	5,200	7,200

At the present time, the concern has funds for cost-saving investments of this nature. However, a current requirement is that annual net savings of at least 10% of the original investment must be demonstrated if a proposal is to be accepted. The management of the concern feels that ample opportunities for investment are available elsewhere in the plant on which at least this rate of return can be made.

Which of the above methods would you recommend? Show all the computations you make, and give reasons for your choice.

10.9   An electrical utility company maintains a large fleet of small panel trucks in customer-service work. The company wishes to establish a replacement policy that determines the life of a truck and when it should be replaced. Information relative to the problem is designated as follows in general terms.

P = purchase price of a new truck plus any costs incidental to readying the truck for service

$S(n)$ = salvage value of the truck at the end of n years as a percentage of the first cost. A study shows that salvage value is of hyperbolic form $S(n) = a + b/x$, where x is the life of the truck in years.

t = income tax rate

i = desired rate of capital recovery after taxes

$A(n)$ = annual costs of operating the truck in the nth year. A study shows that the costs per mile increase linearly: $A(n) = c + d(x)$ per mile, and x is the life of the truck.

g = annual mileage of the truck

(a) Develop a general formula for the derivation of the optimal truck life in terms of uniform annual costs.

(b) Assuming that the following data apply, what is the optimal value of n?

P = $3,200
a =   0.100
b =   0.500
t =   0.54
i =   0.10
g = 15,000 miles
c =   0.060
d =   0.010

10.10   An electrical utility company uses a battery set for energizing circuit breakers in their substations. A study of the maintenance costs on these batteries shows that the costs increase with the service life of the battery set.

n	1	2	3	4	5	6	7	8	9	10	11	12	13	14	15
c_i	40	50	60	80	110	140	170	200	230	260	290	320	360	400	450

The cost of a new set of batteries including installation is $1,000. Salvage value is zero.

(a) Determine an optimal life using an approximate method and an exact method of determining uniform annual costs.

(b) Make a graph of n versus the total equivalent uniform annual costs. What important information does the graph give?

10.11   Verify the annual cost of alternative (b) ($6,137) on page 323.

10.12   The Apex Aircraft Corporation has 10,000 active fluorescent lighting fixtures in its production and storage buildings. A sales engineer for the Brite-Lite Lamp Corporation is trying to sell Apex's chief industrial engineer the idea of "group relamping" to replace the company's present practice of replacing a lamp only after it fails ("failure relamping"). The Brite-Lite sales engineer has presented figures from other companies that now "group relamp" that show annual savings ranging from $500 to $8,000, compared to "failure relamping."

The "group relamp" program presented by the salesman is as follows:

1. Replace each lamp failure as it occurs during the first 3,000 hours (6 periods)

of lamp life. This will be only about 40% of the lamps.

2. At 3,500 hours (7 periods), "group relamp"; that is, replace with new lamps all 10,000 lamps in use.

    (*Note:* Assume that lamps are replaced only at the end of a period.)

The salesman's main argument to support this program is that, although it is true that Apex will be using more lamps, the savings in labor due to group relamping will more than offset this increased lamp cost.

The cost of a lamp to Apex is $.55 each, whether they replace lamps individually or in groups. Estimates by the time-study engineers show that the mean replacement time for failure replacement is 25 minutes per lamp and for group replacement, 15 minutes per lamp. Maintenance labor for this job is rated at $2.00 an hour. The total overhead rate in this department is 100% of the hourly wage. Variable overhead is $1.00 an hour.

The lamp company has supplied the following probability distribution for lamp failures, where each period is 500 hours.

Period	% Failure
1	0
2	2
3	3
4	5
5	10
6	20
7	25
8	20
9	10
10	5
	100%

The expected number of lamps to fail under the "failure replace" program for periods 6 through 20 is as follows:

Period	Expected number of failures	Total expected failures
6	2,029	4,045
7	2,570	6,615
8	2,165	8,780
9	1,323	10,103
10	1,038	11,141
11	831	11,972
12	1,225	13,197
13	1,620	14,817
14	1,841	16,658
15	1,789	18,447
16	1,560	20,007
17	1,330	21,337
18	1,241	22,578
19	1,314	23,892
20	1,475	25,367

Additional information:

1. Lamps burn on an average of 10 hours per day 250 days per year.
2. Neglect interest charges on the investment in lamps.
3. Assume that group replacements are made only at the end of a period under all plans. Failure replacements are made when they occur.

Based on the above data,

(a) What is the expected cost per period for the "failure replace" program, which Apex is now using? (Assume that the probability distribution for lamp failures is the same as on page 352.)
(b) Plot the expected number of failures by periods for this program. How would you expect this curve to appear for the periods beyond the twentieth?
(c) What is the optimum number of periods between "group relamping"?
(d) What is the expected cost per period for the program advanced by the Brite-Lite salesman?
(e) Should Apex undertake "group relamping"?
(f) What is the optimum number of periods between "group relamping" under this plan?
(g) By building a special mobile platform at a cost of $5,000, Apex can "group relamp" at the rate of two minutes per lamp. Would this be a worthwhile investment if the platform lasted for ten years and maintenance costs were $200 per year? Assume $500 scrap value at the end of this period.

Bibliography

Replacement

BRENNAN, J. F., "Optimum Life of Fleet Automobiles," *J. Ind. Eng.*, November–December 1964.

CANADA, JOHN R., "Capital Budgeting: Its Nature, Present Practice and Needs for the Future," *J. Ind. Eng.*, March–April 1964.

CLARE, KENNETH G., "Development of Criteria for Deciding Whether to Rebuild or Replace Major Industrial Equipment," *J. Ind. Eng.*, March–April 1964.

DEAN, BURTON V., "Replacement Theory," *Progress in Operations Research*, vol. I, R. L. Ackoff, Ed. New York: John Wiley & Sons, 1961.

EISEN, M., and M. LEIBOWITZ, "Replacement of Randomly Deteriorating Equipment," *Management Science*, January 1963.

ENGLISH, J. MORLEY, "A Discount Function Comparing Economic Alternatives," *J. Ind. Eng.*, March–April 1965.

GRANT, EUGENE L., and W. GRANT IRESON, *Principles of Engineering Economy*, 4th ed. Ronald Press, 1960.

KRASNOW, HOWARD S., "Rate of Return: A Comparison Between Accurate and Approximate Methods for the Nonuniform Income Case," *J. Ind. Eng.*, November–December 1961.

MAYER, RAYMOND R., "Problems in the Application of Replacement Theory," *Management Science*, April 1960.

NATIONAL INDUSTRIAL CONFERENCE BOARD, *Managing Capital Expenditures*, Studies in Business Policy No. 107.

NORDIN, J. A., "A Method of Replacement Analysis," *Eng. Econ.*, vol. 6, no. 2, Winter 1961.

OLMER, FRANÇOIS J., "A New Approach to the Determination of Replacement Costs," *Management Science*, October 1959.

REISMAN, ARNOLD, and ELWOOD S. BUFFA, "A General Model for Investment Policy," *Management Science*, April 1962.

RIFAS, B. E., "Replacement Models," in *Introduction to Operations Research*, C. W. Churchman, R. L. Ackoff, and E. L. Arnoff, Eds. New York: John Wiley & Sons, 1957, Chapter 17.

SINDEN, FRANK, "The Replacement and Expansion of Durable Equipment," *J. Soc. of Ind. and Appl. Math.*, vol. 8, no. 3, September 1960.

SMITH, VERNON L., "Economic Equipment Policies: An Evaluation," *Management Science*, October 1957.

TAYLOR, GEORGE A., *Managerial and Engineering Economy*. Princeton, N.J.: D. Van Nostrand, Inc., 1964.

Maintenance

BARLOW, RICHARD, and LARRY HUNTER, "Optimum Preventive Maintenance Policies," *Operations Research*, January–February 1960.

CAMPBELL, FORREST, DONALD PIERCE, and PAUL E. TORGERSEN, "The Maintenance Game," *J. Ind. Eng.*, January–February 1964.

KLEIN, MORTON, "Inspection-Maintenance-Replacement Schedules under Markovian Deterioration," *Management Science*, October 1962.

MANN, LAWRENCE, JR., "Toward a Systematic Maintenance Program," *J. Ind. Eng.*, September 1966.

MORSE, P. M., *Queues, Inventories and Maintenance*. New York: John Wiley & Sons, 1958.

PARSONS, JAMES A., "Preventive-Maintenance Policy Selection," *J. Ind. Eng.*, September–October 1965.

PRITSKER, A. ALAN B., "The Setting of Maintenance Tolerance Limits," *J. Ind. Eng.*, March–April 1963.

WAGNER, HARVEY M., RICHARD J. GIGLIO, and R. GEORGE GLASER, "Preventive Maintenance Scheduling by Mathematical Programming," *Management Science*, January 1964.

11

Design and Management of Capacity

INTRODUCTION

The term "capacity" generally refers to the potential of a production or service facility to produce some rate of output. The way in which capacity is measured and the way in which it is changed depend on the kind of facility, its technology, the product mix, the extent of the change, and the term for which the capacity is needed.

The general production format, that is, job or flow shop, conditions the kinds of capacity decisions made. In the job shop format, initial capacity decisions involve the determination of the kinds, numbers, and sizes of the individual machines and equipment. The joint use of the facility by heterogeneous products necessitates the translation of product demand into machine hour requirements through routing analysis. The resulting hourly requirements for each facility must then be inflated to account for machine downtime to yield normal productive standard hours.

In the job shop context, expansion in capacity usually consists in incremental additions to particular machine groups, and the economic problems are quite similar to those encountered in replacement analysis. At the time expansion is required, alternative processing methods should be considered. Besides increasing the number and/or size of machines, additional capacity can be gained by a number of tactical or strategic maneuvers, including accruing capacity through inventories, deferring capacity by backlogging, changing scheduling patterns, deferring preventive maintenance, making minor methods changes, shifting labor pools, changing employment levels, etc. We will discuss some of these methods in Chapters 14, 15, and 16 as they relate to production planning and scheduling.

In the flow shop context, where the product mix is usually small, original capacity decisions often involve major capital commitments to plant and equipment, specifically designed to produce a single product line for the life of that product line. Such situations are typically encountered in chemical, processing, or mass-production plants or in the design or purchase of a single large machine, such as a forging press, printing press, or computer. Capacity expansion often involves the replacement of a major piece of equipment or the addition of like units of equipment at a substantial capital investment.

CAPACITY DECISIONS

While we are interested in the various ways that capacity can be manipulated, in this chapter we will focus on the question of determining the size and scale of plants or facilities. In this respect, the design of initial production capacity or the expansion of existing capacity are topics that can be extrapolated from the discussion of replacement. From the point of view of replacement, one might conclude that the issue of designing capacity is simply one of choosing the desired size or number of machines or equipment to accommodate some forecasted product or service demand, assuming that the choice of production method has been made. However, the problem has some complex ramifications.

The dominant variable in capacity decisions is usually the rate of product demand translated into capacity requirements for different time periods. The rate of demand is seldom static and is more often the function of random, seasonal, general business, and long-term growth determinants. These force the major decision of when and how much capacity should be added. Then there are also probabilistic considerations, including error in requirement forecasts and cost projections, and uncertainty of process performance, which complicate the investment decisions.

Ultimately, the design of an original or expanded plant may include decisions on the production method for alternative output rates, plant size and location, size of individual units of equipment or machines within the plant, and timing of investment. The collection and analysis of the data for such decisions, the structuring of decision models, and the interpretation of analytical results are some of the ingredients of corporate or company planning functions.

In the remainder of this chapter, we will briefly consider some of the ramifications of capacity decisions especially related to flow shop conditions. Since the subject by its very nature involves large and complex issues, our examples will appear grossly simplified. However, they are intended to convey merely the concepts.

Design Uncertainty in Process Capacity

When a process is in the design stages, its *expected rate* of production for some specific design is a matter of risk or uncertainty. It will not be known for certain until the design is implemented and the process is operational.

If a plant is under design and composed of a number of processing facilities in series, then the uncertainty of each facility's expected capacity necessitates a safety factor in the plant design to ensure a specified expected plant output rate. For example, consider a plant that is being designed with m operations in series, Figure 11.1. Obviously, the plant output rate will be confined to the lowest rate of any operation in the series. Suppose that each operation is designed for an expected output rate of $\bar{v}$ tons per year. However, the actual average rate $\bar{v}$ is probabilistically distributed; that is, the actual average output rate of the operation is not known with certainty. Assume that the distribution of $\bar{v}$ is normal with mean $\bar{v}$

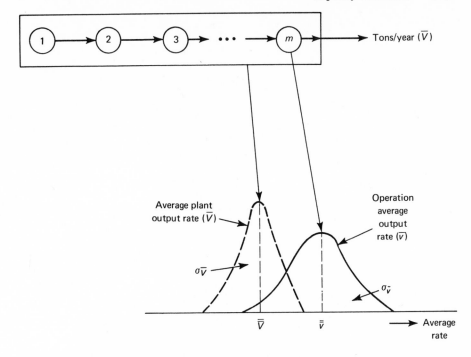

FIGURE **11.1** Influence of uncertainty in operation average capacity on average plant capacity.

and standard deviation $\sigma_{\bar{v}}$. Then, the actual average output rate of the plant will also be a random variable with a distribution that is approximately normal with mean $\overline{\overline{V}}$ and a standard deviation of $\sigma_{\overline{V}}$. If $m > 1$, then $\overline{\overline{V}} < \bar{\bar{v}}$ and $\sigma_{\overline{V}} < \sigma_{\bar{v}}$.

Figure 11.2 shows the cumulative probability distribution of average plant capacity as a function of the normalized standard deviation of average capacity of the individual operations for three values of m. This assumes that the average operation capacities are normally, identically, and independently distributed. We let p equal the probability of one operation's having an average capacity ($\bar{v} < Y$). Then, for m stations, the probability that the average plant capacity will be less than Y is $P(\overline{V} < Y) = 1 - (1 - p)^m$.

Suppose that the over-all plant output rate Y is desired. It can be readily seen that the uncertainty of both the operation rate and the number of operations in series affects the probability of meeting the desired rate. In this situation, the determination of expected capacity, assuming a static demand rate, requires a decision on what risk shall be taken of the plant not being able to meet the desired demand rate. Traditionally this has been handled by adding a safety factor in the design that will probably assure the desired capacity. Optimizing this safety factor involves a tradeoff between the increased capital costs of the added operation capacity versus the cost of insufficient capacity, such as lost sales.

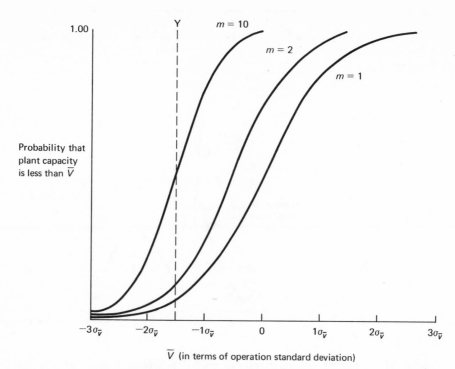

FIGURE **11.2**   Probability that plant capacity is less than $\bar{V}$ for the case of m operations in series.

EXAMPLE **11.1**   Suppose we have the following rather odd chemical process consisting of a single-stage piece of equipment that has yet to be purchased. There are three equipment sizes to select from, namely, X, Y, and Z. The expected production rate for each is $\bar{v}_X = 100,000$ (tons per year), $\bar{v}_Y = 110,000$, and $\bar{v}_Z = 120,000$. However, the actual rate is a matter of risk related to the following distribution:

Actual rate ($\bar{v}$)	$\bar{v} - 10,000$	Average ($\bar{v}$)	$\bar{v} + 10,000$
Prob ($\bar{v}$)	0.30	0.50	0.20

We have the following additional information:

1. The rate of demand for the product is constant and known to be 110,000 tons per year.

2. The capital costs of the equipment are $A = 1,670\bar{\bar{v}}^{0.52}$.

3. The selling price of the product is $2.00 per ton, and the variable operating and manufacturing costs are $1.10 per ton. Fixed costs of operation per year are $F = 0.02A$.

4. The economic life of the equipment is 20 years, which equals the life of the project, and the desired rate of return is 10%. There is no equipment salvage value at the end of 20 years. We will ignore taxes.

We now wish to find the expected present worth of using each equipment size. For a given output rate $\bar{v}$, the expected present worth is

$$EPW = P(\bar{v})[(\text{Annual income} - \text{Annual variable costs} - \text{Annual fixed costs})$$
$$PFW(u)_{0.10}^{20} - \text{Initial capital cost}]$$

Now consider size Y, for example, which has a mean output rate of 110,000.

$$A = 1,670(110,000)^{0.52} = 698,700$$

For $\bar{v} = 100,000$,

$$EPW = 0.30[((100,000)(0.90) - (698,700)(0.02))8.514 - 698,700] = -15,420$$

For $\bar{v} = 110,000$ or $120,000$,

$$EPW = 0.70[((110,000)(0.90) - (698,700)(0.02))8.514 - 698,700] = 17,647$$

Therefore, the total expected present worth for the policy to buy size Y is

$$T(EPW)_Y = -15,420 + 17,647 = 2,228$$

Similarly, the total expected present worth of the policies to buy X and Z are

$$T(EPW)_X = -19,640$$
$$T(EPW)_Z = -12,589$$

Consider now the case where there are two stages in the process, each stage consisting of a single piece of equipment having the same capacity distribution as before but whose capital cost is one-half the cost of the single equipment. We can ignore size X, since it was too small in the previous case. If two size-Y pieces of equipment are used in series, the probability that the output rate of the plant will be less than 110,000 tons per year will be $[1 - (1 - 0.30)^2] = 0.51$. Then,

$$T(EPW)_{YY} = EPW(\bar{v} = 100,000) + EPW(\bar{v} = 110,000)$$
$$= -26,224 + 12,562 = -13,662$$

For two size-Z pieces of equipment in series,

$$T(EPW)_{ZZ} = -12,589$$

If management is willing to accept the lower rate of return, then size Z is required.

Demand Growth

Situations are commonly encountered in the long-term planning of production facilities where the demand for output is an increasing function of time. Figure 11.3 shows the growth in demand for a product in the form of the classical S-curve indicating the typical times for each phase.

A variety of policies exist for meeting the demand function. At one extreme, they include building capacity at the present time to meet all future requirements, and at the other extreme, the addition of small increments of capacity as demand increases. Between these two extremes lie combinatorial possibilities.

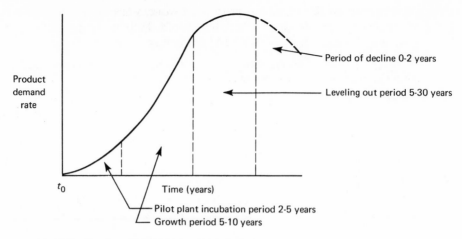

FIGURE **11.3**   Product demand rate growth curve.

The economics of choice involve certain cost tradeoffs. The building of excess capacity offers the economies of scale in construction or initial capital costs. For example, in the building of a warehouse, the larger the warehouse, the lower the costs per square foot of warehouse requirement. Also, expanding now to meet future requirements avoids repeating the fixed costs of preparing for construction. Furthermore, the effects of inflation are reduced. On the other hand, adding in small increments avoids tying up capital in un-utilized capacity. Also, the commitment to smaller future time intervals permits management to take advantage of improvements in technology and to avoid the risks inherent in long-term estimates.

The fundamental issue is the size and timing of both present and future capacity expansion. The problem has been subjected to a number of different approaches using both analytical and simulation techniques. As with most investment decisions, the models are perhaps more useful in suggesting the critical variables in the decision than in assigning an optimum choice. Most models use exact cash flow or rate of return analysis. Additional factors sometimes considered are uncertainty in demand rate and plant capability.

LINEAR GROWTH: The determination of optimum timing of expansion is easiest to demonstrate by linear demand growth. Suppose we wish to determine an expansion policy for gas-fired annealing furnaces for a copper tube plant.[1] Let

a = variable costs of installation in dollars per 1,000 lb of capacity
b = fixed costs of installation regardless of capacity added
k = rate of growth of demand in 1,000 lb per year
i = desired rate of return on capital
t = period between installations

[1] See Ian McDowell, "The Economic Planning Period for Engineering Works," *Operations Research*, vol. 8, no. 4, July–August 1960, for a discussion of both linear and exponential demand cases of this model.

Then, considering that an initial installation is to be made now, the present worth of a series of expansions made at time intervals of length t is

$$PW = (akt + b) + (akt + b)e^{-it} + (akt + b)e^{-2it} + \cdots$$

The second term on the right side is the discounted cost of the second increment of expansion made at the end of the first interval t. The third term is the expansion made at the end of the second interval, etc.

$$PW = (akt + b)(1 + e^{-it} + e^{-2it} + \cdots$$

$$= \frac{(akt + b)}{1 + e^{-it}}$$

Setting the derivative of PW with respect to t equal to zero yields

$$\frac{dPW}{dt} = 0 \quad \text{when} \quad ak/bi = 1/(e^{-it} - it - 1)$$

Figure 11.4 shows the relationship between the ratio ak/bi and the variable t for various values of i.

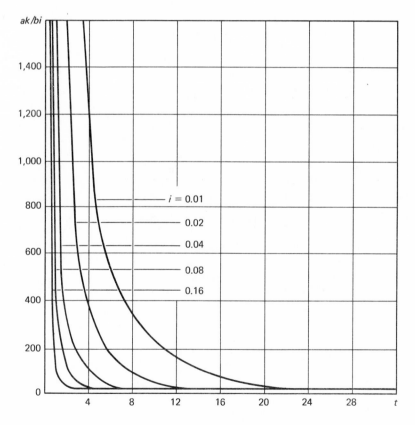

FIGURE **11.4** ak/bi versus t for linear growth. From Ian McDowell, *Operations Research*, vol. 8, no. 4, July–August 1960.

EXPONENTIAL GROWTH: More complex analytical models that relate especially to the design of chemical or engineering facilities and plant capacity have been proposed.

A method proposed by Coleman and York is briefly outlined to suggest the kind of approach taken.[2] The model applies to planning expansion during the demand growth and maximum phases of the S curve. In this case, the demand is assumed to be increasing exponentially to the maximum, so that the demand at any time t is

$$D_t = D_0 e^{kt} \quad \text{for} \quad 0 \leq t \leq t_{max} \quad \text{and} \quad D_t = D_{max} \quad \text{for} \quad t > t_{max}$$

where

D_0 = present rate of demand
D_{max} = maximum rate of demand
k = growth coefficient
t_{max} = time at which maximum demand is reached

The purpose of the model is to determine the timing of expansion and the size of the incremental unit of capacity v. The steps in the formulation of the model are outlined below.

1. *Capital costs*   The capital cost of the capacity addition is given by

$$A = cv^\alpha$$

where

c = capital cost per unit of capacity (dollars per ton) taken at some base capacity
v = size of the capacity addition
α = a coefficient, where usually $\alpha = 0.5$ to 0.8

Thus, α determines the economy of scale in construction. If α equals one, then capital costs are directly proportional to capacity size, and if α equals zero, then capital costs are independent of the capacity and there is no incentive to build early. Thus, α is determined by construction technology.

2. *Present worth of installing v units of capacity*   Suppose that capacity of size v_0 is added at the present. Then the present worth of the estimated costs of this installation, assuming an economic life of m years and a tax rate of 50%, is

$$PW = cv_0^\alpha - 0.5\frac{cv_0^\alpha}{m}PWF(u)_i^m + fcv_0^\alpha(1 - 0.50)\,PWF(u)_i^m = Cv_0^\alpha \tag{1}$$

where

$$C = c\left[1 - \frac{0.5}{m}PWF(u)_i^m + f(1 - 0.50)PWF(u)_i^m\right]$$

f = a coefficient, which is the rate of fixed operating costs per dollar of capital cost

---
[2] John R. Coleman, Jr., and Robert York, "Optimum Plant Design for a Growing Market," *Ind. Eng. Chem.*, vol. 56, no. 1, January 1964, pp. 28–34.

In Equation (1), the first term on the right side is the initial capital cost of installing v units of capacity now. The second term accounts for the tax savings resulting from straight-line depreciation over the m-year life of the asset. The third accounts for the present worth of the fixed operation costs adjusted for the tax rate. All costs are discounted to the time when the capacity v_0 is added.

3. *Present worth of a series of additions*   Now suppose that we add a series of n additions to capacity. Let v_j be the capacity of the unit added at time t_j, and assume that each addition will be identically replaced after m years for perpetuity. The present worth of this series is

$$PW = \frac{Cv_0^{\alpha}}{i}(CRF)_i^m + Cv_1^{\alpha}\frac{(CRF)_i^m}{i} \cdot PWF(s)_i^{t_j} + \cdots + \frac{Cv_n^{\alpha}}{i}(CRF)_i^m \cdot PWF(s)_i^{t_n}$$

$$= \frac{C}{i}(CRF)_i^m \left[v_0^{\alpha} + \sum_{j=1}^{n} v_j^{\alpha} \cdot PWF(s)_i^{t_j} \right] \tag{2}$$

Each right-hand term of Equation (2) converts the present worth of a stream of costs, over the m-year life of the v_j addition of capacity, to time t_j. Then it converts that present worth to a uniform annual series, converts this series back to a present worth, as of t_j, by dividing by i, thus assuming the perpetual series of like replacements. Finally, a conversion is made to the present worth as of time zero.

4. *Conversion of* t_j Suppose at time t_j the total rate of demand corresponds to $\sum_{i=1}^{j-1} v_i$, assuming that v_{j-1} is added to meet the rate of demand at the time v_j is installed. This is shown graphically in Figure 11.5.

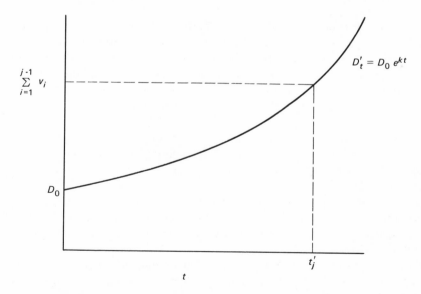

FIGURE **11.5**   Rate of demand increasing exponentially with time.

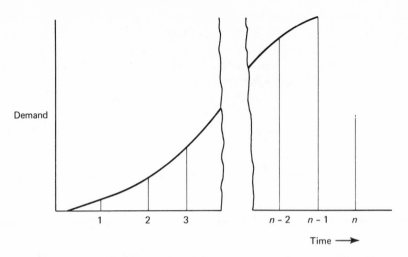

FIGURE **11.6** Designated points in time when expansion can take place.

Then,

$$\sum_{1}^{j-1} v_i = D_0 e^{kt_j}$$

and

$$t_j = \frac{1}{k} \ln\left(\frac{\sum v_i}{D_0}\right) \tag{3}$$

If Equation (3) is substituted into Equation (2), the problem is to find the optimum values of v_j for $j = 0, 1, 2, \ldots, n$. For a given value of n, the optimum value of v_j is found by taking the partial derivative of Equation (2) with respect to v_j and setting it equal to zero. A constraint is that the ultimate capacity must equal the maximum demand. A global optimum for some value of n is found by replicating the above method for $n = 1, 2, \ldots$, until the minimum present worth is found.

DYNAMIC PROGRAMING: The problem of optimizing expansion policies has been approached using dynamic programing. Suppose that expansion can take place at any one or more of n discrete points in time over the growth cycle of a product, Figure 11.6.

Then there are $2^n - 1$ possible expansion policies ranging from building at the first period for all future demand or building at each of n periods. At any one of the points, capacity may be added to cover the incremental demand at one or more of the future periods.

To demonstrate the method of dynamic programing, we offer the following simplified example. Suppose that for a single product we have the following demand schedule for four periods.

Period t	Incremental demand (tons per year) v_t	Total demand rate (tons per year)
1	20,000	20,000
2	40,000	60,000
3	60,000	120,000
4	20,000	140,000

We will assume that capacity is built at the beginning of any period t and that the costs are incurred and discounted as of the end of the period to the present. Let

$_tA_{t'}$ = capital cost of building the requirements of period t in period t'

$V_{t'}$ = capacity (tons per year) built at time period t'

$$= \begin{cases} v_t + v_{t-1} + \cdots + v_{t'} & \text{for } t > t' \\ v_t & \text{for } t = t' \end{cases}$$

$$Z_t = \underset{t'}{\text{minimum}} \{_tA_{t'}PWF(s)_t^{t'} + Z_{t'-1}\}$$

Now suppose that we introduce an economy of scale in capital costs such that

$$_tA_{t'} = \frac{V_{t'}}{(1 + 0.0000010V_{t'})} + 4,000$$

Then the problem involves a tradeoff between the economy of scale and the capital cost of un-utilized capacity.

For convenience, the capital costs are tabulated as follows:

t	t'	$V_{t'}$	$_tA_{t'}$
1	1	20,000	23,608
2	1	60,000	60,604
2	2	40,000	42,461
3	1	120,000	111,142
3	2	100,000	94,909
3	3	60,000	60,604
4	1	140,000	126,807
4	2	120,000	111,142
4	3	80,000	78,074
4	4	20,000	23,608

Table 11.1 summarizes the computations for Z_t, starting with period 1 and ending with period 4. Solutions are shown for rates of interest equal to 0.12 and 0.15. For example, consider period $T = 2$ and $i = 0.12$. The alternatives are to build period 2 requirements in period 1 or period 2. Then,

$$Z_2 = \text{minimum} \begin{cases} (60,604)(0.8929) + 0 & = 54,113 \\ (42,461)(0.7972) + 21,080 & = 54,930 \end{cases}$$

For period 4, and with $i = 0.12$, we have $Z_4 = 109,682$. This corresponds to a solution: "Add capacity in periods 1 and 2." For the case of $i = 0.15$, the optimum solution is "add capacity in periods 1, 2, and 3."

TABLE **11.1**   Computations for dynamic programming solution of capacity expansion problem.

(1) t	(2) t'	(3) $_tA_{t'}$	(4) $PWF(s)^{t'}_{0.12}$	(5) 3×4	(6) $Z_{t'-1}$	(7) $5 + 6$	(8) $PWF(s)^{t'}_{0.15}$	(9) 3×8	(10) $Z_{t'-1}$	(11) $9 + 10$
1	1	23,608	0.8929	21,080	0	21,080	0.8696	20,530	0	20,530
2	1	60,604	0.8929	54,113	0	54,113*	0.8696	52,701	0	52,701
2	2	42,461	0.7972	33,850	21,080	54,930	0.7561	32,105	20,530	52,635*
3	1	111,142	0.8929	99,238	0	99,238	0.8696	95,871	0	95,871
3	2	94,909	0.7972	75,661	21,080	96,741*	0.7561	71,761	20,530	92,291*
3	3	60,604	0.7118	43,138	54,113	97,251	0.6575	39,847	52,635	92,482
4	1	126,807	0.8929	113,226	0	113,226	0.8696	110,271	0	110,271
4	2	111,142	0.7972	88,602	21,080	109,682*	0.7561	84,034	20,530	104,564
4	3	78,074	0.7118	55,573	54,113	109,686	0.6575	51,334	52,635	103,969*
4	4	23,608	0.6355	15,003	96,741	111,744	0.5718	13,499	92,291	105,790

* (min. Z_t)

MANUFACTURING PROGRESS FUNCTION

It is generally understood and intuitively logical that after a new product and/or new process is introduced in production, there may be a reduction in the resources spent per unit of output as the cumulative number of units produced increases. Typically, this is expressed as a decline in the cost, man hours, or machine hours per unit, although other measures are possible, such as reduced fuel consumption or space requirements.

This improvement, related to time or to cumulative production, is often referred to as the *learning function*. Since this term is generally used to connote the improvement in individual worker performance, we use the term *progress function* to suggest the combined efforts of an organization to improve production performance in a number of ways. These can include the results of methods changes, tooling redesign, changes in material, equipment replacement, shop organization, and shop design, as well as operator learning.

An early quantitative expression of the progress function was given by Wright, who observed that the unit cost of each of a series of orders for airframes declined as a function of the number of orders accumulated.[3] Today, his model is the general expression of the manufacturing progress function.

$$y_n = y_1 n^{-b}$$

where

y_n = units of a resource (e.g., labor hours) required to produce the nth unit of output in a series $1, 2, \ldots, n$

y_1 = units of the resource required to produce the first unit of output in the series

b = coefficient of rate of reduction

---

[3] T. P. Wright, "Factors Affecting the Cost of Airplanes," *J. Aeronaut. Sci.*, February 1936.

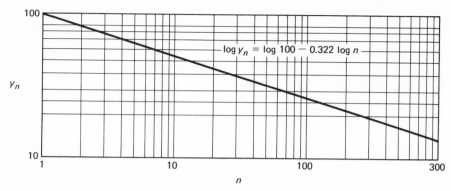

$\log y_n = \log 100 - 0.322 \log n$

FIGURE **11.7**   Progress function for $y_1 = 100$ and $b = -0.322$.

The model can be transformed into logarithmic form

$$\log y_n = \log y_1 - b \log n$$

Figure 11.7 shows graphically the case $y_1 = 100$ and $b = -0.322$. A progress function is often described as a percent function, such as an "80% function." This percent is the complement of the rate of improvement that takes place by doubling the cumulative output. Let

p = percent function
n_1 = an initial cumulative production count
n_2 = a second cumulative production count, where $n_2 = 2n_1$
y_1 = hours per unit at n_1
y_2 = hours per unit at n_2

Then, the percent improvement in hours per unit from n_1 to n_2 is $(y_1 - y_2)/y_1$ and p is y_2/y_1.

The progress function was first used in the aircraft industry to predict cost performance. Because of the relatively small number of cumulative units produced, the use of the model was particularly appropriate. Since that time it has been shown that the progress function is applicable to a wide variety of manufacturing situations. Conway and Schultz investigated the function for various operations of a large electronic equipment manufacturing company.[4] Figure 11.8 shows the progress function for a physically large, low-volume, high-skilled labor content product. The discontinuous function resulted from a disruptive relocation of the operations. Figure 11.9 shows the progress function for a high-volume, physically small part in terms of the machining and assembly labor hours. Improvement was consistent up to a certain point, after which it was highly variable, a characteristic encountered in other cases. In a study of 28 separate cases of new process and product startups

---

[4] R. W. Conway and A. Schultz, Jr., "The Manufacturing Progress Function," *J. Ind. Eng.*, vol. X, no. 1, January–February 1959, pp. 39–54.

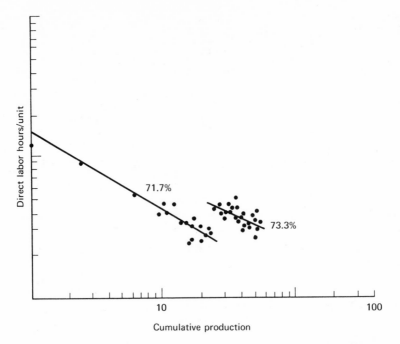

FIGURE **11.8** Progress in final assembly labor. From R. W. Conway and A. Schultz, Jr., *J. Ind. Eng.*, vol. X, no. 1, January–February 1959, p. 47.

occurring in highly mechanized production operations, Baloff found a regular improvement in productivity, which could be described by the progress function.[5] However, his studies indicated an eventual interruption of this improvement by a final leveling-off phase. Hirschmann reports improvement in petroleum refining output as a function of the age of the processing equipment.[6] This improvement in output rate is attributed to the operator's learning to take advantage of the safety margins designed into the equipment.

Thoughtful writers on the subject warn of misinterpretations of the progress function. One misconception is that the function is an inherent characteristic of a process with the parameter values (y_1, b) highly correlated with the kind of product or process. While it is obvious that in any reasonably managed situation, productivity improvements will take place, the exact form of the function must depend on management's improvement tactics and strategies. Neither parameter can assume a value "representative" of a given product-process situation. There is even good reason to believe that a parameter will not assume the same value for highly similar or presumably identical cases.

---

[5] Nicholas Baloff, "Startups in Machine-Intensive Production Systems," *J. Ind. Eng.*, vol. XVII, no. 1, January 1966, pp. 25–32.
[6] W. B. Hirschmann, "Profit from the Learning Curve," *Harvard Business Rev.*, vol. 42, no. 1, January–February 1964, pp. 125–39.

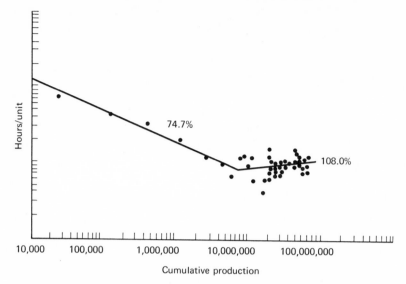

FIGURE **11.9**   Progress in total labor content. From R. W. Conway and A. Schultz, Jr., *J. Ind. Eng.*, vol. X, no. 1, January–February 1959, p. 48.

To be of any use as an estimator of future performance, the progress function parameters themselves must be estimated. The situation appears to be anomalous, since the extrapolation of parameter values from one situation to another introduces error. Baloff makes a tentative suggestion that the parameter b might be estimated from a knowledge of y_1.[7] As a result of observing industrial operations and conducting group problem-solving experiments, he proposes that there is an inverse correlation between b and y_1. He offers no theoretical hypothesis for the results but encourages further research into the subject.

Relation of Progress Function to Demand Growth

The progress function has some bearing on the problem of designing capacity to meet future expansion needs. Suppose, for example, that the demand for a product is expanding at the rate $50e^{kt}$, where t is expressed in years. Then, the incremental number of units demanded in any year t is

$$N_t = \int_{t-1}^{t} 50e^{kt}\,dt - 50$$

Now suppose that if capacity is added at $t = 0$, a progress function, expressed in hours per unit, will operate according to

$$y_n = 544n^{-b}$$

---

[7] Nicholas Baloff, "Estimating the Parameters of the Startup Model—An Empirical Approach," *J. Ind. Eng.*, vol. XVIII, no. 4, April 1967, pp. 248–53.

If we assume 2,000 working hours per year, then the cumulative number of units n_t produced by the end of year t is found by solving the following expression for n_t

$$\int_0^{n_t} 544 n^{-b}\, dt = 2{,}000t$$

The estimated number of units (N'_t) produced in year t is

$$N'_t = n_t - n_{t-1}$$

Figure 11.10 shows the number of units produced per year for three values of the progress function coefficient b, corresponding to 75%, 80%, and 85% functions.

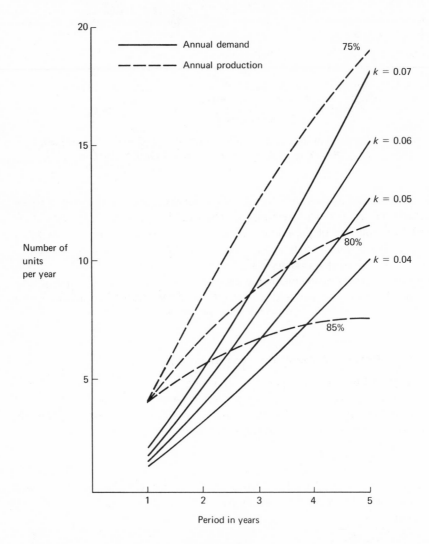

FIGURE **11.10**   Number of units demanded per year with exponential growth rate and number of units produced per year with a progress function.

These are compared with the annual growth requirements for four values of the growth coefficient k. It can be seen that the ability of the expansion increment to meet the future five-year annual demand depends on the actual values of the growth and progress function parameters. The sensitivity of realizable capacity depends on the magnitude of the error in estimating the two parameters. For example, if one estimated a growth parameter of $k = 0.04$ and a progress parameter of $b = 0.45$ corresponding to the 75% curve, there would be sufficient capacity. However, if the actual results were a 75% increase in the k value to 0.07 and a 50% reduction in b (the 85% curve), demand would not be satisfied by the second year.

It appears that the system is sensitive to the estimates of the growth and progress coefficients. With respect to the progress coefficient b, future research may concentrate on determining the critical variables that affect b. But even if the reliability of estimates of b are improved, there will always be some residual error. If the progress function is used as a variable in capacity planning, one may assign probabilities to a range of b values and consider the problem as one of risk.

Bibliography

Plant Investment and Scale of Operations

BOWMAN, EDWARD, "Scale of Operations—An Empirical Study," *Operations Research*, June 1958.

CHAMBERS, JOHN C., S. K. MULLICK, and THOMAS J. PATTERSON, "Strategic New Product Planning Models for Dynamic Situations," Corning Glass Works, Corning, N.Y.

DANIELS, EVERETT J., "A Long Range Planning Model for a New Firm in a Growth Market," *J. Ind. Eng.*, March–April 1964.

HESS, SIDNEY W., and JAMES B. WEAVER, "How Big a Plant?" *Ind. Eng. Chem.*, July 1961.

HOROWITZ, IRA, "Formulation of the Price-Cost Relationship in a Class of Plant Investment Decisions," *J. Ind. Eng.*, November–December 1963.

KLEIN, M., and R. R. KLIMPEL, "Application of Linearly Constrained Nonlinear Optimization to Plant Location and Sizing," *J. Ind. Eng.*, January 1967.

SALETAN, D. I., and A. V. CASELLI, "Optimum Design Capacity of New Plants," *Chem. Eng. Pro.*, May 1963.

STARR, MARTIN K., "Planning Models," *Management Science*, vol. 13, no. 4, December 1966.

WHITE, JAMES M., "A Dynamic Model for the Analysis of Expansion," *J. Ind. Eng.*, May 1966.

Manufacturing Progress Function

ALCHIAN, ARMEN A., "Reliability of Progress Curves in Airframe Production," RM-260-1, The RAND Corporation, Santa Monica, Calif., April 14, 1950.

BALOFF, NICHOLAS, "The Learning Curve—Some Controversial Issues," *J. Ind. Econ.*, July 1966.

HIRSCH, W. Z., "Manufacturing Progress Functions," *Rev. of Econ. and Stat.*, May 1952.

———, "Firm Progress Ratios," *Econometrica*, April 1956.

12

Planning Input Data:
Work Measurement

ALL (12)

MANAGEMENT USES OF TIME ESTIMATES

Work measurement is a generic term designating the class of techniques used to derive time estimates. Time estimating pervades almost every area of production management. The techniques of work measurement and their uses are varied, and we shall examine some of them in this section.

Work measurement, in part, is a sampling procedure, and, therefore, statistical theory is relevant to the problem of determining the reliability of time estimates. While we could lend an aura of academic respectability to the subject by stressing its statistical characteristics, we will concentrate on the more difficult problems in the management of a work measurement program. These include such things as deciding among alternative measurement methods, relating the permissible error in time estimates to their use, maintaining and upgrading a file of time data, and dealing with the reactions of people to the use of time estimates for performance evaluation.

Figure 12.1 indicates the varied uses of time estimates. Time estimates are used 1) for evaluating performance and 2) for predicting future performance. In case 1), a time estimate must represent a *standard* for judging actual performance. In case 2), the time estimate is essentially a forecaster of future actual performance without reference to the time as a standard of performance. There are occasions, in practice, when a given time estimate may serve a variety of purposes. But it is important that these two underlying purposes be understood prior to applying a given technique. A time estimate derived for one purpose may not be functionally or economically useful for a second purpose.

One of the principal and original uses of time estimates is the determination of the labor content of various jobs and operations. A "time standard" is the time estimate that has been derived for evaluating labor performance. Consequently, work measurement is often directly associated with the broader topic of labor-cost control. This fact has resulted in some underlying social and economic problems related both to the manner in which the time standard is derived and to the way it is used. The mismanagement of a program of work measurement and time

372

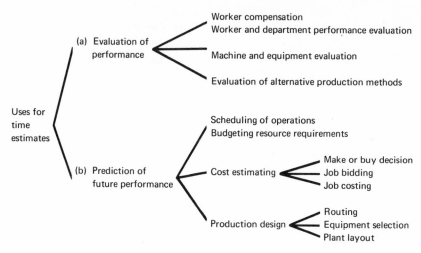

FIGURE **12.1** Uses of time estimates in production management.

standards can often lead to disastrous results and can be the cause of serious labor stoppages and restrictions on output.

ESTIMATING UNIT OUTPUT TIMES

There are two major measures in work measurement. The first is an estimate, for a job or operation, of the average time it takes to produce a unit of work or, conversely, the average rate of output. The second is an estimate of the average proportion of time a production facility spends in various mutually exclusive activities, such as production versus idleness. We will first examine the methods used to determine unit time estimates and then consider the time proportion problem.

Time Study

The term *time study* is often used synonymously with work measurement. In this section, however, we will use the term to designate a means of deriving an estimate of the time needed to produce a unit of output. While there are a number of measuring devices that can be used, the stopwatch seems to have become the symbolic instrument of time study. Other kinds of instruments, either more refined (such as motion pictures) or less refined (such as an ordinary wristwatch), are useful. For most purposes, however, the stopwatch has an inherent error of measurement that is far less than the errors contributed by other factors.

The method used to estimate unit times will depend on the acceptable degree of error. The cost of the measurement consists of the direct cost of measuring, plus the consequences of having an error in the estimate. Generally, the amount of acceptable error may be the predominant criterion, and, in this case, we must consider both precision, which is controlled by the sample size, and accuracy, which is controlled by the measurement procedure.

There are alternative ways of obtaining unit time estimates. These include:

1. *Analysis of production records*   The number of units produced in a given time period yields a gross measure of output rate. Such an estimate does not indicate the quality of performance, but it can be useful for some planning purposes.

2. *Random sampling*   With a stopwatch, a random sample of units produced at a job is measured, yielding an estimate of the actual production time independent of job interruptions. Depending on the use of the estimate, the performance of the operator might be evaluated at the time the observations were made.

3. *Orthodox time study*   This is a formalized procedure based on the traditionally accepted method of time study. It involves more than simple stopwatch measurements and is concerned with the evaluation of the human operator's work methods and pace.

4. *Standard time data*   The results of actual time studies can be extrapolated into an inventory of standard time data. Such data, set forth in charts, tables, or formulas, are elemental task times. A standard time for a given job is set by describing the job method in terms of these fundamental tasks and applying the predetermined standard time to the tasks.

Before considering some of these in more detail, we will discuss the more fundamental issue of determining standard performance for a human operator.

The Issue of Standard Performance

The method of orthodox or traditional stopwatch time study is inextricably and historically linked with the problem of evaluating human performance, generally for the purposes of incentive wage payment. The usual form of incentive wage payment is the piece rate. A piece rate is simply a translation of an hourly rate of pay into a pay rate per unit of output for a job.

In order to set a "fair" piece rate, one must have a notion of what constitutes a reasonable level of worker performance (rate of output), as well as a reasonable hourly rate of pay. That is, suppose one thinks that for a given job the output rate should be 100 pieces per hour and that a fair hourly rate is $2.00. Then the piece rate is $0.02 per piece.

Prior to the advent of scientific management, the piece-rate decisions were made by those most intimately concerned with the production jobs, including the foreman or shop superintendent. There were inherent labor-management antagonisms, manifested by systematic restriction of output by labor and by lack of objective rate setting by management. If the rate was "tight," it meant that the worker would have a difficult time meeting the desired or expected rate of output, and if the standard was "loose," the opposite was true. The former had inherent management advantages, while the latter was to the worker's benefit. Therefore, each side introduced ways, some devious, of making the standard fit their own objectives.

In the case of management, for example, the rate was frequently "cut" or tightened when a worker attained a rate of output well in excess of what was expected. It was, therefore, to the worker's advantage to restrict output rates in order to avoid the possibility of rate cutting.

In the late 1880's, Frederick W. Taylor introduced his system of time study in an attempt to alleviate the basic labor-management stresses over the issue of wage payment. His technique was based on the determination of efficient work methods and the setting of standard times for tasks, using the stopwatch. His original work at the Bethlehem Steel Company involved a degree of experimentation and sophistication that was highly unusual in the field of management. In spite of the relative objectivity of Taylor's approach, the basic problem of determining a fair day's pay for a fair day's work was not completely solved, nor has it been up to this time. There was really no criterion to prove as a scientific fact what the rate of output should be for a certain level of pay. Nevertheless, his methods evolved into a widely used system of time study and represented a superior approach over what had preceded.

Orthodox Time-Study Procedure

The traditional procedure for conducting a time study involves these basic steps.

1. *Setting the standard method* The time that it takes to perform a task depends both on the method used by the operator and on his pace. A standard time, therefore, reflects a method. When the method is changed, theoretically the standard time is no longer valid. In order to reduce the requirements for future changes in the standard, attention must be paid to establishing the best method for the job and then obtaining a detailed description of this method prior to setting the time standard.

2. *Breaking the job down into elements* The job is broken down into a series of elemental tasks capable of being timed with a stopwatch. The basic information about the job, its method, and its elements are recorded on a time-study observation sheet (Figure 12.2).

The purpose of breaking the job down into elements is to derive more information about the method and to permit the observer to eliminate from the raw data elemental times that he feels are not representative of the "normal" conditions affecting the job time. Also, the raw data expressed in terms of these elements can become the basis for deriving standard time data.

3. *The average observed time* Figure 12.2 shows a completed time-study observation sheet for a four-element job. Ten output cycles have been studied. For each element there is a space for the watch reading R in hundredths of a minute, and the element T, which is determined by subtracting the successive watch readings. Note that the watch is read continuously. An average time $\bar{T}$ is then calculated for each element.

4. *Rating the operator to determine the normal time* Each of the observed average elemental times is rated by the observer. Rating is the adjustment made to

Time Study Observation Sheet														

Identification of operation: Assemble 24" × 36" chart blanks   **Date:** 10/9

Began timing: 9:26 **Ended timing:** 9:32 **Operator** 109 **Approval** BM **Observer** A.T.R.

Element Description and Breakpoint			1 0.00	2	3	4	5	6	7	8	9	10	ΣT	T̄	RF	NT
1	Fold over end (grasp stapler)	T	.07	.07	.05	.07	.09	.06	.05	.08	.08	.06	.68	.07	.90	.06
		R	.07	.61	.14	.67	.24	.78	.33	.88	.47	.09				
2	Staple five times (drop stapler)	T	.16	.14	.14	.15	.16	.16	.14	.17	.14	.15	1.51	.15	1.05	.16
		R	.23	.75	.28	.82	.40	.94	.47	⁴.05	.61	.24				
3	Bend and insert wire (drop pliers)	T	.22	.25	.22	.25	.23	.23	.21	.26	.25	.24	2.36	.24	1.00	.24
		R	.45	.00	.50	².07	.63	³.17	.68	.31	.86	.48				
4	Dispose of finished chart (touch next sheet)	T	.09	.09	.10	.08	.09	.11	.12	.08	.17	.08	1.01	.10	.90	.09
		R	.54	.09	.60	.15	.72	.28	.80	.39	¹.03	⁵.56				
5		T														
		R														
6		T												0.55 normal minute for cycle		
		R														
7		T														
		R														
8		T														
		R														
9		T														
		R														
10		T														
		R														

Normal cycle time __0.55__ + Allowance __(0.55 × 0.143) or 0.08__ = Std. time __0.63 min./pc.__

FIGURE **12.2** Completed time study observation sheet for study of "assembly chart blanks." From E. V. Krick, *Methods Engineering*. New York: John Wiley & Sons, 1962, p. 246.

convert the observed time to a value that, according to the observer's judgment, represents the time it would take the "normal" operator to perform the elemental task. The adjustment is made by a percentage multiplication. One hundred percent represents normal or standard performance. A rating factor less than 100% represents performance slower than normal, and vice versa. The normal time for each of the elements is shown in the last column, and the sum of these times yields the normal cycle time for the job. Because rating is the most controversial part of time study, we will devote more to it subsequently.

5. *Adjustment for delays* The normal cycle time (sometimes called base or rated time) is the time it would take the "normal" operator to complete a cycle of work. The standard cycle time differs by the addition of a certain percentage to allow for the condition of delays or interruptions in the job. A certain percentage of the daily work period is consumed by various "unavoidable" delays; therefore, an adjustment must be made to the normal time to account for these delay times. This adjustment is usually a percentage of normal time and accounts for personal needs and rest periods, setup times, acquiring materials, receiving instructions, periodic part inspections, filling out production records, etc. In Figure 12.2, an allowance of 8% is made at the bottom of the observation sheet.

RELIABILITY OF THE ESTIMATE: Several decades ago, there was a good deal of academic interest in attaching a precision to time estimates in order to determine a sample size (number of cycles to be observed). Relating this specifically to the observed time for a given element, we have the following. Let

u = unrated population time for the element
$\bar{T}$ = the estimator of u
T_j = observed time for the element at the jth cycle, $j = 1, 2, \ldots, n$
$\hat{\sigma}$ = the estimator of the population standard deviation
σ_T = the standard deviation of $\bar{T}$

Then,

$$\bar{T} = \sum_{j=1}^{n} \frac{T_j}{n}$$

$$\hat{\sigma} = \sqrt{\sum_{1}^{n} \frac{(T_j - \bar{T})^2}{n - 1}}$$

$$\sigma_{\bar{T}} = \frac{\hat{\sigma}}{\sqrt{n}}$$

Since the distribution of sample means is normal, we may attach a precision to the estimate of u. Or, if a precision is specified, a sample size n may be determined.

The importance of attending to these statistical details is open to question. First, the observations should be random, which is not the case with the orthodox procedure. A more advisable procedure is to take isolated cycle-time observations randomly over some extended period of time to ensure a representative sample and then to attach a precision to the cycle time. Second, the precision is related to the observed times and not to the normal or standard times. The error in a standard time is a composite of the errors in the observed times, the rating, and the allowances for interruptions. Third, lack of accuracy or constant bias may be a much more relevant contributor to the error in a standard time. In the early literature on the statistics of time study, the discussions often neglected to consider a fruitful analysis of accuracy in comparison to precision, and the differentiation is often neglected today.

Performance Rating

In theory, the standard time is defined as "the time it takes the normal operator working at a normal pace and under normal working conditions to produce a unit of output." It is clear that "normal" exists as a concept in this definition and not much more than that in the operational context.

In the time-study procedure, the engineer typically uses his own concept of normal in comparing the pace and skill of the worker and quantifies the difference with the percentage figure. The issue is, of course, how does one know what normal is? Since there is no scientific standard by which one can validate his concept of normal, the matter must be relegated to agreement among individuals. The question then becomes, how can agreement be obtained, and are differences of judgment contained within some range that permits the time-study procedure to be operationally practical and acceptable?

Prior to World War II, this was the major subject of discussion in work measurement. Various ways were proposed to try to eliminate the subjective parts of rating or to defend them as a necessary but practically sound part of work measurement. Experiments were conducted to determine the degree of agreement among "experienced" time-study engineers in the rating of sample jobs, presented either as films or as actual jobs on the shop floor. It has been generally quoted that the agreements are within plus or minus 5 to 10% of the average rating, a result that has apparently never settled the issue once and for all.

A firm requires a system of time standards that can be economically derived and that result in benefits to both labor and management. We offer these observations:

1. Regardless of whether the company chooses to have an incentive system based upon time standards, the issue of a fair day's work will be omnipresent. Any manager has the obligation to his company to give some assurance that labor dollars are being wisely spent. The use of standard times gives him at least some basis for evaluating his worker's performance, even if an incentive system is absent. Therefore, the issue is not time standards, but rather the methods of determining normal or standard performance. The absence of formal time study does not eliminate the problem.

2. If both management and labor fully recognize the purposes and limitations of the time-study procedure, one hurdle toward an effective use of standard times is eliminated. The danger is that management, on the one hand, will claim that

standards are infallibly set by scientific means, while the union, on the other hand, may insist on throttling the system by excessive legal restrictions in the administration of the standards system.

3. The purposes of work measurement should always be clearly defined. The issue of "standard" performance can often be avoided when the purposes of the time estimates are used for planning, rather than for evaluating performance. Often this distinction is not made clear so that arguments about rating are irrelevant when the time estimate is used as a predictor of actual performance.

4. When both management and labor agree on the desirability of time standards, then the question of determining normal performance must be settled. The following methods are possibilities, depending upon the situation involved:

(a) The question may be left entirely to the judgment of the time-study engineers, assuming that they bring to the situation a degree of experience that is satisfactory. This approach is often acceptable to the union if the door is left open to permit negotiations over rates that appear to be too tight in practice. The feasibility of this approach depends to a large extent on the faith the union has in the system and on the ability of line supervisors and engineers to handle grievances over rates without resorting to involved legalistic procedures.

(b) Both management and union personnel may arrive at some concept of normal performance for certain basic tasks or fundamental jobs. In this case, "rating films" are highly useful. These films may depict certain basic operations being performed at different levels of worker effort. Both union members and management can use these films to arrive at some mutually agreed upon level of performance in each operation that they feel is representative of the normal. The reliability of this method depends, of course, on the degree to which the experience gained in the film situation can be extrapolated to the jobs on the shop floor.

(c) The problem is partially avoided, at least on the surface, by the use of predetermined standard data. The times comprising the standard, however, are rated times, and, therefore, when they are applied, the inherent rating is tacitly accepted as the concept of normal.

Standard Time Data

There are many situations where the direct time measurement of a job or operation is inapplicable or economically unjustifiable. If the number of standards to be set in a plant is large, then direct measurement may be costly in terms of engineering time consumed in making the individual studies. It is not uncommon for a firm to require thousands of standards for its various operations; and, consequently, the firm must revert to using standard time data.

The general idea behind standard data depends on the similarity of operations and jobs. If there are common work elements among a certain class of jobs or operations, then the normal times for these common elements can be predetermined by direct measurement and then "inventoried" for future use in synthesizing times for jobs that contain these elements in some mix.

Besides eliminating the need for direct measurement of some jobs, they permit the estimation of times for jobs, products, and operations that are still in the design or planning stages. In certain companies, this is the most important use of standard time data.

The multiplicity of uses to which standard data are applied implies the need for a variety of standard data types and forms. A set of standard time data appropriate for estimating the cost of parts may not be appropriate for estimating the labor requirements for a machine shop for a coming month or quarter. While the former data might be quite detailed in terms of specifying times for individual job elements, the latter might require data expressed in a more aggregate form with less precision. There is the implication that standard data are applicable only to local situations or to conditions in a specific plant or company. However, it should be noted that one can find standard data compiled in handbooks that supposedly have some universal application in all firms. We are more interested at this point in the problems of deriving standard data for a given plant and given situations within that plant. We will describe two basic ways of deriving the standard data, namely, the synthetic and the analytical methods, and will relate these to various kinds of operations.

THE SYNTHETIC METHOD: This method derives its name from the fact that the time for a given job is synthesized by adding together standard times for each of the job elements. In order to explain the method, the following example is offered.

EXAMPLE 12.1   The Softwalk Rug Company has an operation in which the underside of the rug is sprayed with a quick-drying plastic coating. In the course of a year, many different sizes and shapes of rugs pass through this operation. Since the job is on incentive, it is desired to determine a standard time for each rug that passes through the operation.

The elements of the operation are:

Element no.	Description
1	Pick rolled rug off hand truck, place on a platform, and unroll
2	Mask edges of rug with plastic
3	Pick up spray gun
4	Spray exposed rug base with liquid plastic
5	Put spray gun aside
6	Remove plastic edging and roll up the rug
7	Place rolled rug onto overhead conveyor

By taking a sample of representative rug sizes, each of the elements is timed. A sample of representative rug sizes is selected. Then the elements for each rug are timed at the operation. Each element is then studied to find a correlation between the elemental time and some characteristic of the job. For example, a plot of the times for Element 4 (spray rug base) versus rug area might appear as in Figure 12.3.

From this plot, a line is fitted by eye or by a more sophisticated method, such as least squares. Each element is similarly studied, yielding an elemental estimating equation, which is a function of one or more rug characteristics or possibly a constant. Then, the elemental estimating equations are combined to give an estimating equation for the entire job. That is, let

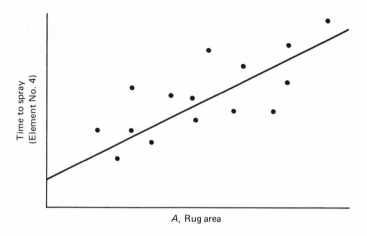

FIGURE **12.3**   Time to spray rug base versus rug area.

t_i = the base time for the ith element; i = 1, 2, . . . 7
P = perimeter of the rug in ft
A = area of rug in ft^2
W = weight of rug in lb
T = normal cycle time
$T = \Sigma\, t_i = f(P, A, W)$

So far we have mentioned only repetitive, direct labor operations. Indirect labor operations or jobs are less well defined in the repetitive sense. They include material-handling jobs, maintenance operations, clerical operations, janitorial jobs, etc. Setting performance standards on these types of jobs requires the derivation and use of standard time data. In each of these job categories, no two days' work may be exactly alike. Therefore, it is necessary to describe each day's work separately and then refer to standard data to derive a standard time for the day's work.

EXAMPLE 12.2   The Xoron Chemical Company has 60 buildings comprising its industrial complex in a certain city. One of the services in the company is a mail and messenger department manned by ten clerks who deliver intracompany mail and messages throughout the 60 buildings. A request is made to place the clerks on an incentive system. In the course of setting up the incentive plan, a set of standard data is derived. The study shows that there are nine basic job elements, including

W	walk
B	ride bicycle
P	push wagon
US	walk upstairs
DS	walk downstairs
UE	ride up elevator
DE	ride down elevator
MaD	mail delivery
MeD	message and package delivery

Standard data for these elements are derived by measuring the elements and corre-
lating the times with the job characteristics. For example, typical equations are

Time (P) = 0.004 (distance traveled in feet) + 0.2
Time (UE) = 0.09 (number of floors traveled) + 2.1
Time (B) = 0.6 + 0.001 (distance traveled in thousands of feet)

ANALYTICAL METHOD: In this method, the estimate of the job cycle time is
determined directly by regression analysis, rather than synthesis of element times.
We hypothesize that the job cycle time is a function of a number of variables.
Then, a sample of observations of the job is taken in which the cycle time and the
job variable values are recorded. The time coefficients are then determined by
multiple regression.

EXAMPLE 12.3   The distribution center for a very large manufacturing company maintains a long dock for loading and unloading trucks. During the week, many trucks
arrive to be loaded or unloaded. The problem is to schedule manpower requirements
to do the jobs. Between weeks, requirements for manpower vary: in heavy weeks,
additional labor is recruited from other areas of the plant at additional cost; in light
periods, labor is either idle or shifted to other jobs. A study of the situation shows that
a forecast of the number of trucks to be loaded and unloaded can be made with some
reliability. The time to unload a truck is less than the time to load, so total manpower
requirements for the week depend on the number of trucks loaded and unloaded. An
estimating formula of the following type can be derived using multiple regression
analysis

$$X_1 = a_1 + a_2 X_2 + a_3 X_3$$

where X_1 is the number of workers required, X_2 is the number of trucks to be loaded,
and X_3 is the number of trucks to be unloaded in a week.

A study of the records shows that, for 30 weeks selected at random from the past
two years, the following number of workers were required for various mixes of loading
and unloading.

Sample observation	X_1	X_2	X_3	Sample observation	X_1	X_2	X_3
1	23	10	12	16	45	37	46
2	28	11	28	17	44	35	58
3	27	15	21	18	51	43	53
4	27	27	16	19	51	48	57
5	45	40	20	20	50	53	58
6	34	35	36	21	46	55	40
7	36	34	32	22	48	55	50
8	34	25	33	23	47	61	50
9	34	17	35	24	52	64	39
10	28	23	46	25	52	63	56
11	34	29	45	26	52	70	58
12	37	43	32	27	53	67	65
13	36	50	33	28	56	78	55
14	42	48	40	29	62	80	60
15	41	45	44	30	32	30	40

A multiple regression analysis gives the following results:

$a_1 = 16.63,$ $a_2 = 0.37,$ $a_3 = 0.21$

The multiple correlation coefficient $R_{1.23}$ equals 0.8698, and the standard error of the estimate $\sigma_{1.23}$ is 3.799.

Several advantages of the analytical method are suggested below:

1. One complaint continually made against the synthetic method is the question of the additivity of element times. The analytical method avoids this by taking the job as a whole and thus permitting an integrative measure of the relationship between tasks. Each job variable is considered in terms of its influence on the cycle time, rather than trying to determine which elements are influenced by which variables.

2. The method permits a determination, with some stated confidence, of the precision of the estimate of the dependent variable.

3. The method allows us to determine which variables make a significant contribution to the standard time, or other dependent measure. In this sense, we are in a position to make some judgment on how many variables should be included in an estimating formula. The greater the number of variables, the greater the cost of deriving and using the standard data but with the advantage of greater precision in our estimates. The fewer the variables, the less the compilation and user cost, but at the price of greater error. Again, this judgment must depend on the use of the data.

4. It would appear that the analytical method costs less to derive and use than the synthetic method. The latter requires an individual study of each element, whereas the former considers cycle times only. However, the use of synthetic standard data perhaps forces a more thorough analysis of the job method. In the analytical method, there may be a greater acceptance of the method implied in the sample.

LINEAR PROGRAMING TIME ESTIMATING EQUATIONS: Linear programing has been proposed as a method for determining estimating formulas for cases where jobs consist of similar elements, but where the proportion of time spent on the elements varies between jobs.[1] The situation is similar to that in which we would apply multiple linear regression. The total time for the job is a function of measurable or countable attributes of the job.

The general formulation of the problem is set forth in the following terms. We are concerned with a job whose performance time T is a function of a set of n job variables, the quantities of which are $a_1, a_2, \ldots, a_i, \ldots, a_n$. We wish an estimating equation of the type

$$T = a_1x_1 + a_2x_2 + \cdots + a_ix_i + \cdots + a_nx_n$$

where x_i is the time coefficient for the ith attribute.[2] We observe the job as it is

---

[1] David W. Anderson, "Linear Programming Time Estimating Equations," *J. Ind. Eng.*, vol. XVI, no. 2, March–April 1965, pp. 136–38.

[2] Note that this is the same kind of estimating equation used in the analytical standard data method. However, the symbols a_i and x_i have been reversed in order to conform with the general linear programing model (Chapter 3).

performed for m distinct periods of time and record the values of the attributes and the total job time T. We then have a set of restricting equations

$$\sum_{i=1}^{n} a_i x_i + W_1 = T_1$$

.
.
.

$$\sum_{i=1}^{n} a_i x_i + W_k = T_k$$

.
.
.

$$\sum_{i=1}^{n} a_i x_i + W_m = T_m$$

$$x_i \geq 0 \quad \text{for all } i$$

where W_k, $k = 1, 2, \ldots, m$ are slack variables that represent the time not accounted for by the job attributes; that is, we assume that, given merely the set of observable attributes, the time to perform the job is less than observed time.

The objective function is to minimize the total time represented by the slack variables over the period of the study. That is,

$$\text{Minimize} \sum_{k=1}^{m} W_k = \sum_{k=1}^{m} T_k - \sum_{i=1}^{n} \left(x_i \sum_{k=1}^{k=m} a_k \right)$$

We can note that this function is minimized by maximizing the last term of the equation, which is a function of the original variables x_i.

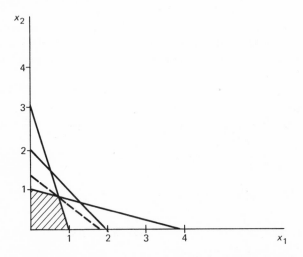

FIGURE **12.4**   Solution space for standard data equations.

TABLE **12.1**   Installation times for 15 jobs.

Job no.	No. of poles a_1	Wire (100 ft) a_2	No. of cross arms a_3	No. of insulators a_4	No. of guy wires a_5	No. of guy guards a_6	Total time T
1	1	4	1	2	1	1	8.0
2	2	10	2	4	0	0	14.0
3	3	6	3	6	1	1	17.5
4	1	2.5	2	3	0	0	7.0
5	2	10	4	6	0	0	16.0
6	4	24	8	12	2	2	37.5
7	4	33	7	11	1	1	39.5
8	1	3	2	4	2	2	10.5
9	0	5	3	3	0	0	5.0
10	2	8	4	8	1	1	17.0
11	3	12	6	12	0	0	23.5
12	2	12	2	4	1	1	16.5
13	3	18	3	6	0	0	22.0
14	1	5	2	3	0	0	8.5
15	4	12	8	12	0	0	28.5

Suppose a job has two attributes a_1 and a_2. A study of the job taken at three different times yields the following:

$$1x_1 + 4x_2 = 4$$
$$5x_1 + 5x_2 = 10$$
$$9x_1 + 3x_2 = 9$$

where x_1 and x_2 are the unknown time coefficients. We wish to find an estimating equation of the type $T = a_1x_1 + a_2x_2$ by linear programing, given the objective of maximizing $15x_1 + 12x_2$. Figure 12.4 displays the solution space and the optimum solution at the point $x_1 = \frac{8}{11}$ and $x_2 = \frac{9}{11}$, at which point the sum of the slack variables equals zero.

Chisman[3] offers an example, which we reproduce here. An electric power company wishes to determine a standard time estimating formula for installing power lines. The coefficients include

x_1 = time to install a pole
x_2 = time to install 100 feet of wire
x_3 = time to install a cross arm on a pole
x_4 = time to install an insulator
x_5 = time to install a guy wire
x_6 = time to install a guy guard

A study of 15 jobs yields the information shown in Table 12.1.

---

[3] James A. Chisman, "Using Linear Programming to Determine Time Standards," *J. Ind. Eng.*, vol. XVII, no. 4, April 1966, pp. 189–91.

There are 15 restriction equations of the following form.

$$1x_1 + 4x_2 + 1x_3 + 2x_4 + 1x_5 + 1x_6 + S_1 - S_2 = 8.0$$
$$2x_1 + 10x_2 + 2x_3 + 4x_4 \qquad\qquad + S_3 - S_4 = 14.0$$

$$\cdots$$

$$1x_1 + 5x_2 + 2x_3 + 3x_4 \qquad\qquad + S_{27} - S_{28} = 8.5$$
$$4x_1 + 12x_2 + 8x_3 + 12x_4 \qquad\qquad + S_{29} - S_{30} = 28.5$$

The slack variables can assume either positive or negative values, and in this case, the objective function is to minimize the sum of the absolute values of the slack variables:

$$\text{Minimize} \quad z = \sum_{k=1}^{k=30} |S_k|$$

The simplex solution gives the following estimating equation:

$$T = 3.17a_1 + 0.50a_2 + 0.92a_3 + 0.21a_4 + 1.50a_5 + 0.0a_6$$

In this case, the time to install a guy wire guard is zero, meaning that it is included in the installation of the guy wire, since every guy wire requires a guard. This simply says that elements that are performed together need be considered only as a single element.

Predetermined Motion Time Systems

We now examine a second kind of standard time data. A predetermined motion time system consists of standard times assigned to basic or fundamental hand and body motions. The data are related to motions or "micro" elements of a job, in contrast to time-study or "macro" elements of standard time data. In this sense, predetermined motion time data are more universally applicable in contrast to time-study standard data, which may be applicable only in the company that derives them.

A number of predetermined motion time systems have been developed by independent consulting firms and are available to the public, advisedly tempered by assistance from the vendor of the system.

In the use of these systems, a time estimate for a job is derived first by describing the job method in terms of fundamental body motions and then synthesizing the job time from the motion-time values found in predetermined tables or charts. The data presented in the tables or charts are derived from studies made in laboratory situations or in actual shop operations. In principle, such data include:

1. The derivation of a system of basic motions, including a precise qualitative description of the motions.
2. The description of the motions in terms of the variables that influence each motion time.
3. The determination of normal times for the motions as a function of the motion variables.

TABLE **12.2**   Data for the motion REACH in the methods-time-measurement system of predetermined standard time data. (1 *TMU* = 0.00001 hour).[4]

Distance moved inches	Time *TMU*				Hand in motion		Case and description
	A	*B*	*C* or *D*	*E*	*A*	*B*	
¾ or less	2.0	2.0	2.0	2.0	1.6	1.6	*A* Reach to object in fixed
1	2.5	2.5	3.6	2.4	2.3	2.3	location, or to object in
2	4.0	4.0	5.9	3.8	3.5	2.7	other hand or on which
3	5.3	5.3	7.3	5.3	4.5	3.6	other hand rests.
4	6.1	6.4	8.4	6.8	4.9	4.3	
5	6.5	7.8	9.4	7.4	5.3	5.0	*B* Reach to single object in
							location which may vary
6	7.0	8.6	10.1	8.0	5.7	5.7	slightly from cycle to
7	7.4	9.3	10.8	8.7	6.1	6.5	cycle.
8	7.9	10.1	11.5	9.3	6.5	7.2	
9	8.3	10.8	12.2	9.9	6.9	7.9	*C* Reach to object jumbled
10	8.7	11.5	12.9	10.5	7.3	8.6	with other objects in a
							group so that search and
12	9.6	12.9	14.2	11.8	8.1	10.1	select occur.
14	10.5	14.4	15.6	13.0	8.9	11.5	
16	11.4	15.8	17.0	14.2	9.7	12.9	*D* Reach to a very small
18	12.3	17.2	18.4	15.5	10.5	14.4	object or where accurate
20	13.1	18.6	19.8	16.7	11.3	15.8	grasp is required.
22	14.0	20.1	21.2	18.0	12.1	17.3	*E* Reach to indefinite loca-
24	14.9	21.5	22.5	19.2	12.9	18.8	tion to get hand in posi-
26	15.8	22.9	23.9	20.4	13.7	20.2	tion for body balance or
28	16.7	24.4	25.3	21.7	14.5	21.7	next motion or out of
30	17.5	25.8	26.7	22.9	15.3	23.2	way.

4. The presentation of the final data in tables or charts.

M.T.M. SYSTEM:[4] A popular system of motion time data is the M.T.M. (Methods Time Measurement) system. For example, the data for the basic motion REACH are shown in Table 12.2. This motion is described as follows:

REACH (symbol *R*) is the basic hand or finger motion employed when the predominant purpose is to move the hand or fingers to a destination.

1. Reach is performed only by the fingers or hand. Moving the foot to a trip lever would not be classified as reach.
2. The hand may be carrying an object and still be classified as a reach provided the predominant purpose is only to move the hand or fingers and not the object. An example would be "reach" for eraser while still holding chalk in the same hand.
3. Short reaches can be performed by moving only the fingers; longer reaches involve motion of the hand, forearm, and upper arm.

---

[4] Information and data are courtesy of M.T.M. Association for Standards and Research, Ann Arbor, Mich.

Note in Table 12.2 that the data are classified in terms of distance and type of hand movement.

The system includes a variety of other finger, hand, arm, and body motions. We need not be concerned with the operating details of this or other systems. Rather, we should be familiar with the functions of the data, the assumptions under which they are applied, and possible sources of error in their use.

Such systems of time data are extensively used in industry today. One major advantage of these systems is that the work method is directly linked to time. This is useful in the stages of designing operations, tools, products, and equipment. Thus, alternative designs in each of these areas may be evaluated in the design stage in terms of manual performance requirements, rather than be timed after the method is operational. Another advantage is that in setting standard times, the method is automatically specified, and future changes in the method, together with the effect on performance time, can be more readily determined. Finally, the standards engineer is provided with a system that may lend some consistency to the setting of standards in the plant, even though there are sources of error inherent in the data and their use.

THE VALIDITY OF PREDETERMINED MOTION TIME DATA: A good deal of academic discussion has centered on the validity of systems of predetermined motion time data.[5,6] It has been made readily apparent that given a certain job, competing systems of this kind of data yield different standard times for the job. This difference is due both to the inherent variations in the systems and to differences in the interpretation of the way in which the data are applied. Although we do not wish to make an exhaustive analysis of these kinds of systems, we should note that the user of such systems must at least consider the possible sources of error in order to evaluate claims about the system that he uses. We may note the following points:

1. The universality of the data depends on the similarity between the sampled populations from which the data were derived and the sample of jobs to which they are applied. The times recorded in the tables and charts represent sample averages of data taken from laboratory studies or from actual industrial situations. Many users of the data often audit the standards that have been set and temper the data with their own experience.

2. The data as presented in charts or tables are usually rated or normal times without allowances for interruptions. The concept of normal or standard performance is therefore inherent in the data and may differ between systems or between the originator of the data and the user. The use of the data does relieve the user, in a direct manner, from the responsibility of rating a job. However, this can be a deceptive advantage, for the simple reason that the use of the system implies the acceptance of the concept of normal that underlies the data.

---

[5] Harold O. Davidson, "On Balance—The Validity of Predetermined Elemental Time Systems," *J. Ind. Eng.*, vol. XIII, no. 3, May–June 1962, pp. 162–65.

[6] Heinz Schmidtke and Fritz Stier, "An Experimental Evaluation of the Validity of Predetermined Elemental Time Systems," *J. Ind. Eng.*, vol. XII, no. 3, May–June 1961, pp. 182–204.

3. The causes for the performance time for a certain motion can be complex. No system can recognize all the variables affecting a motion time. For example, the time required to perform a *reach* motion may depend on the direction of the hand motion, a variable ignored in some systems. Therefore, one source of error is the incompleteness of a system in assigning causes of time variation.

4. The time for a complete job is synthesized by adding the elemental times. The question of additivity of times has been open to considerable debate. It is generally recognized that the time required to perform a certain motion depends on the context of motions comprising the total job, that is, the motions that precede and follow the one in question. Since each job represents a unique sequence of motions, the question of additivity is difficult to assess each time the data are used.

5. Finally, and most importantly, there are sources of error in the application of the data. First, the analyst must decide on the best method. This is the method that will represent standard performance. When considering a job in the detail of micro elements, the method that is "best" for one worker may not be best for another, and skill, as well as pace, is a variable of worker performance. Second, once the method is decided upon, the analyst must interpret it in terms of the system of motions. This is probably the point where a major error can be introduced and where an experienced analyst is required to do the work.

The criteria for the usefulness of systems of predetermined motion times does not lie solely in the degree of errors inherent in the systems or in their application. We must also consider the economics of standards setting. A system of setting standards must be relatively easily applied and understood by its users, as well as by those who must work under the standards. The arguments about the scientific validity of the systems are useful only if they ultimately lead to something operationally better than that which exists. We may expect that, in the future, the improvement of these systems will continue both through the addition to empirical knowledge and through research in the physiology of work.

WORK SAMPLING

We noted earlier that one purpose of work measurement is to estimate the proportion of time consumed by an operation, worker, or machine in various mutually exclusive activities. Work sampling is the technique used to determine such proportions.

The method of work sampling is easy to understand. The procedure involves making a number of instantaneous observations of a job or machine over a protracted period of time. For each observation, we note the activity state of the job. Then, the estimate of the proportion of time spent in a given activity is equal to the number of observations made of that activity, divided by the total number of observations made.

There are two basic ways we can spread our observations over time: we can make our observations at random points in the protracted time period over which the study will be conducted, or we can make "systematic" observations over the study period. Systematic observations are made at regular or equally spaced points in time. We will first outline the random sampling procedure.

Random Work Sampling

In order to clarify the procedure, we will assume that we have a given machine and wish to estimate the fraction of time during which this machine is idle.

DEFINITION OF ACTIVITIES: The first step is to carefully define the activities that will be observed. These activities must be mutually exclusive and exhaustive. In our case, there are two mutually exclusive activities, namely "machine idle" and "machine not idle." Idleness must be carefully defined. We might, for example, say that the machine is idle when it is not actually in the state of producing a part. But even this is open to question, for it might or might not include the time that the operator is loading the machine with material or unloading it with a finished part. Lack of clear-cut definition of activities will leave some doubt in the observer's mind as to what activity is occurring at the time he makes an observation.

THE LENGTH OF THE STUDY: The length of the study is the protracted period over which the random observations will be made. The time period defines the population from which the sample will be extracted. The longer the period, the more idleness will be included, due to a variety of causes. If the amount of idleness varies between days, we might wish to stratify the sample by days to detect the between-day differences in idle time. A representative sample means that the study period is sufficiently long to represent the causes of the idle time.

RANDOMIZING THE OBSERVATIONS: Suppose that the study period is five successive work days and that n observations are taken. We wish to insure that the n observations are randomly dispersed over the five-day period. We might accomplish this in the following manner:

1. Divide the five-day period into discrete time units equal to one minute. Select a number from a table of random numbers:

If the number is	then make an observation on
1 or 6	Monday
2 or 7	Tuesday
3 or 8	Wednesday
4 or 9	Thursday
5 or 0	Friday

We are now assured that each of the five days has an equal likelihood of being selected. Next, we select a three-digit number from the table of random numbers. If the number lies between 000 and 480, it will designate the minute in the chosen day when the observation will be made. We may also use the range 500–980 for corresponding minutes. For example,

Trial no.	First random no.	Day	Next three random nos.	Time of observation
1	3	Wed.	012	8:12 A.M. Wed.
2	6	Mon.	124	10:04 A.M. Mon.
.	.	.	.	.
.	.	.	.	.
.	.	.	.	.
n	5	Fri.	815	1:15 P.M. Fri.

Given n such trials, the observation times are arranged in time sequence, thus giving us a random schedule of observations.

MAKING THE OBSERVATIONS: At each of the chosen random times, the observer visits the machine and, within the designated minute, makes an instantaneous observation of the machine. On an observation sheet, he notes:

1, if the machine is idle
0, if the machine is not idle

Then, when all observations have been taken, let

r = the number of 1's (successes) observed
p = the true fraction of time the machine was idle over the study period
q = the true fraction of time the machine was not idle
$\hat{p}$ = an estimator of p
$\hat{q}$ = an estimator of q
$\quad \hat{p} = r/n$
$\quad \hat{q} = 1 - \hat{p}$

THE PRECISION OF THE ESTIMATE: Since the observations are taken at random, p is constant over all observations. If n is specified prior to the study, and the activities are mutually exclusive and exhaustive, then r is binomially distributed. From this we may determine a precision of the estimate for any desired confidence level. In most cases of work sampling, n will be necessarily large in order to gain a reasonable precision, and p will probably not be less than 5%. Therefore, the normal approximation to the binomial will be a satisfactory model to determine the precision.

The number of observations to be taken is a function of the precision. Assume, for example, that the plant manager hypothesizes that the machine is idle 40% of the time. How many observations must be taken in order to provide an absolute precision of $p \pm 2\%$, with a confidence coefficient of 95%? Assuming that p is 40%,

$$0.02 = 2\sigma_p$$

$$= 2\sqrt{\frac{pq}{n}} = 2\sqrt{\frac{0.4 \times 0.6}{n}}$$

$$n = \frac{4}{0.0004}(0.4 \times 0.6) = 2,400$$

The study would therefore consist initially of 2,400 observations made at random over the period of the study. If $\hat{p}$ is less than 40%, the precision specifications have been satisfied; otherwise, they have not and a larger sample size is required.

THE ACCURACY OF THE ESTIMATE: As in the case of time study, the accuracy of the estimate is unaffected by the number of observations. Accuracy is a function of the manner in which the study is conducted. The factors that could introduce bias into the results are:

1. Lack of randomness in the observations.
2. Bias introduced by the observed medium. If we are observing human performance, the person being observed may alter his behavior intentionally at the time each observation is made.
3. Bias introduced by the observer. The observer might anticipate what the results should be and therefore choose his observations so that they reflect his desired result.
4. Poor definition of activities.

The value of $\hat{p}$ is an estimator of the population parameter p. It is also used as a predictor of future performance, unless conditions are intentionally changed. While $\hat{p}$ may be both precise and accurate, it may still be a poor predictor if it does not represent the conditions that would prevail in the future. In this sense, work sampling may be used to sample the operation at various points over a period of time in order to detect significant changes in the value of p when they occur. That is, we might institute some changes in the operation of the machine, and then we may work sample at a later time to determine the effect of the changes on idle time or whatever activity we are measuring.

Systematic Work Sampling

There are certain conditions where observations at regular intervals are superior to random observations. It would appear that a schedule of regular observations is easier to derive and follow, especially when a number of independent work-sampling studies can be scheduled to fully utilize the time of the observer. Also, the possible mechanization of observation through the use of a photographic device recommends the use of systematic sampling to avoid the cost of randomizing the device. We might also be interested in the times at which certain activities occur, as well as in their uninterrupted duration.

Certain kinds of work measurement are operationally more amenable to systematic work sampling than to continuous stopwatch time studies. Group or crew activities require the observer to keep track of the activities of more than one person or piece of machinery. Work sampling, using short and systematic intervals between observations, approaches continuous time study and permits the observer to systematically record the activities of the individuals in the group over periods of time.

Davidson et al. present a rigorous analysis of systematic sampling and suggest the conditions for using two models to determine estimate precision.[7] If the observation interval is longer than the duration of the activities, then the binomial model

---

[7] H. O. Davidson, W. W. Hines, and T. L. Newberry, "The Error of Estimate in Systematic Activity Sampling," *J. Ind. Eng.*, vol. XI, no. 4, July–August 1960, pp. 290–92.

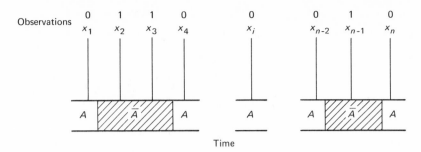

FIGURE **12.5**   Sequence of systematic work sampling observations.

is applicable. If, however, the observation interval is equal to or less than the duration of the activities, then a second type of model is proposed, namely

$$\sigma_{\bar{p}} = \frac{1}{n}\sqrt{\frac{N}{6}}$$

where

    n = sample size or number of observations

    N = number of times the state of the activity changes during n observations. This would be counted by noting the changes from 1 to 0 and from 0 to 1 in the sequence of observations for that activity.

As an example, suppose we have two mutually exclusive activities, A and not A, or $\bar{A}$. A sequence of observations is shown in Figure 12.5. Note that the observation interval is shorter than the duration of either A or $\bar{A}$. A change in activity occurs when the sequence shifts from 0 to 1 or 1 to 0. This model is independent of p and is also more sensitive to sample size.

MANAGEMENT CONSIDERATIONS

Overriding the practical methods of deriving time estimates are the problems of administering a program of work measurement. The economics of work measurement in which the costs of data collection are compared with the losses associated with measurement error are seldom evaluated. While theoretically interesting, the problem may be too difficult to deal with practically. However, the wide variety of management situations requiring time estimates suggests that good estimating procedures other than the microscopic or elemental approaches are needed.

The determination of individual job standards will continue to be important. Where the volume in an individual company is high, we may anticipate partial automation of the standards setting task.

Figure 12.6 shows the basic features of a standard time data-processing system. Information about a job, such as a methods description, a time-study form, and a

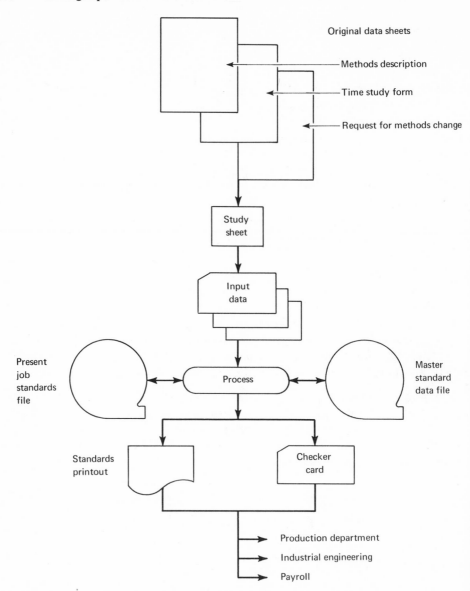

FIGURE **12.6**   Standard time data-processing system.

request for methods change, is recorded on original documents. From this information, a detailed method is recorded on a Study Sheet that codes the elements of the job, frequency of element occurrence, element description, and minutes per occurrence. This information is punched on data input cards and processed. A Master Standard Data File converts the coded work elements into elemental standard times and reconciles the analyst's times if they have been given. The standard time for the job is then stored on a Present Job Standard Tape. The process output consists of a printout of the job standard and checker cards, which are distributed to various departments.

Once a standard is set on a job, it must be periodically audited to see if it has become obsolete due to changes in job methods or conditions. A computer system of the type described is particularly useful, since variations in job method can be read into the system and converted to a new standard, and the standard then compared with the present job standard to determine if a significant difference has occurred.

Through a system of this kind, the data base and computing capacity can be used to aggregate individual job times for the more gross purposes of manpower planning, preliminary job cost estimating, equipment replacement decisions, etc.

Problems

12.1   The term "scientific standard" is often applied to a time standard derived by either stopwatch study or by standard data techniques. Why is this term not appropriate?

12.2   One method of wage payment, which will probably increase in use, is the guaranteed annual wage. Comment on the relationship between work measurement and this kind of wage payment. Does this method preclude the use of work measurement for standards setting?

12.3   The KKJS Company is a job-order machine shop that manufactures a wide variety of products. Many of these products are made in small volume to customers' specifications. In some cases, repeat orders are received several times a year for the product, while in others, the company is called upon to make the product only once. In addition to these customer orders, the company also manufactures and sells a line of fittings used in the oil industry. The company catalog lists 500 different sizes and types of these fittings. Since quick delivery is essential in this business, the 100 most common sizes and types are manufactured in advance and sold from stock. Yearly sales on these 100 standard products range from 4,000 to 12,000 units and make up about 80% of the company's fitting business, with the other 400 types and sizes making up the remaining 20%. The company employs approximately 400 people and does a gross business in excess of $8,000,000 per year divided about equally between their special customer orders and their oil industry fittings. The company is not unionized. In answering the following questions, you may make any reasonable assumptions that you feel are necessary, but clearly state any assumptions you make.
(a) For what purposes would this company need time standards?
(b) What would be some of the most important basic work measurement problems that you would expect this company to encounter?
(c) Describe in detail the work measurement techniques you would recommend this company use, telling why you have selected these particular techniques over others.

12.4   A large retail florist sells preselected and wrapped flowers. An operation for assembling and wrapping a standard bouquet is timed by the continuous method with the following results:

Element	Cycle time in minutes						Performance rating percent
	1	2	3	4	5	6	
(1) Prepare box	0.06	0.60	1.17	1.68	2.33	2.94	1.10
(2) Select eight flowers	0.21	0.72	1.27	1.86	2.44	3.09	0.95
(3) Arrange bouquet and box	0.42	1.02	1.51	2.11	2.75	3.41	1.05
(4) Put box aside	0.50	1.12	1.56	2.20	2.86	3.52	0.90

(a) What is the normal completion time for one output cycle?

(b) Assuming a 15% allowance, what is the standard time for unavoidable delays?

(c) Suppose that the estimated population standard deviation for the cycle time is 0.05 min. What sample size is required to give an estimate of the average cycle time with a precision of ± 0.04 min and a confidence coefficient of 0.95?

12.5   Suppose that a time study of a job yields an average observed time $\overline{X}$ of 1.00 minute. An estimate of the variance of the sample average is $\sigma_{\overline{X}} = 0.10$. The job was rated at $R = 0.80$. Assume that you are 95% certain that repeated ratings of this job under the same conditions will yield a rating factor between 0.70 and 0.90. A work-sampling study using 100 observations yields a percent estimate of unavoidable delays, $p = 0.20$. Can you attach a statement of precision to your estimate of the standard time for this job?

12.6   Kadwell and Klock, Inc., are home builders. In three home developments in a city, the company expects to build some 150 to 200 homes a year for the next five years. There are ten basic models of houses being built. The company has hired an industrial engineer in anticipation of controlling the building operations. The company hires and maintains a core of personnel who build foundations, house frames, etc. However, many of the operations are subcontracted. Mr. Kadwell thinks that standard times should be set on the company operations as a basis for a system of wage incentives. Mr. Klock sees no payoff in this. Present arguments on both sides.

12.7   An industrial engineer has proposed that four operations using semiautomatic machines be collected together and run by a single operator. Individually, these operations require the following normal times:

Operation number	Unload and load machine	Machine time	Inspect finished part
	min	min	min
1	0.50	2.00	0.10
2	0.60	2.30	0.10
3	0.40	0.80	0.10
4	0.70	2.50	0.10

The present average incentive earnings in the plant run about 25% above normal. What problems would you expect in the management of this operation, particularly with respect to incentive earnings?

12.8   The Vitex Valve Company produces a line of large cast valves and fire hydrants. Most of the items are made for stock and then sold to customers in varying batch sizes. Before shipment to the customer, the item is painted to customer specifications. The painting operation is shown in Figure 12.7. The paint booth operator loads a hand truck with a number of items from the stock room and then trucks them to the paint

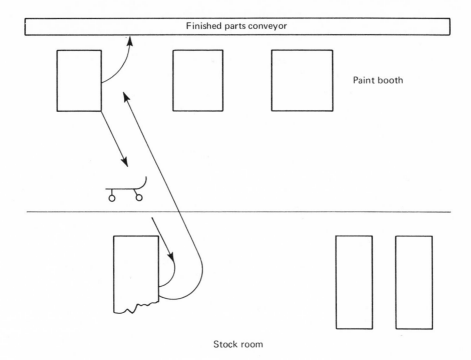

FIGURE **12.7**

booth. When an item is finished, it is placed on an outgoing conveyor. An estimating formula is to be derived based on the distance the man must travel to pick up a load and the gross weight of the items in each load. A study of six jobs shows the following relationships between the total time T to complete the job in minutes, the distance D traveled in feet, and the gross weight W of the load in tons.

$$
\begin{aligned}
Dx_1 + Wx_2 &= T \\
30x_1 + 0.5x_2 &= 60 \\
100x_1 + 1.0x_2 &= 150 \\
200x_1 + 1.14x_2 &= 200 \\
60x_1 + 0.53x_2 &= 105 \\
150x_1 + 2.04x_2 &= 225
\end{aligned}
$$

Compare the derivation of an estimating formula by multiple regression and by linear programing. Why would one prefer to use the linear programing method over the method of multiple regression?

12.9   A large manufacturing plant has three employees whose job it is to change light bulbs in the thousands of lights in five factory buildings. This operation is to be placed on standards for purposes of wage incentive.

(a) Differentiate between the synthetic and analytical methods of deriving standard time data for this operation. You should hypothesize the job elements.

(b) Describe the features of an incentive plan.

(c) How can this job be placed on incentive? Describe the basic features of a plan.

12.10   The general manager of the White Engine Company is considering having the industrial engineering department start using a system of predetermined motion times. He has heard from another plant manager that a system of this kind is more accurate than traditional time study and time-study standard data and that the use of the system relieves management of the responsibility of having to rate job performance. Comment on these claims.

12.11   The Xoron Chemical Company has a large force of janitors. It is requested by the general manager that the industrial engineering department institute a program of janitorial cost control, including the possibility of setting standards for the janitors. Suppose you are a member of the team of engineers attacking this problem and you have been told to consider the possibility of setting standards on the cleaning of offices in the various buildings. A normal job, done after 5 P.M., consists of these elements:

1. Unlock door, push hand cart into office, and turn on lights.
2. Empty wastepaper baskets in hand cart container.
3. Empty and clean all ash trays.
4. Every Friday night dry mop floor.
5. Every Wednesday night dry mop floor and wipe off desk tops.
6. Remove equipment from office, turn out light, and lock door.

(a) What form might the standard data take?
(b) Discuss the problem of using the standards for incentive pay. How can the company install an incentive pay scheme on this type of operation when the volume of work is constant? Suppose that there are three engineers assigned to this project, which is expected to take a year and a half, before the standards program is completed. What is the payoff for this investment in engineering time?

12.12   A work-sampling study is made of a drill press operation. The purpose of the sampling study is to determine allowances for the standard time to be placed on the operation. The allowance will be set for delays that cannot be avoided by the operator. The results of the study are as follows:

Activity	Number of observations	Percent
Total	608	100%
Unavoidable delays	61	10%
Avoidable delays	24	4%
Production	523	86.0%

(a) If the normal or base time for the operation is 0.50 minutes per 100 pieces, what is the standard time per 100 pieces? Show calculations.
(b) Assuming a confidence coefficient of 95%, what is the precision interval for the estimate of 10% unavoidable delays? Show calculations.
(c) List four factors that would contribute to lack of accuracy in the estimate of percentage of unavoidable delays.
(d) What is the name of the correct and underlying probability distribution for the *sampling random variable* in this study? What is its mean and standard deviation?

12.13   The Visco Company has a manual assembly operation for which a standard time has been set. A grievance is registered by the operator that the standard is unfair. The original study was made by stopwatch. A new study is proposed using the method of systematic work sampling. The study is conducted over a period of 240 minutes using observation intervals of two minutes, which is shorter than the duration of any of the mutually exclusive activities comprising the job. Other information about the study is:

Number of pieces produced by the operator = 240
Estimate of the fraction of time the operator was busy = 0.80
Estimate of the fraction of time consumed in interruptions (unavoidable) = 0.10
Count of the number of times the activities shifted from one state to the other = 180
Over-all rating factor = 0.90

From this information, determine a standard time for the operation. Suppose the boss asked you for some measure of the error in your estimate. What figure would you give?

Bibliography

BARNES, RALPH M., *Motion and Time Study*, 5th ed. New York: John Wiley & Sons, 1963.

——, *Work Sampling*. New York: John Wiley & Sons, 1962.

CONWAY, RICHARD W., "Some Statistical Considerations in Work Sampling," *J. Ind. Eng.*, March–April 1957.

DAVIDSON, HAROLD O., "Work Sampling—Eleven Fallacies," *J. Ind. Eng.*, September–October 1960.

DAVIS, H., "A Mathematical Evaluation of a Work Sampling Technique," *Naval Research Logistics Quarterly*, March–June 1955.

FLOWERDEW, D. A., and P. W. MALIN, "Systematic Activity Sampling," *J. Ind. Eng.*, July–August 1963.

HANSEN, B. L., *Work Sampling for Modern Management*. Englewood Cliffs, N.J.: Prentice-Hall, Inc., 1960.

HUDSON, W. R., and ROBERT V. HOGG, "A Chi-Square Test for Monitoring Staff Activity," *J. Ind. Eng.*, January–February 1963.

KERKHOVEN, C. L. M., "The Rating of Performance Levels of the S. A. M. Films," *J. Ind. Eng.*, July–August 1963.

KRICK, E. V., *Methods Engineering*. New York: John Wiley & Sons, 1962.

LADD, GEORGE W., and KEITH L. MC ROBERTS, "A Regression Method for Determining Visual Inspection Times," *J. Ind. Eng.*, September–October 1960.

MADOW, L. H., "Systematic Sampling and Its Relation to Other Sampling Designs," *J. Am. Stat. Assoc.*, vol. 41, 1946.

MAYNARD, H. B., G. J. STEGEMERTEN, and J. L. SCHWAB, *Methods-Time Measurement*. New York: McGraw-Hill Book Co., 1948.

PARKS, GEORGE M., "Multiple Criteria Sequential Work Sampling," *J. Ind. Eng.*, July–August 1964.

SALEM, M. D., JR., "Multiple Linear Regression Analysis for Work Measurement of Indirect Labor," *J. Ind. Eng.*, May 1967.

STUKEY, ARTHUR E., "Work Measurement in Perspective-Universal Time Data," *J. Ind. Eng.*, January–February 1964.

TAYLOR, FREDERICK W., *Shop Management*. New York: Harper & Bros., 1903.

THELWELL, RAPHAEL R., "An Evaluation of Linear Programming and Multiple Regression for Estimating Manpower Requirements," *J. Ind. Eng.*, March 1967.

13

Controlling
Production Quality

To p⁹ 435

INTRODUCTION

The Meaning of Quality

The quality of a product or a service is expressed in terms of a given set of attributes that are required to meet the economic needs for which the product or service is created. If the consumer sets forth a rigid set of specifications for his needs, then a "good" quality product is one that exactly meets those needs. This is in contrast to the general notion that a good or high-quality product is one that is high priced or that maximizes the values of a set of attributes. The term "good quality" means close adherence to a set of specifications.

The difficulty in defining quality lies in the multiplicity of attributes and their specifications. Size, hardness, weight, durability, reliability, attractiveness, low maintenance cost, and economy of operation are only a few of the physical, operating, or economic attributes that can be assigned to a product or service. When a product is mass produced, the quality is relative to the specifications that represent the general market requirements. Each customer has his own set of implicit or explicit specifications, and the best he can do is to search the market for the product that comes closest to his own requirements. A custom-made product or service can be tailor-made directly to the customer's requirements, such as in the case of a spaceship.

The purpose of quality control is to give some degree of assurance that product or service quality standards are maintained. In production, no quality control can take place unless the attributes are quantifiable and measurable with a desired degree of precision. Quality specifications must represent a standard against which actual performance can be compared.

Programs for quality assurance must recognize imperfection. We are familiar with the fact that most standards or specifications must represent a range of acceptable values to allow for the inherent variability in production processes. Also, there must be a recognition that off-standard production is probable and that a certain number of defective units will fall into the hands of the consumer.

In manufacturing systems, quality control refers to both inputs and outputs of a system. Quality is an ultimate agreement between the vendor or "producer" and the "consumer." Within a plant, the producer may be an operation or department that is producing for a second operation or department, the consumer. Beyond measuring various product or part dimensions, quality control demands a good deal of coordination between the groups that form the producer-consumer relationship within a plant and between companies in the stages of production. The risk that the consumer will receive a defective product must be weighed against the producer's costs of quality assurance.

Costs of Quality Assurance

Because quality is such a pervasive concern, the assessment of the total costs related to product or service cost is a difficult or impossible task. If one were to consider all costs associated with designing, maintaining, and controlling quality, one would have to include just about all functions in the actual design and processing of a part. More realistically, we need to consider the costs directly related to controlling quality once the quality standards have been determined by management.

We can classify quality related costs as prevention, appraisal, internal failure, and external failure costs. While some of the cost elements in each of these classes are easy to detect and measure, others are much less so. The typical cost elements in each of these classes are listed below.

PREVENTION: This class includes those costs associated with the design and planning of a quality control (QC) program. Typical elements are:

1. QC administration and systems planning
2. Quality training
3. Quality planning (QC engineering work)
   (a) Incoming, in process, final inspection, and test planning
   (b) Special processes planning
   (c) Quality data analysis and feedback
   (d) Procurement planning
   (e) Vendor surveys, audit and surveillance planning
   (f) Reliability studies
4. Design and development of quality measurement and control equipment
5. Qualification of material

APPRAISAL: These are the costs involved in the direct appraisal of quality both in the plant and in the field.

1. Test
2. Inspection
3. Quality audits
4. Incoming test and inspection and laboratory acceptance
5. Checking labor
6. Laboratory or other measurement service

7. Setup for test and inspection
8. Test and inspection material
9. Outside endorsements
10. Maintenance and calibration of inspection and test equipment
11. Product engineering review and shipping release
12. Field testing

INTERNAL FAILURE: The following are costs directly related to the occurrence of defective production within the plant.

1. Scrap—at full shop cost
2. Rework—at full shop cost
3. Scrap and rework—fault of vendor
4. Material procurement
5. Factory contact engineering
6. QC investigations (of failures)
7. Material review activity
8. Repair and troubleshooting

EXTERNAL FAILURE: The failure of a product or service in the field leads to costs, some of which are difficult to assess. These include:

1. Complaints and loss of customer good will
2. Warranty costs
3. Field maintenance and product service
4. Returned material processing and repair
5. Replacement inventories
6. Strained distributor relations

The cost complex of maintaining and controlling quality suggests that planning effective and efficient programs in this area is not an easy task. The development of decision models in many areas of quality management has not progressed as it has in some other realms of production. Much of the work has been concerned with devising localized economical inspection procedures. The decision whether to invest in quality control procedures is often based on technical factors and is related to the critical nature of a part or product dimension. The potential and explicit costs of internal failure or the implicit costs of external failure are often so high as to necessitate investing in a control procedure for some part of material.

The General Quality Control Structure

The general stages of quality control for a product are shown in Figure 13.1.

PLANNING AND DESIGN SPECIFICATIONS: The basic quality control is executed in the product planning, development, and design stages, just as are the basic product costs. Management assessment of potential markets and demand functions for various combinations of quality, cost, and price determines the set of basic quality specifications for the product. Within this first-order set of specifica-

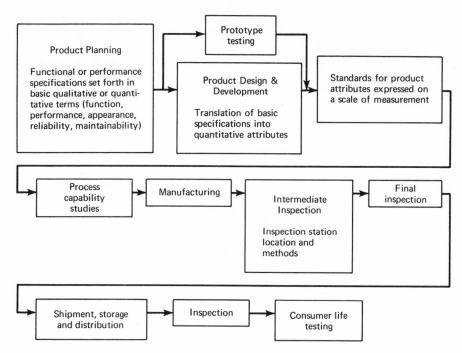

FIGURE **13.1**   Quality control structure.

tions, the engineer must consider the variety of alternative designs that will conform to these specifications.

The result of the final and detailed product design will be an evolved and similarly detailed set of product attributes expressed on a measurement scale and standards for these attributes against which quality can be measured. Of course, for many products, standards are set forth by industry or government authority. Process capability studies may accompany the determination of the product specifications and standards.

OPERATIONAL QUALITY CONTROL: Once the design is finalized, the problem of quality control is operational except, of course, for subsequent design changes. In terms of organization, quality is basically the responsibility of the line organization. The design and operation of an inspection system may reside with a quality control department or division. But the line organization must be responsible for taking the necessary remedial action when specifications are not being met. Top management may be familiar only with reports of total rejects or costs of defective parts or material. At the operational level, the foreman may have a periodic measure of quality for a given operation in the form of a control chart or inspection report.

The management control of quality at the operational level involves a variety of decisions. These relate to the design of the quality control system for a multiproduct material situation, as well as for a given individual part. Included in this is an engineering division for the design and manufacture of technical gauges used for inspection, or their purchase and storage. We will have little to say about this hardware aspect of inspection. There is also the design of specific inspection work methods and work places, which is a part of the over-all operation and job design problem.

With respect to a given item of incoming material or a partially or fully completed outgoing part, there are a number of decisions that must be made. First, it must be decided where in the routing sequence the material should be inspected. Second, what kind of inspection method should be used, that is, complete, or 100%, inspection or sampling inspection? Third, there are the decisions on the disposition of rejected parts, the remedial action that will be taken to correct the process, and, finally, whether or not standards need to be altered to conform more realistically with the process capabilities. If the part is purchased, vendor relationships may have to be altered.

As we have noted, the theoretical content of many of these tactical decisions is difficult to translate into workable decision models. The design of exact inspection methods is a legitimate part of the methods engineering function. This is a design problem. The actions taken at the operating level to remedy off-quality conditions are unique in each case, and the efficiency of corrective action depends on the technical capabilities of the line organization to ferret out the causes, unless redesign of a part or machine is required.

INSPECTION: Inspection is not synonymous with the managerial control of quality. Inspection is the process of verifying the quality of a part or material with respect to some attribute.

There are two fundamental purposes for inspecting parts. The first is to ascertain the quality of some portion of the parts being turned out by the process. This portion is referred to as a *lot* of parts. Usually a lot is an identifiable batch of the production, such as an hour or day's production, the output of a given machine, or the shipment from a given vendor. The problem is to decide whether to accept or reject the lot on the basis of its quality; this is called *Acceptance Control*. The actual measurement of the attribute is compared with a standard, resulting in the acceptance or rejection of a batch of the part. The remedial action is a management problem involving both technical and economic considerations.

The second purpose is to ascertain the condition of an operation, machine, or process in terms of its quality-producing performance. In this case, the problem is *Process Control*. A given inspection may serve both purposes.

There are two basic methods for determining the lot quality with respect to some dimension of the part. The first is *100% inspection*, or screening. The second is *sampling inspection*.

1. *100% inspection*   Each unit in the lot is subjected to inspection. The defective parts are then segregated from the lot and reworked or disposed of, and the remainder of the lot is passed to the consumer. In cases of a very critical dimension, 100% inspection may be the only possible way of maintaining the required quality.

However, there are certain disadvantages and limitations to this method of inspection. First, if the measurement process is destructive, such as with ammunition or candy, 100% screening is unfeasible. Second, there is no guarantee that the residual lot, after screening, is free of defects, particularly if the inspection is manual. Studies have indicated that inspectors may fail to remove as many as 10% to 50% of the defective units in a lot, on a single screening. Third, this method of inspection is costly and may not be justified in cases where the number of defects in the lot is very small.

2. *Sampling inspection*   In sampling inspection, a sample of parts is selected from the lot (the statistical population). The individual parts in the sample are subjected to 100% inspection. Based on the number of defective units found in the sample, the lot is either accepted or held up for more intensive inspection. The subject of statistical quality control is concerned with the derivation of the decision rules that are used as the basis for accepting or rejecting the lot.

In the case of both 100% and sampling inspection, we may use either an *attribute* measure or a *variable* measure. An attribute measure is one in which the inspected part is assigned a value 1 or 0 if the part is rejected or passed, respectively. The measuring instrument or gauge is calibrated with a nominal scale. This is called a Go or No-Go gauge. For example, suppose we have a lower weight limit for boys who will be allowed to play on the varsity football team. We set the balance of the weighing scale to that limit. When a boy stands on the scale, the balance will either rise or remain stationary. If it rises, the boy is passed; otherwise, he is rejected. Or, on a less precise scale, a barrel of wine is to be tested by a jury of tasters. Each taster takes a sample from the barrel and judges the wine to be acceptable or not.

In the case of the variable measure, the gauge provides a value for the dimension from a scale of values. The football player's actual weight is recorded. The wine is subjected to chemical analysis for, say, alcohol content.

Both kinds of measure are used in both methods of inspection for either acceptance or process control. We will subsequently examine the essential features of sampling inspection for both acceptance and process control.

LOCATION OF INSPECTION STATIONS

When a part is introduced into production, an important question is where or at what points in the sequence of operations comprising the part routing inspection should take place.

We have the condition shown in Figure 13.2. There are N distinct operations through which the part is routed, and there is the possibility of inspecting the part after each operation. There is also the possibility of inspection during an operation. This implies an inspection device built into the machine, such that the part is checked automatically with respect to the dimension being imparted or to previously generated dimensions. Otherwise, the part is inspected either automatically or manually after it is processed at some point in its routing.

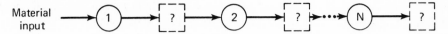

FIGURE **13.2** Operation-inspection sequence.

Given a set of N potential inspection points, a location choice is one of 2^N subsets of ordered numbers, where a subset

$$A = \left\{ a_i;\ a_i = \begin{bmatrix} 1 & \text{if an inspection station is located after operation } i \\ 0 & \text{otherwise} \end{bmatrix} \right\}$$
$$i = 1, 2, \ldots, N$$

For example, if there are three independent operations performed on a part, then the possible subsets are:

Subset A	Number of stations	Operation 1	Operation 2	Operation 3	
1	0	0	0	0	1—inspection point
2	1	1	0	0	0—no inspection
3	1	0	1	0	point
4	1	0	0	1	
5	2	0	1	1	
6	2	1	0	1	
7	2	1	1	0	
8	3	1	1	1	

Location of station spans Operation 1, Operation 2, Operation 3 columns.

The problem of selecting a minimum cost inspection scheme from among the set of possibilities is a difficult task. If each subset is to be costed, then a good deal of analysis is involved. The costs certainly include the direct costs of inspection, which depend mainly on the design of the inspection method at each station. For example, in alternative 5, the inspection station located after operation 2 would presumably be checking the dimension generated at operations 1 and 2. In alternative 8, the inspection station after operation 2 would check only the dimension imparted at operation 2. The other cost is that of processing at a given operation parts that have been made defective in previous operations. In alternative 4, the last operation would process those parts that have been made defective at the previous two operations, since they were not removed from the system by previous inspection.

Pragmatic Rules

Before considering a decision model for the inspection station location problem, we should recognize that the decision is often based on certain pragmatic rules, which are outlined as follows:

1. *Reception of raw material*   It seems logical to inspect incoming raw material and purchased parts at the point of their reception into stores. This is often a normal routine prior to issuing the voucher for payment. If the material is subject to possible deterioration in stores, a second inspection may be necessary prior to its release to production.

2. *Prior to a costly operation*   If a given operation is extremely costly, then inspection just prior to that operation prevents the generation of costs on parts that are already defective. Examples are gold plating a watch or performing a difficult assembly operation.

3. *Prior to potential damage*   An off-standard part or material can sometimes cause damage in subsequent operations. For example, a weak section of paper can cause a roll breakage and require an expensive setup in paper making, or a defective part may cause a machine to jam in the next operation.

4. *Prior to a series of operations*   In certain processes, there may be a series of operations in which inspection is impossible or difficult to perform. This might be the case in a chemical process where accessibility is impossible or the rate of flow is extremely high.

5. *Point of no return*   After certain operations, a defective part cannot be reworked. For instance, a metal part may have been hardened to the point where it cannot be remachined if found defective. Errors in the text of a book cannot be economically corrected after the book has been bound. Cutting a keyway in an undersized hole means that the hole cannot be enlarged in a rework operation.

6. *Masking attributes*   Some operations mask certain attributes of a part and thus eliminate the possibility of checking the attribute. Painting a part covers up any surface indication of defects. Locating a part or subassembly in an inaccessible location in the main assembly precludes the inspection of the part or subassembly. Therefore, inspection is necessary prior to assembly of the part.

7. *Prior to stocking*   Just as in the case of raw materials, partially finished parts should be inspected if the cost of not having them available later is high. A shelf of off-standard subassemblies may throw a final assembly operation off schedule.

8. *Process control*   If the potential cost of out-of-control processes is high, inspection may be necessary to detect out-of-control situations. This is related to process variability and capability.

9. *Quality responsibility*   Inspection points are often set up at the point where a part is transferred from one area of responsibility to another. This is important because the responsibility for costly off-standard quality cannot always be clearly attributed to a single area of responsibility after the part has passed a certain point in its routing. In many cases, of course, a defect in some dimension can be traced exactly to the point where the dimension was imparted.

10. *Quality incentives*   In many incentive plans, the operator receives pay only for good pieces produced, or there may be a quality factor in the incentive pay calculation. This demands the inspection of the work subsequent to the incentive operation and possibly just before it to establish the worker's responsibility for any defective work.

Quantitative Methods

In order to consider some quantitative approaches to the problem of locating the inspection station, we will use the following variables. Let

i = index number for an operation and the possible inspection point following it:

$i = 1, 2, \ldots, N$

s = number of units of the part entering the first operation, $i = 1$
p_i = expected percentage of parts made defective at the ith operation
d_i = number of good parts made defective at the ith operation
u_i = cost of processing a unit at the ith operation
b_{ij} = cost of inspecting j dimensions of a unit at the ith inspection station
F_i = fixed cost of locating an inspection station at the ith point
z_i = cumulative number of defective parts removed before the ith inspection point
$m_i = \begin{cases} 1 \text{ if an inspection station is located at the } i\text{th point} \\ 0 \text{ otherwise} \end{cases}$

The system is indicated in Figure 13.3, where each operation generates new defectives d_i whose number is a function of the starting quantity, the percentage p_i, and the number of defectives made at previous stations.

We wish to choose a subset of inspection station locations that will minimize the total cost of rejected parts and inspection costs. The cost of a rejected part will depend on how many operations it will go through after it has been made defective. The inspection costs depend on how many dimensions must be checked at an inspection station.

EXAMPLE 13.1   Suppose that a certain critical part is routed through five operations. It is assumed that an inspection station must be located after the last operation, but the location of any other inspection stations is still undecided. Information about the operations is as follows:

Operation-inspection point i	Unit processing cost u_i	Expected percent defective p_i	Number of defects d_i	Variable cost of inspection for j number of dimensions b_{ij}				
				1	2	3	4	5
1	$1.25	5%	50	$0.25				
2	2.20	3	28	0.20	0.30			
3	0.95	10	92	0.15	0.30	0.40		
4	1.60	6	50	0.20	0.35	0.45	0.60	
5	1.32	4	30	0.15	0.30	0.45	0.60	0.90

Assume that the starting quantity is 1,000 units and that there is a fixed cost of $50 to set up an inspection station ($F_i = \$50$ for all i).

A HEURISTIC RULE: In order to gain insight into the problem, we can try the following rule. This is to compare the costs of locating or not locating a station at any point relative only to the next point in the line. If the cost of not locating a station is less than the cost of locating, then no station will be added and vice versa. The costs are calculated as follows.

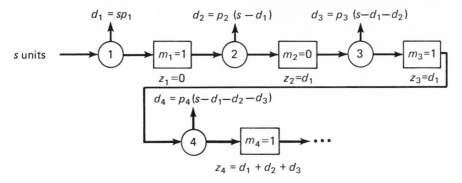

FIGURE **13.3**   Generation of defects.

For any given point k let

CN_k = cost of not establishing an inspection station at k
CY_k = cost of establishing an inspection station at k

Then,

$$CN_k = (u_{k+1})\left(\sum_{i=h}^{i=k} d_i\right) + (b_{k+1,j+1})(s - z_k)$$

where h is the point following the last point where an inspection station was located, $j = k - h + 1, h \geqslant 1$, and

$$CY_k = (b_{kj})(s - z_k) + (b_{k+1,1})\left(s - z_k - \sum_{i=h}^{i=k} d_i\right) + F_k$$

Note that both CN_k and CY_k assume that there will be a station at $k + 1$.

If we apply this rule to the data given in the example, we find that the steps are as follows:

Station point	CN	CY
1	$410.00	$490.00
2	474.10	488.00
3	872.00	616.00
4	315.00	333.00

The rule then says that the location indices are $m_1, m_2, m_4 = 0$ and $m_3, m_5 = 1$.

COMPLETE ENUMERATION: We can test the above rule by enumerating the costs of all subsets of inspection station locations. Thus, we have for c_i, the cost of the ith operation inspection point,

$$c_i = \begin{cases} (\mu_i + b_{ij})(s - z_i) + F_i & \text{if } m_i = 1 \\ (\mu_i)(s - z_i) & \text{if } m_i = 0 \end{cases}$$

and $C_l = \sum_{i=1}^{N} c_i; l = 1, 2, \ldots, 2^{N-1}$

For the case of our example we have

l	C_l	Subset
1	8270.00	0.0.0.0.1.
2	7846.00	0.0.0.1.1.
3	7570.51	0.0.1.0.1.
4	7588.83	0.0.1.1.1.
5	7830.88	0.1.0.0.1.
6	7718.35	0.1.0.1.1.
7	7584.16	0.1.1.0.1.
8	7602.48	0.1.1.1.1.
9	7936.50	1.0.0.0.1.
10	7736.00	1.0.0.1.1.
11	7598.01	1.0.1.0.1.
12	7616.33	1.0.1.1.1.
13	7910.88	1.1.0.0.1.
14	7798.35	1.1.0.1.1.
15	7664.16	1.1.1.0.1.
16	7682.48	1.1.1.1.1.

and we see that the previous rule gave the minimum cost, but by chance, since the rule is nonoptimal and one can construct a counterexample to show the nonoptimality of the rule.

OPTIMAL METHODS: Several published articles have proposed methods for determining optimal solutions to this kind of problem.[1,2] These methods employ dynamic programing as the basic technique and differ in the way the problem has been structured and in the assumptions made. We will not attempt to reproduce them here, for they involve a complexity beyond the desired scope of this problem.

LEAST-COST TESTING SEQUENCE

In the inspection of a given part, we might be confronted with the following problem. A certain part is to be subjected to n different tests in sequence. The problem is to determine the sequence of the tests. Each individual test entails a certain cost and a certain probability of rejecting the part. The tests are independent, so we may choose any one of $n!$ sequences for the tests. If a part is found to be defective at any test, it is rejected and not subjected to the subsequent tests in the sequence.

In the general case, we have the following: Let

C_i = cost of making the ith test per unit; $i = 1, \ldots, n$
R_i = reject rate for the ith test or the probability of rejecting the item
S = a particular test sequence chosen among $n!$ possible sequences
$C(S)$ = total unit cost for the given sequence S

[1] Glenn F. Lindsay and Albert B. Bishop, "Allocation of Screening Inspection Effort—A Dynamic Programming Approach," *Management Science*, vol. 10, no. 1, January 1964, pp. 342–52.
[2] Leon S. White, "The Analysis of a Sample Class of Multistage Inspection Plans," *Management Science*, vol. 12, no. 5, May 1966, pp. 685–93.

The problem, then, is to find $C(S) = \min$.

The rule to use is as follows:[3]

1. For each test j, determine the ratio C_j/R_j.
2. Run the tests starting with the one that has the smallest ratio C_j/R_j, followed by the one that has the second smallest ratio, etc. Or, $C_1/R_1 \leqslant C_2/R_2 \leqslant \cdots \leqslant C_n/R_n$.

The proof is as follows:

Suppose we have to make three tests. If they are conducted in the order 1, 2, 3, then the cost for each test is

$$C_1 = C_1$$
$$C_2 = C_2(1 - R_1)$$
$$C_3 = C_3(1 - R_1)(1 - R_2)$$

Assume that we have sequenced the tests such that $C_i/R_i < C_{i+1}/R_{i+1}$. Suppose we transpose the positions of tests 2 and 3 so that 3 precedes 2. Let $C(S)$ be the total inspection cost for the sequence 1, 2, 3. Then

$$C(S) = C_1 + C_2(1 - R_1) + C_3(1 - R_1)(1 - R_2)$$
$$= \frac{C_1}{(1 - R_1)} + C_2 + C_3(1 - R_2) = \frac{C_1}{(1 - R_1)} + C_2 + C_3 - C_3 R_2$$

Let $C(S)'$ be the total inspection cost for the sequence 1, 3, 2. Then

$$C(S)' = C_1 + C_3(1 - R_1) + C_2(1 - R_1)(1 - R_3)$$
$$= \frac{C_1}{(1 - R_1)} + C_3 + C_2 - C_2 R_3$$

We wish to prove $C(S) < C(S)'$.

$$C(S) < C(S)'$$

$$\frac{C_1}{(1 - R_1)} + C_2 + C_3 - C_3 R_2 < \frac{C_1}{(1 - R_1)} + C_3 + C_2 - C_2 R_3$$

and therefore

$$-C_3 R_2 < -C_2 R_3 \tag{1}$$

But, since $C_2/R_2 < C_3/R_3$, then $C_2 R_3 < C_3 R_2$, which agrees with (1).

ACCEPTANCE CONTROL BY SAMPLING

In acceptance control, we wish to judge the quality of a homogeneous batch of parts called a lot. The homogeneity of the lot is based on some common source of the parts in the lot. This could be a given vendor's shipment, a day's production

---

[3] L. G. Mitten, "An Analytical Solution to the Least Cost Testing Sequence Problem," *J. Ind. Eng.*, vol. XI, no. 1, January–February 1960, p. 17.

from a given machine or process, a batch of parts transferred from one department to another, parts from a given batch of raw material, etc. In these cases, the parts are transferred between producer and consumer on a discrete lot-by-lot basis. Each lot may be subjected to independent inspection. In other cases, we may encounter a continuous flow of material between two operations in the system, thus requiring a continuous inspection scheme of some sort.

There are a variety of sampling methods that may be applied to the acceptance control situation. These depend on whether there is a lot-by-lot or continuous transfer of material or parts, attributes or variables measures, or single or multiple sampling plans. In the following pages, lot-by-lot single sampling plans using both attributes and variables will be emphasized, and we will avoid a detailed discussion of the many other kinds of plans.

Lot-by-Lot Sampling by Attributes

In our discussion, we will use the following notation. Let

N = number of items in the lot, that is, the lot size
p = the proportion of defective parts in the lot
n = the number of items in the sample, that is, the sample size
c = the number of defective parts in the sample
$\hat{p}$ = the sample estimate of p; $\hat{p} = c/n$

Given a lot to be inspected, the general sampling procedure is to select a random sample from the lot and use this to estimate the value of p, which is the lot quality. Depending on the findings, the lot will be accepted or rejected.

ACCEPTABLE QUALITY LEVEL: In order to make a decision about the lot quality, we must have a standard of what is good or poor quality. We therefore define good quality in terms of some value of p. This value is called AQL (acceptable quality level).

The determination of the AQL often involves decisions that are independent of our immediate problem of designing the sampling plan. What is good quality is basically an economic issue and depends, of course, on the kind of product or parts being inspected. We might naturally expect an AQL for a drug to be much lower than the AQL for pencils. Theoretically, an optimum AQL is one for which the total costs relevant to the decision are minimized. These include the consequential costs of having defects reach the consumer, as well as the costs of inspection and manufacturing.

Regardless of the method of specifying AQL, we would like to accept all lots whose value of p is equal to or less than AQL and reject those lots whose value of p is greater than AQL. Or, putting it another way, we would like to have a probability of 1.0 of accepting a lot whose p is equal to or less than AQL and a probability of 0.0 of accepting a lot for which $p > AQL$. This is represented in the diagram in Figure 13.4, which shows the relationship between the probability $P(A)$ of accepting the lot and the value of p. This is called an operating characteristic curve (OC curve) of the sampling plan. In this particular case, the plan would

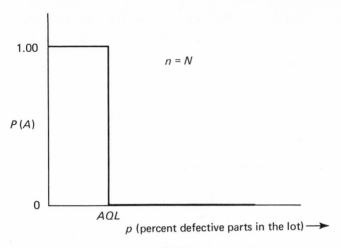

FIGURE **13.4**   OC curve for 100% inspection plan.

have to be 100% inspection without human error, or the sample size must equal the population.

If we sample a lot, rather than subject it to 100% inspection, we must infer the value of p as estimated from c/n. We therefore take a *risk of rejecting* a lot for which $0 \leq p \leq AQL$ and a *risk of accepting* a lot for which $p > AQL$. In this sense, acceptance sampling is hypothesis testing. Given a homogeneous lot of parts (the population), we make a hypothesis about the value of p and then proceed by sampling to accept or reject the hypothesis. Therefore, the probability of acceptance is a function of p, given a certain sample size and a specified value of c, which we will use as the criterion for accepting the lot. The form of the operating characteristic curve is shown in Figure 13.5.

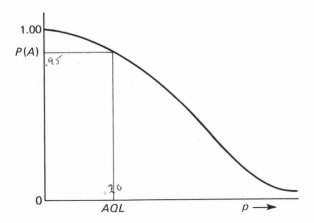

FIGURE **13.5**   Typical form of an OC curve for a sampling plan.

TABLE **13.1**   Sampling distributions of c and conditions where they are appropriate.

Sampling distribution of c	N	n	p	np
Hypergeometric series	small	0.20N or larger	—	—
Binomial series	large	$n/N < 0.20$	—	—
Poisson	large	$n/N < 0.20$	less than 0.10	—
Normal approximation to binomial	large	large	$p \geq 0.10$	greater than 5

THE SINGLE SAMPLING PLAN: The single sampling plan is the procedure that will be used as the basis for accepting or rejecting the lot. The procedure is as follows: Given a lot size of N homogeneous parts, select a random sample of size n. Count the number of defective parts in the sample. If the number of defective parts in the sample is equal to or less than a predetermined number c', then accept the lot; otherwise, reject it.

Subsequent to the rejection, the remaining $N - n$ units may be subjected to 100% inspection and passed on after rejects are removed, or the lot is scrapped or submitted to further sampling if destructive testing is used. We will not be concerned about these actions for the moment.

The problem in acceptance sampling, then, is to determine a sampling plan expressed in terms of the sample size n and the value of c' that will give the required degree of protection. Each independent value of n and c' results in a distinctive OC curve from which we can determine the probability of accepting a lot with a given value of p.

THE DEVELOPMENT OF THE OC CURVE: The OC curve is constructed from the distribution of the random-sample variable c. Therefore, it is necessary to know what the appropriate sampling distribution of c is for any situation. The suggested distributions for various conditions are summarized in Table 13.1.

EXAMPLE 13.2   Suppose that we construct an OC curve for the following situation. A lot of 5,000 parts is to be sampled. If a plan $n = 50$ and $c' = 1$ is used and we use the Poisson distribution, then the probability of accepting lots with various values of p is as follows:

p	Probability of acceptance $P(c \leq c')$
0	1.00
0.02	0.736
0.03	0.558
0.04	0.406
0.05	0.287
0.06	0.199
0.08	0.092
0.10	0.04

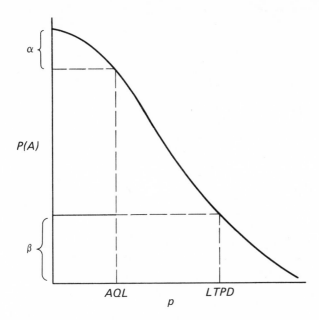

FIGURE **13.6**   OC curve showing the two quality levels and probabilities α and β.

LOT TOLERANCE PERCENT DEFECTIVE: No sampling plan is of any use unless management is prepared to define the "goodness" of quality. Good quality has been designated as AQL, the acceptable quality level, and we desire a high probability of accepting a lot with that level of quality or better. However, as the general shape of the OC curve indicates, there is also a high probability of accepting a lot that has a value of p close to AQL. Therefore, we need to state a second level of quality for which we wish to have a low probability of acceptance. We will call this second value of p the Lot Tolerance Percent Defective ($LTPD$).

Associated with each of these two levels of quality is a probability of accepting the lot. The probability that we will *reject* a lot that has a percent defective *equal* to AQL is called the producer's risk and is symbolized by α (Type I error). Thus, $1 - \alpha$ is the probability of accepting the lot. The probability that we will *accept* a lot with a percent defective *equal* to $LTPD$ is called the consumer's risk and is symbolized as β (Type II error). Given AQL, $LTPD$, α, and β, we can design a sampling plan whose OC curve fits these specifications. See Figure 13.6. Just as with AQL and $LTPD$, α and β must be determined by management decision. This is not particularly easy to relegate to a quantitative cost minimization model, particularly when the relevant costs are difficult to assess. In subsequent pages, we will examine an expected cost model in which the specific setting of α and β is not the important issue.

EXAMPLE 13.3   Suppose we wish to specify a sampling plan for the following specifications: $AQL = 1\%$, $LTPD = 6\%$, $\alpha = 0.05$, $\beta = 0.10$. Using the cumulative Poisson distribution, we construct a table as follows:

	$p_1 = AQL = 0.01$		$p_2 = LTPD = 0.06$	
c'	$n_1 p_1$	$n_1 = \dfrac{n_1 p_1}{p_1}$	$n_2 p_2$	$n_2 = \dfrac{n_2 p_2}{p_2}$
0	0.05	5	2.3	38
1	0.35	35	3.9	65
2	0.82	82	5.3	88
3	1.37	137	6.7	112

1) Start with $c' = 0$ @ $p_1 = .01$ to be 95% sure if $n_1 p_1 = .05$ $n_1 = \dfrac{n_1 p_1}{p_1} = 5$

Step 1. Set $c' = 0$. Then, examining Column 1 of Table B (Appendix), we note that the probability of accepting the lot will be 0.95 if the mean of the distribution $(n_1 p_1)$ is equal to 0.05. Since p_1 has been designated as 1%, then n_1 must be equal to 5 (or 0.05/0.01). Similarly, if $n_2 p_2$ is equal to 2.3, the probability of accepting the lot is 0.10, and since $p_2 = 0.06$, the sample size n_2 will be 38.

Step 2. Set $c' = 1$ and repeat the process described in Step 1. This results in a sample size of 35 for the α level of protection and a sample size of 65 for the β level.

Step 3. Set $c' = 2$, which gives $n_1 = 82$ and $n_2 = 88$.

Step 4. Set $c' = 3$. Now the sample sizes diverge, indicating that the desirable value of c' is 2 and the sample size is chosen as 85. The relation between c' and n_1, n_2 is shown in Figure 13.7.

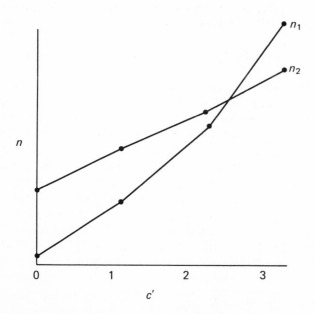

FIGURE **13.7**

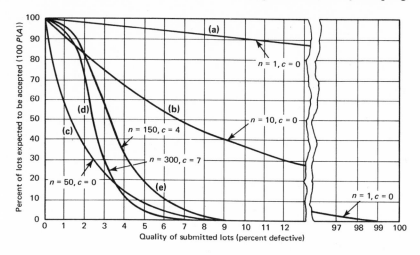

FIGURE **13.8** Comparative OC curves. From B. L. Hansen, *Quality Control*, ©
1963, p. 127. Reprinted by permission of Prentice-Hall, Inc., Englewood Cliffs, N.J.

When the difference between good and poor quality, as presented by AQL and
$LTPD$, respectively, decreases, then the power of the sampling plan to discriminate
between the two quality levels must be increased by increasing n, or decreasing c',
or both. One might assume that reducing c' will do the job. We can see in Figure 13.8 that $c' = 0$ results in a concave upward curve, which is biased in favor
of the producer at lower values of n and in favor of the consumer at higher values
of n. The curve assumes the inverted S shape as c' is increased. Also, the increase
in the sample size produces a more favorable consumer risk, as illustrated by the
difference between curves (d) and (e).

AVERAGE OUTGOING QUALITY: The quality of an outgoing lot after sampling
is as good as or better than the incoming lot, assuming that the defective units
have been culled from the rejected lots. The average outgoing quality is of interest
to the consumer and is often expressed, therefore, as AOQ. An AOQ curve is
shown in Figure 13.9, together with a table of the calculated points on the curve.
The AOQ is the expected percent of defective units in the outgoing lot and is
approximated by $pP(A)$.

The curve characteristically reaches a maximum between the lower limit of
$p = 0$ and some upper limit, in this case $p = 0.015$. Incoming lots with a small
number of defects are passed with a correspondingly high outgoing quality. At
the other extreme, incoming lots with a large percentage of defects are not passed
but given 100% inspection. The resulting outgoing quality is again high. In between, there is a point where the outgoing quality will reach a maximum; this is
called the Average Outgoing Quality Limit ($AOQL$). It should be remembered

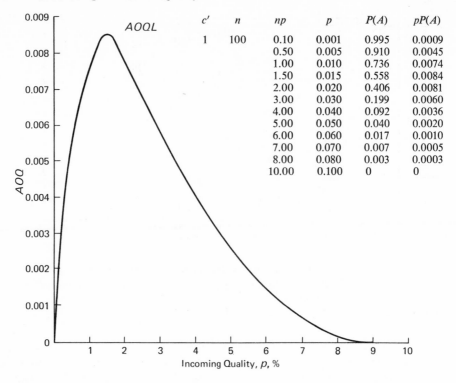

	c'	n	np	p	P(A)	pP(A)
	1	100	0.10	0.001	0.995	0.0009
			0.50	0.005	0.910	0.0045
			1.00	0.010	0.736	0.0074
			1.50	0.015	0.558	0.0084
			2.00	0.020	0.406	0.0081
			3.00	0.030	0.199	0.0060
			4.00	0.040	0.092	0.0036
			5.00	0.050	0.040	0.0020
			6.00	0.060	0.017	0.0010
			7.00	0.070	0.007	0.0005
			8.00	0.080	0.003	0.0003
			10.00	0.100	0	0

FIGURE **13.9** AOQ curve, $n = 100$, $c' = 1$.

that this is an average, and the actual outgoing quality may be greater than this for any particular lot.

Besides specifying a plan in terms of AQL, $LTPD$, α, and β, it is possible to select a plan based on $AOQL$ or upon the minimum total inspection necessary. Such plans have been tabulated in various forms and are readily available to those having to manage a quality control system.[4]

DOUBLE SAMPLING: A double sampling plan is based on the following procedure. Select a sample of size n_1 from a given lot. If it contains c_1 or fewer defective units, accept the lot. If it contains more than c_2 defective units, reject the lot. If the number of defective units is greater than c_1 but less than c_2, take a second sample of size n_2. If in the combined sample $n_1 + n_2$ there are c_2 or fewer defective units, accept the lot; otherwise, reject it. The two major advantages of this plan are as follows. The first sample size n_1 is less than the sample size for a comparable single sampling plan. Therefore, inspection is reduced for lots accepted or rejected on the first sample. Also, the second sample need not be completely inspected

[4] H. F. Dodge and H. G. Romig, *Sampling Inspection Tables—Single and Double Sampling*. New York: John Wiley & Sons, 1944; and Military Standard 105—*Sampling Procedures and Tables for Inspection by Attributes*.

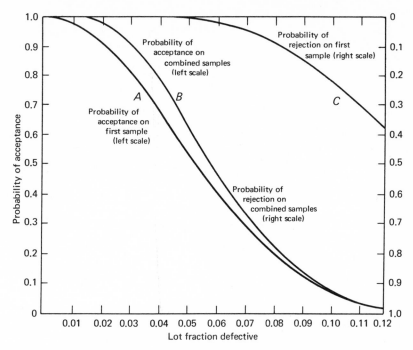

FIGURE **13.10**   Operating characteristic curves of the double-sampling plan $N_1 = 50$. From A. J. Duncan, *Quality Control and Industrial Statistics*. Homewood, Ill.: Richard D. Irwin, Inc., 1965, p. 165.

before rejecting the lot. The plan also has the psychological advantage to the producer of giving the lot a second chance before a final decision is made.

A characteristic curve for a double sampling plan is shown in Figure 13.10.

The construction of the OC curves is done in the following way. Assume that $p = 0.04$ and that the use of the Poisson distribution is valid.

Curve A. This is the normal OC curve for the first sample of size 50. For $np = 50 \times 0.04 = 2$, the probability of accepting the lot is 0.677.

Curve B. This is called the principal OC curve because it gives the final probability of acceptance, given that the second sample is selected. We wish to find the probability of getting six or fewer defective units in the combined sample of 150. This is a compound probability of the events that occur in the first and second sample and yields a total number of defects less than 7.

Sample 1 $n = 50$	$P(c_1)$	Sample 2 $n = 100$	$P(c_2)$	$P(c_1) \times P(c_2)$
c_1		c_2		
3	0.180	3 or less	0.433	0.0780
4	0.090	2 or less	0.238	0.0214
5	0.036	1 or less	0.092	0.0033
6	0.012	0	0.018	0.0002
				0.1029

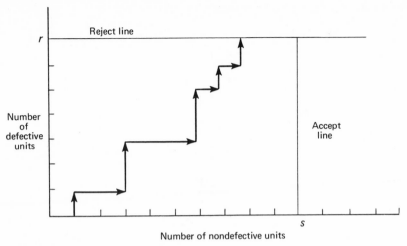

FIGURE **13.11**   A random walk.

The total probability of accepting the lot is, therefore, $0.677 + 0.103 = 0.780$.

Curve C. When read from the right-hand scale, this gives the probability of getting more than six defective units in the first sample, which for $p = 0.04$ is 0.005. The difference between Curves B and C is the probability of rejecting the lot on the second sample.

SEQUENTIAL SAMPLING: The method of sequential sampling consists in selecting a sequence of items from a lot and making a decision after each selection in the sequence. At any given step in the sequence, the item selected is measured and found to be either defective or not. The decision rule is as follows:

1. If the cumulative number of defective units in the sample up to and including the item just selected is equal to a number r, then the lot is rejected.
2. If the cumulative number of nondefective units in the sample up to and including the item just selected is equal to a number s, then the lot is accepted.
3. If neither condition 1 nor 2 exists after the selection, then additional items are selected from the lot until the decision rule can be applied.

The sequential sampling process, therefore, continues until either r or s is inevitably reached.

The method is called a random walk and is illustrated in Figure 13.11. Each step in the walk corresponds to the selection of an item from the lot. If the item is defective, we move one step in the vertical direction, otherwise, one step in the horizontal direction. The probability of going one step in the vertical direction is equal to p, the lot fraction of defects, and, similarly, $1 - p$ for a step in the horizontal direction. The walk will cease when either the reject line r or the accept line s is reached, whichever occurs first.

One of the original contributors to the theory of sequential sampling was

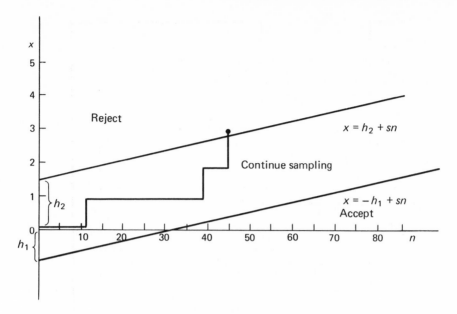

FIGURE **13.12**   Sequential-sampling chart. From A. J. Duncan, *Quality Control and Industrial Statistics.* Homewood, Ill.: Richard D. Irwin, Inc., 1965, p. 176.

A. Wald, who developed methods of designing sequential sampling plans to satisfy specifications for *AQL, LTPD*, α, and β. Figure 13.12 is a sequential sampling chart based on Wald's work.[5]

The equations for the two limiting lines are

$$x = -h_1 + sn$$
$$x = h_2 + sn$$

where

$$h_1 = \log \frac{1 - \alpha}{\beta} \bigg/ \log \left[\frac{LTPD(1 - AQL)}{AQL(1 - LTPD)} \right]$$

$$h_2 = \log \frac{1 - \beta}{\alpha} \bigg/ \log \left[\frac{LTPD(1 - AQL)}{AQL(1 - LTPD)} \right]$$

$$s = \log \left[\frac{1 - AQL}{1 - LTPD} \right] \bigg/ \log \left[\frac{LTPD(1 - AQL)}{AQL(1 - LTPD)} \right]$$

Tables have been developed that give h_1, h_2, and s for selected values of *AQL, LTPD*, α, and β.[6]

[5] A. Wald, *Sequential Analysis.* New York: John Wiley & Sons, 1947.
[6] Statistical Research Group, Columbia University, *Sequential Analysis of Statistical Data: Applications.* New York: Columbia University Press, 1945.

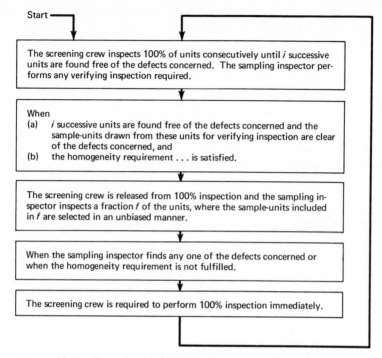

Start

The screening crew inspects 100% of units consecutively until *i* successive units are found free of the defects concerned. The sampling inspector performs any verifying inspection required.

When
(a)   *i* successive units are found free of the defects concerned and the sample-units drawn from these units for verifying inspection are clear of the defects concerned, and
(b)   the homogeneity requirement . . . is satisfied.

The screening crew is released from 100% inspection and the sampling inspector inspects a fraction *f* of the units, where the sample-units included in *f* are selected in an unbiased manner.

When the sampling inspector finds any one of the defects concerned or when the homogeneity requirement is not fulfilled.

The screening crew is required to perform 100% inspection immediately.

FIGURE **13.13**   Procedure for CSP-1 plans. From B. L. Hansen, *Quality Control,* © 1963, p. 189. Reprinted by permission of Prentice-Hall, Inc., Englewood Cliffs, N.J.

Continuous Sampling by Attributes

In many processes, it is impossible or undesirable to identify the product in terms of homogeneous and segregated lots. In such cases, a continuous acceptance sampling plan by attributes can be invoked. The general procedure for this type of plan is noted in the flow diagram in Figure 13.13.

For this kind of plan, one design criterion is the *AOQL*, which depends on the given values of *i* and *f*. The same *AOQL* can be obtained from different values of *i* and *f*. The plan indicated in Figure 13.13 is called Continuous Sampling Plan 1 and is the first of a variety of continuous sampling plans.[7]

A Cost Model for Attributes Sampling

So far we have said nothing about determining a sampling plan based on the minimization of relevant costs. Here we will examine, for a nondestructive single sample attributes plan, the behavior of the expected total cost as a function of *p*, the percent defective units in the lot.

---

[7] For a general discussion on such plans, see Acheson J. Duncan, *Quality Control and Industrial Statistics*, 3rd ed. Homewood, Ill.: Richard D. Irwin, Inc., 1965, pp. 321–33.

BREAK-EVEN VALUE OF p: We might pose the following question. Should a lot with a given percent of defective units be inspected or permitted to pass on to the consumer? It can be shown that the answer depends on a critical value of p.[8]
Let

$C(I)$ = cost of inspecting a unit
$C(R)$ = cost of reworking or replacing a defective unit
$C(A)$ = cost of passing a defective unit on to the consumer

The expected number of units inspected for a given value of p will be $n + (N - n)(1 - P_a)$, where, as usual, n, N, and P_a are the sample size, lot size, and probability of accepting the lot, respectively. Then, the expected inspection cost *per unit* will be

$$\frac{C(I)}{N}[nP_a + N(1 - P_a)] \tag{2}$$

The expected number of items replaced or reworked will be p times the expected number inspected, or $p[nP_a + N(1 - P_a)]$, and, therefore, the expected replacement cost per unit is

$$\frac{C(R)}{N}p[nP_a + N(1 - P_a)] \tag{3}$$

Finally, the consequences of letting defective units pass on to the consumer are as follows. The expected number of defective units passed is $pP_a(N - n)$, and the unit cost is

$$\frac{C(A)}{N}pP_a(N - n) \tag{4}$$

Then, the total expected cost per unit is

$$\frac{TC}{N} = \frac{C(I)}{N} + \frac{C(R)}{N} + \frac{C(A)}{N} \tag{5}$$

If we let the expected unit cost of not inspecting the lot be $[C(A)/N]pN = pC(A)$, then there will be a break-even value of p such that the expected unit cost of not inspecting the lot will equal the total expected cost of sampling. That is,

$$pC(A) = \frac{C(I)}{N}[nP_a + N(1 - P_a)] + \frac{C(R)}{N}p[nP_a + N(1 - P_a)]$$

$$+ \frac{C(A)}{N}pP_a(N - n) \tag{6}$$

from which

$$p_b = \frac{C(I)}{C(A) - C(R)}$$

It is interesting to note that p_b, the break-even fraction of defective units, is

[8] C. A. Martin, "The Cost Breakeven Point in Attribute Sampling," *Ind. Qual. Control*, vol. 21, no. 3, September 1964, pp. 137–44.

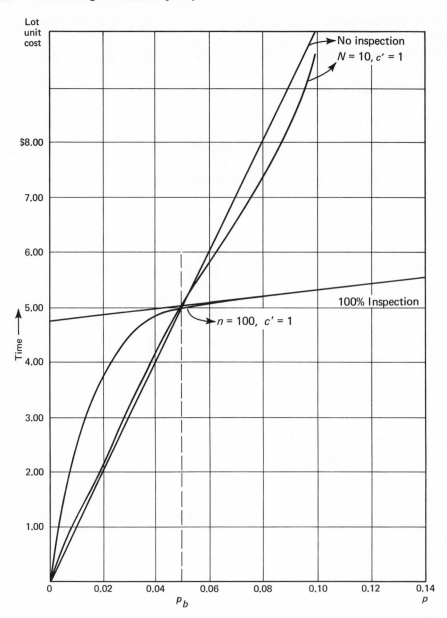

FIGURE **13.14**   Lot unit cost as a function of p.

independent of the sampling plan as specified by n and c'. For any $p < p_b$, the minimum cost scheme is to let the lot pass uninspected. For any $p > p_b$, the limiting minimum cost plan is one in which $P_a = 0$. For this situation, the total cost function, that is, the right-hand side of (6), will equal

$$TC = C(I) + pC(R)$$

EXAMPLE 13.4   Suppose we have the following parameters:

$$N = 1,000$$
$$C(A) = \$100.00$$
$$C(I) \ \ = \$4.75$$
$$C(R) = \$5.00$$

Figure 13.14 shows the unit cost as a function of p for four policies, namely, 1) no inspection, 2) 100% inspection, 3) a sampling plan, $n = 100$, $c' = 1$, and 4) a sampling plan, $n = 10$, $c' = 1$. The break-even value of p is $p_b = 5\%$. The two limiting curves are no inspection for $p \leq p_b$ and 100% inspection for $p > p_b$.

UNKNOWN p: The practical problem is to determine, for a given lot, the value of p. If we know that the process capability produces a range of p values that are all less than p_b, then we can avoid inspection or, more reasonably, submit the lot to a loose inspection (i.e., $n = 10$, $c' = 1$). Conversely, if the range of p is above p_b, we can use the loosest plan for which $P(A) = 0$ for $p = p_b$.

If p varies within a range including p_b, the issue is more difficult. Suppose we assume that the between-lot variation of p is probabilistically distributed around p_b. Figure 13.15 shows the behavior of total expected cost, for a lot size $N = 2,000$ using Equation (5) (not divided by N). There are two cases, each using a hypothetical discrete distribution of p around p_b, as shown in the figure. Unit costs are also indicated. In each of the two cases, both the sample size n and the reject number c' are varied.

In Figure 13.15a, p is uniformly distributed with $E(p) = p_b$, range 1% to 10%, and probability function $f(p) = \frac{1}{10}$. Each curve represents a distinct value of c' and indicates a local minimum expected cost. A global minimum exists for $c' = 10$ and $n = 280$. However, the local minima are insensitive to values of c' above 5. For any given value of c', the expected cost is particularly sensitive over the range of n from 1 to the optimum. In this range, the increase in n results in significant savings due to the high cost of passing defective parts on to the customer.

In Figure 13.15b, the distribution of p is skewed to the left. The absolute expected costs are less, due to the lower number of defects in the lots. The global minimum is not reached in the range of curves studied. The local minima are more focal, and the costs of inspection and rework have greater impact.

ACCEPTANCE SAMPLING BY VARIABLES

In the variables sampling plan, we revert to measuring some variable quantity. In this case, we are interested in estimating the *lot average value* for the variable in question. The standard of quality is some level of the lot average or mean, below and/or above which the lot should not be accepted. For example, we might be interested in accepting a barrel of bolts based on the average sheer strength of the bolts. A lower limit would be specified as the division between good and poor

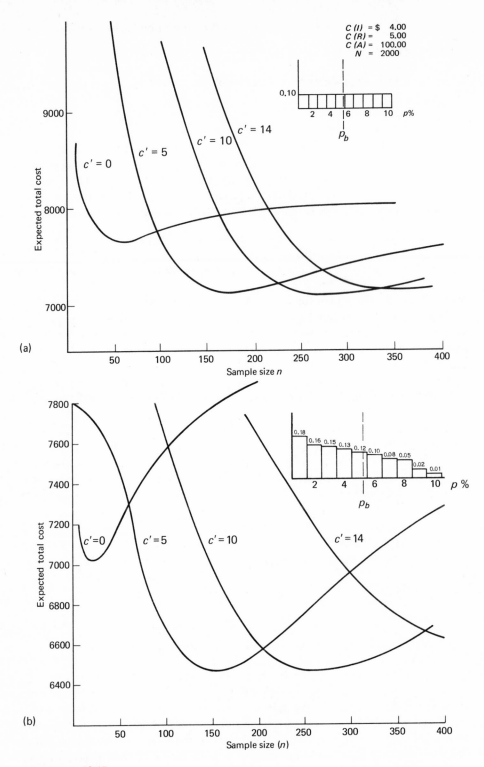

FIGURE **13.15**

quality. If the lot is made up of candy bars, we might be interested in an upper and lower weight limit.

The following notation will be used. Let

μ = lot (population) mean
n = sample size
$\bar{x}$ = sample mean
σ = lot standard deviation
$\sigma_{\bar{x}}$ = standard deviation of sample means
L = lower limit of acceptance
U = upper limit of acceptance

The Sampling Plan

The purpose of the sampling plan is to estimate the value of μ. The estimator is $\bar{x}$, and the lot is accepted or rejected based on predetermined limits for $\bar{x}$. The procedure is as follows:

Given a lot size of N homogeneous parts, select a random sample of size n. Measure each item in the sample with respect to the quality variable. Calculate the sample mean $\bar{x}$. If $\bar{x}$ is less than L (or greater than U), reject the lot; otherwise, accept it.

The problem of variable sampling design is to determine values for n, U, and L such as to provide some required degree of protection. The performance of the plan is indicated by an operating characteristic curve, as was the case for the attributes plan.

EXAMPLE 13.5   A company manufactures spools of wire, and the quality factor to be measured is the tensile strength of the wire. A preliminary study of the process yields the following information: the process yields tensile strengths that are normally distributed with a population standard deviation of 320 lb. Poor quality is defined as tensile strengths of less than 6,000 lb. A sampling plan is desired such that the probability of accepting a lot of spools in which 2.5% are defective (i.e., have tensile strengths less than 6,000 lb) is 0.95.

In Figure 13.16, the upper part of the diagram shows the population or lot distribution position when 2.5% of the spool tensile strengths fall below 6,000 lb. At this point, the average of the lot is $\mu = 6{,}000 + 2(320) = 6{,}640$.

If we select a sample of size n from this population, its average will come from a sampling distribution indicated on the lower part of the figure. The mean distribution of sample means is the mean of the population from which the sample is taken, and the variance is $\sigma/\sqrt{n}$.

Suppose we choose a sample of size 4. We now choose a value of L. If the sample mean falls below L, we will reject the lot; otherwise, we will accept it. Since we have stipulated that the probability of rejecting the lot is 0.05 when the lot average is 6,640 lb, then $L = 6{,}640 - 1.645\sigma_{\bar{x}} = 6{,}640 - 1.645(320/\sqrt{4}) = 6{,}377$.

Characteristic Curve

Just as in the case of attributes, the plan does not tell us anything about the probability of accepting lots that have lower quality than those with 2.5% defects. Figure 13.17 shows the characteristic curve for $n = 4$ and $L = 6{,}377$. Note that the probability of accepting a lot whose average is equal to L is 0.50, as expected.

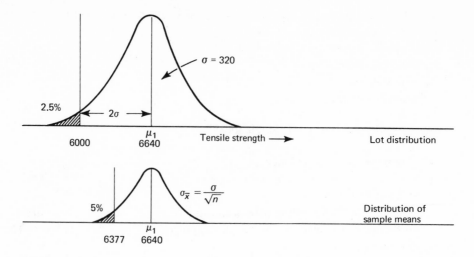

FIGURE **13.16**   Population and sampling distribution for $\mu = 6,640$.

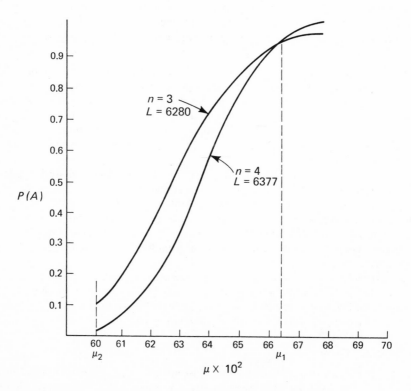

FIGURE **13.17**   Characteristic curves for two variable plans.

We may have two levels of process average quality, which correspond to the *AQL* and *LTPD* in the attributes case. These are expressed as μ_1 and μ_2 with associated α and β values, respectively. The problem is to find the required sample size and limit of acceptance to meet the specifications. We can demonstrate this kind of situation by specifying two quality levels for this example.

Assume the following:

Acceptable quality level = 2.5% defects. This corresponds to a quality level of $\mu_1 = 6,640$ lb (i.e., $6,000 + 2.0 \times 320$).
Poor quality level = 50.0% defects or a lot average of 6,000 lb
Probability of rejecting a lot with average 6,640 = $\alpha = 0.05$
Probability of accepting a lot with average 6,000 = $\beta = 0.10$

Set up two simultaneous equations as follows:

$$\frac{L - 6,640}{320/\sqrt{n}} = -1.645$$

$$\frac{L - 6,000}{320/\sqrt{n}} = 1.282$$

Figure 13.18 shows the two positions of the lot distribution and the corresponding sampling distributions when the lot averages are at the two specified quality levels, 6,640 lb and 6,000 lb. Solving the simultaneous equations for n and L, we obtain $n = 2.15$ and $L = 6,280$ lb. The characteristic curve for this plan is shown on Figure 13.17 with n chosen as the next highest integer value.

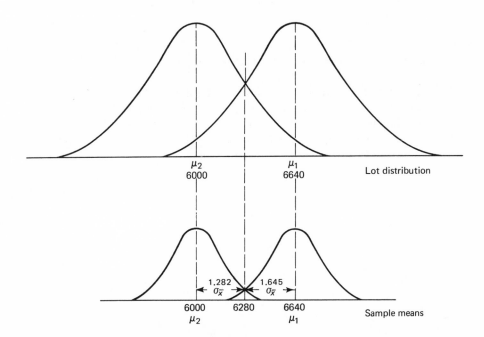

FIGURE **13.18**   Distributions for μ_1 and μ_2.

Comparison of Attributes and Variables Plan

If both good and poor quality can be expressed as percent defectives and as lot averages, then either an attributes plan or a variables plan can be designed to give the required protection.

EXAMPLE 13.6   A company has an inspection station where electric motor coils are tested for resistance. The resistance variation between motors is normally distributed with a mean of 100 ohms and a standard deviation of 5 ohms. Good quality is considered to be 90 ohms or greater and poor quality less than that. Management wishes a sampling plan that will give a 5% chance of rejecting a lot in which 2% of the motors have less than 90-ohm resistances and a 10% chance of accepting a lot in which 8% of the motors have less than 90-ohm resistances. Design both an attributes plan and a variables plan that will assure to these specifications.

The specifications are summarized as follows:

Attributes	Variable
$AQL = 2\%$	$\mu_1 = 100.2$[9]
$LTPD = 8\%$	$\mu_2 = 97.0$[10]
$\alpha = 0.05$	$\alpha = 0.05$
$\beta = 0.10$	$\beta = 0.10$

Attributes Plan[11] $n = 100$ $c' = 4$ From Poisson table
Variables Plan $n = 21$ $L = 98.4$ From solution of simultaneous equations

The variables sampling plan requires a smaller sample size than the attributes plan for the same degree of protection. However, a variables measurement usually requires more time per unit than an attributes measurement.

PROCESS CONTROL BY SAMPLING

The discussion in this section is a natural extension of the material covered in the section on process capability. The classical treatment of process control by statistical sampling was set forth in 1931 by Walter A. Shewhart[12] of the Bell Telephone Laboratories. Since that time, the subject has grown considerably, and the most we can do here is to present its essential features.

---

[9] $\dfrac{90 - \mu_1}{\sigma} = -2.05;\ \mu_1 = 100.2$

[10] $\dfrac{90 - \mu_2}{\sigma} = -1.40;\ \mu_2 = 97.0$

[11] An attributes plan can also be approximated by solving the following set of equations:

$$\frac{\dfrac{c' + 0.5}{n} - 0.02}{\sqrt{\dfrac{0.02 \cdot 0.98}{n}}} = 1.645; \qquad \frac{\dfrac{c' + 0.5}{n} - 0.08}{\sqrt{\dfrac{0.08 \cdot 0.92}{n}}} = -1.282$$

[12] W. A. Shewhart, *Economic Control of Quality of Manufactured Product.* Princeton, N.J.: D. Van Nostrand Co., 1931.

Criterion of Control

The criterion of process control is the degree of statistical stability exhibited in the variability of some particular dimension of process input or output. The function of the control procedure is to place limits on the degree of variability and to signal when causes for excessive variation should be ferreted out and corrections made to the process.

We have already noted that the variability in a process is contributed by random or chance causes and by assignable causes. The contributors of chance variation are usually many, but their aggregative effect is considered to be minor and economically perhaps not worth remedying. This is particularly the case when no single cause is a major contributor to the variability.

The second kind of variability can be assigned to various causes that presumably can be detected and remedied or explained. Assignable causes of variation include such things as differences in the properties of a material between batches, differences among machines, differences in a given machine over time, etc.

The theory of statistical control is related to these kinds of variation. A process "under control" is presumably exhibiting the properties of chance variation in its output. The process then gets out of control when this variability exceeds the limits of random variation and reflects the influence of assignable causes. Intuitively, statistical stability suggests that the distribution parameters of the chance variable are constant over time, and an out-of-control situation implies that the parameters are changing over time. We should note, however, that even if the process appears to be operating under a system of random variation, there may be insignificant changes in the parameters of the system. The object of control is to signal when these parameter changes become significant. The timely detection of such changes is the object of the sampling method. However, the corrective measures that must be taken involve technical judgment, as well as analysis of the control data, in order to pinpoint the offending factors.

The Control Chart

The central feature of the control plan is the control chart. The output of a process is periodically sampled to estimate the statistical parameters of the particular dimension of interest. These estimators are plotted in the form of a time series on a control chart. In one sense, the control chart is a running analysis of the process capability over time.

The form of the control chart is shown in Figure 13.19. Suppose that we wish to detect changes in the average of a process. We select an output sample of the process at a given point in time. The sample average is calculated and its value plotted on the chart. If the process is in control, we expect the sample average to fall in the normal distribution between the upper control limit and the lower control limit with some degree of confidence. The degree of confidence depends on the location of the limits, which are a function of the standard deviation of the sample means and the confidence coefficient k. That is, if the limits were located

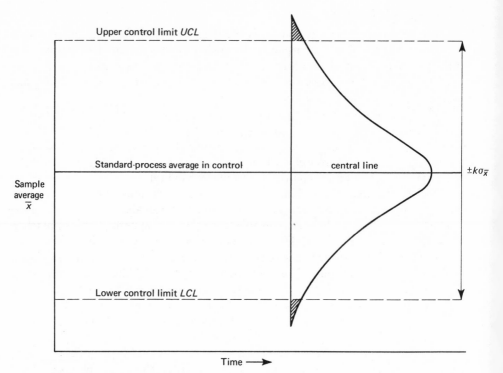

Upper control limit *UCL*

Standard-process average in control   central line $\pm k\sigma_{\bar{x}}$

Sample
average
$\bar{x}$

Lower control limit *LCL*

Time ⟶

FIGURE **13.19**   Control chart form.

at $k = 1.96$ standard deviations from the mean, we would expect five samples in 100 with means outside the limits.

The population or process parameters can be measures of either central tendency or dispersion. Also, either a variable or an attribute plan can be used. We will first briefly examine various kinds of control charts and then consider the economics of their use.

Variables Control Charts

$\bar{X}$-CHART: The purpose of the $\bar{X}$-chart is to detect changes in the process average. An example of this chart is as follows. A milling machine mills a certain thickness on a part. A study of the process shows that when it is in control, the distribution of the thickness dimension is normal with a mean of 0.500 inch and a standard deviation of 0.002 inch. The process is to be controlled by periodically taking samples of size 4, calculating the sample mean, and plotting it on the control chart.

Population mean	$\mu = 0.500''$
Population standard deviation	$\sigma = 0.002''$
Sample mean	$\bar{x}$
Standard deviation of sample means	$\sigma_{\bar{x}} = \sigma/\sqrt{n} = \dfrac{0.002}{\sqrt{4}} = 0.001$

Confidence level
$$k = 3$$
$$UCL = 0.500 + 3(0.001)$$
$$LCL = 0.500 - 3(0.001)$$

The control chart for the plan is shown in Figure 13.20. The time scale is represented as the number of the sample drawn. The chart shows the plot for 15 sample means taken periodically. The fourteenth sample point is outside the upper limit. Since the limit represents three sigmas, the probability of having a point outside the limit, if the process is in control, is very small.

A process may be out of control even though the sample means fall within the control limits. Figure 13.21 shows various behaviors of the sample points which indicate possible out-of-control conditions.

CHARACTERISTIC CURVE: The performance of a process control sampling plan can be shown in the form of a characteristic curve. Such a curve for the milling machine example is shown in Figure 13.22. This curve shows the probability that a sample mean will fall within the control limits when the process average is greater or less than the control mean. Suppose that the process average shifts to 0.503″. Then, of course, there is a fifty-fifty chance that the sample will not show this change if the sample is taken after the change occurs.

R-CHARTS: An R-chart shows the variation in samples ranges. The central line represents the average of sample ranges, and the limits are based on the standard deviation of the sample ranges σ_R, which is either calculated from past data or is a function of the process standard deviation. The assumption is usually made that the population individual values are normally distributed.

The R-chart is frequently constructed prior to determining the $\overline{X}$-chart in order to insure that the process variability is under control before determining the process standard deviation.

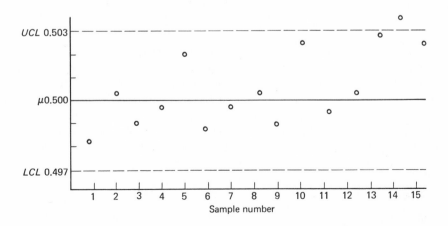

FIGURE **13.20** $\overline{X}$-chart.

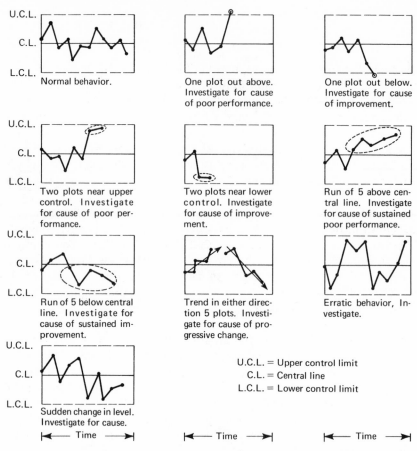

FIGURE **13.21**   Control chart evidence for investigation. From B. L. Hansen, *Quality Control*, © 1963, p. 65. Reprinted by permission of Prentice-Hall, Inc., Englewood Cliffs, N.J.

In the construction of an *R*-chart, we will assume that historical data are used in the following way. Suppose for the milling machine case that we take 20 samples of size 5. For each sample, we calculate the sample range *R*. Then, the estimated process average range $\overline{R}$ is the average of the ranges of the twenty samples. The standard deviation of the range σ_R may be calculated by using the standard quality control formula $\hat{\sigma}_R = d_3(\overline{R}/d_2)$, where d_2 and d_3 may be obtained from tables for various sample sizes. Such tables may be found in quality control or statistics books.

Attributes Control Charts

Basically, the attributes control chart is the same as the variables charts except that the unit of measurement is discrete. The two common forms are the *p*-chart and the *c*-chart.

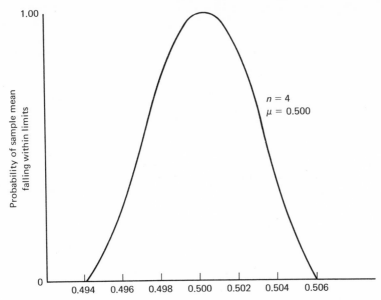

FIGURE **13.22**   Characteristic curve for sampling plan.

p-CHART: The *p*-chart shows the variation in the percent defective units. The *variable Control Charts* normal approximation to the binomial is used to determine the control limits set at $\pm k \sqrt{\dfrac{pq}{n}}$. Since the limits are a function of *n*, the charts can have either constant or variable limits, depending on the constancy of *n* from sample to sample. In cases where 100% inspection is performed, *n* can represent the entire production for some unit time.

EXAMPLE 13.7   A process for assembling auto horns is to be controlled by a *p*-chart. An examination of the process over a two-week period shows that the average percent defective units in a day's production was 15%. Figure 13.23 shows the chart for the plan to be used with a constant sample size of 100. Samples taken on each of twenty successive days after the plan was installed are shown below and plotted on the chart.

Day	*n*	No. of defects *c*	Day	*n*	No. of defects *c*
1	100	17	6	100	13
2		15	7		20
3		9	8		18
4		20	9		13
5		2	10		12
11		16	16		6
12		18	17		10
13		26	18		7
14		28	19		5
15		15	20		12

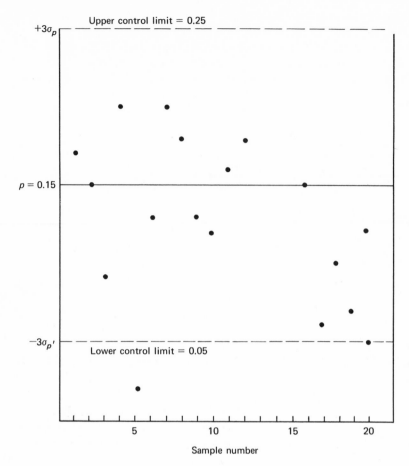

FIGURE **13.23** *p*-chart.

c-CHART: A second kind of attribute sampling chart is the *c*-chart, in which the number of defects per some unit of production is used, rather than the percent defective. In certain cases, the number of defects is a logical and economical control measurement. This is the case where the production unit represents a large number of points where defects can occur. For example, in inspecting a unit length of 25 yards of fly-fishing line, the number of defects per unit is a random variable. Another case is the number of defects in a television set in which there are a large number of points where defects may occur.

In these cases, the "unit of inspection" is the basic physical domain in which the defects can occur. When the unit of inspection is sufficiently large and the probability of a defect at any point in the unit is small and constant, then the number of defects can be considered Poisson distributed. The assumption is that we can also express the results as percent defective. In the case of the fishing line, the inspection unit consists of the number of inches n in the 25 yards, and the percent defective is the fraction of inches containing some defect.

The sample size is expressed as the number of inspection units examined. That is, in the case of the fishing line, while the inspection unit of 25 yards is fixed, the sample size can consist of 50 yards, 12.5 yards, or any other multiple of the inspection unit. The inspection units represent a convenient accounting form, while the sample size determines the statistical properties of the control procedure.

The c-chart is constructed by using either the cumulative Poisson tables or the normal approximation, depending on the average number of defects. The mean of the chart consists of the process average. The limits are set to give the desired degree of protection, depending on the sample size.

The Economics of Control Charts

The kind of plan, the size of samples, and the frequency of sampling are basic issues in determining the economics of a sampling control plan. It is difficult to arrive at general conclusions, because the plan depends on specifics such as its purpose, process output rates, relative costs of inspection, and undetected, out-of-control situations.

PURPOSES OF CONTROL CHARTS: The general purpose of control charts is to detect assignable (nonrandom) causes of variation in a process. Within this framework, control charts may be used for more specific purposes. A few of the possibilities are suggested below.

1. *New process* When a process is new or has been redesigned, the progress of implementation can be studied with a control chart. Typically, during the first runs, we would expect an out-of-control situation, due to assignable causes of variation. As these causes are removed from the system, the control chart limits may be constricted, until a situation of stability is reached. Figure 13.24 shows the progress reduction in control limits on a p-chart over a four-month shakedown period after a part redesign. The idea of increasing the precision over time as assignable causes are removed applies to control charts in general.

2. *Evaluation of process technology* A study of process variability, particularly through the use of variables charts, may lead to a better understanding of the operational characteristics of the process. We might imagine that the results of designed manipulation of the physical components of a complex process will be reflected in the control charts. This, in turn, can lead to optimum control settings or to changes in the design of machine components to provide the desired system stability.

3. *Process capability* Control charts are natural devices for studying the capability of a process to meet the product design specifications. But we must be careful to note that product design tolerance limits must be compared with the variation in the individual values, that is, the variance of the population. For example, Figure 13.25 shows the behavior of individual measurements around the nominal dimension (process average) as compared to the upper and lower toler-

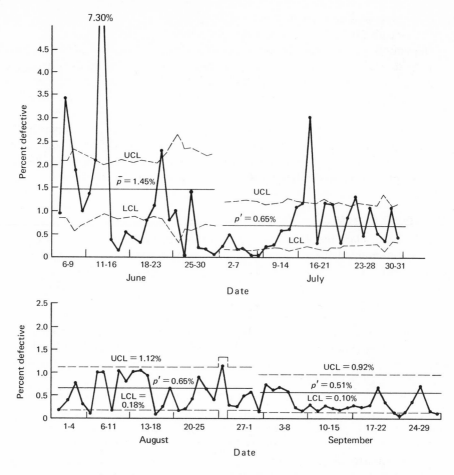

FIGURE **13.24**   Control chart for percent defective—four month's production of an electrical device. From *Statistical Quality Control* by E. L. Grant, p. 257. Copyright 1946 by McGraw-Hill, Inc. Used by permission of McGraw-Hill Book Company.

ances of the part. We note that the process is incapable of producing all parts within the tolerance limits, although the process is in statistical control, as indicated by the $\overline{X}$- and R-charts (b and c). Therefore, a change in the tolerance specifications will be required if the process is to produce all units within the tolerance limits.

In cases where the process capability greatly exceeds the tolerance specifications, an $\overline{X}$-chart with modified control limits may be used. Figure 13.26 shows such a chart, in which the control limits are offset from the tolerance limits, rather than being located as a function of the central line. Thus, adjustments for changes in process average will not be taken until the change entails a risk of producing parts outside the tolerance limits. We can modify the risk of producing off-tolerance parts by a more general formula:

$$UCL = UTL - k\sigma' + 3\sigma'/\sqrt{n}$$

$$LCL = LTL + k\sigma' + 3\sigma'/\sqrt{n}$$

VARIABLES VERSUS ATTRIBUTES CHARTS: One important decision, of course, deals with the kind of chart to use. The major difference between the $\overline{X}$- and

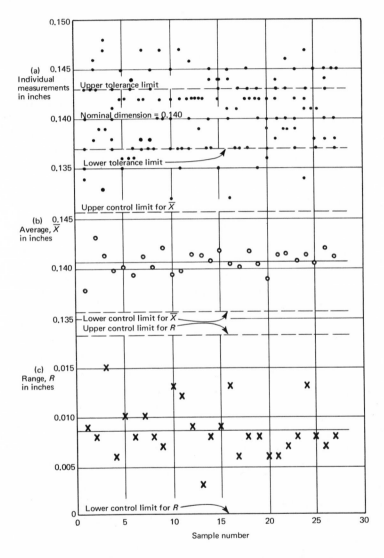

FIGURE **13.25**   Measurements of dimension on rheostat knob. (a) Individual measurements. (b) Control chart for average (X). (c) Control chart for ranges (R). From *Statistical Quality Control* by E. L. Grant, p. 29. Copyright 1946 by McGraw-Hill, Inc. Used by permission of McGraw-Hill Book Company.

R-charts on the one hand and the p- and c-charts on the other hand is the specificity of information. The variables charts apply to a single dimension and are therefore particularly useful in focusing attention on specific causes for variation, especially where the $\overline{X}$- and R-charts are used jointly. The p-chart, on the other hand, is useful in evaluating the over-all quality performance of a process, particularly where a single chart represents all possible kinds of defects. If a separate p-chart is used for each kind of defect observed, then the information can be used to indicate where variables charting may be helpful in diagnosing the exact causes of trouble.

The cost of collecting data for attributes charts is likely to be less than for the variables charts, especially where the former is used for all defects, rather than for a given kind. The attributes sample size, in contrast, must for a given desired level of protection be larger than the variables sample size, similar to the case of acceptance sampling.

SIZE AND FREQUENCY OF SAMPLING: Attempting to specify an optimal cost plan in terms of sample size and frequency of sampling for a specific process may be difficult. One factor is the manner in which the process will change over time. Changes in central tendency and variance can be random in time and magnitude, as well as in step functions or gradual and continuous shifts.

The size of the sample affects both the control chart limits and the OC curve. The larger the sample size, the closer the limits to the central line and the higher the probability of detecting a causal change for a given value of the confidence coefficient k. For a given number of observations to be taken over a protracted period for current control, the alternatives range from a few large samples to a number of small samples taken more frequently.

The decision about sample size and frequency depends on the cost of sampling, on the costs of not detecting changes in the system, and on a knowledge of the behavior of the process. An important rule is that samples should represent populations of homogeneous output so that changes in the system will result in different samples, rather than appear as differences between the observations within individual samples. Small samples taken frequently will often display the between-sample variations, whereas larger samples may mask these differences.

Duncan[13] made a general study of the design of *variables control charts* for the process average and arrived at the following principal conclusions.

    1. The customary sample sizes of 4 or 5 are close to optimum if the shifts to be detected are relatively large, e.g., if the assignable cause produces a shift of $2\sigma'$ or more in the process average. If it is the aim of the chart to detect shifts in the process average as small as one σ', sample sizes of 15 to 20 are more economical than sample sizes of 4 or 5.

    2. If a shift in the process average causes a high rate of loss, i.e., high relative to the cost of inspection, it is better to take small samples quite frequently than large samples less frequently. For example, when the rate of loss is high, samples of 4 or 5 taken every half hour are better than samples of 8 or 10 taken every hour.

---

[13] Acheson J. Duncan, *Quality Control and Industrial Statistics*, 3rd ed. Homewood, Ill.: Richard D. Irwin, Inc., 1965, p. 398.

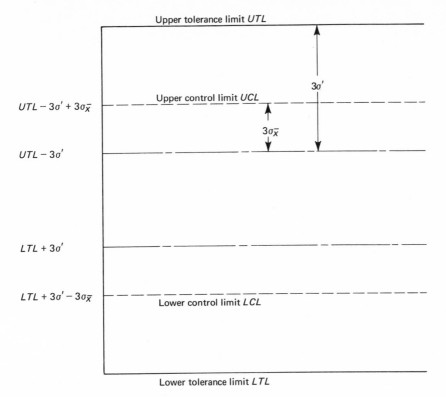

Upper tolerance limit *UTL*

$3\sigma'$

$UTL - 3\sigma' + 3\sigma_{\overline{X}}$ — — — — Upper control limit *UCL* — — — — —

$3\sigma_{\overline{X}}$

$UTL - 3\sigma'$ — — — — — — — — — —

$LTL + 3\sigma'$ — — — — — — — — — —

$LTL + 3\sigma' - 3\sigma_{\overline{X}}$ — — — — Lower control limit *LCL* — — — — —

Lower tolerance limit *LTL*

FIGURE **13.26**   Modified control chart.

3. Under certain circumstances charts using 2σ or even 1.5σ limits are more economical than charts using the conventional 3σ limits. This is true if it is possible to decide very quickly and inexpensively that nothing is wrong with the process when a point (just by chance) happens to fall outside the control limits, i.e., when the cost of looking for trouble when none exists is low. Contrariwise, it will be more economical to use charts with 3.5σ to 4σ limits if the cost of looking for trouble is very high.

4. If the unit cost of inspection is relatively high, the most economical design is one that takes small samples (say, samples of 2) at relatively long intervals (say, every 4 to 8 hours) with narrow control limits, say, at $\pm 1.5\sigma$.

PROCESS SIMULATION: Simulation offers a reasonable way of evaluating alternative sampling control schemes. Barish and Hauser[14] used a rather extensive computer simulator to study the economical design of sampling plans for control decisions. The method consisted in simulating a process subjected to both chance and adjustable causes of variation. An adjustable cause is one that can be corrected by making adjustments to the process inputs, in contrast to an assignable cause, which implies the need to stop the process, search for, and correct the cause.

Figure 13.27 shows a general logic diagram of the method. Design variables

---

[14] Norman N. Barish and Norbert Hauser, "Economic Design for Control Decisions," *J. Ind. Eng.*, 14, no. 3, May–June, 1963, pp. 125–34.

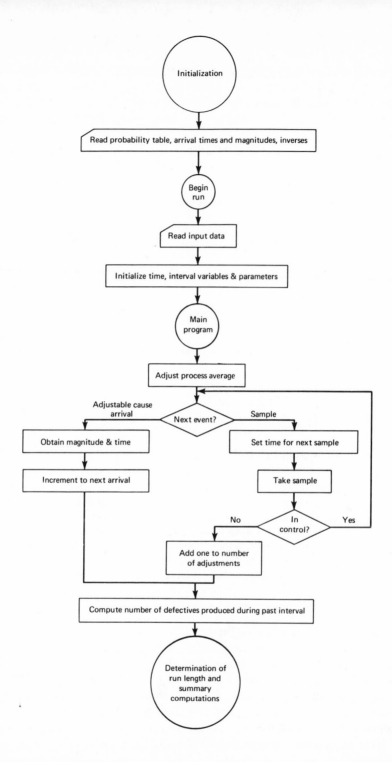

FIGURE **13.27** Flow chart of process model. From N. Hauser, N. N. Barish, and S. Ehrenfeld, *J. Ind. Eng.*, vol. XVII, no. 2, February 1956, p. 80.

include the process capability as related to tolerance limits, sample size and frequency of sampling, probability distributions of the arrival time and magnitude of disturbances to the system, and methods of evaluating the samples (control limits, run lengths, etc.). The model is described mathematically by the following equation:

$$X_t = u'' + \sum_{k=1}^{t} \delta_k + \sum_{k=1}^{T} \rho_k + \epsilon_k$$

where

X_t = a random variable denoting the process level at time t

u'' = the desired process mean

δ_k = a random variable denoting adjustable cause magnitude ($\delta_k = 0$, unless an adjustable cause arrival is indicated at time k)

ρ_k = the change introduced by the control scheme at time k

ϵ_k = a random variable representing the effects of chance causes of variation

The economic criterion is a total cost function

$$C_t = C_D + C_F + C_V + C_I + C_A$$

where, on a unit time basis,

C_D = cost of defectives

C_F = fixed cost of sampling

C_V = variable costs of sampling

C_I = cost of interpretation and decision making

C_A = cost of adjustment

We will not attempt to reproduce the results of these experiments, since they are extensive and depend on the particular sets of chosen design variables. However, as an example of the kind of results obtainable from simulation, it should be noted that in none of the tests of Barish and Hauser was the popular 3σ decision rule the most economical, and in many cases it was the least economical of the rules used. For other interesting results and details, we refer the reader to the literature cited.

SUMMARY

The control of quality is a pervasive issue in the management of a production or service system. A quality level is designed into the product or service commensurate with price and cost parameters. This is part of the over-all strategy of introducing new products. Once the quality level is specified, the issue is one of determining production process capabilities as a part of the production engineering function.

When process capabilities are satisfied, then the role of operational quality control is to provide assurance that desired quality levels will be sustained in production. The major purpose of operational quality control is to maintain a surveillance over the quality of both inputs and outputs of production. The design of inspection methods and tools falls within the realm of methods or job design. The designation of the inspection plan, that is, where and when inspection shall take place and how much will be inspected, are distinctive quality control problems.

The matter of locating inspection stations is usually decided on the basis of pragmatic rules and judgments of the consequences of producing off-standard parts. The problem may be structured as a dynamic programing problem, provided that reliable costs and determination of defect-generating characteristics of the process can be determined.

We have examined a number of sampling inspection schemes related to accepting process output or controlling a process. The subject of sampling inspection is vast. Fortunately, the practitioner can use predetermined standard sampling plans to fit a wide variety of specifications. It is suggested that future developments will include the design of cost models, which, coupled with a computer, can be used to provide decision rules for both location, acceptance sampling, and process inspection sampling decisions.

Problems

13.1   An airplane bushing has six different dimensions to be inspected. Suppose the part is checked in all dimensions at a single work station. If the part is defective in any dimension, it is rejected. A study yields the following information:

Dimension	Unit cost to inspect	Expected rate of rejects
A	$0.20	0.005
B	0.15	0.001
C	0.25	0.002
D	0.30	0.008
E	0.40	0.010
F	0.20	0.004

In what order should the stations be located in the line to minimize the total cost of the inspection operation?

13.2   Attributes sampling involves sampling from the following distribution:

X	1	0
$f(x)$	p	q

(a) What is the name of the above distribution, and what are its mean and variance?
(b) What are the mean and variance of the true sampling distribution?
(c) What two distributions are used to approximate the true sampling distribution? What are their means and variances?

13.3   The production manager of the Gelder Company wants a part inspected by an attributes plan. If a sampling plan of $n = 100$ and $c' = 2$ is chosen, what will be the probability of accepting a lot with a fraction defective of $p = 0.02$? a lot with a fraction defective of $p = 0.10$? Compare the probabilities obtained by using the Poisson distribution and the normal approximation to the binomial. Assume that the lot size is large.

13.4   The acceptable quality level for a part is 2.2%. Management would like to reject all lots with a lower quality and accept all lots having 2.2% or higher quality level. Which of the following would be the best plan to achieve this?

Plan 1 $N = 1,000$, $n = 100$, $c = 0$
Plan 2 $N = 1,000$, $n = 170$, $c = 1$
Plan 3 $N = 1,000$, $n = 240$, $c = 2$

13.5   Construct an OC curve by plotting the information for the plan $n = 50$, $c' = 1$. Construct an OC curve for the same plan, using the normal approximation to the binomial as the sampling distribution. Why does this curve differ from that obtained using the Poisson distribution? Why is the binomial series inappropriate when the sample size is 20% of N or greater?

Assume that the value of AQL is 2%. What is the probability of accepting a lot that has quality equal to AQL? What is the probability of accepting a lot that has $p = 2.5\%$?

Construct an OC curve for a sampling plan for which $n = 100$ and $c' = 0$.

13.6   Suppose the University Library Committee considers the following solution to the space problem in the library. Move all books printed earlier than 1920 to a storage area, thus releasing stack space for current acquisitions. The chairman will authorize a thorough study if the percent of books printed earlier than 1920 is 0.20 or more; otherwise, the idea will be dropped. A sample of 400 books is taken randomly, and the number of successes r is counted (success is books printed earlier than 1920). The hypothesis to be tested is $H_0: p = 0.20$ versus $H_1: p < 0.20$. A level of significance $c = 0.05$ is set.
(a) What is the critical value of r for the test?
(b) Sketch an OC curve for the test, indicating the coordinate values for three points on the curve other than $r = 0$ or $r = 400$.
(c) What is the probability of accepting H_0 when it is a false error (approximately) if $p = 0.16$? What does this mean in terms of this particular experiment; that is, what will happen?

13.7   The average breaking strength of cotton yarn is one measure of its quality. Let the acceptance quality level for a given use be an average of 90 lb, and let the lower tolerance limit be an average of 80 lb. The standard deviation of the breaking strength of the particular grade of cotton yarn is 11 lb. Design a sampling plan based on sample averages that will yield a 0.95 chance of accepting yarn of 90-lb quality and a maximum chance of 0.10 of accepting yarn of 80-lb quality. Draw the OC curve for the plan.

13.8   The manufacturer of floor tile (9 in. by 9 in. sections) has a process that makes the tile in strips. The strip comes from the machine automatically into a slitter, which cuts the strip into the individual sections. A production lot consists of a half hour's production of individual tiles. The lot is checked for tile thickness. Management desires a 0.95 probability of accepting a lot with 2.5% defectives and a 0.10 probability of accepting a lot with 6.7% defectives. The process is set up for an average of 0.25 in. and a standard deviation of 0.01 in. A defective tile is one whose thickness is greater than 0.30 in. or less than 0.20 in..

Specify a variable sampling rule in terms of sample size and rejection limits.

13.9   You are a dealer in high-quality tree seedlings, and you wish to control the quality (in height) of the trees you sell to your customers. Past research has indicated that the height of two-year-old spruce seedlings varies significantly between shipments from tree farms, but that the standard deviation of the variation among trees within any given shipment apparently remains constant at 1.0 in.. Trees that are less than 4 in. in height are considered to be below the standard of your trade (i.e., defective). To control the quality of your purchases, you wish to find a variables sampling plan that will do the following: 1) accept 95% of the shipments that have only 10 out of 1,000 trees below standard; 2) accept only 10% of the shipments that have 60 out of 1,000 trees below standard.

(a) Find a variables sampling plan that will meet these criteria.

(b) Find an attribute plan that will meet these criteria, and compare it with the variables plan in terms of cost.

13.10 In the milling machine case on page 432, what is the probability that if the process mean shifts to 0.503, none of five successive samples taken after the shift will show the parameter change?

13.11 The following data pertain to a process for assembling a piece of equipment. For 32 samples of size 5, the average number of labor hours and range are shown. Are these data from a controlled process in terms of an $\overline{X}$- and R-chart? (For samples of size 5, $d_2 = 2.326$ and $d_3 = 0.8641$.)

Sample no.	$\overline{X}$	R	Sample no.	$\overline{X}$	R
1	40.0	15.5	17	48.0	15.5
2	51.7	24.8	18	58.4	17.4
3	54.0	76.7	19	57.6	24.1
4	51.1	11.8	20	27.1	21.5
5	40.4	2.6	21	44.4	21.9
6	45.5	25.5	22	39.9	13.4
7	50.6	35.2	23	64.0	7.1
8	48.4	13.7	24	43.2	11.5
9	60.2	40.0	25	46.6	28.2
10	78.4	12.9	26	52.5	12.6
11	45.6	21.5	27	47.6	5.9
12	59.2	25.2	28	55.5	13.3
13	84.7	17.4	29	44.6	97.1
14	75.8	10.0	30	71.8	20.6
15	58.5	20.0	31	27.9	24.8
16	55.8	24.8	32	42.5	18.2

13.12 Plot an OC curve for a p-chart with the *UCL* and *LCL* set at 0.430 and 0.064, respectively, and $n = 50$.

13.13 Oven timers are inspected at the end of an assembly line. Below are data for the number of rejects in each day's production lot for a one-month period. Is the manufacturing process under control with respect to the fraction defective?

Date of production	Units in lot	No. of defectives
April 3	1,239	146
4	1,162	107
5	1,208	201
6	645	60
7	668	77
10	660	74
11	732	71
12	773	87
13	636	54
14	609	41

Date of production		Units in lot	No. of defectives
April	17	618	49
	18	728	58
	19	643	48
	20	656	47
	21	628	46
	24	687	48
	25	592	42
	26	645	56
	27	675	60
	28	685	42
May	1	640	35
	2	621	42
	3	645	40
	4	648	51
	5	700	50

13.14   A 25-yd length of fishing line is inspected by passing the length under a magnifying glass to detect imperfections in the line. A c-chart is to be set up to control the process. Suppose that the average number of defects per 25 yd is 5 when the process is considered to be under control. Discuss the relative merits of sample sizes of 50 yd, 25 yd, or 12.5 yd, assuming that the control limits are set so as to yield a probability of 0.025 of a point exceeding the upper and lower limits, unless the lower limit is 0. Support your discussion by use of the characteristic curves for the three cases.

13.15   A radio manufacturer wishes to set up a control chart on the *number of defects* in a certain radio model. The radio has n different points where it could be defective. A study of past quality was made by counting the number of defects in 25 groups of five radios each. The average number of defects per group from the study was 55.7. The data from the original study looked like this:

Group no.	No. of defects per group	Group no.	No. of defects per group
1	77	14	87
2	64	15	40
3	75	16	22
4	93	17	92
5	45	18	89
6	61	19	55
7	49	20	25
8	65	21	54
9	45	22	22
10	77	23	49
11	59	24	33
12	54	25	20
13	41		

Was the process for making the radios in or out of control? Show all computations and assumptions.

13.16   A part is inspected by attributes sampling. A study of the relevant costs shows that the inspection cost is $5.00 per unit. Defective units must be replaced at a cost of $30.00 per unit. The cost to the user of receiving a defective unit is $100.
(a) Construct a cost curve, plotting the cost per lot unit versus the percent defective for the case of 100% inspection, no inspection, and two sampling plans: Plan I $(n = 50, c' = 0)$ and Plan II $(n = 100, c' = 1)$. Let the lot size equal 1,000.

(b) Discuss the implications of the cost curves. How would you use this cost information to determine a sampling plan?

(c) Suppose you know that the process yields a percent defective for a lot between the values $0.05 \leq p \leq 0.10$ with uniform probability. Can you relate this to the determination of a sampling plan?

Bibliography

BEIGHTLER, CHARLES S., and L. G. MITTEN, "Design of an Optimal Sequence of Inter-related Sampling Plans," *J. Amer. Stat. Assoc.*, vol. 59, 1964.

BEIGHTLER, CHARLES S., and JAMES E. SHAMBLIN, "Sequential Process Control," *J. Ind. Eng.*, March–April 1965.

FEIGENBAUM, A. V., *Total Quality Control*. New York: McGraw-Hill Book Co., 1961.

GRANT, E. L., *Statistical Quality Control*. New York: McGraw-Hill Book Co., 1961.

HANSEN, BERTRAND L., *Quality Control: Theory and Applications*. Englewood Cliffs, N.J.: Prentice-Hall, Inc., 1963.

HAUSER, NORBERT, N. N. BARISH, and SYLVAIN EHRENFELD, "Design Problems in a Process Control Simulation," *J. Ind. Eng.*, February 1966.

MANKEKAR, P. S., and L. G. MITTEN, "The Constrained Least Cost Testing Sequence," *J. Ind. Eng.*, March–April 1965.

PRICE, H. WALKER, "Least Cost Testing Sequence," *J. Ind. Eng.*, July–August 1959.

14

Production Planning

THE PLANNING HORIZON

Production planning is concerned with specifying how the production resources of the firm are to be employed over some future time period, in response to the predicted or forecasted demand for the product or services. The composition of the planning function, such as the techniques used, the number of people involved, and the degree of detail depends in part on the planning horizon or the length of the period for which plans are to be made.

Long-term planning, for a period of two or more years, would consider such things as programs for plant expansion, allocation of a product mix to various plants, opportunities for diversification, replacement of major facilities, etc. These kinds of strategic decisions are not considered in this chapter.

At the other extreme is short-term planning, for periods of one month or less. This falls under the heading of tactical production control and will be covered in the following chapters.

In this section, we will concentrate on planning for intermediate time periods of four to twelve months. The purpose of such planning is to specify the resource requirements for each of a series of time increments up to the planning horizon. In this case, the resources include those factors contributing to production capacity, such as employment levels, inventory levels, available machine hours, etc. The series of time increments may be weeks, months, or quarter-years.

The function of planning is important to the degree that the demand for products or services varies over time. The problem of production planning in the sense that we discuss it evaporates when there is only one product, the rate of demand is known and constant over time, and the production capacity is sufficient to meet the demand. At the other extreme, the problem becomes most complex when the product mix is large, demand for each product and in the aggregate is variable, production facilities consist of jointly used nonidentical equipment, and capacity is limited. In between these two extremes lie a variety of situations, which have some common characteristics that permit us to generalize the methods used in planning.

449

The kinds of demand variability that contribute to operating problems and for which planning is an antidote are significant periodic (week or month) changes in demand. Seasonal variation is a typical case, but there are also changes introduced by exogenous factors, such as general or specific business conditions, competitive changes, etc. When their effect is felt in the aggregate, that is, over all products, then the purpose of planning is to specify the kinds of capacity adjustments that should be made in response to the predicted changes in demand.

There are four essential ingredients to the production planning function. First, there must be a forecast of demand. The degree to which demand can be reasonably forecasted determines the planning horizon. If the organization cannot predict demand for more than several weeks into the future, then it must revert to a system of tactical manipulation of production capacity from week to week to meet the unforeseen changes in demand. Second, there must be alternative ways of adjusting the production capacity over time in response to demand variation. Third, there must be some measures of effectiveness of various alternative production plans. Fourth, there must be some means of economically determining an optimal or good plan from among the alternatives.

CAPACITY REQUIREMENTS

Measures of Capacity

Capacity can be measured in terms of either inputs or outputs of the system. We normally think of capacity as the measure of the potential of the system to produce a certain kind of output. Output measures, such as numbers of parts, tons, cubic yards, etc., are applicable in cases where products are equivalent or require equal inputs. In many cases, however, different products or services produced from the same facilities cannot be reduced to equivalent output units. Therefore, some equivalent units of input are used, such as labor hours or machine hours.

At any given time, the theoretical capacity of a facility, as measured in machine or labor hours, must be adjusted to a normal or net operating capacity. The latter allows for operating interruptions due to ordinary repairs, setups, machine failures, management errors, absences, vacations, material delivery delays, etc.

Capacity measurements are translations of the demand for products or services into equivalent units of capacity. In the case of a large and variable product mix, a major data-processing task is the translation process. If the planning is to be carried out in detail, then each product must be examined through its routing sheet to determine the demands made on each type of facility used in making the product. The aggregate equivalent labor or machine hours for all parts constitutes a future load on a particular facility. For a firm producing several thousand products, each with five or more components, one can easily visualize the extent of the computational problem involved in determining capacity requirements for a large number of facilities.

Methods of Adjusting Capacity

The methods of adjusting capacity to meet changes in demand constitute the set of decision variables in a planning problem. These methods depend on the planning horizon. Clearly, the methods for gaining additional capacity on a short-term basis, such as a week, are different and perhaps more restricted than those possible for the coming year. Generally and without reference to specific planning horizons, these are methods of altering production capacity.

1. *Changes in employment levels*   This obviously includes the hiring and layoff of personnel directly affected by demand changes. When done selectively, an individual at a time, this permits a continuous response to small changes in demand. Adding or dropping an entire shift forces a stepwise response.

2. *Over- and undertime*   This pertains to the retention of the normal working force, but with additions and reductions in the number of standard work hours in the week. Overtime can be used as a tactical method for meeting short-term changes in demand and can also be a planned response to longer term forecasts of changing demand.

3. *Inventories*   Both finished goods and work-in-process inventories represent "accrued" capacity to be used at some future time. The shifting of capacity from one period to another through inventories is a major planning variable.

4. *Backlogs*   This is the accumulation of demand to be satisfied at some future time. A backlog is in one sense a negative inventory or "deferred" capacity. Certain industries tend to operate with a backlog as a normal operating procedure, in lieu of maintaining inventories or using other methods of adjusting capacity.

5. *Make or buy*   The alternative of shifting capacity to an outside producer is both a short-term and long-term tactic of altering capacity. A small manufacturing firm may rely heavily on subcontractors to provide most of the production capacity, thus reducing the risks of investment in idle facilities.

6. *Design changes*   This includes a variety of things, such as methods improvements, machine and equipment acquisitions, and improved layouts and material handling. While these are important, we will not consider them in our discussion of planning and control procedures, since their effect must be related to a specific situation.

7. *Routing*   Alternative part routes provide the opportunity for choice of facilities in making a part and thus offer a degree of flexibility in the utilization of individual machines and equipment on a short-term basis.

8. *Lot sizes*   The size of production lots for different products affects the amount of time spent by facilities in set-up or make-ready. Increasing the batch sizes reduces set-up time requirements, at the expense, however, of limiting the number of different kinds of jobs that can be processed in the shop due to longer runs.

9. *Deferred preventive maintenance*   Periods of both under- and over-capacity can be dealt with by revisions in preventive maintenance schedules, which affect machine utilization and requirements at any given time.

10. *Increasing the skill base*   Short-term flexibility in capacity can be gained

by having employees who are skilled in more than one job. This permits the shifting of labor between machines or facilities, depending on the facility loads.

11. *Dispatching*   This refers to the manner in which individual shop orders or jobs are sequenced through the production system. The utilization of facilities, the extent of machine set-up and tear-down time, and the rate at which work flows through the production system are affected by dispatching rules.

The extent to which the various methods of altering production capacity enter into the planning decisions depends on the futurity of the plan. If the product mix is large and forecasting limited, management may resort to all the above methods in some combination dictated by the circumstances at a given time. Even if there is a well-devised production plan for the year, there is need for tactical control of the various methods, but within the constraints of the plan.

While the tactical manipulations may be directed toward individual products or product groups, yearly production planning is usually concerned with the aggregate input and output. Plans are expressed not in terms of individual products, but rather in terms of some common denominator, such as dollars, labor hours, machine hours, or equivalent units. The planning variables are often limited to aggregate employment levels, inventory levels, overtime, and backlogs. Sometimes the questions of lot sizes, setups, and make or buy decisions are also a part of planning.

The degree of aggregation may be relaxed to include in the planning the allocation of capacity to individual products or product classes if the mix is small or if there is a degree of commonality among the products. In such cases, planning tends to merge with tactical control at a pseudodetailed level. In any event, the production plan specifies the general capacity levels, which become the constraints for detailed tactical control on the short-term basis. That is, once the general employment levels, overtime, inventory levels, or anticipated backlogs are specified in the aggregate, some control procedures are used to handle the week-to-week production of the individual products.

OBJECTIVES OF PRODUCTION PLANNING

The objective of production planning is to minimize the total costs of meeting a stated future demand within the constraints of a given system design. We could, of course, consider the question of redesigning the system or adding physical capacity as part of the planning problem, but these issues are arbitrarily eliminated from consideration. The planning variables are those capacity factors which can be manipulated by management and for which capital investment is not important.

One key to good planning is, of course, a knowledge of the costs to be minimized in the decision. We are interested in the spectrum of alternative plans and the relevant or escapable costs associated with each one. Given a projected forecast of demand for the coming year, there is a whole range of alternative production-inventory plans, one of which will result in minimum cost. Such a plan would express the weekly, monthly, or quarterly capacity level in regular hours, added shifts, overtime, and inventory or backlog levels. The determination of a theoretically optimal plan is a challenging problem, and much of the literature of management science has been devoted to this question. We will explore superficially some of the models that have been developed.

Relevant Costs

In comparing alternative production plans, we are interested in the set of relevant costs for each alternative. Two major problems immediately confront us. The first is the determination of which costs are relevant, and the second is understanding their behavior with changes in the planning variables.

Regarding the first problem, the relevant costs are not the typical product costs set forth by standard accounting procedure. As with most decisions, planning involves an independent study of the behavior of costs with changes in planning variables. Such costs are usually indirect, and only a few may be normally collected by orthodox accounting, such as overtime premiums or setup costs. The determination and measurement of relevant costs can be a task of large magnitude. It commences with the recognition of the variables over which the planner has control, followed by an exhaustive listing of the costs that will likely change with the variables, and an assessment of which ones are likely to be critical.

McGarrah[1] has compiled a rather comprehensive list and description of costs that typically increase or decrease with changes in production capacity and inventory levels. An outline of these costs follows.

A. Costs of increasing the production level.
1. Employment and training.
    (a) Interview and selection.
    (b) Investigation of references, security check.
    (c) Physical examinations.
    (d) Payroll entry preparation.
    (e) Training new employees.
    (f) Rehiring of employees temporarily laid off.
2. Additional service and staff activities.
    (a) Production and inventory control.
    (b) Purchasing, receiving, inspection, materials handling, etc.
    (c) Additional materials handling personnel.
3. Added shifts (included only when a change involves an extra shift).
    (a) Supervision.
    (b) Shift premiums.
4. Overtime costs.
B. Costs of decreasing the production level.
1. Unemployment compensation insurance.

---

[1] R. E. McGarrah, "Production Programming," *J. Ind. Eng.*, vol. VIII, no. 6, November–December, 1957, pp. 264–65.

2. Contributions to wage stabilization funds.
3. Other employee costs.
   (a) Employee transfers.
   (b) Plant-community relations.
   (c) Excessive recruiting costs.
4. Staff clerical and service activities.
   (a) Purchasing.
   (b) Inventory and production control.
   (c) Personnel and payroll expenses.
5. Idle time costs.

PLANNING MODELS

Leveled Production

Among the many possible alternative production plans, there are two extreme possibilities. The first is to meet the fluctuations in demand directly with corresponding changes in the employment level. This includes the hiring and layoff of single shift personnel, or the addition or elimination of extra shifts. Such a policy is mandatory in some seasonal businesses dealing with products or services that cannot be backlogged or inventoried. Otherwise, while such a policy is possible, it has been noted that it can be very costly. Besides the direct and indirect costs previously cited, there are the social costs, which, while obvious, are not easy to measure.

The second possibility is to stabilize the labor force at some predetermined level and meet changes in demand mainly by altering inventories, backlogs, overtime, and other means. This is called leveled production.

In many cases, a production plan may consist of some mixture of these two extremes. A basic policy of leveled production can be augmented by temporary periods of overtime and added shifts or part-time personnel. Periods of low demand can be utilized for internal service or maintenance operations or complemented with vacation scheduling, besides reducing backlogs or increasing inventories.

Linear Decision Rules for Production Planning

Perhaps the most comprehensive experiment in production planning was conducted at the Carnegie Institute of Technology in 1955.[2] The problem was to determine a decision rule for making production and labor-force decisions in successive time periods that would minimize the expected value of total costs over a large number of periods. The study resulted in the formulation of a mathematical model consisting of a set of linear decision rules. We will consider the basic features of the method.

---

[2] Charles C. Holt *et al.*, *Planning Production, Inventories, and Work Force.* Englewood Cliffs, N.J.: Prentice-Hall, Inc., 1960.

STUDIES OF COST BEHAVIOR: The method employs a rigorous analysis of the behavior of the relevant planning costs with changes in the planning variables. The following notation is used:

W_t = the number of workers required for the period t; $t = 1, 2, \ldots, T$

P_t = the number of units to be produced in period t

I_t = the inventory minus backlogs at the end of period t

S_t = forecast of the number of units to be ordered for shipment during the period t

C_k = cost coefficients to be determined for a given plant or situation

Figure 14.1 shows the hypothetical behavior of the planning costs (solid line) and a quadratic approximation to these costs in each case. Each cost function expresses the change in cost corresponding to a change in the planning variable from one month to the next. The values of the cost coefficients must be determined individually for each plant in which the model is used.

From such analysis, a total cost function of the following kind is derived.

$$C_T = \sum_1^T C_t$$

and

$$
\begin{aligned}
C_t = [\,&(C_1 W_t) && \text{Regular payroll costs} \\
&+ C_2(W_t - W_{t-1})^2 && \text{Hiring and layoff costs} \\
&+ C_3(P_t - C_4 W_t)^2 + C_5 P_t - C_6 W_t && \text{Overtime costs} \\
&+ C_7(I_t - C_8 - C_9 S_t)^2] && \text{Inventory connected costs}
\end{aligned}
$$

subject to constraints

$$I_{t-1} + P_t - S_t = I_t$$

Once such a cost function is obtained, the decision rule that minimizes the expected value of C_T is obtained by differentiating with respect to each decision variable. This results in a set of *linear* equations whose solution, in turn, yields the decision rule. Note that the assumption of quadratic cost functions results in linear equations after differentiating, and finally in linear decision rules.

The resulting linear decision rules are of the following form:

$$P_t = \sum_{t=1}^T \lambda_t S_t + k_1 W_{t-1} + k_2 - k_3 I_{t-1} \tag{1}$$

$$W_t = k_4 W_{t-1} + k_5 - k_6 I_{t-1} + \sum_{t=1}^T \alpha_t S_t \tag{2}$$

Consider Equation (1) for calculating the production level P_t. First, it is a function of the forecasted sales for T periods in the future. λ_t is a specific weight given to each forecast. The more immediate period forecasts are given a higher weight than the more distant ones. The implication is that it is not economical to produce currently for shipments that are far into the future, because of inventory costs. Second, production is also a direct function of the employment level at the beginning of the period, thus reflecting the desirability of avoiding the cost of changing

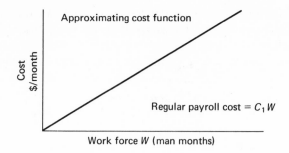

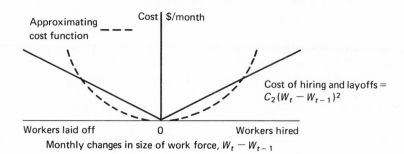

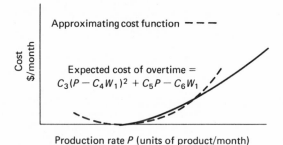

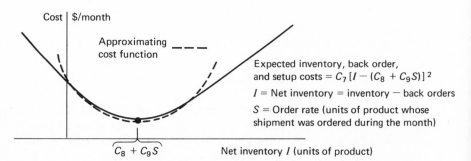

FIGURE **14.1**   Hypothetical cost behavior as a function of planning variables. From Charles C. Holt, Franco Modigliani, and Herbert A. Simon, "A Linear Decision Rule for Production and Employment Scheduling," *Management Science*, vol. 2, no. 1, October 1955.

the level. Finally, if the inventory at the beginning of the period is high, then production may be reduced in order to lower the inventory.

With respect to Equation (2) for the employment level W_t, we note that it is also a function of the forecasted sales for which a weight α_t is used. Typically, the value of α_t declines as t increases. However, the weights extend further into the future before they become negligible, such that forecasts into the more distant future influence employment level decisions. For example, in one study of a paint factory, the values of λ_t and α_t were

t	1	2	3	4	5	6	7	8	9	10	11	12
λ_t	+0.458	+0.233	+0.111	+0.046	+0.014	−0.001	−0.007	−0.008	−0.008	−0.007	−0.005	−0.004
α_t	+0.010	+0.009	+0.007	+0.005	+0.004	+0.003	+0.002	+0.002	+0.001	+0.001	+0.001	+0.000⁺

Thus, changes in sales that will take place in the distant future are reflected in present changes in employment levels, whereas more immediate changes in sales are reflected in current production level changes through overtime.

The two equations yield a dynamic response system to changes in demand. The production level for one period influences the inventory level, which in turn affects the employment level for the next period, which then affects the production level for the third period. Short-term fluctuations in demand, such as random variations, are absorbed by varying production levels, whereas long-term trend and cyclical changes are met by gradual changes in employment levels.

This method of planning production was tested in several actual situations by the originators of the method. One study was made of a paint factory in which the decision rules were applied to a history of sales over the 1952 to 1954 period. A moving-average forecast was used to provide the forecast requirements for the model. If the rules had been used during the study period, the reduction in cost, as compared to the company's actual performance, would have been 7.8%, as shown in Table 14.1.

This method of using linear decision rules has not been widely employed. Undoubtedly, this is due to the amount of analysis required to obtain the necessary

TABLE **14.1**   Comparison of performance using
decision rules with actual performance.[a]

Costs (thousands of dollars)	Actual company performance	Decision rule (Moving-average forecast)
Regular payroll	$1,256	$1,149
Overtime	82	95
Inventory	273	298
Back orders	326	246
Hiring and layoffs	16	12
Total cost $	1,953	1,800
%	108.5	100

[a] From Holt, Modigliani, and Simon, *Management Science*, vol. 2, no. 1, October 1955.

cost data, as well as to the mathematical sophistication of the method. However, the derivation of the linear rules can be accomplished on a computer with reasonable efficiency. This method represents a very thorough approach to an important problem and should not be ignored because of its mathematical complexity.

Linear Programing

A number of linear programing approaches have been taken to solve the problem. A rather straightforward use of the simplex method in terms of a single facility and single product is the following.[3] Let

i = index of planning period; $i = 1, 2, \ldots, k$

$d(i)$ = forecasted demand in units for the ith period

$h(i)$ = maximum number of units that can be produced on regular time in ith period prior to change in employment level

$w(i)$ = maximum number of units that can be produced on overtime in ith period

$r = w(i)/h(i)$

$p(i)$ = number of units produced on regular time in ith period

$y(i)$ = number of units produced on overtime in ith period

b = overtime marginal cost per unit of product

c = inventory carrying charge per unit per period

a' = cost to add one product unit of capacity to production

a'' = cost to remove one product unit of capacity from production

       (note that both a' and a'' are equivalent to employment level changes)

$u(i)$ = number of units of capacity added in period i

$v(i)$ = number of units of capacity removed in period i

Note that all capacity and cost measures have been expressed in terms of units of product. This permits an expansion of the method for the case of more than a single product.

We now have the following restrictions:

1. Restrictions on regular production

$$p(1) - u(1) + v(1) \leq h(1)$$
$$p(2) - u(1) - u(2) + v(1) + v(2) \leq h(2)$$

$$\vdots \qquad \vdots \qquad \vdots \qquad \vdots$$

$$p(k) - u(1) - \cdots - u(k) + v(1) + \ldots + v(k) \leq h(k)$$

2. Restriction on overtime production

$$y(1) + r[-u(1) + v(1)] \leq w(1)$$
$$y(2) + r[-u(1) - u(2) + v(1) + v(2)] \leq w(2)$$

$$\vdots \qquad \vdots$$

$$y(k) + r[-u(1) - \cdots - u(k) + v(1) + \cdots + v(k)] \leq w(k)$$

---

[3] John F. Magee and David M. Boodman, *Production Planning and Inventory Control*. New York: McGraw-Hill Book Co., 1967, pp. 369–73.

3. Restrictions on inventories (assuming no opening inventory in first period)

$$p(1) + y(1) \geq d(1)$$
$$p(1) + p(2) + y(1) + y(2) \geq d(1) + d(2)$$

$$\sum_{j=1}^{i} p(j) + \sum_{j=1}^{i} y(j) \geq \sum_{j=1}^{i} d_j; \; i = 1, 2, \ldots, k$$

4. Capacity added and removed

$$u(1) - p(1) \geq -p(0)$$
$$u(2) - p(2) + p(1) \geq 0$$

$$u(k) - p(k) + p(k - 1) \geq 0$$

and, similarly,

$$v(k) + p(k) - p(k - 1) \geq 0$$

Now the objective function to be minimized is

$$C(p, y, u, v) = a' \sum_{1}^{k} u(i) + a'' \sum_{1}^{k} v(i) + \alpha(p, y)$$

where

$$\alpha(p, y) = b \sum_{1}^{k} y(i) + c \left[\sum_{i=1}^{k} \sum_{j=1}^{i} p(j) + y(j) - d(j) \right]$$

$$= \sum_{1}^{k} cp(i)(k - i + 1) + \sum_{1}^{k} y(i)[b + c(k - i + 1)] + D$$

and

$$D = -c \sum_{i=1}^{k} \sum_{j=1}^{i} d(j)$$

Dynamic Programing

Another approach to production planning uses dynamic programing. For our example we will use the following notation. Let

P_t = the number of regular production hours used in period t

I_t = the inventory level, in equivalent hours, at the beginning of period t

D_t = the period t demand for the product in equivalent hours

ϕ_t = the number of hours of overtime used in period t

S_t = an index of changes in production level (employment level)

$$S_t = \begin{cases} 1 \text{ if the production level is changed from period } t - 1 \\ \quad \text{ to period } t \\ 0 \text{ if no change in production level takes place} \end{cases}$$

$c_t(P)$ = the cost per hour of regular production in period t

$c_t(I)$ = the cost of carrying one hour of inventory for period t.

We will assume that the inventory at the beginning of the period is carried for the full period.

$c_t(\phi)$ = the cost per hour of overtime in period t

$c_t(E)$ = the cost of shifting the regular production level from period $t - 1$ to period t. We will assume that the production level in any period can assume one of two values.

$C_t(1)$ = the total cost of regular production in period t
$\quad = P_t c_t(P)$

$C_t(2)$ = the total inventory cost in period t
$\quad = I_t c_t(I)$

$C_t(3)$ = the total cost of overtime in period t
$\quad = \phi_t c_t(\phi)$

$C_t(4)$ = the total cost of changing production level in period t
$\quad = S_t c_t(E)$

$TC_t(P_t, \phi_t : P_{t-1}, I_t)$ = the total cost for period t given the choice of the regular production level P_t and overtime ϕ_t conditioned by a production level change of $P_{t-1} - P_t$ and by a beginning period inventory of I_t
$\quad = C_t(1) + C_t(2) + C_t(3) + C_t(4) + \text{minimum } TC_{t+1}(: P_t, I_{t+1})$

Now consider an example with arbitrarily restrictive assumptions. Let there be four planning periods. Regular production levels P_t can be changed by going from one shift (1,000 hours) to two shifts (2,000 hours) or vice versa. The present employment level (preceding period 1) is 2,000 hours. Overtime for any period ϕ_t can have the value zero or 500 hours. The beginning period inventory I_t can assume the alternative values of 500, 1,000, or 1,500 hours. The inventory at the end of period 4 must be 500. The inventory at the beginning of period 1 is zero. The following data are relevant:

| | | $c_t(P)$ | | | | |
| | | One | Two | | | |
t	D_t	shift	shifts	$c_t(\phi)$	$c_t(I)$	$c_t(E)$
1	1,000	$2.50	$3.00	$4.00	$1.00	$5,000
2	2,500	2.50	3.00	4.00	1.00	5,000
3	2,000	2.50	3.00	4.00	1.00	6,000
4	1,500	3.00	4.00	5.00	1.00	6,000

The problem is to determine the regular production hours (number of shifts) and overtime for each of four periods, which results in the minimum total cost of production, overtime, inventory, and production level changes. That is, we wish to minimize $TC(1)$, subject to

$$P_0 = 2,000$$
$$I_1 = 0$$
$$I_5 = 500$$
$$I_{t+1} = I_t + P_t + \phi_t - D_t$$

For any period, the decision alternatives are to use one shift only, one shift with overtime, two shifts only, or two shifts with overtime. We commence with period 4. The four alternatives are listed across the top of Table 14.2. The rows of the table are labeled with possible combinations of period 3 employment level and period 4 opening inventory. Each cell in the table indicates the total cost $TC(4)$ of the production plan labeling the column. For example, if, in period 4, we produce at a level of 1,000 hours with 500 hours of overtime, the total cost will be $3,000 production, $500 inventory, $2,500 overtime, and zero for a change in employment level, since we assumed 1,000 hours in period 3. Since the ending inventory for the fourth period is specified as 500 hours and the demand for that period is 1,500 hours, certain plans are inadmissible, as indicated by the dashes.

TABLE **14.2**   Chart for period 4 decision.

P_4		1,000	1,000	2,000	2,000
P_3	ϕ_4 / I_4	0	500	0	500
1,000	500	—	$C(1)$ 3.0 $C(2)$ 0.5 $C(3)$ 2.5 $C(4)$ 0.0 $TC(t+1)$ 0.0 6.0	—	—
2,000	500	—	3.0 0.5 2.5 6.0 0.0 12.0	—	—
1,000	1,000	3.0 1.0 0.0 0.0 0.0 4.0	—	—	—
2,000	1,000	3.0 1.0 0.0 6.0 0.0 10.0	—	—	—
1,000	1,500	—	—	—	—
2,000	1,500	—	—	—	—

The chart for period 3 is shown in Table 14.3. Note that each element is standardized as follows:

$$
\begin{array}{|c|}
\hline
\boxed{I_{t+1}} \\[2pt]
C_t(1) \\
C_t(2) \\
C_t(3) \\
C_t(4) \\
\min TC(t+1) \\
\hline
\end{array}
$$

For example, if we produce at 2,000 hours without overtime, and assuming the opening inventory is 500 and the period 2 production level was 1,000, then the total cost would be production \$6,000, inventory \$500, overtime zero, and change in production level \$6,000. Since this plan would result in an ending inventory of 500 hours, we must add to this the minimum fourth period plan for the conditions $P_3 = 2,000$ and $I_4 = 500$, which is \$12,000. Thus, the total cost is \$24,500. Note that we carry back each period the optimum costs from the following period for the given value of P_t and I_{t+1}. The student may continue the problem until a production plan is derived.

APPLICATIONS: In reviewing the problem of production planning under conditions of seasonal demand, Vergin conducted a study of eight firms having highly seasonal products.[4] He noted that in most of the firms, management tended to concentrate on methods of removing the seasonal influence, rather than determine low-cost production plans. For example, one method was to hire the kind of labor that would easily adapt to the seasonal requirements, such as farm labor for a product for which there is high demand in the winter. For three of the firms, he applied different planning methods and compared them to the normal operating schedule used by the firm in terms of annual variable costs. The results of the tests are shown in Table 14.4. The two methods used were linear decision rules and simulation. Line 4 indicates a base assuming a completely level rate of demand. Then, the difference between the costs in lines 3 and 4 is attributable to seasonal factors, while the difference between lines 1 and 4 is due to both seasonal conditions and inefficient planning.

Figure 14.2 shows the general structure of a modular computer simulation program for the production planning problem, which is used to obtain the information in line 3 of Table 14.4. The planning process is essentially a trial-and-error procedure using guide rules developed by considering the cost figures and operating characteristics of the firm. Starting with a given plan, the effects of successively varying employment levels, overtime, inventory, subcontracting, etc., are evaluated successively until there is a convergence on a low-cost plan.

---

[4] Roger C. Vergin, "Production Scheduling Under Seasonal Demand," *J. Ind. Eng.*, vol. XVII, no. 5, May 1966, pp. 260–66.

TABLE **14.3**   Chart for period 3 decision.

P_2	I_3	P_3 = 1,000, ϕ_3 = 0	P_3 = 1,000, ϕ_3 = 500	P_3 = 2,000, ϕ_3 = 0	P_3 = 2,000, ϕ_3 = 500
1,000	500	—	—	[500] 6.0, 0.5, 0.0, 6.0, 12.0, 24.5	[1000] 6.0, 0.5, 2.0, 6.0, 10.0, 24.5
2,000	500	—	—	[500] 6.0, 0.5, 0.0, 0.0, 12.0, 18.5	[1000] 6.0, 0.5, 2.0, 0.0, 10.0, 18.5
1,000	1,000	—	[500] 2.5, 1.0, 2.0, 0.0, 6.0, 11.5	[1000] 6.0, 1.0, 0.0, 6.0, 4.0, 17.0	—
2,000	1,000	—	[500] 2.5, 1.0, 2.0, 6.0, 6.0, 17.5	[1000] 6.0, 1.0, 0.0, 0.0, 4.0, 11.0	—
1,000	1,500	[500] 2.5, 1.5, 0.0, 0.0, 6.0, 10.0	[1000] 2.5, 1.5, 2.0, 0.0, 4.0, 10.0	—	—
2,000	1,500	[500] 2.5, 1.5, 0.0, 6.0, 6.0, 16.0	[1000] 2.5, 1.5, 2.0, 6.0, 4.0, 16.0	—	—

OPTIONS

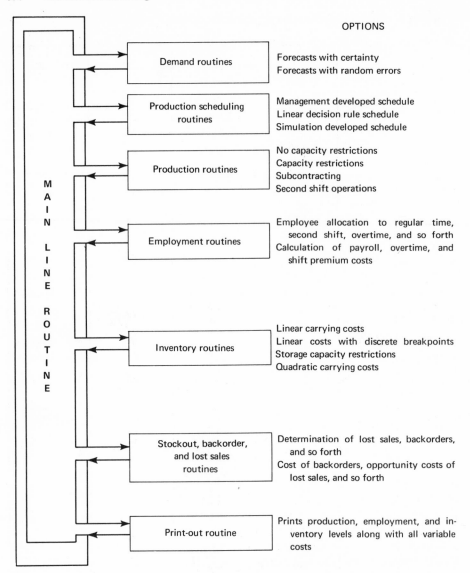

FIGURE **14.2**   Flow diagram of simulation scheduling process. The main line routine sends controls of the program to each of the decision rule routines in turn. Each routine passes control back to the main line when it has performed its designated function. From R. C. Vergin, *J. Ind. Eng.*, vol. 17, no. 5, May 1966, p. 265.

TABLE **14.4**   Annual variable costs of alternative scheduling methods.[a]

	Firms		
	A	*B*	*C*
1. Operating schedule	$1,616,023	$225,128	$255,988
2. Linear decision rule schedule	983,307	152,950	176,350
3. Simulation schedule	401,701	91,213	90,914
4. Level demand schedule	0	0	0
5. Total annual costs of firm	$54.5 millions	$9.0 millions	$16.5 millions

[a] The "Operating Schedule" is the schedule developed by management and actually being used in the firm. From R. C. Vergin.[4]

SHOP LOADING

In the discussion of production planning, we generally avoided the problem of planning the production of individual items by considering production in the aggregate. If the final product mix consists of assemblies, then we are faced with the task of determining the production requirements for subassemblies and components and establishing purchasing schedules for raw materials with appropriate allowances for production time lags. Of course, these detailed schedules can be combined to form the basis of a general production plan. Our concern here will be with the task of synthesizing these data.

Alternative Assembly Plans

If the mix of final products consists of assemblies, then two basic approaches may be taken to meet assembly schedules. At the one extreme is the use of a work-in-process or subassembly and component inventory, which acts as a buffer between the final assembly department and the fabricating and subassembly operations. In this case, the requirements for subassemblies and components are met directly from this intermediate inventory. The orders for subassemblies, components, or materials, in turn, are triggered when it is necessary to replenish the inventory levels. Therefore, the demand schedule for final assemblies or completed parts is translated into production requirements through the control of the intermediate inventory system. We will delve into this kind of operation in a later chapter.

At the other extreme is a system of *product explosion* and *shop loading*. The demand for final assemblies is translated into an equivalent demand for subassemblies, components, and raw materials necessary to satisfy the final product demand. The requirements for subassemblies and component parts are then translated into hourly requirements for various production centers. Almost invariably this translation process must also consider the "lead" times necessary to prepare the production orders, order materials, and process parts so that the subassemblies and components will arrive at the final assembly point when they are needed. In this system, an intermediate inventory may exist solely as a buffer for random fluctuations in demand. Product explosion and shop loading constitute the two aspects of this kind of program, the former being the translation of final assembly into component requirements, and the latter, the determination of the hours required in the shop to meet these demands.

Obviously, any plant may use a mixture of these two approaches. For example, suppose a company manufactures three lines of pleasure boats. Production planning might be confined to converting forecasted customer demand (distributors) into a schedule or plan for the assembly department. The woodworking shop, where the components or subassemblies are made, might operate on the basis of a production control plan under which shop orders are placed to replenish component inventories set up for the assembly lines. Or, the requirements for the final products might be translated directly into a plan for shop production with the necessary lead times taken into consideration.

Product explosion and subsequent shop loading can be effected either from a backlog of orders or from a forecast. If a system of backlogging orders is in effect, then as new orders arrive and are added to the backlog, they are exploded into the component requirements and translated into shop hour requirements, and the results are accumulated over time to provide a basic running schedule of future hourly requirements. The future shop load will depend on the lead time for the parts, as well as on the size of the order backlog.

In contrast to this is the possibility of forecasting the demand for final assemblies and then, again by explosion and shop loading, converting the forecast into a production schedule. The forecast period will have to be at least as long as the lead time necessary to complete the final product. Which scheme a company uses depends on the product, the company policies regarding customer service requirements, forecasting ability, etc.

Product Explosion

Determining the requirements for subassemblies and components is not a trivial task, especially if parts and subassemblies are standardized for use in more than one final product. For large product mixes, the use of a computer is mandatory because of the magnitude of the arithmetic task. The mathematics of product explosion is essentially matrix algebra. We explore the subject by considering first a very simple problem.

EXAMPLE 14.1   Suppose a company makes two final products, A and B, two subassemblies, a and b, and a basic component, x. The assembly relationships of the part, subassemblies, and final products are shown in Figure 14.3 in the form of a flow diagram (or Gozento Chart). The arrows indicate the assembly relationship between two parts. The part at the tail of the arrow is used directly in the assembly of the part at the point of the arrow. The numbers next to the arrow are the quantities of the parts to be used in an assembly unit.

The parts are arranged in levels. Thus, a part located at one level may be used in any part in higher levels but never in a part at the same or lower level.

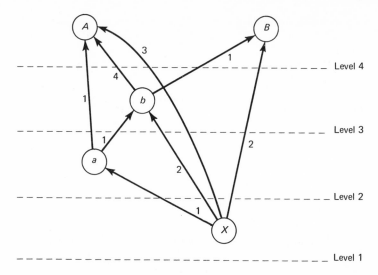

FIGURE **14.3**   Flow diagram of assembly relationships between parts.

THE N MATRIX: We now convert the information on the flow diagram into a matrix, $N = (n_{ij})$, where n_{ij} is the quantity of the ith part (component or subassembly) used directly in the assembly of the jth part. The matrix contains exactly the same information found in the flow diagram but in a more useful form. Considering the matter of levels, we will code each part with a number, k. A part k always goes into parts with numbers greater than k but never into parts with numbers smaller than k.

k		1	2	3	4	5
k	i \ j	x	a	b	A	B
1	x	0	1	2	3	2
2	a		0	1	1	0
3	b			0	4	1
4	A				0	0
5	B					0

N matrix.

THE T MATRIX: The N matrix gives only the quantities of a part directly used in any other part. We are interested now in determining the total numbers of a part used directly and indirectly in any other part. For example, the number of x's used to subassemble one unit of b is 3. b uses two x's directly and also one x contained in the a that goes into the b.

The T matrix gives us this information: $T = (t_{ij})$, where t_{ij} is the quantity of the ith part required to assemble one unit of the jth part. T will be a square matrix with the same dimension as N.

The diagonal of the T matrix will be 1, or $t_{ii} = 1$. It can be shown that

$$T = I + N + N^2 + N^3 + \cdots$$

where I is the identity matrix. Since this is a geometric series of the form $a + an + an^2 + \cdots + an^k$, an equivalent form is

$$T = \frac{I}{(I - N)}$$

since

$$\lim_{k \to 0} T = \frac{I}{(I - N)} = (I - N)^{-1}$$

Therefore, T can be found by a matrix inversion operation. If the dimension of the N matrix is large, the inversion process can consume a good deal of computing time.

We may also calculate T by using the following algorithm:

$$t_{ij} = \sum_k (n_{ik} \cdot t_{kj}) \quad \text{for} \quad i \leq k \leq j \quad \text{and} \quad t_{ii} = 1 \tag{3}$$

That is,

$$T = N \times T + I$$
$$I \times T - N \times T = I$$
$$[I - N][T] = I$$

Therefore,

$$T = \frac{I}{I - N} = (I - N)^{-1}$$

		1	2	3	4	5
i \ j		x	a	b	A	B
1	x	1	1	3	16	5
2	a	0	1	1	5	1
3	b	0	0	1	4	1
4	A	0	0	0	1	0
5	B	0	0	0	0	1

T matrix.

It is fairly easy to systematically complete the T matrix given the N matrix. That is, suppose that we are given the N matrix shown at the left below and we wish to complete the first row of the T matrix indicated to the right of the N matrix. We proceed as follows:

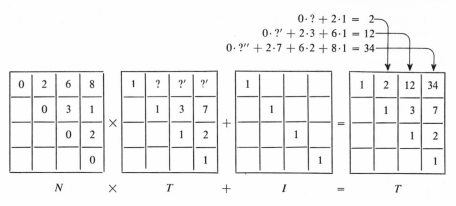

$$0 \cdot \; ? + 2 \cdot 1 = 2$$
$$0 \cdot \; ?' + 2 \cdot 3 + 6 \cdot 1 = 12$$
$$0 \cdot \; ?'' + 2 \cdot 7 + 6 \cdot 2 + 8 \cdot 1 = 34$$

$$N \times T + I = T$$

TOTAL PERIOD REQUIREMENTS: We may convert the requirements for a unit of end product into total requirements for some end product demand schedule. Suppose, for example, that we have a matrix, $S = (s_{ip})$, where s_{ip} is the number of units of the ith part demanded in period p. We may convert this into a demand schedule for subassemblies and components as follows:

Let $S =$

i \ p	1	2	3
A	6	4	5
B	5	3	2

In order to obtain the total requirements of x, a, and b necessary to make the required number of A and B for each of the three periods, we carry out the following multiplication, using part of the T matrix:

i \ j	A	B
x	16	5
a	5	1
b	4	1

$\times$

i \ p	1	2	3
A	6	4	5
B	5	3	2

$=$

i \ p	1	2	3	Total:
x	121	79	90	290
a	35	23	27	85
b	29	19	22	70

SHIFTING THE TIME BASE: Usually, components and subassemblies must be produced in advance of the time they are actually required. For instance, suppose that part b must be subassembled one period prior to its use in A and B. This means that all x's and a's going into b must be prepared in the same period or, more likely, in a preceding period. In other words, each level of parts constitutes an increment of lead time between the point where components are processed (or materials ordered) and the final assembly of A and B.

For purposes of demonstration, we will assume that the x's and a's can be produced in the period for which they are demanded. Using the N matrix, we can determine the distribution of this demand over the subassemblies and components required in the third period.

$i \backslash j$	x	a	b	A	B
x	0	1	2	3	2
a	0	0	1	1	0
b	0	0	0	4	1
A	0	0	0	0	0
B	0	0	0	0	0

$\times$

$i \backslash p$	3
x	90
a	27
b	22
A	5
B	2

$=$

$i \backslash j$	x	a	b	A	B
x	0	27	44	15	4
a	0	0	22	5	0
b	0	0	0	20	2
A	0	0	0	0	0
B	0	0	0	0	0

This shows that, in terms of the third period demand, 19 x's are required directly for A and B, 44 are required directly for the b's, which will be made in period 2, and 27 are required for the a's that go directly into A and will be used in period 2 for the b's. An entire production schedule for four periods is shown below and can be verified by extending the analysis to periods 1 and 2.

Period	Part A	B	a		b		x	
3	5	2	5	for direct use in A	0		19	direct in A and B;
							5	direct in a's;
2	4	3	4	direct in A	22	for period 3 A and B	18	direct A and B;
			22	direct in b's			4	direct a's for A;
							44	direct in b's;
							22	direct in a's for b's;
1	6	5	6	direct in A	19	for period 2 demand	28	direct A and B;
			19	direct in b's			6	direct a's for A;
							38	direct for b's;
							19	direct a's for b's;
1-1	0	0	29	direct in b's	29	for period 1 demand	58	direct in b's;
							29	direct in a's for b's.
Total:		85	85		70		290	

Loading the Facilities

Suppose we have four facilities in the above example. Designating a facility by the letter m, we have an A matrix, $A = (a_{im})$, where a_{im} is the time to process one unit of part i in facility m.

$A =$

i \ m	1	2	3	4
x	1	2	1	0
a	0	1	2	3
b	0	0	3	5
A	0	0	6	5
B	0	0	7	6

Hours required to produce one unit
of part i in facility m

To determine the total hourly requirements for each of the four facilities for each of the four periods, we summarize the production schedule in the form of a total parts requirements matrix:

p \ i	x	a	b	A	B
3	24	5	0	5	2
2	88	26	22	4	3
1	91	25	19	6	5
1-1	87	29	29	0	0

Total part requirements for four periods

Then, the total hourly requirement is calculated as follows, giving us an H matrix, $H = (h_{pm})$, where h_{pm} is the number of hours required for the mth facility in the pth period:

p \ i	x	a	b	A	B
3	24	5	0	5	2
2	88	26	22	4	3
1	91	25	19	6	5
1-1	87	29	29	0	0

$\times$

i \ m	1	2	3	4
x	1	2	1	0
a	0	1	2	3
b	0	0	3	5
A	0	0	6	5
B	0	0	7	6

$=$

p \ m	1	2	3	4
3	24	53	78	52
2	88	202	251	226
1	91	207	269	230
1-1	87	203	232	232

Generalizing the Problem with Constant Lead Times

In the preceding example, we derived a schedule of part requirements, considering that only part b was subjected to a lead time. Suppose we generalize the problem by saying that all final products will be processed in the month they are demanded and all components and subassemblies will be processed in one time period prior to the time they are needed.

Let

u = the number of final products
r = the number of components and subassemblies
p_t = the number of periods for which a forecast of final product shipments is made, $t = 1, 2, \ldots, T$, where T is the most advanced period
N^* = a submatrix from the N matrix
S = a shipment schedule
D = a parts requirement schedule

Then we have the following computation:

$$r \left[\; N^* \;\right]_u \times u \left[\; S \;\right]_{\substack{p_t \\ T, \ldots, 1}} = r \left[\; D_1 \;\right]_{\substack{p_t \\ T-1, \ldots, T-T}}$$

D_1 is the requirements for the r parts to meet the shipment schedule S, but to be made in period $T - 1, T - 2, \ldots, T - T$.

$$
\underset{r}{\boxed{\overset{r}{N^*}}} \times \underset{r}{\boxed{\overset{T-1,\ldots,T-T}{D_1}}} = \underset{r}{\boxed{\overset{T-2,\ldots,T-(T+1)}{D_2}}}
$$

D_2 is the requirements for the r parts to meet the requirements schedule D_2, but to be made one period in advance of the requirements D_1. In this manner, we continue until we generate a requirement schedule, $D = 0$.

Now we combine the requirement schedules thus derived into a total schedule of production for each of the parts for each of the periods, $T, T - 1, T - 2, \ldots$. Given this schedule, we proceed to load the facilities in the manner previously described. We should note that a check on the part requirements can be made by comparing the total number of parts with the product of $T \times S$.

Estimating Shop Load Requirements by Regression

In a job shop, where each part is made to customer specification, it may be difficult to estimate the hourly requirements of individual parts for various facilities because of the variety of parts produced. However, the experience gained in the past may be used to predict or estimate requirements for a new part by using multiple linear regression analysis.

For example, this method has been used by the Westinghouse Electric Corporation to estimate labor time requirements for building up the laminations that form the core of a shell-type power transformer.[5] An engineering drawing of the part is provided several months before production time. For this kind of part, the following variables, each a dimension of the part, were considered to contribute to the core building time.

X_1 = number of stacks
X_2 = yoke area (in.^{2})
X_3 = short area (in.^{2})
X_4 = leg area (in.^{2})
X_5 = total weight of iron (k lb)
X_6 = $\frac{1}{6}$ opening volume (k in.^{3})
X_7 = $\frac{1}{2}$ core volume (k in.^{3})
X_8 = stack height (in.)

By examining a sample of 400 parts produced in the past, each with varying dimensions, and using multiple linear regression analysis, the following estimating formula was developed:

$$Y = T_0 + T_1 X_1 + T_3 X_3 + T_5 X_5 + T_7 X_7 + T_8 X_8$$

[5] Francis L. Canning, "Estimating Load Requirements in a Job Shop," *J. Ind. Eng.*, vol. X, no. 6, November–December 1959, pp. 447–49.

where Y is the estimated time and T_i is the coefficient derived from the sample. Note that a preliminary study of a random sample of 50 resulted in the elimination of variables X_2, X_4, and X_6 as being redundant.

A test of this estimating equation on a sample of 100 current shop orders showed that 30% of the estimated times were within $\pm 1\%$ of the actual times, 75% were within $\pm 5\%$, and the maximum error, which occurred in 2% of the cases, was $\pm 20\%$.

This method has been successfully used in other shops of the company and has provided a rudimentary method of scheduling.

SUMMARY

We have considered how a set of resources is to be allocated in the aggregate over a future planning period to meet a variable demand. This demand is either a backlog, a forecast, or both. We have considered the resources to be employment levels, facility hours, over- and undertime, and inventories (accrued capacity) or backlogs (deferred capacity).

The degree of aggregation depends on the extent of product and facility mix. The typical planning model requires the translation of heterogeneous product demand into equivalent demand for production capacity. Both product explosion and shop loading are procedures for making this translation. When this is done, planning is concerned with the economics of satisfying the capacity requirements, given constraints on some of the capacity factors for each future period. We should be cognizant of the fact that the design and implementation of production plans can be a formidable task. The effectiveness of optimum-seeking methods depends on the reliability of forecasts, the economics of data collection, the accuracy of cost estimates, and the ability of the model to entertain the relevant planning variables. Plans never represent a firm commitment for the future but must be updated periodically during the planning year. Simulation appears to offer the ultimate in flexibility in terms of ability to experiment with alternative planning policies and to consider a wide variety of planning variables.

The next two chapters will consider the more tactical problems of operating the production system on a short-term basis in terms of individual products and facilities. The control of production at the operational level is executed within or without the framework of aggregate planning. The latter case exists in those situations where forecasting is difficult, product and facility mixes are large, and relatively minor increments and decrements in capacity area are easy to make on a short-term basis. When planning has been carried out, a problem of tactical production control is to reconcile operating decisions with constraints set forth by aggregate planning. That is, the actual aggregate result of decisions on the size of production batches, which product inventories are to be replenished, and how production is to be scheduled in the shop must be reconciled with the desired or planned aggregate inventory levels, anticipated shop loads, and employment and overtime levels.

Problems

14.1 The Riga Woodworking Company has a plant containing some 50 different woodworking machines comprising a general-purpose shop. The output consists of a large mix of small and medium-sized wooden products and novelties sold through department stores, mail-order houses, and jobbers. Fifty percent of the items are catalogued and carried in stock for an average of two to four years. New products are created by a design department or submitted by customers. Explain why planning aggregate production for a year ahead is difficult for this kind of business. Make a list of tactical ways the plant superintendent can alter production capacity to meet current changes in the demand for the capacity of the shop facilities.

14.2 Calculate an efficient production plan for one year, given the following cost estimates and forecast information:

Initial inventory	3 units
Production rate	1 unit per person per month
Regular time labor cost	$400 per person per month
Overtime labor cost	$600 per unit (maximum of 2 units per month)
Hiring cost	$200 per person
Layoff cost	$500 per person
Carrying cost	$100 per unit per month
Desired closing inventory	4 units at end of December
Labor force needed	1 unit per person per month
Marginal revenue	$100 per unit

Month	Inventory	Sales forecast	Labor force
January	3	10	7
February		6	
March		6	
April		7	
May		7	
June		9	
July		9	
August		8	
September		8	
October		6	
November		4	
December		6	

14.3 Set up a simplex tableau for the following production planning problem.

Number of periods	$k = 3$
Demand per period	$d(1) = 45$; $d(2) = 52$; $d(3) = 60$ units
Hourly rate of production	$g = 100$ hours per unit
Constraint on regular production	$h(1) = h(2) = h(3) = 45$ units
Constraint on overtime	$w(1) = w(2) = w(3) = 11.25$ or 25% of regular capacity
Overtime marginal cost per unit	$b = \$200$
Inventory holding cost per unit per period	$c = \$12$
Cost to add one unit of capacity	$a' = \$240$
Cost to subtract one unit of capacity	$a'' = \$180$

14.4 Jim's Jam Factory produces a variety of preserves, jams, jellies, and marmalade. One plant is involved in making just preserves and marmalade. The varieties of preserves produced are shown below.

Code number	Variety	Cost per lb	Approximate percentage of total sales	Opening inventory (lb)
1	Apricot	$0.20	0.05	0
2	Cherry	0.17	0.03	0
3	Strawberry	0.12	0.25	1,500
4	Grape	0.30	0.22	0
5	Purple plum	0.27	0.04	600
6	Red raspberry	0.15	0.11	2,000
7	Red raspberry and currant	0.15	0.02	0
8	Blackberry	0.25	0.04	100
9	Black raspberry	0.25	0.07	500
10	Peach	0.15	0.04	0
11	Pineapple	0.20	0.03	2,000
12	Marmalade	0.12	0.10	100
			1.00	

The following is a forecast of the demand for each variety for each of the next 13 weeks. The figures shown represent computer output and therefore exhibit an unrealistic precision.

				Week			
Variety	1	2	3	4	5	6	7
1	5925.	6518.	6221.	5925.	5629.	5333.	5925·
2	30574.	33631.	32102.	30574.	29045.	27516.	30574·
3	4242.	4667.	4454.	4242.	4030.	3818.	4242·
4	13616.	10893.	9985.	9077.	8623.	8170.	7716·
5	6435.	5148.	4719.	4290.	4075.	3861.	3646·
6	10630.	8504.	7795.	7086.	6732.	6378.	6023·
7	4835.	4835.	4835.	4029.	4029.	4029.	4029.
8	5148.	5148.	5148.	4290.	4290.	4290.	4290·
9	14846.	14846.	14846.	12372.	12372.	12372.	12372·
10	3754.	2920.	2503.	3337.	4171.	3754.	5006.
11	25575.	19892.	17050.	22733.	28417.	25575.	34100.
12	12244.	9523.	8162.	10883.	13604.	12244.	16325.
Total	137823.	126522.	117821.	118838.	125017.	117338.	134247.

				Week			
Variety	8	9	10	11	12	13	Total
1	5925.	7110.	6221.	5333.	5333.	5629.	77026.
2	30574.	36688.	32102.	27516.	27516.	29045.	397456.
3	4242.	5091.	4454.	3818.	3818.	4030.	55151.
4	9077.	9985.	9077.	8170.	6354.	6808.	118004.
5	4290.	4719.	4290.	3861.	3003.	3217.	55767.
6	7086.	7795.	7086.	6378.	4960.	5315.	92123.
7	3828.	3626.	4029.	3828.	3223.	4029.	52378.
8	4075.	3861.	4290.	4075.	3432.	4290.	55767.
9	11753.	11134.	12372.	11753.	9897.	12372.	160831.
10	5423.	4171.	3754.	5840.	4171.	4171.	54226.
11	36942.	28417.	25575.	39783.	28417.	28417.	369418.
12	17685.	13604.	12244.	19046.	13604.	13604.	176852.
Total	140900.	136201.	125495.	139400.	113729.	120927.	

The production process is straight-line flow consisting of five major steps, including the preparation of the frozen fruits, vat cooking, container filling, container sealing and cooling, and packaging. Once the line is set up, the rate of production is about 4,000 lb per hour. The time to set up the process is a function of the sequence of the varieties made. A schedule of setup times in hours is shown below:

						Brand						
	1	2	3	4	5	6	7	8	9	10	11	12
1	0	2.0	1.0	0.5	1.5	0.5	2	0.5	2	2	2	3.0
2		0	1.0	1.0	1.0	2.0	2.0	1.0	2.0	2.0	1.0	3.0[a]
3			0	0.2	1.0	2.0	2.0	1.0	2.0	2.0	1.0	3.0
4				0	1.0	1.5	2.0	0.5	0.2	0.2	0.5	3.0
5					0	1.0	2.0	0.2	0.5	0.5	0.5	3.0
6						0	2.0	1.0	2.0	2.0	1.0	3.0
7							0	2.0	2.0	2.0	2.0	3.0
8								0	1.0	1.0	1.0	3.0
9									0	1.0	1.0	3.0
10										0	1.0	3.0
11											0	3.0
12												0

(The left-side label "Brand" runs vertically alongside rows.)

[a]That is, three hours are required to change over from brand 3 to brand 12.

Because the raw materials can be stored in the frozen state, and because demand is somewhat stable over time, the plant runs for 52 weeks of the year. Prepare a production plan for the coming 13 weeks, assuming the following:

1. Regular production time is a five-day week, eight-hour day. Overtime can be used to the extent of five hours per week at a premium of $20 per hour. Interruptions to the line cause a 2% reduction in capacity.
2. The basic output is a case of containers weighing 24 lb. Marginal profit is 33% of the cost per pound.
3. Output can be inventoried. The annual inventory rate is 25% of cost per lb.
4. The process has just completed a run of variety 6.
5. The demand for a week must be met in the week it occurs. If demand cannot be met, then 50% of it will be lost and the other 50% can be satisfied by transshipments from another warehouse at an additional cost of $0.03 per pound, or by backlogging orders for one week. If an order is backlogged for more than one week, it is lost.

14.5   You are given the following:

$k \times m$ matrix A, where a_{ij} is the time required by department j for the production of one unit of part i.
$l \times m$ vector C, where c_j is the time available in department j.
$l \times k$ vector D, where d_i is the maximum quantity of part i that can be sold.
$l \times k$ vector M, where m_i is the unit margin for part i.

Describe the machine loading problem in terms of these vectors and matrices.

14.6   Two final assemblies, X and Y, consist of a combination of two subassemblies *a* and *b*, and two basic components, 1 and 2. The relationship between the parts is shown in the flow diagram below:

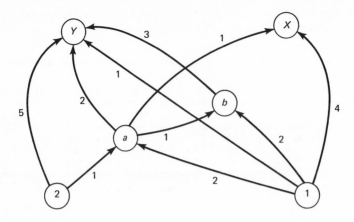

A shipping schedule for the final products and the two subassemblies is shown below for a two-month period. The subassemblies represent replacement parts:

	a	*b*	*X*	*Y*
December	5	5	10	20
November	10	5	20	30

The lead times are as follows: Products that are shipped are made in the month of shipment. However, all components and subassemblies must be made in the month prior to the month in which they are needed. There are three facilities, and the unit times for processing the parts in these departments are shown in the following matrix:

Part	Facility		
	11	12	13
1	0	2	1
2	0	5	2
a	5	0	0
b	3	1	0
X	20	2	0
Y	10	1	0

Prepare a schedule of required facility hours for as many months as you can.

Bibliography

BOCK, ROBERT H., and WILLIAM K. HOLSTEIN, *Production Planning and Control*. New York: Chas. Merrill Books, Inc., 1963.

BOWMAN, EDWARD H., "Production Scheduling by the Transportation Method of Linear Programming," *Operations Research*, vol. 4, no. 1, 1956.

BRONSON, M. E., "Program Loading," *J. Ind. Eng.*, November–December 1960.

COLEMAN, J. R., JR., S. SMIDT, and R. YORK, "Optimal Plant Design for a Seasonal Production," *Management Science*, July 1964.

DZIELINSKI, B. P., and RALPH E. GOMERY, "Optimal Programming of Lot Sizes, Inventory, and Labor Allocations," *Management Science*, July 1965.

ELMAGHRABY, S. E., "A Note on the Explosion and Netting Problems in the Planning of Material Requirements," *Operations Research*, July 1963.

GIFFLER, BERNARD, "Mathematical Solution of Parts Requirement Problems," *Management Science*, July 1965.

GLEIBERMAN, LEON, "The Engineering Change of the Total Requirements Matrix for a Bill of Materials," *Management Science*, April 1964.

HANSSMAN, FRED, and SIDNEY W. HESS, "Linear Programming Approach to Production and Employment Scheduling," *Management Technology*, January 1960.

MAGEE, J. F., "Linear Programming in Production Scheduling," *Operations Research*, February 1953.

MC GARRAH, ROBERT E., *Production and Logistics Management*. New York: John Wiley & Sons, 1963.

SMITH, SPENCER, "An Input-Output Model for Production and Inventory Planning," *J. Ind. Eng.*, January–February 1965.

SYMONDS, G. H., "Stochastic Scheduling by the Horizon Method," *Management Science*, January 1962.

THOMPSON, GERALD L., "On the Parts Requirement Problem," *Operations Research*, May–June 1965.

VAN DE PANNE, C., and P. BOSJE, "Sensitivity Analysis of Cost Coefficient Estimates: The Case of Linear Decision Rules for Employment and Production," *Management Science*, October 1962.

15

Production
and Inventory Control

INTRODUCTION

In this and the next chapter, we will be concerned with tactical decisions made in the course of controlling production and inventory levels. These are decisions that are made daily or weekly about how the production system is to be employed in the immediate future. They are related to such questions as when jobs should be released to the shop, production lot sizes, choice of machines if alternative routings are possible, choice of worker assignments, sequencing of jobs through a machine, etc.

Our discussion will apply to a wide variety of production systems, where one or more products must be produced and inventoried. Many of the concepts can be extrapolated to service systems. However, we will concentrate on manufacturing systems which must accommodate a large product mix and which comprise non-identical machines jointly used by this product mix.

We have categorized production control into three areas, namely, inventory control, scheduling, and dispatching. The focal issues of inventory control are when to replenish the inventory for an item and what the size of the replenishment order should be. Scheduling focuses on the work content of a set of facilities in a future time period. Dispatching is the function of specifying the sequence or order in which jobs that are competing at a given time for a facility will be processed through that facility. In this chapter, we will focus on inventory control, and then, in the next chapter, we will cover scheduling and dispatching.

We should keep in mind that the tactical decisions of production control may or may not be made within the constraints laid down by aggregate planning. If production is planned along the lines discussed in the previous section, then we have to reconcile the results of planning with the control decisions. On the other hand, a company may find it difficult to plan with any economy or reliability and will therefore rely on the control decisions to minimize the costs of operations.

Figure 15.1 shows the essential features of the system to be controlled.

1. *Sales orders* are received daily and filtered by the *production control* function. These are used to update final product forecasts, or backlogs, or both,

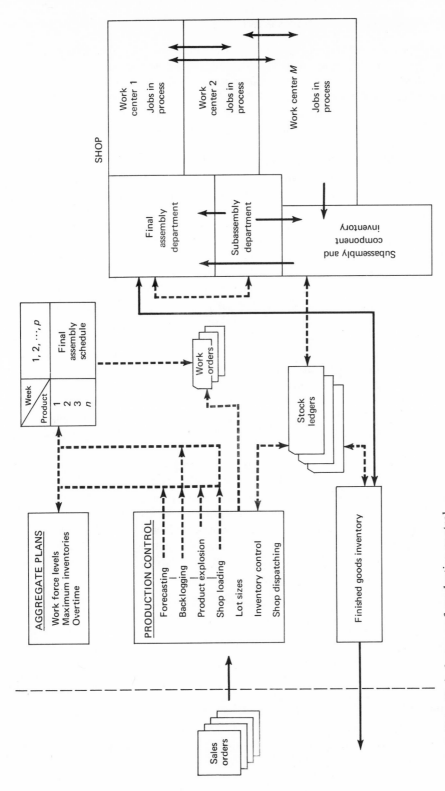

FIGURE **15.1** Basic features of production control.

depending on the circumstances. Both forecasts and backlogs are used to update the aggregate plan as discussed in the previous chapter.

2. *Product explosion and shop loading* translate the final product demand into an equivalent demand for subassemblies and components, as well as raw materials. The shop loads may be used for aggregate planning and/or for setting up actual shop schedules based on a backlog.

3. *Finished goods inventory* may exist if the products are standard. Current demand is met directly from these inventories. Then, inventory replenishment requirements become the demand on the production system, assuming that shop loading of the direct customer demand is not carried out. However, a combination of strategies may be used between the extremes of producing directly to meet inventory replenishment requirements to shop loading a forecast demand and using inventories to make adjustments for forecasting errors.

4. *Work orders* are issued to final assembly either to make an inventory replenishment order, or to adhere to the shop loading schedule, or both. Work orders are also issued currently to subassembly and component fabrication work centers. Such work orders authorize the start of a *job* to assemble a batch of final products or subassemblies, or to start fabricating a batch of a given part.

5. *Final assembly* operations may be supplied from intermediate subassembly and component inventories. In this case, work orders for subassemblies and components reflect replenishment requirements for those inventories. Or, subassembly and component work orders may reflect a shop loading schedule, in which case intermediate inventories are used for replacement parts or for reserves.

6. *Shop orders* of jobs commence in one of the shop work centers. Each job then proceeds through the shop according to its routing instructions. Since facilities are jointly used, each job may compete at a given time for a certain facility, and thus there is a work-in-process inventory consisting of jobs waiting to be processed at a given machine or facility. The time that the job spends waiting to be processed is usually a significant proportion of the total time it spends in the shop prior to entering inventory or assembly operations.

There are other features of the typical system involving a large product mix and jointly shared facilities. Before a job can be started, the shop requirements for tools, quality control devices, raw materials, subcontracting, etc., must be geared to the schedules. If the product is nonstandard, then it must have a preliminary routing through product and production engineering.

Measures of Effectiveness

In production planning, the measure of effectiveness was the degree to which total costs were minimized. The costs were changes in employment levels, inventory, and overtime and were expressed in monetary terms. In production control, the measures of effectiveness are more local and likely to be indices of costs not expressed in monetary terms. An "optimal" production control decision is difficult to make because of the number of criteria and their often conflicting natures.

In trying to assess the efficiency of production control, we might look at the following:

1. *Finished goods inventory* The idea of an optimum inventory is relevant. A large inventory could be the result of leveled production or an essential guard against a highly unpredictable customer demand pattern. Low inventory levels could signify a high risk of running out of stock, as well as low inventory holding costs.

2. *Work-in-process inventory* While a low work-in-process inventory may indicate corresponding minimum holding costs, the problem of efficient plant utilization is eased by having backlogs of work in the shop from which to construct alternative schedules. A work-in-process inventory permits each machine to be an independent processing unit and thus capable of working at its own maximum rate of output without having to be linked directly to subsequent operations.

3. *Inventory shortages* The occurrence of inventory shortages can lead to lost sales, or to the backlogging of jobs, or to the costs of expediting a replenishment order through the production system. The cost of avoiding shortages is to have a reserve inventory capable of meeting unexpected changes in demand. If the cost of holding stock is high, then the toleration of occasional shortages may be advisable.

4. *Facility utilization* When potential demand is greater than capacity, the occurrence of idle facilities due to poor scheduling is obviously costly. On the other hand, an idle machine may result from the judicious shifting of workers from one machine to the other as the work load in the shop shifts between facilities.

5. *Setup or changeover time* The time consumed in setting up a facility to produce a different product is nonproductive and costly and reduces the potential shop capacity. However, the introduction of setups due to small lot production must be weighed against the reduced working inventory.

6. *Late shipments* The difference between shipment date and due date is the measure of the degree of job lateness. Obviously, this must be controlled. The absolute elimination of late deliveries must be bought at the expense of other factors, including larger work-in-process inventories, disrupted schedules due to expediting, and decreased facility utilization.

None of the above measures by itself is a reliable indicator of good or poor production control except as it appears in the extreme.

Batch Production

In the multiproduct-multifacility manufacturing system, parts or products are usually produced intermittently in batches or lots such that no facility is used exclusively throughout the year for the production of a single product. There is, therefore, a joint use of facilities by different parts.

The choice of batch or lot size for a part is a basic decision in production and inventory control. Consider some of the factors that determine lot-size decisions under varying circumstances.

1. If a part is made directly for customer order, then the lot size is obviously determined by the order size unless the order is split into sublots for delivery over a protracted time period.

2. The lot size may be determined by aggregate planning rules. For a seasonal item, leveled production may be chosen such that the part is produced in large lots for inventory during the slow part of the seasonal cycle and then in small lots later on, depending on the difference between the accumulated inventory and current demand. Conversely, another item may be produced directly for current demand throughout the annual cycle.

3. In a system of relatively stable demand, an item may be produced directly for inventory. The production lot size will depend on the economics of holding the item in inventory versus setup costs for its manufacture.

4. The lot size may be determined by scheduling restrictions. In periods of heavy shop loading, lot sizes may be reduced in size to permit a greater product mix to be produced during a given time period. However, if setup time requirements are significant, then larger lot sizes may be produced to reduce the frequency of setting up or changing over facilities.

5. Lot sizes for subassemblies and components may be geared directly to final assembly schedules. Thus, product explosion routines determine the periodic part requirements, which become the production lot sizes.

6. Sometimes lot sizes are determined by machine operating characteristics. For example, in the woodworking industry, lot sizes are sometimes equal to the number of units that can be produced between successive tool sharpenings. Similarly, a chemical batch size may be limited to the production between successive process shutdowns and cleanings.

There are other factors, depending on the specific circumstances. In this section, we will examine the problem of setting batch sizes for products that are produced for inventory and where the decision is focused on the inventory replenishment requirements.

Degree of Control

In a company manufacturing thousands of parts for inventory, some thought must be given to the degree of control to be exerted over the item inventory. The extent to which an item is controlled should depend on the relative importance of the item on some scale. One typical approach is to use the *A-B-C* classification.

In many industries, the classification of items according to their contribution to inventory value follows a particular pattern. That is, a few items may account for a large percentage of the total value of inventory, while, conversely, a large number of items contribute a small amount to the total inventory value.

Figure 15.2 shows the *A-B-C* classification. The subset of items *A* accounts for the largest percentage of inventory value. It is not uncommon to find situations

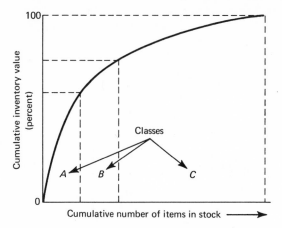

FIGURE **15.2**   *A-B-C* classification of inventory.

where 10% of the items carried in stock contribute 80% of the inventory value. The *C* items fall at the other end of the scale. The implication is, of course, that *A* items deserve a relatively high degree of control, which is facilitated by the relatively small numbers involved. In contrast, control procedures of *C* items need to take into consideration both their low value and their large numbers.

FIXED ORDER SIZE-REORDER POINT MODELS

We now consider the lot-size decision for *A* or *B* items when the items are produced directly for an inventory from which demand is satisfied. If we focus on the inventory, there are two basic decisions to make. The first concerns the size of the lot we should order for inventory and the second when the order should be placed.

The way we attack the problem depends on the manner in which we keep track of the item in inventory. One way is to keep a continuous surveillance over the inventory so that at any given point in time we know exactly how many units are in stock. This is referred to as the *two-bin* system of control. The other method is to periodically review the inventory status either at regular intervals or at random points in time. This is called the *periodic review* system or cyclical ordering. We will first examine the two-bin system (or fixed order size-reorder point models) and then later the periodic review situation.

The two-bin system derives its name from the idea of using two stock bins for each item. The time to replenish the stock is signaled when the first bin is emptied. The second bin then theoretically contains enough items to meet the demand during the "lead time" or the interval of time between the issuance of the order and the arrival of the item on the shelf. Actually, there need not be two bins as long as we keep a physical count of the inventory level so that we know when the level has been reduced to the reorder point—a fact that can be noted on a perpetual inventory record.

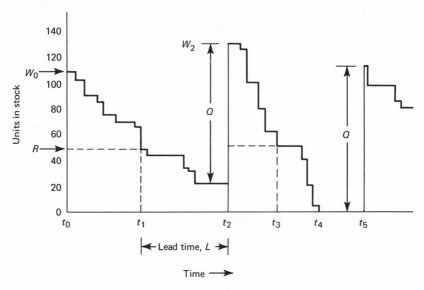

The behavior of a typical inventory under the two-bin system is indicated in Figure 15.3. At time t_0, the inventory is at level W_0. At time t_1, the inventory has been reduced to a level of R units, where R is the *reorder point*. At this time, an order for Q units is issued either as a production or as a purchase order. At time t_2, the order of Q items arrives and replenishes the stock to a level of W_2. The cycle is then repeated with a production order being issued every time the stock drops to the reorder point R. We may note that during any one cycle, the ending stock level just before replenishment is either negative, zero, or positive. If negative, a shortage or stockout occurs, and if positive, the total inventory just after replacement consists of the working inventory Q plus the residual.

The practical problem is to determine good values for both Q and R, which tend to minimize the relevant costs. Theoretically, we can shoot for an optimum Q and R, but, as we shall see, optimal answers may be difficult to obtain in practice or the assumptions underlying them are oversimplified.

Economical Production Lot Size

BASIC MODEL: We will first examine the classical, economical lot-size model (abbreviated as the EOQ model, or economical order quantity). The purpose of this model is to determine the optimum value of Q, given some very severe assumptions or restrictions. The optimum lot size is that quantity which minimizes the costs of inventory and setting up or preparing to produce the lot.

Let us assume that we have a single production facility and a single product to produce for inventory. The inventory status of the product is shown in Figure 15.4. At time t_0, the inventory is exactly at zero level, and we commence to replenish the

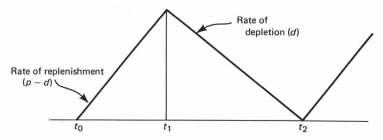

FIGURE **15.4**   Inventory level for economical lot-size model.

stock until time t_1, when the production order is completed. From t_1 to t_2, the inventory diminishes to zero level, at which time the cycle is repeated.

Let

d = annual rate of demand for the item
Q = production lot size; $0 < Q < \infty$
p = annual rate of production; $p > d$
i = annual inventory holding cost
c = item unit marginal cost of production
S = cost to set up or prepare to produce a lot
TC = total cost of inventory policy
Q^* = economical lot size
TC^* = total cost of inventory policy when Q is equal to Q^*

Assume the following:

d is constant and known
p is constant and known
the lead time is constant and known
the system is never out of stock
the product is never obsolete

We have

$$\text{Maximum inventory} = \frac{Q}{p}(p - d)$$

$$\text{Average inventory} = \frac{Q}{2p}(p - d)$$

$$\text{Annual cost of holding inventory} = \frac{ciQ}{2p}(p - d)$$

$$\text{Annual cost of setup} = \frac{Sd}{Q}$$

Then, the total annual cost is

$$TC = \frac{Sd}{Q} + \frac{ciQ(p - d)}{2p}$$

Differentiating with respect to Q and setting the result equal to zero, we have

$$\frac{dTC}{dQ} = \frac{-dS}{Q^2} + \frac{ci(p-d)}{2p} = 0$$

Solving for Q, we obtain

$$Q^* = \sqrt{\frac{2Sdp}{ci(p-d)}}$$

If the capacity of the facility is very large relative to the annual demand rate, then the ratio $p/(p-d)$ approaches 1 and the formula can be simplified to the classical form

$$Q^* = \sqrt{\frac{2S\,d}{ci}}$$

and

$$TC^* = \sqrt{2dSci}$$

We can further simplify the formula by substituting C for ci, thus giving[1]

$$Q^* = \sqrt{\frac{2Sd}{C}}$$

This model first appeared in the literature in the late 1910's. It has appeared since that time in various forms such as nomographs and slide rules to facilitate computations. Its validity in a real-life situation is open to question, and there are probably many situations where the formula has been abandoned for various reasons. However, it is the first step to more involved models, and, therefore, its limitations should be thoroughly understood. For example, you might consider the following questions:

1. A firm has a general policy of keeping two months' supply of a certain item in stock. A two-month supply means that the stock should be sufficient to meet a two-month demand. What is the effect on inventory under this policy if the demand rate suddenly doubles? How does this compare with the EOQ model?
2. How does management judgment enter into the use of the formula? For instance, how might the matter of possible obsolescence of the product be handled by the formula?
3. What kinds of problems would arise in scheduling the demand created by replenishing inventories based on economical lot-size quantities?
4. What will happen if we relax the assumption that we have only one facility and one product?
5. Can the value of Q^* be larger than d?
6. If we had to control 20,000 items in stock, how would we reconcile the computational problems?

---

[1] This model applies to a purchased item, where S is the order preparation cost and C is the annual holding cost based on the purchase price of the item.

7. How can we reconcile the use of the model with the specifications laid down for aggregate inventory levels by the planning function?

SENSITIVITY OF TOTAL COST TO DEVIATIONS IN Q: One important point is the effect on total cost if the lot size differs from the optimum. That is, if for various reasons we cannot produce the economical lot size, what will be the effect on the total cost?

Suppose we are forced to produce a lot size $Q = \dfrac{Q^*}{2}$. Then,

$$\frac{TC}{TC^*} = \frac{dS}{Q\sqrt{2dSC}} + \frac{CQ}{2\sqrt{2dSC}}$$

Multiplying the top and bottom of the first term by $\sqrt{2dS}$ and the top and bottom of the second term by $\sqrt{C}$, and recalling that $Q^* = \sqrt{\dfrac{2dS}{C}}$, we have

$$\frac{TC}{TC^*} = \frac{dS\sqrt{2dS}}{Q2dS\sqrt{C}} + \frac{CQ\sqrt{C}}{2C\sqrt{2dS}} = \frac{1}{2}\left[\frac{\sqrt{2dS}}{Q\sqrt{C}} + \frac{Q\sqrt{C}}{\sqrt{2dS}}\right]$$

$$\frac{TC}{TC^*} = \frac{1}{2}\left[\frac{Q^*}{Q} + \frac{Q}{Q^*}\right]$$

Since $Q = Q^*/2$,

$$\frac{TC}{TC^*} = \frac{1}{2}\left[2 + \frac{1}{2}\right] = 1.25$$

This says that if Q deviates from Q^* by $Q^*/2$ or $2Q^*$, the total cost increases by only 25%. We can conclude that the total cost is insensitive to minor deviations of the lot size from the optimum (Figure 15.5).

THE EFFECT OF PRICE BREAKS: It is not unusual to experience a change in production costs as the lot size increases due to shifting from one kind of process to another. Suppose that the unit production cost is c_1 for a lot size ranging from 1 to $Q_2 - 1$, c_2 for a lot size from Q_2 to $Q_3 - 1$, and c_3 for a lot of Q_3 or larger. Then, there is a set of three cost functions. Figure 15.6 shows three such functions with price breaks occurring at lot sizes Q_2 and Q_3. The optimum Q is the lowest point on the stepwise function that satisfies the price break restrictions.

ECONOMICAL LOT SIZE WITH AGGREGATE CONSTRAINTS: If we aggregate the production requirements of a large number of items using the individual economical lot-size formulas, then the results may be inadmissible due to restrictions on the aggregate value of some resource. For example, the number of setup hours available in a plant may be insufficient to meet the setup requirements generated by economical lot-size formulas. This, for example, is a real constraint in certain metal-working shops, where skilled setup labor is at a premium. Or, there may be insufficient inventory space available or a restriction on total capital for inventory investment.

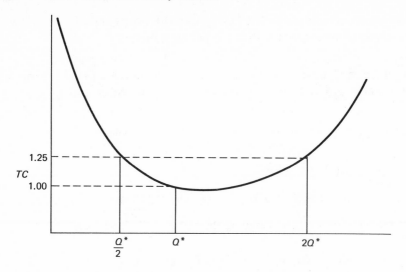

FIGURE **15.5**   Effect on total cost of deviations from Q.

In these situations, the problem is to allocate the limited resource to the individual items so that total cost is minimized.

Suppose we have a restriction on the total setup hours available, and we wish to determine the economical lot size for items in stock. Let

d_i = annual rate of demand for the ith item, $i = 1, 2, \ldots, N$

Q_i = lot size for the ith item

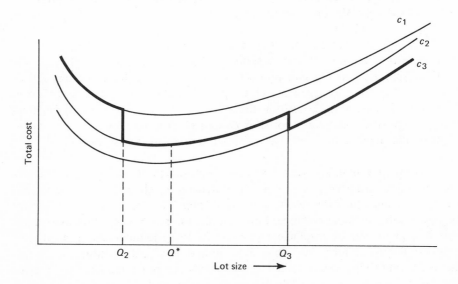

FIGURE **15.6**   Effect of price breaks on total cost.

$_rQ_i^* =$ economical lot size for the ith item considering the restriction
$Q_i^* =$ economical lot size without considering the restriction
$C_i =$ unit annual inventory holding cost for ith item
$s =$ rate of cost per setup hour
$H_i =$ annual setup hours required for the ith item
$_rH_i^* =$ annual setup hours required for the ith item when $_rQ_i^*$ is produced
$S_i =$ cost to set up a lot of the ith product
$M =$ total annual setup hours available
$T_i =$ total annual cost for the ith item
$TC =$ total annual cost for all products $= \sum\limits_1^N T_i$

The objective is to minimize TC. Now

$$H_i = \frac{d_i S_i}{Q_i s} \quad \text{or} \quad Q_i = \frac{d_i S_i}{H_i s}$$

$$T_i = \frac{d_i}{Q_i} S_i + \frac{Q_i}{2} C_i$$

Substituting for Q_i,

$$T_i = \frac{H_i s \, d_i S_i}{d_i S_i} + \frac{d_i S_i C_i}{2 H_i s}$$

Let

$$a_i = \frac{d_i S_i C_i}{s}$$

Then,

$$T_i = s H_i + \frac{a_i}{2 H_i}$$

$$TC = s \sum_1^N H_i + \sum \left(\frac{a_i}{2 H_i} \right) \tag{1}$$

subject to $\sum H_i - M \leq 0$ \hspace{2em} (2)

Now we define a new variable λ (Lagrange multiplier).

$$\lambda = 0 \quad \text{if} \quad \sum H_i - M < 0$$
$$\lambda > 0 \quad \text{if} \quad \sum H_i - M = 0$$

If we multiply Equation (2) by λ, the product is always 0. Now add Equation (2) to both sides of Equation (1), giving the Lagrangian expression.

$$TC + \lambda(\sum H_i - M) = \left(\sum s H_i + \sum \frac{a_i}{2 H_i} \right) + \lambda(\sum H_i - M)$$

$$= \sum H_i(s + \lambda) + \sum \frac{a}{2 H_i} - \lambda M$$

We next set the partial derivative with respect to H_i equal to zero.

$$\frac{\partial[TC + \lambda(\sum H_i - M)]}{\partial H_i} = s + \lambda - \frac{a_i}{2 H_i^2} = 0$$

$$_rH_i^* = \sqrt{\frac{a_i}{2(s + \lambda)}} \tag{3}$$

$$\frac{\partial[TC + \lambda(\sum H_i - M)]}{\partial \lambda} = \sum H_i - M = 0$$

$$\sum H_i = M \tag{4}$$

Now our problem is to find a value of λ that will satisfy both Equations (3) and (4) for all H_i. Note that if λ is equal to zero, $_rH_i^* = H_i^*$, and the regular EOQ formula yields Q^*, since $\sum H_i - M \leq 0$. The first thing to do is to set λ equal to zero and determine if the restraint is satisfied by the sum of the H_i's. If not, increase λ by trial and error until the restriction is exactly satisfied.

In this particular case, we can relate Q_i^* to $_rQ_i^*$. If we substitute for a_i,

$$_rH_i^* = \sqrt{\frac{d_i S_i C_i}{2s(s + \lambda)}}$$

$$_rQ_i^* = \sqrt{\frac{d_i S_i 2(s + \lambda)}{C_i s}}$$

$$\frac{_rQ_i^*}{Q_i^*} = \sqrt{\frac{(s + \lambda)}{s}}$$

If $\lambda = 0$,

$$_rQ_i^* = Q_i^*$$

Since we are already familiar with the sensitivity of the total cost to deviations from Q^*, we could use the above information to estimate the total savings if additional setup hours could be obtained and compare these with the costs involved in gaining the additional hours.

C STOCK ITEMS: The detailed analysis of each item in inventory may be quite uneconomical if the number of items in inventory is large. C stock items usually account for the largest percentage of items in stock but contribute, in the aggregate, the smallest percent of inventory value or use. Generally, therefore, we must apply some sort of aggregate rule to all items in this class or break the total number of items into a manageable number of subsets to which rules can be individually applied.

A general policy may be applied to C items such as "order one-quarter, one-half, or even one year's supply." If the order quantities for C items are kept small under the impression that inventory costs will be reduced, then there will be a large number of purchase orders written, since, by definition, C items account for the largest number in stock. Also, the opportunity for price breaks may be ignored. The over-all effect of shifting a general policy from ordering one-quarter to one-half year's supply or from one-half to one full year's supply can be tested by sampling some C items at random to determine the effect of the desired policy on inventory costs and price breaks. The results of the sample can be used to judge the effect of the policy on all C items with an appropriate measure of precision and confidence.

For example, Table 15.1 shows the hypothetical results of sampling 50 C items at random.[2]

The total net annual savings for the sample is \$142.20, and the estimated savings per item is therefore \$2.85. Assume that there are 1,000 items comprising the C class. Then the total savings for this class will be \$2,850, and we may associate a precision to this estimate based on the sample variability. The estimated savings do not reflect certain variables, namely:

1. The inventory costs (Column 13) do not consider any additional storage costs nor item obsolescence. These might be reflected in a higher inventory holding rate.
2. Order preparation costs are ignored, and this factor would favor the larger order quantity.
3. The investment in inventory fails to consider a reserve stock. However, the larger order quantity would reduce the risks of annual shortage due to fewer reorder cycles.

SINGLE MACHINE CYCLIC PRODUCTION: Certain production systems consist of a single process jointly shared by a number of products that are made in sequence. A typical case would be a food processing machine in which a number of brands are made in sequence during a single production cycle. The problem is to determine the optimum cycle length through which all products are to be made, as well as the optimum batch size for each product. Presumably the number of products is small, so that the cycle will be repeated a number of times during the year. Let

p_i = production rate for the ith product, $i = 1, 2, \ldots, n$
d_i = annual rate of demand for the ith product—a constant
t_i = length of run time for the ith product in years
c_i = inventory cost per unit per year
Q_i = production batch size for the ith product
S = total setup cost for all products. This assumes that the sequence has been chosen such that S is a minimum.
m = number of cycles per year
I_i = average inventory for the ith product
TC = total cost over all i

Then,

$$I_i = \frac{t_i}{2}(p_i - d_i)$$

Since

$$Q_i = p_i t_i \quad \text{and} \quad Q_i = d_i/m$$

[2] J. W. Gavett, "Sampling to Determine Price Break Advantages in 'C' Stock Items," *J. Ind. Eng.*, vol. XII, no. 6, November–December 1961, pp. 406–11.

TABLE **15.1**   Sample data for C items.

1	2	3	4	5	6	7	8	9	10	11	12	13	14	15
									Ave. inv't. in inv.		Added investmt.	Added holding cost	Net annual savings	
Item number	A = annual demand-units	Q_1 units	P_1 $	Q_2 units	P_2 $	$(A)(P_1)$ $	$(A)(P_2)$ $	Savings Col. 7 − Col. 8 $	$Q_2P_2/2$ $	$Q_1P_1/2$ $	Col. 10 − Col. 11 $	$i\times$(Col. 12) $	Col. 9 − Col. 13 X $	Col. 14 squared X^2 $
1	200	12	0.207	100	0.145	41.40	29.00	12.40	7.25	1.24	6.01	0.60ᵃ	+11.80	139.24
2	2,000	1,000	0.051	1,000	0.051	102.00	102.00	—	—	—	—	—	—	—
3	60,000	15,000	0.007	30,000	0.007	420.00	420.00	—	105.00	52.50	52.50	5.25	−5.25	27.56
4	24	6	1.700	12	1.500	40.80	36.00	4.80	9.00	5.10	3.90	0.39	+4.41	19.45
5	1,000	200	0.805	500	0.765	805.00	765.00	40.00	191.25	80.50	110.75	11.07	+28.93	836.94
6	30,000	15,000	0.011	15,000	0.011	330.00	330.00	—	—	—	—	—	—	—
7	160	25	2.200	80	2.000	352.00	320.00	32.00	80.00	27.50	52.50	5.25	+26.75	715.56
8	600	100	0.351	300	0.281	210.00	168.60	41.40	42.00	17.55	24.45	2.46	+38.34	1,469.96
9	200	100	0.294	100	0.294	58.80	58.80	—	—	—	—	—	—	—
10	480	120	0.290	240	0.290	139.20	139.20	—	34.80	17.40	17.40	1.74	−1.74	3.03
11	144	24	0.470	72	0.470	67.68	67.68	—	16.92	5.64	11.28	1.13	−1.13	1.28
47	400	400	0.200	200	0.235	80.00	94.00	−14.00	23.50	40.00	−16.50	−1.65	−12.35	152.52
48	5,000	1,000	0.080	2,500	0.072	400.00	360.00	40.00	90.00	40.00	50.00	5.00	+35.00	1,225.00
49	1,200	300	0.202	600	0.202	242.40	242.40	—	60.60	30.30	30.30	3.03	−3.03	9.18
50	100	20	2.500	50	2.300	250.00	230.00	20.00	57.56	25.00	32.56	3.26	+16.74	280.23
Total													$142.20	$4,335.16

Adapted from *J. Ind. Eng.,* November–December 1961, p. 407.

ᵃ i = interest rate = 10 percent in this example.

Column 1—Code number or name of item.

Column 2—Estimated average annual demand for the item.

Column 3—(Q_1) Quantity ordered under the present policy, which averages one-quarter year's supply with individual variation.

Column 4—(P_1) Unit price when buying in quantities equal to Q_1.

Column 5—(Q_2) Quantity to be ordered under new policy, which is equal to one-half year's supply.

Column 6—(P_2) Unit price when buying in quantities equal to Q_2. In some cases, this reflects a price break, while in others, no price break is possible.

Column 7—(AP_1) Total annual purchase cost of the item under present policy.

Column 8—(AP_2) Total annual purchase cost of the item under proposed policy.

Column 9—(Col. 7 − Col. 8) Annual savings due to price break.

Column 10—($Q_2P_2/2$) Average annual investment in inventory of the item under the proposed policy.

Column 11—($Q_1P_1/2$) Average annual investment in inventory of the item under the present policy.

Column 12—(Col. 10 − Col. 11) Added investment in inventory due to buying in larger quantity.

Column 13—(Col. 12 × 10%) Added holding cost, assuming a rate of 10%.

Column 14—(Col. 9 − Col. 13) Net savings or loss for the item.

we have

$$\frac{t_1}{2}(p_i - d_i) = (p_i - d_i)\frac{Q_i}{2p_i} = (p_i - d_i)\frac{d_i}{2mp_i} = \frac{d_i}{2m}\left(1 - \frac{d_i}{p_i}\right)$$

and

$$TC = mS + \frac{1}{2m}\sum_{i=1}^{n} c_i d_i \left(1 - \frac{d_i}{p_i}\right)$$

Setting $\dfrac{dTC}{dm} = 0$ and solving for m, we have

$$m^* = \sqrt{\frac{\sum\limits_i c_i d_i(1 - d_i/p_i)}{2S}}$$

and since $Q_i = d_i/m$,

$$Q_i^* = \sqrt{\frac{2d_i^2 S}{\sum\limits_i c_i d_i(1 - d_i/p_i)}}$$

The Reorder Point

In the economical lot-size model, the lead time is known and constant. A reorder is issued when the inventory falls to a point where the stock on hand exactly meets the demand that occurs during the lead time. Because demand and possibly lead time are seldom known with certainty, there is always the possibility that the residual stock at the time the replenishment order arrives will be other than zero. The problem is to set the reorder point such that there is some balance between being out of stock on the one hand and having too large a residual inventory on the other hand. An optimum reorder point R^* is one that balances the costs of being out of stock and the costs of the residual inventory.

The fact that demand and lead time are variables and not known with certainty results in the necessity of maintaining a *reserve* stock in inventory. Thus, the average inventory is equal to one-half the reorder quantity Q plus the average size of the reserve stock. The size of the reserve stock is proportional to the value of R, the reorder point.

The determination of an optimum value of R is difficult in practice due to the problems of determining both the costs of shortages and the variable nature of demand and lead time. The value of R may be set by management dictum. If management is sensitive to shortages, then the reorder point may be set high enough so that there is a very small chance that shortages will occur under maximum possible rates of demand. If the dictum is to reduce inventory levels, then either R or Q or both will be lowered.

The number of shortages that will occur in a year is not just a function of R. There is a certain probability of a shortage occurring every time a reorder is to be made. Therefore, the number of reorders made in a year, which is determined by Q, affects the shortages that will occur in the year. However, for any given reorder cycle, the probability of a shortage is determined solely by R.

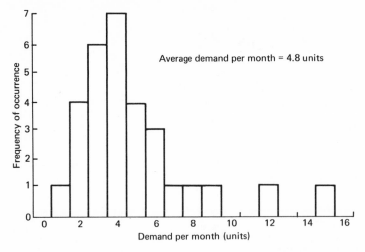

FIGURE **15.7** Frequency distribution of monthly demand for model K.

SETTING R BY PROBABILITY OF A SHORTAGE OCCURRING: In trying to set R, we may concentrate only on the probability of a shortage of the item in a given reorder cycle, assuming that lead time demand is a random variable. This can be theoretically determined rather easily if we know the probability distribution of demand during the lead time and if the lead time is constant.

Consider the following example. A manufacturer of ice-making machines has a certain model K, which he makes for stock. The following is a record of the monthly sales of the model for the past 30 months, in number of units sold.

	Jan.	Feb.	Mar.	Apr.	May	Jun.	Jul.	Aug.	Sept.	Oct.	Nov.	Dec.
1965	3	2	4	5	6	9	3	3	4	7	2	4
1966	3	2	4	4	5	3	6	2	4	5	4	3
1967	6	1	5	15	12	8						

This information is also displayed in Figure 15.7 as a frequency distribution of the demand for model K. If we assume that the lead time to manufacture the item is exactly one month, then the reorder point can be set in terms of the risk of a shortage occurring. Presumably, for example, if the reorder point is set at 15, then the chances of a shortage are zero, if we assume that the past is a good predictor of the future. Or, setting the reorder point at 12 units indicates a probability of 0.033 of having a demand greater than 12.

If the manufacturer stocked a large number of items, the construction of frequency distributions for each item could well be a tedious task. In order to avoid this, he may assume that the lead-time demand for his products reflects some theoretical distributions that would be easy to work with. Figure 15.8, for example, shows the superimposition of a Poisson distribution on the actual distribution, using the actual average of 4.8 units per month. The approximation of actual demand using such a theoretical distribution facilitates the task of determining

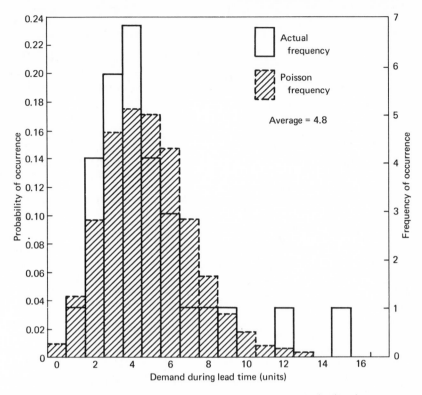

<small>Probability of occurrence</small> — <small>Frequency of occurrence</small>

Average = 4.8

Demand during lead time (units)

FIGURE **15.8** Comparison of Poisson and actual demand distribution.

shortage probabilities but obviously introduces risks of error. Note that the two distributions differ at the right tail, which is where we would hope they agree. In this case, the difference might be explained by an unusually large order in one month, or perhaps the average demand is shifting due to a product growth pattern.

Summarizing this method of setting the reorder point, assume that X is the lead time demand, a random variable with a probability distribution $f(x)$. Then, assuming that the desired probability of a shortage occurring is θ, we set R such that Prob $(x > R) = \theta$. The safety stock level is then $R - E(X)$.

VARIABLE LEAD TIME: The problem can be compounded if the lead time, as well as the demand, is a random variable. Then the lead-time demand is a joint probability distribution. For example, assume that a company has a product for which the demand per unit time D is a random variable and the lead time T is a random variable with the following probability distributions:

D	0	1	2		T	1	2
$f(d)$	0.2	0.5	0.3	;	$g(t)$	0.4	0.6

Let X be the lead-time demand with a distribution $h(x)$ calculated as follows:

X	$t = 1$		$t = 2$			$h(x)$
	$d; t = 1$	$P(d; t = 1)$	d_1 1st period	d_2 2nd period	$P(d_1 \cap d_2; t = 2)$	
0	0	(0.2)(0.4) = 0.08	0	0	(0.2)(0.2)(0.6) = 0.024	0.104
1	1	(0.5)(0.4) = 0.20	0 1	1 0	$\left.\begin{array}{l}(0.2)(0.5)(0.6)\\(0.5)(0.2)(0.6)\end{array}\right\} = 0.120$	0.320
2	2	(0.3)(0.4) = 0.12	0 2 1	2 0 1	$\left.\begin{array}{l}(0.2)(0.3)(0.6)\\(0.3)(0.2)(0.6)\\(0.5)(0.5)(0.6)\end{array}\right\} = 0.222$	0.342
3			1 2	2 1	$\left.\begin{array}{l}(0.5)(0.3)(0.6)\\(0.3)(0.5)(0.6)\end{array}\right\} = 0.180$	0.180
4			2	2	(0.3)(0.3)(0.6)	0.054

If the reorder point R is set at 3 units, then the probability of a shortage in any reorder cycle is the probability of getting a demand for 4 units, or 0.054. The average lead-time demand is $\sum_0^4 xh(x) = 1.760$, and therefore the expected value of the reserve stock will be $3 - 1.76 = 1.24$.

VARIABLE CUSTOMER ORDER SIZE: In trying to set a reorder point, it is important to recognize the character of the demand for the item in stock. Usually demand consists of two components, namely the number of orders received in a given time period and the size of each order. When order size, as well as the number of orders, is a random variable, then we have to consider a joint probability distribution of demand. Table 15.2 shows the value of the reorder point for an average lead-time demand of 200 units made up of different values of average number of orders, order size, and lead time to give a probability of shortage equal to 0.05.

TABLE **15.2**   Reorder point required to give a probability of shortage equal to 0.05.

Case	Average number of orders (Poisson variable)	Average order size (negative exponential variable)	Average lead time (Poisson variable)	Average lead-time demand	R
1	200	Constant (1)	Constant (1)	200	225
2	50	4	"		255
3	40	5	"		275
4	30	6.7	"		290
5	20	10	"		310
6	10	20	"		355
7	5	40	"		425
8	1	67	3		490

In each case, the average lead-time demand is 200 units. In case 1, the order size and lead time are constants. In all but the last case, the lead time is a constant. The number of orders is a Poisson random variable, and the order size has a negative exponential distribution. Note that when the number of orders, order size, and lead time are random variables, the reorder point required to give a probability of shortage equal to 0.05 is just over twice the value for the first case, where only the order size is a variable.

Figure 15.9 shows the influence of a negative, exponentially distributed order size on the size of the reorder point for different values of shortage probability.

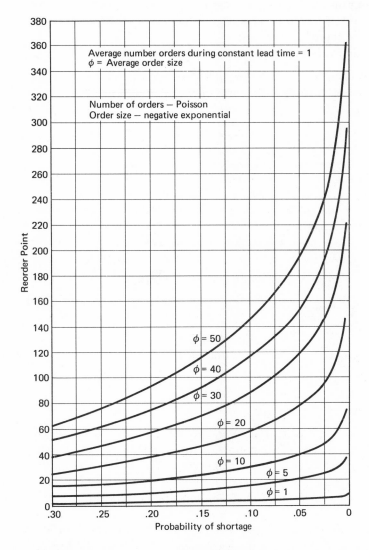

FIGURE **15.9** Reorder point for different values of average customer order size.

In this case, the average number of orders during a constant lead time is Poisson distributed with a mean of 1.00. Note the sensitivity of the reorder point to low values of the shortage probability, and for large average order sizes.

LINEAR INVENTORY HOLDING AND SHORTAGE COSTS: If both the holding costs and shortage costs are directly proportional to the number of units held in stock and the number of units out of stock, respectively, then there is a very simple rule of thumb that can be applied to obtain an optimal value of R. Let

C = unit annual cost of holding an item in stock
Q = reorder quantity
A = unit cost of having an item out of stock
d = average annual rate of demand
$P(S)$ = probability of having a shortage

Then the optimum value of R is such that the expected cost of holding the item in stock is equal to the expected cost of not having the item in stock.

$$C(1 - P(S)) = \frac{Ad}{Q} P(S)$$

$$P(S) = \frac{C}{\frac{Ad}{Q} + C}$$

This says that the optimum R should be set such that the probability of having a shortage is equal to the ratio of the annual holding cost to the sum of the annual holding and shortage costs, assuming that the costs are linear.

Consider, for example, the case of the ice-machine manufacturer (page 496). For the particular model, C = $100, Q = 4, A = $50, and d = 57.5. Then,

$$P(S) = \frac{100}{\frac{50 \times 57.5}{4} + 100} = 0.12$$

Then, considering the empirical distribution of demand, the reorder point would be set at 8 units.

A (Q, R) Model

It may be obvious that there is an interdependence between Q and R when the objective is to minimize costs. The optimum reorder point R^* is a function of the number of reorder cycles per year, which, in turn, is a function of Q. Then Q is a function of the shortage costs. Therefore, choosing Q^* and R independently of each other introduces an error. The (Q, R) model considers the joint optimum value of the two variables.

In the event of a shortage, we may assume either that the order is backlogged or that a sale is lost. In the following development, we will assume the lost sales case. We will use the following notation:

X = the lead-time demand—a random variable with a probability distribution $f(x)$

$u = E(X)$

Q = reorder quantity

Q^* = economic reorder quantity

R = reorder point

R^* = optimum reorder point

C = unit annual inventory holding cost

A = unit marginal cost of a shortage

a = number of units stocked out in a reorder cycle

d = average annual rate of demand

S = setup cost per lot

$P(S)$ = probability of a shortage in a reorder cycle

TC = total annual cost

Now consider the matter of lost sales. If, given R, we let $E(a; R)$ be the expected number of units short in a reorder cycle, then

$$E(a; R) = \sum_{R+1}^{\max} (x - R)f(x)$$

The average annual cost related to the number of reorder cycles is

$$(d/Q)[S + AE(a; R)]$$

The average annual inventory cost is

$$C\left[\frac{Q}{2} + (R - u) + E(a; R)\right]$$

The first and second terms in the brackets account for the working inventory and safety stock, respectively. The last term is included under the assumption that the expected demand will be decreased by the amount of the lost sales, and therefore average inventory will be increased by that amount. Now the total cost is

$$TC = \frac{d}{Q}[S + AE(a; R)] + C\left[\frac{Q}{2} + (R - u) + E(a; R)\right]$$

Differentiating this expression with respect to Q and setting it equal to zero, we have

$$\frac{dTC}{dQ} = -\frac{2d}{Q^2}[S + AE(a; R)] + C = 0$$

$$Q^* = \sqrt{\frac{2d[S + AE(a; R)]}{C}} \tag{5}$$

Now we note that Q^* cannot be determined unless $E(a; R)$ is known. This is a function of R, which, in turn, is a function of Q, and therefore we need a second relationship between Q and R. We can use the same argument presented earlier for the case of linear costs of shortage and inventory. That is, we equate the expected annual holding cost of increasing R by one unit with the expected annual shortage cost.

$$[1 - P(S)] \frac{CQ}{d} = AP(S)$$

$$P(S) = \frac{C}{\dfrac{Ad}{Q} + C} \tag{6}$$

The procedure for determining Q^* and R^* is reiterative:

1. Set $E(a; R) = 0$.
2. Solve for Q using Equation (5).
3. Solve for $P(S)$ using Equation (6).
4. Determine the value of R that corresponds to $P(S)$ from the distribution $f(x)$.
5. Solve for a new Q using Equation (5), where $E(a; R) = \sum\limits_{R+1}^{max} (x - R)f(x)$.
6. Repeat the steps until a solution is converged upon.

Note from Equation (5) that Q^* deviates from the deterministic economical lot size (EOQ) by a factor $AE(a; R)$, which is added to S. If this factor is a small increment to S, then Q^* will not differ greatly from the EOQ.

If in practice we wish to avoid using a joint model of the above type, then probably little error will be involved if we simply choose Q^* using the deterministic lot-size model $\sqrt{\dfrac{2dS}{c}}$ and then choose R using a predetermined probability of shortage or the ratio of the holding cost to the sum of the shortage and holding costs. Using the EOQ model would always result in a smaller Q^* than the one determined by the joint model. But the difference can be negligible and not worth worrying about in light of our knowledge of the sensitivity of total cost to non-optimal Q.

PERIODIC REVIEW SYSTEMS

In contrast to the preceding system, where inventory was kept under constant surveillance, the periodic review system examines the inventory only at periodic or random times. At the time of the review, the manager must decide how much to order to replenish the inventory. His decision, of course, will depend on the status of the inventory at that time, as well as on the nature of the replenishment lead time and the time interval between reviews. He must also fix the time interval between successive reviews.

In this system, there are costs of both working and reserve inventories, as well as costs associated with stockouts, both of these costs being dependent on the decisions in question. Periodic review systems are required in cases where continuous inventory surveillance is impossible, as in the case of off-premise gas or liquid storage tanks, or uneconomical, as in the case of class B or C items. First we will assume that the time interval between reviews has been fixed, and the problem will be to determine an ordering policy when the review takes place. Then we will consider the problem of determining an optimal review period.

An Elementary Rule

A simple rule to use, given a fixed lead time, is as follows:

1. A forecast of demand is made for a period equal to the delivery lead time plus one reorder cycle.
2. An order is placed equal to the demand forecast over the reorder cycle plus lead time less the inventory on hand and on order at the time the order is placed.

In such a system, the average inventory on hand and on order can be viewed as composed of three elements.

1. The *safety stock* or average level of minimum balances on hand. The safety stock is designed to absorb fluctuations in the minimum balances, as in the two-bin system. In the fixed period system, the amount of stock on hand at the minimum points will fluctuate by the same amount as the differences between actual and expected demand over the period of lead time plus cycle time. Thus, the required safety stock can be determined from an analysis of these fluctuations, together with a specified risk of running out.
2. The *cycle stock*, equal to half the average quantity ordered, that is, half the average consumption during one cycle.
3. The *stock on order but undelivered*, which will equal the average consumption during the lead time.

In this system, the orders will arrive periodically if the lead time is constant, and the time between deliveries will equal the review cycle time. There will be a time lag between the order arrival and the time the review is made. If t_i is the time of the ith review, L the lead time, O_i the time of arrival of the order placed at t_i, and T the review period, then

1. If the review cycle is longer than the lead time, an order O_{i-1} will arrive $T - L$ periods prior to t_i.
2. If the review cycle is less than the lead time, an order O_{i-1} will arrive $L - T$ periods after t_i.

EXAMPLE 15.1   Suppose we have a single product for which the past average demand per month has been 30 units. A review period is equal to one month, and the lead time for replenishment is one month. Thus, an order placed in month t becomes available in month $t + 2$. The ordering rule is

$$Q_t = S_{t+2} - I_t - \phi_{t+1}$$

where

Q_t = order size placed at the end of month t
S_{t+2} = demand forecast for the next two periods, $t + 1$ and $t + 2$
I_t = inventory at the end of period t
ϕ_t = order due in period t

The performance of the rule is shown in Table 15.3.

The forecast demand is a simple moving average starting with 30 units in the period just prior to the first period; for example, for period 1, $S = 2[(30 + 28)/2]$.

TABLE **15.3**

Month	t	1	2	3	4	5	6	7	8	9
Inventory on hand at beginning of month	B_t	0	2	0	0	11	14	6	0	4
Order size arriving during month	ϕ_t	30[a]	30	26	36	25	22	25	30	30
Actual demand during month	D_t	28	35	29	25	34	30	31	26	34
Inventory on hand at end of period $I_t = B_t + \phi_t - D_t$	I_t	2	0	0	11	14	6	0	4	0
Demand forecast for periods $t+1, t+2$	S_{t+2}	58	62	61	58	61	61	60	59	60
Order quantity $Q = S_{t+2} - I_t - \phi_{t+1}$	Q_t	26	36	25	22	25	30	30	25	35
Shortages		0	−3	−3	0	0	0	0	0	0

[a] Ordered in period $t - 2$.

The s,S Rule

A second decision rule under the periodic review system, the *s,S* rule, is applied to conditions of random demand during the review cycle. The rule is to order an amount to bring the inventory up to a level *S*, but only if the inventory level at the time of review and prior to ordering is less than an amount *s*. Otherwise, no order is placed. Let

y = the inventory level at the start of a period after an order has been placed
x = the inventory level at the start of the period, but before placing an order
Q = the amount ordered

Then

$$Q = \begin{cases} y - x \text{ if } x \le s \\ 0 \text{ otherwise} \end{cases}$$

The problem is to determine optimal values of $x = s$ and $y = S$ for given shortage and holding costs.

ZERO OPENING INVENTORY: The problem appears in its simplest form when I is equal to zero. That is, we start out each period with no inventory on hand and we wish to determine how much to order given a random demand for the item over the review cycle. This form of the problem is identical with setting an economical reorder point in the two-bin system, in which we balance the costs of shortage and the costs of holding a reserve stock. A practical example of this problem is the ordering of a perishable item that is to be sold over a time period equal to the reorder cycle. At the end of the cycle, the item has either been completely sold or the remainder must be disposed of at a loss.

The general formulation of the problem in this form is as follows. Let

$f(d)$ = probability distribution of demand d during the review period (reorder cycle)

y = the number of units to be ordered at the beginning of the reorder cycle

A = cost of disposing of an unsold unit at the end of the reorder cycle

B = unit cost of a shortage of the item

$E(C)$ = expected cost of a policy of ordering y units

Then, if $d < y$, the cost of disposing of residual units is $A(y - d)$, and if $y \le d$, the shortage cost is $B(d - y)$. The expected cost of a policy of ordering y units at the beginning of the reorder cycle is

$$E(C) = \int_0^y A(y - d)f(d) \, dd + \int_y^\infty B(d - y)f(d) \, dd$$

Now the optimum number y of units to order that will minimize $E(C)$ is found by setting the derivative of $E(C)$ with respect to y equal to zero and solving for y.

EXAMPLE 15.2   A Christmas tree grower has a stand of premium silver firs. He wants to know how many he should cut and sell at his distribution center located in a city 200 miles away. Since it is one week before Christmas, he will make one trip to the tree farm and cut as many trees as he thinks he can sell. If the demand during the week is greater than the number of trees he has cut, the opportunity cost of lost sales is $10. If the demand is less than the number he has cut, the extra trees must be disposed of at a loss of $5 each. How many trees should he cut if the weekly demand during the week prior to Christmas is randomly distributed with a uniform distribution having a range of 0–100?

Let

d = weekly demand

$f(d) = 1/100; \quad 0 \le d \le 100$

y = number of trees cut

$E(C)$ = total expected cost

If $y < d$, then the cost of stockout will be $10(d - y)$. If $y > d$, then the cost of overstocking is $5(y - d)$.

The expected total cost is

$$E(C) = \int_0^y 5(y - d)f(d) \, dd + \int_y^\infty 10(d - y)f(d) \, dd$$

$$= \int_0^y 5(y - d)(1/100) \, dd + \int_y^\infty 10(d - y)(1/100) \, dd$$

$$= (1/100)[5dy - 5d^2/2]_0^y + (1/100)[5d^2 - 10dy]_y^{100}$$

$$= (1/100)[5y^2 - 5y^2/2 + 5(100)^2 - (10)(100)y - 5y^2 + 10y^2]$$

$$= (1/100)[5y^2/2 + 50{,}000 - 1{,}000y + 5y^2]$$

$$= (1/100)[7.5y^2 - 1{,}000y + 50{,}000]$$

$$= 7.5y^2 - 1{,}000y + 50{,}000$$

$$\frac{dE(C)}{dy} = 0 = 15y - 1,000$$

$$y^* = 67$$

Consider a more direct solution to the previous problem. This may already be apparent to the reader from the earlier discussion of reorder points. Let A be the unit cost of overstocking and let B be the unit cost of understocking. Then again, the expression for expected total cost is

$$E(C) = \int_0^y A(y - d)f(d) \, dd + \int_y^\infty B(d - y)f(d) \, dd$$

$$= Ay \int_0^y f(d) \, dd - A \int_0^y df(d) \, dd + B \int_y^\infty df(d) \, dd - By \int_y^\infty f(d) \, dd$$

Differentiating with respect to y and setting the results equal to zero, we have

$$\frac{dE(C)}{dy} = Ayf(y) + A \int_0^y f(d) \, dd - Ayf(y) - Byf(y)$$

$$+ Byf(y) - B \int_y^\infty f(d) \, dd = 0$$

and

$$A \int_0^y f(d) \, dd = B \int_y^\infty f(d) \, dd$$

That is, the expected total cost is minimized when the expected cost of overstocking equals the expected cost of understocking. Since

$$\int_0^\infty f(d) \, dd = 1,$$

we have

$$A \left[1 - \int_y^\infty f(d) \, dd \right] = B \int_y^\infty f(d) \, dd$$

$$A = \int_y^\infty f(d) \, dd \, [A + B]$$

or

$$\int_y^\infty f(d) \, dd = \frac{A}{A + B}$$

Or, when the costs of overstocking and understocking are linear, the probability of a shortage is equal to the ratio $A/(A + B)$.

FIXED ORDERING COST: Now assume that an item left over at the end of the reorder cycle has value and is stored. Furthermore, we will introduce a fixed ordering cost. Again, remember that x is the inventory at the start of the reorder cycle prior to making an order, and y equals the inventory level at the start of the reorder cycle after making an order and assuming that the order is immediately placed in stock.

Since a fixed ordering cost is incurred, an order for small values of $y - x$ will not be placed. The problem is to find the value for both y and x, which is the optimal cutoff point for ordering. Consider the following example. Let

$x =$ inventory at the start of the reorder period prior to making an order
$y =$ inventory level at the start of the period after making an order assuming that the order is immediately placed in stock
$f(d) =$ probability distribution of demand $= 1/100,\ 0 \le d \le 100$

Storage cost $= \$1$ per unit stored at end of period
Order cost $\quad = \$10 + \$1(y - x)$, if $y > x$
Sales price $\quad = \$10$

If $y > x$, an order is placed. Then

for $y > d \qquad$ cost $= C_1 = 10 + 1(y - x) - \underset{\text{(income)}}{10d} + \underset{\text{(inv cost)}}{1(y - d)}$

$\phantom{for y > d \qquad \text{cost} = C_1 = 10 + 1(y - x)}$ (order cost) (income) (inv cost)

for $y \leq d \qquad C_2 = 10 + 1(y - x) - 10y + 0$

Expected Cost (for $y > x$) $= \displaystyle\int_0^y C_1 f(d)\, dd + \int_y^{100} C_2 f(d)\, dd$

If $y = x$, no order will be placed. Then

for $y > d \qquad C_3 = 0 - 10d + 1(y - d)$
for $y \leq d \qquad C_4 = 0 - 10y + 0$

Expected Cost (for $y = x$) $= \displaystyle\int_0^y C_3 f(d)\, dd + \int_y^{100} C_4 f(d)\, dd$

If an order is placed, $y > x$, and

$$G(y) = \text{Expected Cost (for } y > x)$$
$$= (1/100)[(11/2)y^2 + 1,000 - 900y - 100x] \qquad (7)$$

$$\frac{d(G(y))}{dy} = 0 = 11y - 900$$

$$y^* = 82$$

with no fixed cost the rule would be

$$\text{order} \begin{cases} 82 - x & \text{if } y > x \text{ and } x < 82 \\ 0 & \text{if } x \geq 82 \end{cases}$$

If $x < y^*$ and we do not order, we incur a penalty K for not ordering at y^*. Now we wish to find a value of x, x^*, which is the critical cutoff point.

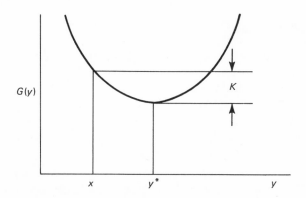

FIGURE **15.10** Penalty K for not ordering y^*.

If we do not place an order, then $y = x$.

$$H(y) = \text{Expected Cost (for } y = x) = \tfrac{1}{100}[\tfrac{11}{2}y^2 - 1{,}000y] \tag{8}$$

Now substitute y^* for y in Equation (7):

$$G(y) = \frac{1}{100}\left[\frac{(11)(900^2)}{(2)(11^2)} + 1{,}000 - \frac{(900)(900)}{11} - 100x\right] \tag{9}$$

and substitute x for y in Equation (8):

$$H(y) = \left[\frac{\tfrac{11}{2}x^2 - 1{,}000x}{100}\right] \tag{10}$$

If we set $G(y) = H(y)$, then we can determine the value of x where the expected cost of ordering is equal to the expected cost of not ordering.

$$G(y) = H(y)$$
$$x^* = 68.3$$

Let

$$s = x^*$$
$$S = y^*$$

Then order an amount

$S - x$ if $x \leq s$
0 otherwise

Setting the Reorder Cycle and Reorder Quantity

We will now discuss a simple and approximate model for setting the review period and the amount to be ordered. We will assume that orders are backlogged and that the variable costs of the system include order preparation costs, costs of reviewing the inventory, inventory holding costs, and backlog costs. Furthermore, demand is a random variable with a probability function $f(x; t)$, the probability of x units being demanded in a time period t. The expected demand in period t is λ.

Let

$T =$ review period in years
$r =$ lead time in years for delivery of replenishment order
$I =$ inventory level at the time of review and before an order is placed
$Q =$ amount ordered
$R =$ level of inventory just after placing order $= Q + I$
$K =$ sum of order preparation and review costs for a review cycle
$u =$ expected lead time demand $= \lambda r$
$C =$ unit annual inventory holding cost
$\pi =$ cost of a backorder per unit backordered

The inventory rule is to review the inventory periodically at intervals of T. Then, order an amount sufficient to bring the inventory level up to a value R at the time the order is placed. The problem is to determine optimum values of T and R.

The total annual variable costs of the system include three components as follows:

1. *Order preparation and review costs: K/T*
2. *Inventory holding costs:* Inventory consists of two components. If we look at Figure 15.11, which shows the expected behavior of inventory for a set of arbitrary parameters, we note that the inventory peaks at a value $(R - u)$ and reaches an expected minimum of $(R - u - \lambda T)$. Therefore, the expected inventory level is

$$\frac{(R - u) - (R - u - \lambda T)}{2} + (R - u - \lambda T) = \frac{(R - u)}{2} + \frac{(R - u - \lambda T)}{2}$$

$$= R - u - \frac{\lambda T}{2}$$

and therefore the expected annual inventory holding cost is

$$C\left[R - u - \frac{\lambda T}{2}\right]$$

where we assume that the number of backorders is small relative to the number of units stocked, since otherwise we would need a more precise statement of inventory, considering that the backorders are satisfied immediately by the arrival of an order.

3. *Backorder cost:* The number of backorders accumulated is a function of the demand during the time interval T, considering that we start out with the quantity $(R - u)$ at the start of the interval. The expected number of backorders per cycle is

$$\int_{R-u}^{\infty} x - (R - u)f(x; T)\, dx$$

This is equivalent to

$$\int_{R}^{\infty} (x - R)f(x; r + T)\, dx$$

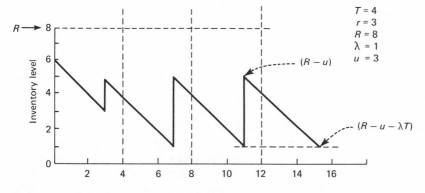

FIGURE **15.11**   Expected inventory behavior.

TABLE **15.4** Total cost as a function of T given $C = 1$, $\pi = 2$, $r = 0.50$, $u = 18$, $\lambda = 36$, $K = 2$.

T yrs	$T+r$ yrs	$\dfrac{CT}{\pi}$	R	$\dfrac{K}{T}$	$C\left[R - u - \dfrac{\lambda T}{2}\right]$	$\delta = \lambda(T+r)$	$\dfrac{\pi}{T}\sum\limits_{R+1}^{\max}(x-R)\dfrac{e^{-\delta}\delta^x}{x!}$	TC
1	1.50	.50	54	2	18.0	54	5.8	25.8
$\frac{1}{2}$	1.00	.25	41	4	14.0	36	2.8	20.8
$\frac{1}{3}$	.83	.167	36	6	12.0	30	2.5	20.5
$\frac{1}{4}$	.75	.125	34	8	11.5	27	2.8	22.3
$\frac{1}{6}$	.66	.083	31	12	10.0	24	2.4	24.4
$\frac{1}{12}$	.58	.042	30	24	10.5	21	2.4	36.96

and therefore the expected number per year is

$$\frac{1}{T}\int_R^\infty (x - R)f(x; r + T)\, dx$$

The total average annual cost is therefore

$$TC = \frac{K}{T} + C\left[R - u - \frac{\lambda T}{2}\right] + \frac{\pi}{T}\int_R^\infty (x - R)f(x; r + T)\, dx \qquad (11)$$

For a given value of T, the value of R that minimizes TC satisfies

$$\frac{\partial TC}{\partial R} = 0 = C - \frac{\pi}{T}\int_R^\infty f(x; r + T)\, dx$$

Therefore,

$$\int_R^\infty f(x; r + T)\, dx = CT/\pi \qquad (12)$$

The optimum value of T can be found by tabulating TC as a function of T. First R^* is found from Equation (12), and the total cost is then determined from Equation (11). Table 15.4 shows the calculation of total cost for six values of T indicating an optimum review period of around four months. Demand is assumed to be Poisson distributed.

Extrapolations

We have so far presented some of the simplified models of inventory behavior. The wide variety of situations encountered in inventory control and the extensions of the simple models justify extensive coverage beyond the scope of this book. A serious constraint on the kinds of inventory models discussed up to this point is the assumption that the system is in a steady state or, in other words, that the statistical and cost parameters are constant over time. This assumption, of course, is highly fictitious in most cases. The kinds of changes that take place may be gradual enough to allow the more simple dynamic models to be used and then updated periodically. However, if the changes are rapid, they must be explicitly accounted for in the model.

A good deal of work has been done on dynamic inventory models, particularly by using dynamic programing. Because of its relative complexity, we will not venture into this subject in this book.

Besides the issue of dynamic inventory behavior, other questions confront the inventory controller. Important problems include the relative economics of the two-bin versus periodic-review models, bulk control versus individual control of items, the proper handling of obsolescence in stocked items, the determination of shortage and backlogging costs, the relative economics of producing sub-assemblies and components for inventory or manufacturing directly for final assembly schedules, etc. These and other topics provide the substance of past and continuing articles and books on inventory planning and control.

In the remainder of this chapter, we will present several more selected topics related to inventory control chosen to suggest the variety of problems encountered rather than as an exhaustive study of the subject.

THE SMALL- LOT PROBLEM

Many companies that carry a large number of standard sales items find themselves in the position of having to set some kind of policy for producing "small-lot" or "slow-moving items." These are finished goods or replacement parts for which the total annual customer demand is small. Pressure is exerted by the marketing department to retain such items in the catalog and possibly to have a few in stock at any one time. Manufacturing resists this due to the cost of inventory maintenance as well as the cost of producing the small numbers involved.

In many such cases, if the item is catalogued, the product is not made unless there is a specific customer order. At the time the job is set up for a specific order, the question of production lot size arises. Producing only an amount equal to the customer order avoids the inventory cost but, nevertheless, introduces a large per-unit setup cost and, of course, precludes fast customer delivery. If the price of the product includes a premium for small-lot production, then the issue is academic. However, if such a premium cannot be added to the normal price and if shortage is an important issue, then the question of economical lot size is relevant.

We should note that this is not necessarily the same problem as dealing with C stock items. The C stock items are of low unit value but are regularly used in the normal conduct of the business. The small-lot production items may be individually of high value, but demand for them may be infrequent.

A Compromise Rule

In between the extremes of producing only for a specific customer order or producing to replenish a formally maintained inventory we might use a compromise production rule. This is to produce the item only when a customer order is received but also, at that time, overproduce for inventory. Future customer orders are met from this inventory until the stock is reduced to zero by a given customer

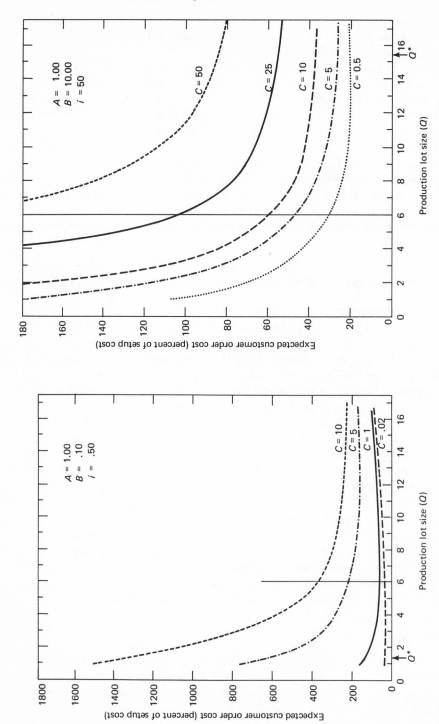

FIGURE 15.12   Expected customer order cost as a function of production-lot size for different values of setup and shortage costs. From J. W. Gavett, *Production and Inventory Management*, vol. 8, no. 1, pp. 69, 71.

order. Under this system, inventory control is reduced to a minimum. No formal inventory records are kept, except for fiscal accounting and for item location in the stock room.

A possible rule is as follows. Let

d_t = the number of units ordered by a customer in time period t
x_t = the number of units carried in inventory just before d_t is satisfied
Q = the production lot size to be set by policy

The rule is:

if $d_t - x_t \leq 0$, then fill the customer order from stock
if $d_t - x_t > 0$ and

1. if $d_t - x_t \geq Q$, then produce an amount $d_t - x_t$ to complete the customer order
2. if $d_t - x_t < Q$, then produce an amount Q. Complete the customer order and place the remaining items in stock.

One can easily visualize an alternative rule, which would be to produce enough units to bring the inventory level up to a value S each time the item is set up for production. It can be shown that such a rule is equivalent to the one we will examine and that the long-term results of the two rules are the same.

SIMULATION: In order to determine what the value of Q should be, the issue has been subjected to a computer simulation. For a given set of system parameters, including inventory, setup and shortage costs, number of orders, and order-size distributions, the simulator determines the expected customer order cost for a chosen value of Q by simulating a specified period of time during which the rule is applied.

Figure 15.12a and b show the results of two trials for different values of A, B, C, and i. In general, the results for these and other trials seem to indicate that savings can be incurred by overproducing the item for stock, especially in cases where the setup and shortage costs are greater than the unit production costs. In most of the cases studied, a severe penalty is incurred by producing only directly for customer order or by limiting the lot sizes to very small values. In the case we have used, the expected annual demand is 6 units (average demand of 4 times the average order size of 1.5), and it would appear that the average customer order cost is sensitive to lot sizes of less than 5 or 6 units. Even the imposition of a large carrying cost i does not seem to affect this general statement. Figure 15.13 shows the behavior of the average customer order cost for different values of inventory carrying cost ranging from $i = 0.10$ to $i = 2.00$.

THE REJECT ALLOWANCE PROBLEM

Material spoilage is an inherent characteristic of most production processes. As material is routed through a series of production operations, there will be a diminution of the size of the batch of material between the point of its introduction into

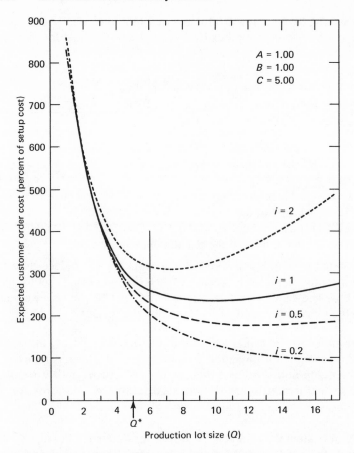

FIGURE **15.13**   Effect of rate of inventory holding cost on expected customer order cost for different production-lot sizes. From J. W. Gavett, *Production and Inventory Management*, vol. 8, no. 1, p. 74.

the production and the point of its completion as a finished or semifinished product. Therefore, if the number of units of finished product is rigidly specified, the starting batch size must be inflated to allow for the rejects that will occur at various steps in the routing. We are now interested in the allowance that must be made in the starting quantity for spoilage rejects.

The problem is easy to deal with under certain conditions. If it is known exactly how much spoilage will take place, then the allowance is exactly equal to this loss. But this is rarely the case, and the spoilage, as a percent of the desired end quantity, is usually a chance variable. But even if this latter condition prevails, the problem may not be serious if the item in question is made directly for inventory. If the inventory replenishment batch size is less than the optimum amount, due to random spoilage, then the additional cost is negligible if the difference between the actual and optimum batch size is small. Also, if the unit costs used to calculate the optimum batch size do not contain a pro-rated amount for spoilage, then a less-than-optimum batch size is warranted if an actual spoilage cost occurs, and, therefore, the starting quantity might equal the desired end quantity.

The problem is more serious when a product is made specifically for customer order or to meet a final assembly schedule. If the end quantity is less than desired, a makeup batch must be scheduled and the facilities set up again for that batch if they are jointly used for other products. Furthermore, a delay in the delivery of the batch is incurred. If the end quantity is larger than desired, the extra units represent a loss of some kind. This loss is either the full cost of the material and applied labor, or it is the cost incurred in disposing of the parts, such as selling them at a reduced price, inventorying them in anticipation of a future repeat order, or converting them for another use.

We wish to determine an optimum production starting quantity that will minimize the total relevant costs. These are the "overage" costs of ending up with more than the required ending quantity and the "shortage" costs of ending up with less than the required quantity.

We might recognize that the problem is quite similar to a periodic review inventory problem, where overage and shortage correspond to inventory surpluses and shortages occurring at the end of a review cycle. The problem can be dealt with analytically but, of course, depending on the assumptions made. Besides knowing the costs of both over- and underproducing, it is necessary to determine the characteristics of the spoilage rate in the process. This latter factor requires knowledge about the process capabilities, which can be difficult to obtain if the item is custom-made.

There are both exact and approximate methods of solving the problem. The approach depends on assumptions made about the operation of the control system, the distribution of the shrinkage rate, the relevant costs included in the model, and the degree of refinement of the model itself.

One approximate method is to specify a starting quantity equal to the ending quantity plus the expected amount of shrinkage. For example, if experience shows that on the average we lose p percent of the starting quantity and the desired final quantity is Y units, then the starting quantity X will be

$$X = Y(1 + p)$$

This method is nonoptimal and ignores the relative costs of overages and shortages. Depending on the nature of these costs, there may be a substantial difference between actual and optimum costs.

An Expected Cost Model

A general approach is to select a starting quantity that minimizes the expected cost of over- and underproducing on the first production run and assumes that makeup runs are nondeteriorating. We can frame this model in terms of the following example.

A company subcontracts its casting work to an outside foundry. It experiences faulty castings, which show up in subsequent machining operations. It therefore wishes to make an initial order that will make allowances for the faulty castings. This is done by ordering an initial batch size larger than the desired final quantity. Let

X = number of castings ordered—the starting quantity
Y = number of castings desired—the required ending quantity, and $X \geq Y$
r = actual number of castings rejected as defective at the last operation— a random variable
p = probability that a part will be rejected
$Z = X - Y$
C_1 = unit processing and material cost for casting
C_2 = setup cost to run an extra batch, independent of batch size
TC = expected total cost

Now, if a shortage occurs, then $r > Z$, and the expected loss L is

$$L_1 = \sum_{r=Z+1}^{r=X} [C_2 + C_1(r - Z)]f(r) \tag{13}$$

On the other hand, if an overage occurs, then $r < Z$.

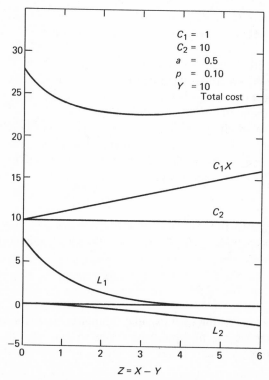

FIGURE **15.14**   Cost components for reject allowance problem.

TABLE **15.5**   Optimum starting quantities for binomially distributed rejects.[3]

Required order quantity	Expected average yield							
	0.99		0.95		0.90		0.75	
	C_2 10C_1	C_2 100C_1	C_2 10C_1	C_2 100C_1	C_2 10C_1	C_2 100C_1	C_2 10C_1	C_2 100C_1
1	1	2	1	2	2	2	2	4
2	2	3	3	3	3	4	4	6
3	3	4	4	5	4	5	5	8
4	4	5	5	6	5	7	7	9
5	5	6	6	7	7	7	7	11
6	6	7	7	8	8	9	10	13
7	7	8	8	9	9	11	11	14
8	8	9	9	11	10	12	13	16
9	9	10	10	12	11	13	14	17
10	11	11	12	13	13	14	16	19

Let us assume that each overage item can be salvaged at a value equal to aC_1, where $0 < a < 1$. The expected overage loss L_2 is

$$L_2 = -\sum_{r=0}^{r=Z} aC_1(Z - r)f(r) \tag{14}$$

Then the total expected cost is

$$TC = C_2 + XC_1 + L_1 + L_2 \tag{15}$$

EXAMPLE 15.3   A company makes a part in small batches on a particular process, The number of rejects is binomially distributed. Suppose that $p = 0.10$, $Y = 10$. $C_1 = 1$, $C_2 = 10$, and $a = 0.5$. Then the optimum starting quantity is $X = 13$. The behavior of the costs as Z increases is shown in Figure 15.14. Note that for $Z > 3$, the total cost for the given set of parameters is insensitive to an increase in Z.

Additional Factors

In the practical sense, we can think of alternative ways of handling the problem and, consequently, of refining the model.

First, the preceding model ignores the possibility that a rerun will experience rejects, thus requiring a sequence of reruns until the final quantity is satisfied. Goode and Saltzman consider this problem for small lots assuming a binomial distribution for the reject rate and a probability of shortages occurring in each successive rerun.[3] Table 15.5 shows the optimum starting quantities for different desired ending quantities, yields, and ratios of setup costs (C_2) to variable costs (C_1), and for a value of the coefficient a equal to 0.5. You might compare the results of the previous example with the value given in their table.

---

[3] Henry P. Goode and S. Saltzman, "A Method for Determining the Optimum Starting Quantity When Manufacturing to Fixed Order Size," A.S.M.E. paper No. 60-SA-29, 1960.

Second, we have assumed that the rejects absorb the full cost of processing the part. Obviously, the rejects may be filtered out of the process before the final processing operation, thus reducing the cost of the rejects. This depends on the location of the inspection points.

Third, sequential decisions can be made at each operation in the part routing. Depending on the status of the batch after the first operation, it might be possible to hold the batch in limbo until an extra re-order is made for the first operation. Then, the new batch proceeds through the next operation, where the decision is repeated, etc.

THE ASSORTMENT PROBLEM

A special kind of inventory problem is the following. A company uses a certain resource that can be purchased and stocked in a range of standard sizes. The product or service using this resource demands varying sizes of the resource. The problem is to determine which standard sizes should be purchased and inventoried.

The problem arises because, if all standard sizes are not stocked, then the product must be produced by using the next largest suitable standard size, or reverting to some other alternative, with an attendant loss of efficiency. However, the more standard sizes stocked, the higher the inventory or other resource control or maintenance costs.

The following are some examples of situations where this problem might arise:

Standard size resource	Product or service	Loss of efficiency by not having standard size for a given job
Length of steel bar stock	Structural form	Cutoff loss in using the next larger standard size
Diameter of steel bar stock	Motor shafts	Cutoff loss when turning to exact diameter when using next larger size
Width of paper roll	Printed business forms	Trim loss on paper margins
Truck size	Long distance movers	Use of large truck for small job
Metal cutting dies	Cut a thread on metal parts	Turn thread on slower operation or subcontract job at premium

Suppose we consider the first example, that of carrying standard sizes of bar stock. We wish to minimize the sum of two costs, namely, the cost of carrying the standard sizes in stock and the cutoff loss. The cutoff loss occurs as follows. If a particular job requires a bar-stock length that is not carried in inventory, it must be cut from the next larger bar stock carried in inventory with an associated loss in material. What, then, should be the mix of standard sizes to be carried in inventory? Here we wish to determine the makeup of inventory, rather than its economical size.

We will use the following notation. Let

A_i = $\{a_i \mid a_i$ is the number of the ith standard bar stock size on a nominal scale$\}$, $i = 1, 2, \ldots, n$

s_i = standard length of a_i; $s_1 < s_2 <, \ldots, < s_n$

d_i = annual requirement for a_i in number of bars

b_i = purchase cost per foot of a_i

c_i = a variable cost of inventorying a_i per a standard unit per year

H = a fixed cost of having to inventory a standard size

$m_i = \begin{cases} 1 & \text{if } a_i \text{ is stocked} \\ 0 & \text{otherwise} \end{cases}$

Suppose the actual data are as follows:

a_i	s_i	d_i	c_i
1	10	3	1
2	12	4	2
3	14	2	2
4	16	6	3
5	18	5	4
6	20	1	5

H = \$10 and b_i = \$1.00 for all i.

To facilitate the discussion, we will make the very unrealistic assumption that no piece can be produced without loss from standard sizes that are multiples of the piece size. That is, we will ignore the possibility of making two 10-foot lengths from one 20-foot length without loss.

Now there will be $2^{n-1} = 32$ possible stocking policies. Each policy will constitute a subset of m_i values. For example, the policy 0 1 0 0 1 1 will mean that numbers 2, 5, and 6 will be stocked. Note that 6 must always be stocked, since a_6 cannot be made from any size other than the 20-foot length. The cost of this particular policy is:

(a) *Cutoff loss:*

parts demanding a_1 must be made from s_2 at a loss of 2 ft/unit $\times$ 3 units = \$6

parts demanding a_3 and a_4 must be made from s_5 at a loss of $4 \times 2 + 2 \times 6$ = \$20

(b) *Inventory and handling costs:*

a_i		
1	3 units requiring 12-foot lengths at \$2/length =	\$ 6
2	4 units requiring 12-foot lengths at \$2/length =	8
3	2 units requiring 18-foot lengths at \$4/length =	8
4	6 units requiring 18-foot lengths at \$4/length =	24
5	5 units requiring 18-foot lengths at \$4/length =	20
6	1 unit requiring 20-foot lengths at \$5/length =	5
		\$71 Total

plus three sizes stocked at a fixed cost of \$10 = \$30

TABLE **15.6**   Alternative policies and their costs.

Alternative		Cutoff loss	Inventory cost incl. fixed	Total costs
1	0 0 0 0 0 1	108	135	223
2	0 0 0 0 1 1	68	115	173
3	0 0 0 1 0 1	48	105	143
4	0 0 1 0 0 1	54	108	152
5	0 1 0 0 0 1	52	114	156
6	1 0 0 0 0 1	78	123	191
7	0 0 0 1 1 1	38	100	138
8	0 0 1 0 1 1	32	97	129
9	0 1 0 0 1 1	26	101	127
10	1 0 0 0 1 1	44	106	150
11	0 0 1 1 0 1	30	96	126
12	0 1 0 1 0 1	20	98	118
13	1 0 0 1 0 1	30	99	129
14	0 1 1 0 0 1	30	108	138
15	1 0 1 0 0 1	42	105	147
16	1 1 0 0 0 1	46	111	156
17	0 0 1 1 1 1	20	91	121
18	0 1 0 1 1 1	10	93	113
19	1 0 0 1 1 1	20	94	124
20	0 1 1 1 0 1	16	96	122
21	1 0 1 1 0 1	18	93	121
22	1 1 1 0 0 1	34	105	149
23	1 0 1 0 1 1	20	94	124
24	0 1 1 0 1 1	18	97	135
25	1 1 0 0 1 1	20	98	128
26	1 1 0 1 0 1	14	95	119
27	0 1 1 1 1 1	6	91	117
28	1 1 1 0 1 1	12	94	126
29	1 1 0 1 1 1	4	111	114
30	1 0 1 1 1 1	8	88	116
31	1 1 1 1 0 1	10	93	123
32	1 1 1 1 1 1	0	88	118

Thus, $TC = 26 + 71 + 30 = \$127$, of which \$15 is inescapable because the last size must be stocked.

An enumeration of the alternative policies and their costs is shown in Table 15.6.

The optimum solution can be determined by dynamic programing starting with the largest standard size bar and working back to the first size in the following way. For any successive pair of standard sizes, a_j, a_{j+1}, let

$$C_{m_j, m_{j+1}} = \min (C_{m_{j+1}, m_{j+2}}) + b_j d_j (s_k - s_j) + d_j c_k + 10 m_j$$

where k is the next value of i such that $k \geq j$ and $m_k = 1$. Starting with the last two standard sizes and assuming that $m_6 = 1$, we want to find C_{m_5, m_6} for the cases $m_5, m_6 = 0, 1$ and $1, 1$.

		m_6
$C_{m_5, m_6} =$	m_5	1
	0	35*
	1	30

* that is, cutoff loss $= b_5 d_5 (s_6 - s_5) = 10$
  inventory cost $= d_5 c_6 \quad\quad\quad = 25$
  fixed cost $= 10 m_5 \quad\quad\quad\ \ = \underline{\ \ 0}$
  $\ 35$

The min $(C_{0,1}) = 35$ and the min $(C_{1,1}) = 30$. Now we will examine the cases $m_4, m_5, m_6 = 0, 0, 1; 1, 0, 1; 0, 1, 1; 1, 1, 1$.

		m_5	
$C_{m_4, m_5} =$	m_4	0	1
	0	89*	66
	1	63	58

* that is, min C_{m_5, m_6} $\quad\quad\quad\quad = 35$
  cutoff loss $= b_4 d_4 (s_6 - s_4) = 24$
  inventory cost $= d_4 c_6 \quad\quad\ = 30$
  fixed cost $= 10 m_4 \quad\quad\quad = \underline{\ \ 0}$
  $\ 89$

Note that min (C_{m_4, m_5}) is 66 for $m_4 = 0$ and 58 for $m_4 = 1$. Therefore, we will now examine the cases $m_3, m_4, m_5, m_6 = 0, 0, 1, 1; 1, 0, 1, 1; 0, 1, 1, 1; 1, 1, 1, 1$.
Continuing,

examine alternatives $m_i = \left\{ \begin{array}{c} i = 3\ 4\ 5\ 6 \\ \hline 0\ 0\ 1\ 1 \\ 1\ 0\ 1\ 1 \\ 0\ 1\ 1\ 1 \\ 1\ 1\ 1\ 1 \end{array} \right\}$ C_{m_3, m_4}

		m_4	
$C_{m_3, m_4} =$	m_3	0	1
	0	82	68
	1	80	72

$$\text{examine alternatives } m_i = \begin{cases} i = 2\ 3\ 4\ 5\ 6 \\ \hline 0\ 0\ 1\ 1\ 1 \\ 1\ 0\ 1\ 1\ 1 \\ 0\ 1\ 1\ 1\ 1 \\ 1\ 1\ 1\ 1\ 1 \end{cases} C_{m_2,m_3} =$$

m_2 \ m_3	0	1
0	96	88
1	86	90

$$\text{examine alternatives } m_i = \begin{cases} i = 1\ 2\ 3\ 4\ 5\ 6 \\ \hline 0\ 1\ 0\ 1\ 1\ 1 \\ 1\ 1\ 0\ 1\ 1\ 1 \\ 0\ 0\ 1\ 1\ 1\ 1 \\ 1\ 0\ 1\ 1\ 1\ 1 \end{cases} C_{m_1,m_2} =$$

m_1 \ m_2	0	1
0	106	98*
1	101	99

The optimum stocking policy is therefore to stock sizes a_2, a_4, a_5, and a_6 with a minimum cost of \$98 plus the inescapable cost of stocking a_6, which is \$15.

SEQUENTIAL INTRAPLANT INVENTORY SYSTEMS

Up to now, our discussion has centered on the determination of production-lot sizes and inventory levels for individual parts, with respect to a single work-in-process for finished-goods stock point. Furthermore, we have considered a well-structured demand pattern originating from the customer.

However, it is generally common for an individual part to pass through a sequence of work-in-process, finished goods, and distributor inventories until it reaches the final consumer. We are interested, therefore, in the way these sequential inventories behave as the original customer demand is filtered down through the series of inventories. The control of intraplant sequential inventories will be discussed in the remainder of this chapter.

Figure 15.15 shows possible alternative routings of customer and shop orders for replenishing inventories or meeting customer orders directly. Where standard items are concerned, two basic questions are: Where should intermediate component and subassembly inventories be established in the manufacturing sequence, and how should these and finished-goods inventories be replenished?

Subassembly Configurations

Before deciding on subassembly and component inventory policies, the number of feasible subassemblies must be chosen. A subassembly is a rational set of components and subsubassemblies that are permanently combined to form an identifiable unit, which is subsequently used as a component of a larger order assembly. The composition of a subassembly is based on a number of criteria, of which some are technological and some economic.

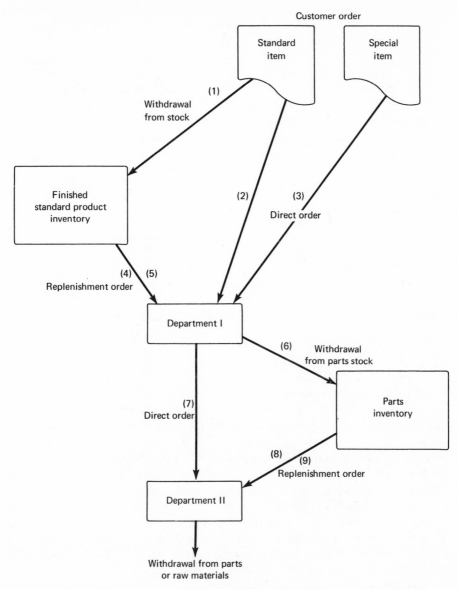

FIGURE **15.15** Alternative order-routing methods, standard and special items. From *Production Planning and Inventory Control*, 2nd ed., by John F. Magee and David M. Boodman. © 1967 by McGraw-Hill, Inc. Used by permission of McGraw-Hill Book Company.

1. Certain parts have to be combined as a subassembly for technological reasons. For example, some parts must be joined together by mechanical methods or manual methods, which preclude the possibility or feasibility of joining them in the context of a larger assembly. The riveting of two parts, for example, must be

done on a rivet machine before the parts are added to a final assembly. A set of small parts must be subassembled manually prior to their addition to the interior of a housing where manual handling is impossible.

2. A subassembly may consist of a set of replacement parts. Their union into a subassembly is much more economical prior to shipping than if done in the field.

3. The testing of a final assembly is facilitated by tests of subassemblies before they are added to the main assembly. Not only is the physical testing easier, but the removal of a defective part is facilitated.

4. In general, the use of subassemblies permits economies of production, including the specialization of labor and the facilitation of parts handling at the main assembly. Also, if parts are standard components in a variety of final products, their assemblage in the form of subassemblies permits economies of scale. Finally, the inventorying of subassemblies permits the reduction in final product assembly lead times, albeit at the cost of inventorying.

Inventorying Subassemblies

Once the decision has been made to establish a subassembly, the issue is whether or not to establish an inventory of that subassembly. For purposes of discussion, we assume that the decision to create a subassembly and the decision to inventory are independent. That is, a subassembly may be produced directly at the time it is needed for the next assembly stage or replacement, or it may be produced independently for stock.

It is not particularly easy to structure an analytical model on which to base the inventory decision. For example, Figure 15.16 shows a hypothetical situation involving a hierarchy of assemblies, including a final assembly $A4$, two subassemblies $A3$ and $A2$, and a component 1 made for stock. Each assembly has certain components that are added directly (numbered dashed lines). Each flow chart shows alternative inventory policies ranging from inventorying $A3$ and $A2$ (a) to combining all components and subassemblies (d), except for component 1, at the time they are needed for the final assembly. Obviously, we could structure more complex and realistic situations.

For each subassembly, we must decide either to inventory it or produce and combine it with the next higher assembly. Intuitively one might favor the inventorying of subassemblies. If demand for the final product is variable and uncertain, then subassembly inventories will tend to minimize the risks of final product shortages by reducing and stabilizing their lead times. For example, if we choose alternative (b) and an order is placed to replenish stock point 4, then assembly operation on subassembly $A3$ will have to be carried out at that time to provide the requirements for $A4$. Thus, the lead time on $A4$ is partially governed by the production time for $A3$. Another intuitive argument for inventorying $A3$ is based on the demand. If the demand for $A3$, assuming that it is used for other final products, is large relative to the demand for each individual final product, we would expect the production-lot size for $A3$ to be also large. Therefore, the number of times we set up to produce $A3$ for inventory may be significantly less than the

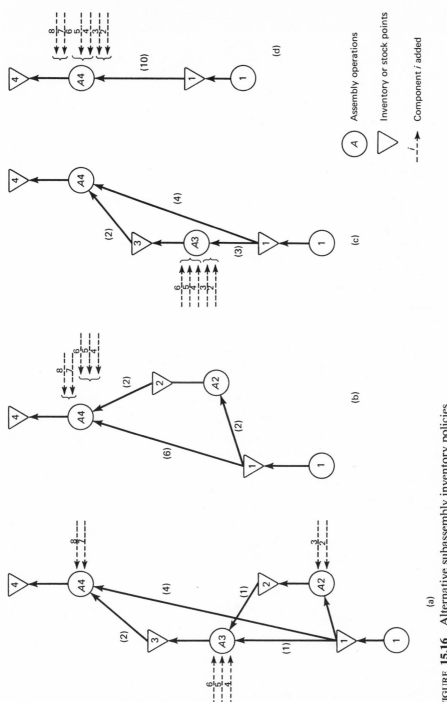

FIGURE **15.16** Alternative subassembly inventory policies.

number of times we set up to produce it independently and directly for each final product, thus achieving savings in the costs of setup and handling.

On the other hand, there are arguments for not inventorying subassemblies but rather combining them with next-stage assemblies. We can reverse the previous argument about the number of setups and show that the setups for $A3$ might be fewer if combined than if inventoried.

When a final product is produced for customer order, either forecasted or back-logged, then assembly schedules may be prepared through shop-loading techniques. Subassembly production schedules can then be integrated with final assembly schedules, thus eliminating the concern for long or unpredictable lead times and the need for subassembly inventories.

AN ANALYTICAL APPROACH: Smith proposes a model for making the sub-assembly inventory decision as follows.[4] Let

A_i = ith assembly
m_i = number of times per year a production order is issued to make A_i
n_{ij} = number of A_i used in one A_j
p_i = number of parts used on A_i
s_i = production setup cost for A_i
u_i = annual use of A_i
v_i = unit cost of A_i
c_1 = clerical cost of issuing a production order
c_2 = cost of withdrawing an item from stores and delivering it to the assembly department
c_3 = cost of putting away one order in stores
c_4 = cost of carrying one dollar of inventory for one year

The four possible cases examined by Smith are diagramed in Figure 15.17. For Case I, the annual savings from combining A_i into A_j are

$$s_{ij} = v_i n_{ij} u_j c_4 / 2m_i + m_j c_2 - m_j(p_i c_2 + s_i) \tag{16}$$

The first term on the right is the avoided cost of inventorying A_i. The second term is the avoided cost of withdrawing A_i every time A_j is set up. The third term is the cost of having to pull individual components for A_i from stores and setting up to produce A_i. Note the assumption that A_i is being inventoried anyway for sales. In this sense, the model ignores the economy of scale.

For Case II, there is an additional savings S_i, which is the avoided cost of having to handle the orders for replenishment of the $A3$ inventory. Note that this term partially offsets the third term of Equation (16).

$$S_i = m_i(c_1 + p_i c_2 + s_i + c_3) \tag{17}$$

---

[4] Spencer B. Smith, "Optimum Configuration of Assemblies in Intermittent Manufacture," *J. Ind. Eng.*, vol. XIV, no. 6, November–December 1963, pp. 327–31.

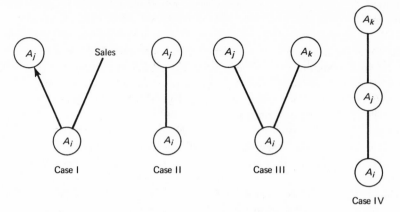

FIGURE **15.17** Disposition of subassemblies—four cases. From Smith, *J. Ind. Eng.*, vol. XIV, no. 6, November–December 1963.

For Case III, we have

Alternative	Savings	Equation
1. Combine A_i into A_j	S_{ij}	1
2. Combine A_i into A_k	S_{ik}	1
3. Combine A_i into A_j and A_k	$S_{ij} + S_{ik} + S_i$	$1 + 1 + 2$
4. Do not combine at all	0	0

In a similar fashion, the conditions and relevant equations are set forth for Case IV.

The critical variables in Smith's model are m_i and m_j and their differences. In order to justify inventories, where parts are not made directly for sales or for more than one subassembly, the only possible negative term is $p_i c_2(m_i - m_j)$ and $s_i(m_i - m_j)$. Therefore, m_j must be larger than m_i to give any advantage to inventorying. Then, also, his model neglects the factor of lead time and shortage risks.

Inventory Behavior and Control

Once it is decided to establish a subassembly inventory, the method of controlling that inventory must be determined.

INDEPENDENT INVENTORY POINTS: One method, obviously, is to operate each stock point independently using an economical reorder quantity-reorder point system. For example, when the finished goods inventory is depleted by distributor orders to the level of a reorder point, an economical order quantity is placed with the assembly department. This department, in turn, draws upon component and subassembly inventories that are controlled independently by their own Q, R formulas. The inventory at each stock point in the sequence will be equal to one-half the economical reorder quantity plus the safety stock required to meet the replenishment lead times.

Alternative methods include a periodic review, in which minimum stocks are a function of the length of the review period plus the lead time and order quantities are based on the maximum desired inventory level. Or, replenishment orders for finished goods may be exploded directly into requirements for various subassemblies and components that are either made directly, with possible long lead times, or made for intermediate stock points.

The major problem of operating each stock point independently is that the demand for the item becomes progressively more erratic the further the stock point is removed from the point of original customer demand. For example, we can visualize what happens to demand in terms of economical reorder quantities. Suppose that the demand for a certain finished product is relatively constant and continuous. When the reorder point is reached, an economical replenishment order will be placed with the assembly department. This demand on the assembly department is passed on to the next stock points for subassemblies and components. In this sense, the demand on the intermediate stock points is bunched. The effect of this is to force a large safety stock to take care of this more erratic demand.

The problem is magnified in another way. If the original customer demand is variable, either randomly or otherwise, then adjustments made to finished goods inventory parameters (the lot size and reorder point) will have a marked effect on subsequent operations and inventories. For example, suppose that demand for a certain finished product suddenly increases, causing the reorder point to be reached. The initial response to this might be to increase the reorder point and possibly the reorder quantity for this and other like items. The former results in more reorder points being reached for other items and the latter in larger order quantities. Both of these have an immediate impact on the production system, which, in turn, passes on the increase to stock points down the line. The sudden

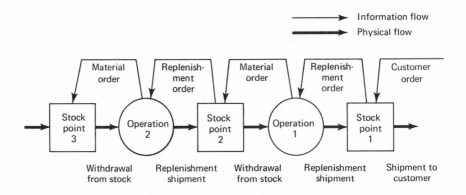

FIGURE **15.18**   Pattern of information flow, base-stock system. From *Production Planning and Inventory Control*, 2nd ed., by John F. Magee and David M. Boodman. © 1967 by McGraw-Hill, Inc. Used by permission of McGraw-Hill Book Company.

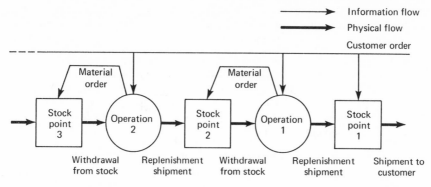

load on the whole system causes lead times to be increased and thus another possible adjustment of reorder points to account for this. If the customer demand continues at the new increased level, or if it continues to increase, then the response may be justified. But, if the demand falls off to its original forecast level, then the process is repeated, but in a different direction.

The sensitivity of a system of sequential inventories to fluctuations in original customer demand is fairly well understood as a theoretical and practical phenomenon. The major remedy for unstable response is to pass customer demand information directly back to each point in the sequence. Figures 15.18 and 15.19 show the two contrasting situations in which stock points respond to replenishment orders in one case and to original customer orders in the other. The general characteristics of the latter system, as put forth by Magee, are[5]

1. Reporting customer demand is separated from actual replenishment runs or shipments. In this way, demand can be reported frequently to control operations, but runs or shipments can be made in economical lots.
2. Each operation works against customer demand to maintain a constant supply of each item in the system, except only for fluctuations due to lot processing, that is, cycle stock.
3. At each stock point, a base stock is established adequate to meet customer demand and demand fluctuations, translated into demand for the particular item stocked over the lead time for the operation supplying the stock point, plus the interval between reports of demand, less the allowed service delay at the next following operation.
4. Replenishment of a stock point is initiated by the supplying operation on the basis of reported customer demand, rather than by the stock point itself through a replenishment order.

Problems

15.1   What are six distinctly different reasons why a company that manufactures a reasonably large product mix might avoid using the economical lot-size formula to derive an economical reorder quantity for manufactured parts?

15.2   Suppose that a manufacturing company has a large product mix and product demand is subject to variation. The company perfects a system of aggregate production-inventory planning in which employment levels, inventory, and overtime are balanced. How can you reconcile a system of economical lot-size formulas for items in finished goods with the aggregate production plan?

15.3   (a) Using a new production line, we can produce at the following rates:

first day	2,800 units
second day	3,500 units
remaining days	4,200 units/day

Two operators, each paid $150 a week, are required. About 20 units are scrapped in setting up. Maintenance cost on a given run is $12 the first day, $9 the second, and about $3 each of the remaining days. It costs $120 to set up equipment to make a batch. The line is being depreciated at $40 a day. However, there is not enough work to keep it busy. It will probably become obsolete before it wears out.

(b) Using older equipment, we can produce 700 units per day. This equipment also uses two operators, who are paid $100 a week. The operators do their own maintenance, but the setup costs $10 of their time before anything is produced. This equipment is not fully utilized. It is written off (fully depreciated).

1. Which method would you select to produce an order of:

Order size	Unit cost
2,800	1.00
6,300	1.00
6,300	10.00
10,500	1.00

Show calculations of order cost.

What order size, with a $1.00 unit cost, could be made at the same cost on either line?

2. Using the same equipment as Problem 15.3a, and that same data, three products are to be made. Product 1 is sold steadily the year around at a rate of 20,000 units per month. Product 2 is sold at a rate of 10,000 units per month. Product 3 is sold at a rate of 5,000 units per month. If Product 3 is made immediately after Product 2, the setup cost is only $40 and only 10 units will be scrapped. Otherwise, it has the same characteristics as Product 1. All products have a unit cost of $1.00.

What is an economical run for each product by Method (a)?
What is an economical run for each product by Method (b)?
How would you plan to make Product 3 by Method (b)?

How would you plan to make Product 3 by Method (a), if all products were made by (a)?

Assume an inventory carrying cost of 20% per year.

If all were made by Method (a), and always back to back (1, 2, 3, —, 1, 2, 3, —, etc.), what would the run sizes be?

15.4   The Maxium Machine Company stocks several thousand finished items. The company recently set up an economical reorder quantity-reorder point system on an electronic computer, which has been in operation for a year. The manager of the system has just discovered an error in the program, which has resulted in the economical lot sizes being 10% too high. In a fit of anxiety, he loses several nights sleep worrying about what he is going to tell his superior. Since the investment in finished goods inventory is $5,000,000, he figures the increased cost to be about $80,000 using a 20% inventory holding cost. He asks you to help him prepare a statement for his boss, which will set forth the consequences of the error in the least damaging terms.

15.5   Develop a formula for determining the economical order quantity for an item in stock, if there is a constraint on available inventory space. Let

W_i = cubic feet of space required by the ith item

M = total cubic space available

$W_i Q_i / 2$ = average space required by the ith item. Here we assume that the product mix is large so that in the aggregate, only the average inventory is on hand

$$\sum_i W_i Q_i / 2 \le M$$

15.6   The Atlas Air Compressor Company presently maintains a finished goods inventory investment of $10,000,000. In the interest of improving the working capital structure of the firm, top management orders the inventory investment to be reduced to $8,000,000. The present inventory level is the result of aggregating the economical order quantity for the items carried in inventory. Assume that the annual cost of holding an item in inventory is calculated at a rate of 10%. The Operations Research Department is asked to recalculate the economical order quantities considering the $8,000,000 investment restriction. If management's policy is followed, what will be the net increase in total cost, assuming that the present sum of inventory and setup costs, in the aggregate, is $2,000,000? What adjustment will be made in the present economical order quantity Q_i^*, and by how much? Prove.

15.7   A mustard manufacturer makes five varieties of mustard on the same facility. The varieties are produced in sequence in a given production cycle. How much of each variety should be produced in each cycle, and how many cycles will there be in a year, given the following information?

Variety	Annual demand, lbs	Annual rate of production, lbs	Annual inventory cost/unit	Setup cost per cycle = $500
1	2,000	10,000	$5.00	
2	1,000	5,000	6.00	
3	3,000	20,000	7.00	
4	4,000	20,000	5.00	
5	10,000	50,000	6.67	

15.8 The following three items have been selected at random from those carried in stock for the Excelsior Company. The average weekly rate of demand for the three products are 6, 10, and 64, respectively. Assuming a Poisson distribution of demand during a constant lead time of one week, what should a reorder point be for each product if a 0.025 probability of shortage per reorder cycle is desired? Suppose that the product with the average demand of 64 is reordered four times a year. What is the probability of shortage occurring in a year?

15.9 The demand per period for an inventory item seems to have the following probability distribution:

Demand (D)	Probability $f(D)$
5	0.2
6	0.4
7	0.3
8	0.1
	1.0

All stock to meet the demand for a period must be acquired at the start of the period. The product costs $4 per unit and sells for $7 per unit. Any leftover at the end of a period must be disposed of as "seconds" at a selling price of $3 per unit. On the other hand, if the stock becomes depleted, there is no cost associated with this shortage.
(a) Under the above conditions, will it be more profitable to stock six units or seven units at the start of each period?
(b) What will be the respective expected profit amounts for each of the above possibilities?
(c) Suppose that in addition to the costs given above there is an inventory carrying cost of $2 per item per period or a fraction of this amount, if an item is stored for a fraction of a period. Assume that demand (at any specified number) will be uniform over the period. That is, if Y is the starting stock and D is the demand, the stock remaining after x percent of the period has elapsed is $-Dx + Y$ or zero, whichever is larger. What will be the expected carrying costs for the case in which seven items are stocked at the start of each period?

15.10 Suppose that an item in stock has a variable demand with a weekly demand that is normally distributed with a mean of four units and a variance of one unit. The lead time is normally distributed with a mean of six weeks and a variance of four weeks. What should the reorder point be to give a probability of shortage in a reorder cycle equal to 0.025? Assume that the demand and lead time variables are independent.

15.11 A company has an item in stock for which the unit annual holding cost is $10, the unit stockout cost is $4, the average annual demand is 468 units, and the lot size is 47 units. If the lead-time demand is a Poisson variable with a mean of 36 units, what should the reorder point be?

15.12 The Bigelow Biological Research Laboratories deposit the residue of biological experiments in a large trash container located in the back of their building. The capacity of the container is four cubic yards. The rate at which material is added is uniformly distributed with a mean of $\frac{1}{4}$ cubic yard per hour and a range of $\frac{1}{2}$. The company must call the disposal contractor to have the container emptied. The average lead time for the contractor to arrive after being called is four hours. A study of his response to calls shows that the lead time is Poisson distributed. How full will the container be when the janitor should call the contractor if everyone is willing to accept a five percent chance of the container overflowing before the contractor's truck arrives? If you cannot do this analytically, design a simulator.

15.13   In a small Adirondack township, electric power is supplied by a local private company. The facilities consist of one small hydro plant, three diesel generators, and a tie-in to a New York State Power Authority Line (which never fails). At the beginning of each day, the manager must decide on how many diesel generators to start and keep in a warmed-up condition, including whether or not, as the last increment of capacity, to tie into the State Line. There is a cost associated with starting a unit and keeping it warmed up as well as in synchronizing into the State Line. This is $100 per diesel started and held ready and $150 for the tie-in. On the other hand, it costs $900 per day if capacity is not available when needed. The demand distribution is:

kw required	Probability	Capacity needed in addition to hydro
100–200	0.5	1 diesel
201–300	0.3	2 diesels
301–400	0.1	3 diesels
401–500	0.1	3 diesels plus tie-in

Based on this information, what capacity should the manager set up at the beginning of each day?

15.14   Determine a complete inventory policy for the following situation. An order may be placed only at the beginning of a period to satisfy demand during that period. Any quantity may be obtained at the beginning of the period for a total charge of $100. The commodity sells for $5 per pound. Any material left over at the end of the period has no value. There is an initial inventory X. The demand during the period is a chance variable D with a probability function

$f(d) = 1/100$ for $0 \le d \le 100$
0 otherwise

15.15   This refers to the inventory rule for slow moving items on page 513. What other rule could be used that would be equivalent to the one mentioned?

15.16   Determine an optimal periodic inventory review period T and an optimal maximum inventory level R for the following conditions.

Unit annual inventory holding cost $= 2$
Unit cost of backorder $= 2$
Cost of order preparation and review $= 2$
Lead time for replenishment $= 0.5$ years

Demand during lead time plus review period $(T + r)$ is uniformly distributed with mean $100(T + r)$ and range

$$h = \begin{cases} 200 \text{ if } 100(T + r) \ge 100 \\ 200(T + r) \text{ if } 100(T + r) < 100 \end{cases}$$

15.17   Consider a single facility manufacturing a certain part. Determine an optimum starting quantity for a batch of the parts if the following conditions apply:

Desired ending quantity $\qquad$ = 10

Unit processing cost $\qquad$ = 1

Setup cost $\qquad$ = 10

Recovery value of overproduced item = 0.50

Rejects are uniformly distributed with a mean equal to $(X + 1)/2$ and a range from 0 to X units.

15.18 Suppose that a part is manufactured at n successive operations. Let p_i equal the probability that a unit will be rejected at the ith operation, $i = 1, 2, \ldots, n$. p_i is independent of p_j for all i, j. How would you determine an economical starting quantity under these conditions assuming that all the cost parameters are known?

15.19 Control production for the 13-week period for Problem 14.4 (Jim's Jam Factory). Your instructor will supply you with the actual demand for each variety week by week.

Bibliography

BROWN, ROBERT G., *Decision Rules for Inventory Management*. New York: Holt, Rinehart and Winston, Inc., 1967.

HADLEY, GEORGE, and T. M. WHITEN, *Analysis of Inventory System*. Englewood Cliffs, N.J.: Prentice-Hall, Inc., 1962.

STARR, M. K., and D. W. MILLER, *Inventory Control Theory and Practice*, Englewood Cliffs, N.J.: Prentice-Hall, Inc., 1962.

WAGNER, H. M., *Statistical Management of Inventory Systems*. New York: John Wiley and Sons, 1962.

Economic Lot Size and Reorder Points:

DZIELINSKI, B. P., and A. S. MANNE, "Simulation of a Hypothetical Multi-Item Production and Inventory System," *J. Ind. Eng.*, November–December 1961.

GRASSI, R. C., and A. J. GRADWOHL, "Obsolescence and Economic Lot Size," *J. Ind. Eng.*, September–October 1959.

GROSS, DONALD, and JACK L. RAY, "Choosing a Spare Parts Inventory Operating Procedure—Bulk Control versus Item Control," *J. Ind. Eng.*, November–December 1964.

HADLEY, G., "Comparison of Order Quantities Computed Using the Average Annual Cost and the Discounted Cost," *Management Science*, April 1964.

KRONE, L. H., JR., "A Note on Economic Lot Sizes for Multipurpose Equipment," *Management Science*, April 1964.

MAXWELL, WILLIAM L., "The Scheduling of Economic Lot Sizes," *Naval Research Logistics Quart.*, June–September 1964.

RUTENBERG, Y. H., "Calculation of Economic Order Quantities Using Ranges of Setup Cost," *J. Ind. Eng.*, January–February 1964.

Assortment Problem:

BELLMAN, R., "On a Routing Problem," *Quart. of Appl. Math.*, vol. XVI, 1958, pp. 87–90.

FRANK, CHARLES R., JR., "A Note of the Assortment Problem," *Management Science*, May 1965.

GILMORE, P. C., and R. E. GOMERY, "A Linear Programming Approach to the Cutting Stock Problem," *Operations Research*, November–December 1961.

SADOWSKI, W., "A Few Remarks on the Assortment Problem," *Management Science*, October 1959.

WOLFSON, M. L., "Selecting the Best Lengths to Stock," *Operations Research*, July–August 1965.

Small Lot Problem:

HEYVAERT, A. C., and A. HURT, "Inventory Management of Slow Moving Parts," *Operations Research*, October 1956.

WHITEN, T., and J. YOUNGS, "A Method for Calculating Optimal Inventory Levels and Delivery Times," *Naval Research Logistics Quart.*, September 1955.

Reject Allowance Problem:

HILLIER, FREDERICK S., "Reject Allowances for Job Lot Orders," *J. Ind. Eng.*, November–December 1963.

LEVITAN, R. E., "The Optimum Reject Allowance Problem," *Management Science*, January 1960.

LLEWELLYN, R. W., "Order Sizes for Job Lot Manufacturing," *J. Ind. Eng.*, May–June 1959.

WADSWORTH, HARRISON M., and SING HOON CHANG, "The Reject Allowance Problem: An Analysis and Application to Job Lot Production," *J. Ind. Eng.*, May–June 1964.

SOLOMON, M. J., "The Use of an Economic Lot Range in Scheduling Production," *Management Science*, July 1959.

WAGNER, H. M., and T. M. WHITEN, "Dynamic Version of the Economic Lot Size Model," *Management Science*, October 1958.

Periodic Review Models:

BALINTFY, JOSEPH L., "On a Basic Class of Multi-Item Inventory Problems," *Management Science*, January 1964.

INGLEHART, DONALD L., "Optimality of (s, S) Policies in the Infinite Horizon Dynamic Inventory Problem," *Management Science*, January 1963.

POPP, W., "Simple and Combined Inventory Policies, Production to Stock or to Order," *Management Science*, Series A, July 1965.

RESH, M., and P. NAOR, "An Inventory Problem with Discrete Time Review and Replenishment by Batches of Fixed Size," *Management Science*, October 1963.

VEINOTT, ARTHUR F., and HARVEY M. WAGNER, "Computing Optimal (s, S) Inventory Policies," *Management Science*, March 1965.

16

Scheduling and Dispatching

INTRODUCTION

Long-term production planning, scheduling, and dispatching represent stages in a hierarchy of allocating productive resources to meet a demand for products or services. Their differences are reflected in the length of the planning horizon, the degree of detail in the techniques used, and the measures of performance used to evaluate them. There is a margin of commonality between successive stages in the hierarchy such that the terms scheduling and planning on the one hand and scheduling and dispatching on the other hand are often used interchangeably in practice.

The function of scheduling is to specify when, in calendar time, certain events are to take place with respect to both the inputs and outputs of a system. In the manufacturing context, scheduling is typically concerned with specifying the time that certain jobs are to be processed on a given facility or, conversely, when certain facilities are to be allocated to a given set of jobs. Scheduling also applies to service functions such as maintenance, tooling operations, and trucking and shipping operations, where resources are allocated on a time basis.

Shop loading is a kind of aggregate scheduling procedure that commits the capacity of one or more facilities to future production requirements. Then, at a more tactical level, the assignment of specific jobs to be processed on specific machines constitutes short-term or detailed scheduling.

The tactical limit of scheduling is the dispatching function. Dispatching is the specification of the sequence or order in which a set of jobs, jointly assigned to a machine, will be processed by that machine. Dispatching is often carried out locally at the shop level and takes advantage of current information about the status of the shop and the jobs in it. The differences between scheduling and dispatching are, again, a matter of degree. However, we can note that scheduling decisions focus on the time of events, whereas dispatching focuses on the sequence of events.

The decisions about the timing and sequencing of work must be related to certain measures of system performance. The theoretical complexity of these functions resides in the combinatorial nature of alternatives and the existence of multiple objectives or measures of performance. As we noted in the previous chapter, the effectiveness of scheduling and dispatching is usually measured in terms of localized criteria or cost indices. If these functions are carried out efficiently, we might expect that:

1. Jobs are completed when due, or the lateness of shipments is minimized.
2. Machine, facility, and manpower utilization are maximized.
3. Work-in-process inventory is held to a desirable level.
4. Lead times are held to a desirable minimum.
5. Employee incentive opportunities are equalized.
6. Facility downtime due to job changeovers or setups is minimized.

As in most cases of multiple criteria, there is seldom one schedule or job sequence that will satisfy all the above objectives. The problem of scheduling and particularly dispatching is to determine the critical objective and then to use a decision rule that will maximize that objective. Most of the theoretical work in this area has been done to determine the effect of different decision rules on various measures of effectiveness.

In the remainder of this chapter, we will briefly consider short-term planning, mainly as an introduction to a more extensive discussion of dispatching. We will then consider the special topic of planning and scheduling project activities.

SHORT-TERM SCHEDULING

Short-term scheduling emerges as a distinctive endeavor when, on the one hand, the planning and aggregate shop loading lack job specificity and, on the other hand, the product mix is not so large as to preclude the economical, detailed scheduling of each individual job. When the product mix is small, such as in many continuous or flow shop situations, the aggregate plans may in fact detail a plan for each product. When the product mix is extremely large, then scheduling may be limited to the timing of job releases to the shop, while the subsequent progress of a job is left to dispatching.

Information Procedures

The essence of short-term scheduling is to interrelate size of job orders, desired dates of completion, and capacity of production facilities. Interrelating these to maximize the utilization of facilities and at the same time meet job delivery dates requires information procedures that update the progress of each job in the shop and the capacity status of facilities. The procedures for doing this vary widely depending on the detail desired, the number of products involved, and the capabilities of the communications system.

Historically, scheduling has depended on the use of visual aids, which plot both the progress of a job and current facility capacities. The venerable scheduling

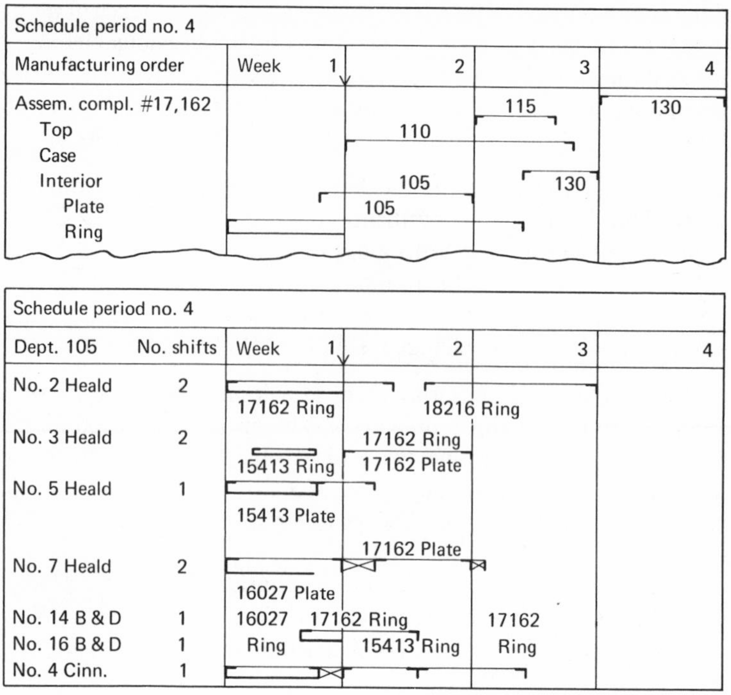

Schedule period no. 4					
Manufacturing order	Week 1		2	3	4
Assem. compl. #17,162				115	130
Top			110		
Case					
Interior			105	130	
Plate		105			
Ring					

Schedule period no. 4					
Dept. 105	No. shifts	Week 1	2	3	4
No. 2 Heald	2	17162 Ring	18216 Ring		
No. 3 Heald	2	15413 Ring	17162 Ring / 17162 Plate		
No. 5 Heald	1	15413 Plate			
No. 7 Heald	2	16027 Plate	17162 Plate		
No. 14 B & D	1	16027 17162 Ring		17162	
No. 16 B & D	1	Ring 15413 Ring		Ring	
No. 4 Cinn.	1				

FIGURE **16.1**   Gantt charts. From Gordon B. Carson, Ed., *Production Handbook*, 2nd ed. New York: Ronald Press, 1958, p. 321.

device for portraying both job and facility information has been the Gantt Chart, an innovation of the era of scientific management. Figure 16.1 shows two variants of the Gantt Chart. In the top section, the projected four-week schedule is shown for various parts listed in the first column. The horizontal lines indicate the planned or projected time the job will be scheduled in the numerically indicated department. The lower part of the chart shows the scheduled load on each of a number of machines listed in the first column and represents graphic machine loading. In both the part schedule and machine loading schedule, the progress of jobs is updated by the heavier black lines. The principle of the Gantt chart can be employed in various forms, including graphic charts, card systems, and control boards using pegs and strings. However, these are rapidly being displaced by electronic and magnetic tape storage and printout systems. We will devote more attention to this matter in the next chapter.

Scheduling Decisions

While the means of displaying information about jobs and machine status are important, they are not, of course, a substitute for decision making. Short-term scheduling decisions include the timing of job releases to the shop, suggested ordering of jobs, the choice of facilities if alternative routings are possible, and possibly the choice of methods of increasing or decreasing capacity.

In scheduling, optimizing procedures are often of only academic interest. For one thing, the multiplicity of objectives and changes in their relative importance over time preclude an unambiguous decision-making environment. If the objective is mainly to maximize facility utilization or meet delivery dates, the problem becomes one of optimal job sequencing via scheduling, if the number of jobs and facilities is small, or via dispatching, if the opposite is true.

There are presumably situations where alternative product routings may minimize processing costs under conditions of constraints in the available facility capacity. We can imagine such a situation, which can be structured as a linear distribution programing problem.

Suppose we can identify a backlogged set of jobs that are to be scheduled on a set of facilities. Each job requires processing on only one of the machines; however, there exist alternative choices of which machine will be used. If the alternatives yield different costs, then the problem is to allocate the hours representing the job requirements to available machine hours. Since the transportation method assumes that a unit of input (at the origin) is equal to a unit of output (at the destination), we must structure our problem in "equivalent" hours, because the machines have unequal production rates.

Let

i = job index; $i = 1, 2, \ldots, n$

j = machine index; $j = 1, 2, \ldots, m$

n_{ij} = rate at which machine j can produce job i in units per hour

a_i = number of units of i in the backlog

b_j = available number of hours for machine j

c_{ij} = cost of producing a unit of i on j

We now assume that there is a constant ratio, that is,

$$\gamma_j = \frac{n_{ij}}{n_{i,j+1}} = \text{constant for all } i$$

This means that all machines produce at a rate that is proportional to the rates of all other machines, regardless of the job being produced.

Let machine k have that index j for which n_{ij} is maximum. We will let

$$\gamma_j = \frac{n_{ij}}{n_{ik}}$$

which is called the equivalency ratio for machine j.

$$\gamma_j = \left\{ \begin{array}{l} 1.00 \text{ for } j = k \\ \leq 1.00 \text{ for } j \neq k \end{array} \right\}$$

The problem must now be structured in standard or equivalent hours:

c'_{ij} = cost for allocating one standard hour requirement of i to j

$c'_{ij} = c_{ij} n_{ik}$

a'_i = requirements for job i in equivalent standard hours

$a'_i = a_i/n_{ik}$

$b'_j =$ equivalent standard hours of available capacity on j

$b'_j = b_j\gamma_j$

We minimize $\sum x'_{ij}c'_{ij}$ subject to

$$x'_{ij} \geq 0; \sum_j x'_{ij} = a'_i; \sum_i x'_{ij} = b'_j; \sum_j a'_i = \sum_i b'_j$$

where x'_{ij} is equal to the number of equivalent standard hours of job i allocated to machine j. Our final solution is then

$$x_{ij} = x'_{ij}/\gamma_j$$

where x_{ij} is number of actual hours allocated.

DISPATCHING

In large single machine processes and where a finite batch of jobs is to be integrally allocated to a set of machines, scheduling and dispatching merge as common functions. When this is not the case, dispatching, or job sequencing, is a localized problem. For a particular facility in a large network of jobs and machines, jobs are dispatched by the foreman or machine operator, and the dispatching decision is based on immediate or current shop information.

In the past decade and a half, the dispatching function has been subjected to a good deal of research involving both analytical and simulation methods. In this chapter, we will examine theoretical approaches to a variety of situations and assumptions. In general, the elements of a dispatching problem include the structure of the "shop" in terms of number of facilities and jobs, decision rules that state the priority with which competing jobs will be sequenced, and the effect of these rules upon measures of performance. The specific theoretical problem is usually to determine, for a given shop structure, the priority dispatching rule that will optimize a given measure of performance or effectiveness. (For an excellent and thorough coverage of the theory of scheduling and, more particularly, of dispatching, see Richard W. Conway, William L. Maxwell, and Louis W. Miller, *Theory of Scheduling*. Reading, Mass.: Addison-Wesley, 1967.)

Priority Dispatching Rules

A dispatching rule states the priority system that will guide the selection of a job from among a batch of jobs waiting to be serviced by a facility. If there is a finite batch of N jobs waiting to be processed by a single facility, then there are $N!$ possible sequences or orders of the jobs through the facility. A priority rule will designate one sequence among the set of $N!$ possible sequences. Once a job is chosen from the set of waiting jobs, the priority rule may be changed so that more than a single rule can be applied to the set of N jobs.

One can conceive of a large number of priority rules to govern the selection of jobs competing for processing time on a given machine. For example, some obvious ones are:

1. Use a random rule such that each job has an equal likelihood of being selected.
2. Use a first-come-first-served rule such that highest priority is given to the job that arrived earliest at the machine.
3. Assign highest priority to the job that requires the least amount of processing time on the machine.
4. Assign highest priority to the job that has the earliest due-date for completion.
5. Select the job that requires the least amount of setup time relative to the job that has just been completed on the machine.
6. Select the job that has the fewest number of remaining operations to completion.

This list can be easily expanded to include a wide variety of priority schemes.

Some general characteristics of priority rules are the following:

1. *Independent versus universal application*   In a system of many jobs and machines, the rules can be applied independently and locally to each machine, or a given rule can be applied universally to all machines in the system. However, we can anticipate that no rule is invoked for long periods of time without change. Such things as machine failures, material shortages, engineering design changes, rework requirements, and other phenomena contribute to the necessity of altering schedules and dispatching rules.

2. *Economy of use*   Priority rules vary in the ease with which they can be applied in terms of the information needed. The first-come-first-served rule is easy to implement, as is the earliest due-date rule, providing the information accompanies each job. On the other hand, such rules as fewest number of remaining operations, or assigning highest priority to the job that subsequently goes to an idle facility, require more information.

3. *Local versus global rules*   A local rule assigns priority on the basis of the immediate status of the job with respect to the machine in question. A global rule requires information about the status of some aspect of the system beyond the local boundaries. The first-come-first-served rule can be applied to the arrival status of the job to the machine (local) or to the shop (global). A rule that examines the status of other machines in the system as a basis for assigning priority to a given job on a given machine requires global information.

4. *Time-dependent rules*   Certain rules require some time measurement of each job, such as processing times or due dates. Thus, time-dependent rules include priority on the basis of the processing time on the immediate machine, the remaining operations, the time the job has waited in a queue, or the due date. Time-independent rules include first come first served or selection on the basis of machine utilization in subsequent operations.

5. *Simple versus compound rules*   A simple rule requires the evaluation of a single factor (first come first served). A compound rule jointly evaluates several

measures. For example, we might assign priority on the basis of the ratio (the time to process the job on the immediate machine) ÷ (the number of remaining operations) calculated for each job.

Each priority rule affects the various measures of effectiveness (machine utilization, job lateness, etc.) to some degree. The basic management problem is to know which measures of effectiveness are important and then to apply priority rules that will maximize these objectives. Choosing the critical value objectives is an economic problem involving tradeoffs among incompatibilities. Attempting to minimize machine downtime may have an adverse effect on job lateness, for example. However, before tradeoffs can be evaluated, it is necessary to know how measures of effectiveness are influenced by dispatching rules, and it is on this aspect that we will now focus our attention.

Classification of Problems

Dispatching problems can be broken down into two broad categories. The first is the situation where there is a fixed number of jobs N to be sequenced through the facility system. That is, all jobs have the same starting time in the system and no job arrivals occur after the decision has been made how the batch of N jobs is to be sequenced. The opposite case is where jobs arrive in a continuous but random fashion to the system.

A second classification is in terms of both the batch size N and the number of machines or facilities M. Problems in which the batch size N is fixed and in which $M \geq 1$ are often referred to as $M \times N$ dispatching or scheduling problems. In the case of random arrivals, the dispatching problems are queuing problems, and when $M > 1$, the problem is one of a network of queues.

More detailed classifications include such things as the character of setup times, that is, whether or not they are dependent on the sequence, the similarity of part or job routings, and the fixity of the processing time estimates.

First we will consider the case of fixed batch size and then look at the case of random arrivals. Throughout this section we will use the following notation.

i = index of job; $i = 1, 2, \ldots, N$

j = index of machine; $j = 1, 2, \ldots, M$

R_{ij} = the time that the ith job is ready to be processed on the jth machine. R_{i1} is therefore the time the job is released to the shop.

P_{ij} = the interval of time required to process the ith job on the jth machine

g_i = number of different operations required on the ith job as prescribed by the routing function

C_{ij} = completion time of the ith job on the jth machine. C_{ig} is therefore the completion time of the job in the shop. Completion time can be interpreted either as a date of completion or as an interval of time spent by a job in the shop, including the sum of processing and waiting times. In the following discussions, completion time is used to mean time interval and is variously called flow, shop, or scheduling time, depending on the particular problem.

D_i = due date for the ith job
L_i = the lateness of the ith job
    = $C_{i_0} - D_i$

DISPATCHING RULES FOR FIXED NUMBER OF JOBS

We now consider the general class of cases where all jobs of a finite and fixed number N are to be scheduled to a finite and fixed number of machines M. The distinctive feature is that all jobs have the same starting time such that $R_{i1} = 0$ for all i. We wish to sequence the jobs on each of the M machines to optimize a given measure of effectiveness.

Single Machine Case (M = 1)

We first examine the single machine case. Many production systems can be considered as single machines for scheduling purposes. Examples include a food processing line, a high-speed computer, an electric utility maintenance truck, and a large expensive boring mill. Isolating such relatively high investment facilities for scheduling purposes leads to economic gains that would be sacrificed if they were relegated to the status of components of a multi-machine system. For this discussion, we will adjust our notation as follows:

j = 1 and will be ignored as a subscript for the machine

C_N = time the last job in the batch is completed. Since $R_i = 0$ for all i, C_N is the total interval of time necessary to complete the job batch (the schedule time).

s_{ij} = time to set up the machine if the jth job follows the ith job. Note that in this case we use j as a job subscript.

SETUP TIME (s_{ij}) IS SEQUENCE INDEPENDENT: In the following cases, we assume that the setup time is not dependent on the sequencing of the jobs. That is, $s_{ij} = 0$; $i = 1, 2, \ldots, N; j = 1, 2, \ldots, N; i \neq j$.

1. *Minimize C_N* We wish to sequence the N jobs such that the completion time of the last job is minimized. Clearly, any dispatching rule will yield the same result. That is,

$$C_N = \sum_1^N s_{ij} + \sum_1^N P_i$$

The first term is zero or constant, as is the second term, regardless of the ordering of the jobs through the machine.

2. *Minimize average completion time* The average completion time for the jobs is $\bar{C} = \sum_1^N C_i/N$. We can easily show that this is sequence dependent. For example, suppose that we have just two jobs X and Y having processing times of 2 and 10 time units, respectively. Then,

a. The sequence X, Y yields $C_X = 2$ and $C_Y = 12$, or an average of 7.

b. The sequence Y, X yields $C_X = 12$ and $C_Y = 10$, or an average of 11.

Suppose that we sequence the jobs on the basis of increasing processing times such that $P_1 \leq P_2 \leq \cdots \leq P_N$. Then,

$$C_1 = P_1$$
$$C_2 = P_1 + P_2$$
$$\vdots$$
$$C_N = P_1 + P_2 + \cdots + P_N$$

We wish to minimize $\sum_1^N C_i$:

$$\sum_1^N C_i = NP_1 + (N-1)P_2 + \cdots + P_N$$

This sum is equal to a minimum, because the addition of a series of products is minimum when one factor increases in order and the other factor decreases in order. Therefore, the rule is to assign the jobs to the machine in order of ascending processing times. We can call this the *shortest processing time* rule.

3. *Minimize average number of jobs in the system*   The average number of jobs in the system between the starting time and the completion time of the last job is equal to

$$\overline{N} = \frac{\sum_1^N C_i}{C_N} = \frac{NP_1 + (N-1)P_2 + \cdots + P_N}{\sum_1^N P_i}$$

This is minimized by using the shortest processing time rule since the rule minimizes $\sum_1^N C_i$.

4. *Minimize average job lateness*   The average job lateness is $\overline{L} = \sum_1^N \frac{(C_i - D_i)}{N}$

$$= \frac{\sum_1^N C_i - \sum_1^N D_i}{N}.$$ Since $\sum D_i$ is a constant, average lateness is minimized by sequencing to minimize average completion time; therefore, the shortest processing time rule is optimum.

5. *Minimize maximum job lateness*   We wish to minimize the lateness of the latest job in the sequence. It can be shown that the optimum rule is to assign the jobs in the sequence $D_1 \leq D_2 \leq \cdots \leq D_N$.

Suppose we consider two jobs i and j in a sequence, where $D_i < D_j$. We want to show that the maximum lateness of the ordering i, j is equal to or less than the ordering j, i.

$$L_i = P_1 + P_2 + \cdots + P_i - D_i$$
$$L_j = P_1 + P_2 + \cdots + P_i + P_j - D_j$$

Now suppose that we reverse the order of the jobs such that j precedes i and let L' indicate the lateness of the reverse ordering.

$$L'_j = P_1 + P_2 + \cdots + P_j - D_j$$
$$L'_i = P_1 + P_2 + \cdots + P_j + P_i - D_i$$

But, $L_i \leq L'_i$ and $L_j \leq L'_i$, and, therefore,

$$\max(L_i, L_j) \leq L'_i \leq \max(L'_i, L'_j)$$

6. *Minimizing a lateness penalty*   Suppose that we attach a value to each job that is a function of the job's completion time. For example, let there be a penalty K_i, which is a linear function of the job's completion time, and let a_i be the unit cost per unit time of completion. That is,

$$K_i = a_i C_i$$

The objective function is minimize $\sum_1^N K_i$. In what sequence should the jobs be processed?

The optimal rule is to sequence the jobs in the order $1, 2, \ldots, n$ such that

$$\frac{p_1}{a_1} \leq \frac{p_2}{a_2} \cdots$$

The proof is very much like the one used in determining a part routing, which minimizes work-in-process inventory investment (see page 172). We proceed as follows: Suppose we sequence N jobs according to the above rule. Then, consider two successively ordered jobs i and j, where $(p_i/a_i) < (p_j/a_j)$. If job i is done before job j and the total cost up to job i is α, then the total cost including i and j is

$$K = \alpha + a_i p_i + a_j(p_i + p_j)$$

If the two jobs are reversed in order and j is done before i, then the loss K' is

$$K' = \alpha + a_j p_j + a_i(p_j + p_i)$$

and, therefore,

$$K - K' < 0 \quad \text{since} \quad \frac{p_i}{a_i} < \frac{p_j}{a_j} \quad \text{or} \quad a_j p_i < a_i p_j$$

SETUP TIME (s_{ij}) IS SEQUENCE DEPENDENT: Now we consider the case where the time to set up the machine is dependent on the order in which the jobs are assigned to the machine. In this case, we will concentrate only on minimizing the completion time for the last job, which means we wish to minimize the total time the machine is nonproductive while being set up for job changes over the batch of N jobs.

For each pair of jobs there is a unique setup time s_{ij}. Then there is a setup time matrix, $S = \{s_{ij}; i = 1, 2, \ldots, N; j = 1, 2, \ldots, N; i \neq j\}$. There are $N!$ possible job sequences. Then, for any given sequence there will be a given total setup time, consisting of the sum of s_{ij} values, one from each row and one from each column of S as determined by the sequence. Let this sum be T_k, $k = 1, 2, \ldots, N!$.

We encountered this problem in Chapter 1, where the printing company was interested in minimizing the downtime of its presses (see page 26). This class of problems is known as the "Traveling Salesman Problem." The analogy is that a salesman has a route in which he will visit each of N cities. There is a unique distance between each pair of cities, and he wishes to determine the sequence of

From job i	To job j					
	A	B	C	D	E	F
A	0	3.0	2.8	2.2	2.5	1.7
B	0	0	1.7	2.3	1.8	0.9
C	0	3.4	0	3.5	2.7	1.9
D	0	1.8	1.2	0	1.2	2.2
E	0	2.5	2.4	3.6	0	2.5
F	0	1.5	2.6	3.4	2.4	0

FIGURE **16.2**   Setup time matrix $S = (s_{ij})$.

cities that will minimize the total distance traveled. In our particular case, the paired job setup times correspond to the paired city distances, and the total setup time corresponds to the total travel distance.

EXAMPLE 16.1   Suppose the manager of a print shop assigns N jobs to be done each day on a large rotary press. Each job has its own specification for paper dimension, ink color, type size, etc. After each job is completed, the press must be shut down and made ready for the next job. Suppose that five jobs are to be assigned to the press on a given day. The press has just completed job A on the previous day, and the problem is to sequence jobs B, C, D, E, and F.

Each pair of jobs will have a changeover time s_{ij}, which depends on the difference in their printing requirements. The changeover or setup times are shown in the Setup Time Matrix (Figure 16.2).

1. *Optimal sequence*   Historically, the traveling salesman problem has been the subject of considerable research. With today's computers, complete enumeration is feasible for problems ranging up to $N = 10$. The problem is a special case of the linear assignment problem, and branch and bound has been used to economically solve rather large problems.[1] Dynamic programing has also been successfully applied.[2]

In the context of the job sequencing problem, the determination of an optimal sequence may be more of academic than of practical interest. In the case of a processing or production line in which a relatively small product mix is recycled in some particular sequence, the determination of an optimal sequence may be

---

[1] J. D. C. Little *et al.*, "An Algorithm for the Traveling Salesman Problem," *Operations Research*, vol. 11, no. 6, November–December 1963.
[2] M. Held and R. L. Karg, "A Dynamic Programming Approach to Sequencing Problems," *J. Soc. of Ind. and Appl. Math.*, vol. 10, 1962.

important, since the sequence is repeated a large number of times. However, in the context of a job shop, such as the printing plant, each unique batch of jobs requires separate computation of an optimal sequence. This not only demands currently available computational facilities, but requires the repeated construction of the setup time matrix, including the estimation of the times contained in it. From a work measurement point of view, the latter may not be feasible.

2. *A heuristic rule* A logical but simple rule can be applied without necessarily having the setup time matrix available. We will call this the "next best rule," which is as follows: Given that the facility has just completed job i, select the unassigned job j for which s_{ij} is a minimum. In terms of the example, we would assign job F after A because s_{AF} is the minimum in row A. Then, given job F, we would assign job B. Continuing in this fashion would result in the assignment A-F-B-C-E-D with a total setup time of 11.2 time units. This rule is nonoptimal, since, for example, in this case the minimum is 8.6 time units, corresponding to the sequence A-D-C-F-B-E.

The obvious importance of the next best rule is that assignments can be made on the basis of the relative merits of each job in the set of unassigned jobs. Presumably in many cases, the scheduler can assess the jobs and select the job that results in the minimum value of s_{ij} without having to actually measure the times. It is therefore important to know just how good this rule is compared to the optimum and to random assignment.

The efficiency of this rule has been studied by Gavett.[3] The test procedure involved generating a sample of setup time matrices. Each matrix was subjected to the next best rule, and the resulting setup time (or tour time) was compared with the optimum found by branch and bound. The setup time matrix elements s_{ij} were generated from a normal distribution of mean 1 and given variance.

Figure 16.3 shows the ratio of the average of the setup times using the next best rule ($\overline{T}_{nb}$) to the average of the optimal tour times ($\overline{T}_{min}$) for various batch sizes and for various coefficients of variation for the distributions of s_{ij}.

As would be expected, the setup time resulting from the application of the next best rule deviates from the minimum in proportion to the coefficient of variation of the s_{ij} values, and the difference is slightly sensitive to the value of N, particularly for the larger values of the coefficient of variation.

Figure 16.4 shows the efficiency of the next best rule compared to the random selection of a sequence $\overline{T}$. For example, the use of the next best rule would result in a reduction of about 50% in downtime over the random sequencing of jobs for which $N = 21$ and the coefficient of variation 0.4. Over all the samples investigated, the average reduction in setup time using the next best rule rather than random sequencing was 26%. In contrast, the use of the optimum sequence, as compared with random sequencing, resulted in an average 31% reduction in setup time.

---

[3] J. W. Gavett, "Three Heuristic Rules for Sequencing Jobs to a Single Production Facility," *Management Science*, vol. 11, no. 8, June 1965, pp. B166–76.

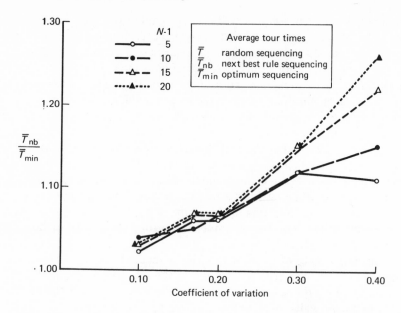

FIGURE **16.3**   Efficiency of the *NB* rule compared to optimum rule. From J. W. Gavett, "Three Heuristic Rules for Sequencing Jobs to a Single Production Facility," *Management Science*, vol. 11, no. 8, pp. 13–17.

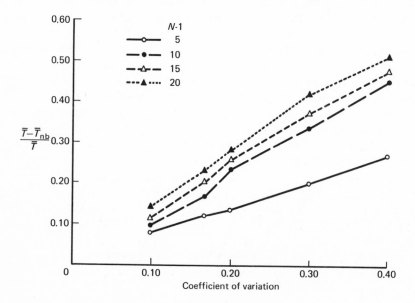

FIGURE **16.4**   Efficiency of the *NB* rule compared to random rule. From J. W. Gavett, "Three Heuristic Rules for Sequencing Jobs to a Single Production Facility," *Management Science*, vol. 11, no. 8, pp. 13–17.

The Multiple Machine Case (M ≥ 2)

Previously, we dealt with a production system involving only one facility. We will now briefly consider systems of more than one machine. Again, we will assume that N is finite and fixed and that all starting times are equal.

The problem of maximizing certain objectives is now considerably more difficult to handle analytically than in the single machine case. If all N jobs must be processed on all M machines, but in any order on each machine, then there are $(N!)^M$ possible unique schedules.

The order in which a given job proceeds through the machines is technologically determined by the routing function. In the flow shop, all jobs have the same routing, while in the pure job shop, the individual job routings are independent. Within each of these extremes, additional constraints can be added. For instance, some pairs of jobs may have to be performed in succession. Furthermore, there may be a time interval between the end of one job and the start of another job on a given machine due to setup requirements that may be sequence dependent or independent. Routings and constraints can be displayed as matrices.

For example, suppose we have three jobs and two machines. Let the jobs be $i = 1, 2, 3$ and the machines be $j = A, B$.

1. There is an R matrix that specifies the routing of each job. We might assume that these orderings are technologically determined, although we should recall that flexible routings are possible and sometimes advisable.

$$
R = \begin{matrix} 1 \\ 2 \\ 3 \end{matrix} \begin{vmatrix} A & B \\ A & B \\ B & A \end{vmatrix}
$$

2. There is a job matrix J that specifies the ordering of jobs on each machine. This ordering might be specified, for example, to minimize machine downtime if setup times are sequence dependent. Usually, however, we might expect this matrix to be partially specified or unspecified.

$$
J =
$$

A	2	1	3
B	3	1	2

3. A feasible schedule is shown in the form of a Gantt chart. There are two kinds of Gantt charts. One indicates a schedule of machines for each job, $G(R)$, and the other a schedule of jobs on each machine, $G(J)$.

$$
G(R) =
$$

1	—	A	B	—
2	A	—	—	B
3	B	—	A	—

$$G(J) = \begin{array}{c|cccc} A & 2 & 1 & 3 & - \\ B & 3 & - & 1 & 2 \end{array}$$

4. There is a P matrix in which an element p_{ij} is the time required to process each job on each machine.

$$P = \begin{array}{c|cc} & A & B \\ \hline 1 & 4 & 3 \\ 2 & 2 & 2 \\ 3 & 3 & 1 \end{array}$$

The Gantt charts may now be expressed using a time scale as follows:

$$G(R) = \begin{array}{c|l} 1 & -- \; A \; A \; A \; A \; B \; B \; B \; -- \\ \hline 2 & A \; A \; -\; -\; -\; -\; -\; -\; -\; B \; B \\ \hline 3 & B \; -\; -\; -\; -\; -\; A \; A \; A \; -- \end{array}$$

$$G(J) = \begin{array}{c|l} A & 2 \; 2 \; 1 \; 1 \; 1 \; 1 \; 3 \; 3 \; 3 \; -- \\ \hline B & 3 \; -\; -\; -\; -\; -\; 1 \; 1 \; 1 \; 2 \; 2 \end{array}$$

The numbers of columns in both charts are equal and correspond to the length of the chart, which is also the time for the entire schedule (schedule time).

The problem is to construct a schedule that will maximize some objective function. In the following discussion, we will be concerned only with the objective of minimizing the schedule time, which as we noted is equivalent to minimizing the maximum completion time of a job in the set N. Because of the variety of situations and constraints that can be encountered in problems of this type, we will make some simplifying assumptions. First, the J matrix is unspecified and a facility can process jobs in any order. Second, for all jobs and machines, once a job is started on one machine it must be completed in its entirety before being scheduled on another machine and before the following job can be started. Third, the processing time for a job is sequence independent, and setup times are equal to zero. Fourth, no job is processed twice on the same machine.

THE CASE $M = 2$: Besides the assumptions listed above, we will assume a flow shop format such that each job must go to Machine A first and then to Machine B. Johnson[4] has shown that the jobs should be processed on both machines in the same order if the completion time for the last job is to be minimized. Assume that we have five jobs with the following P matrix:

		A	B
	1	4	5
	2	4	1
$P =$	3	30	4
	4	6	30
	5	2	3

Rule:

1. Determine the minimum of all p_{ij}.
2. If the minimum is p_{i1}, place the corresponding job first, and if the minimum is p_{i2}, place the corresponding job last.
3. Cross off both times for that job.
4. Repeat the procedure on the reduced set, $N - 1$.
5. In case of ties, select p_{i1}.

That is,

1. Select Job 2 and place it last.
2. Cross out p_{21} and p_{22} equal to 4 and 1, respectively.
3. Select Job 5 and place it first.
4. Select Job 1 and place it just after Job 5, etc. The resultant schedule is 5-1-4-3-2.

THE CASE $M = 3$: Johnson's method of minimizing maximum job completion time also applies to the case of three machines and N jobs, provided that either or both of the following conditions prevail:

1. The smallest processing time for Machine A is at least as great as the largest processing time for Machine B.
2. The smallest processing time for Machine C is at least as great as the largest processing time for Machine B.

The method is to generate a set of two new times for each job

$$P'_i = A_i + B_i \quad \text{and} \quad P''_i = B_i + C_i$$

where A_i, B_i, and C_i are the processing times for the ith job on Machines A, B, and C, respectively. The two-machine rule is then applied to P'_i and P''_i.

[4] S. M. Johnson, "Optimal Two and Three Stage Production Schedules with Setup Times Included," *Naval Research Logistics Quart.*, vol. 1, March 1954, pp. 61–68.

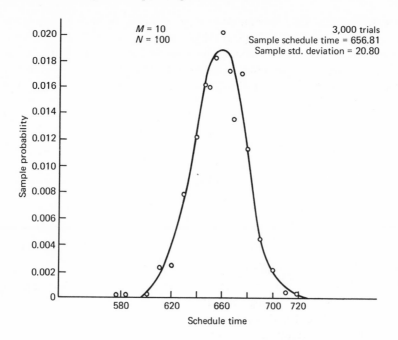

FIGURE **16.5** Distribution of schedule times. From J. Heller, *Operations Research*, vol. 8, no. 2, March–April 1960, p. 182.

THE CASE $M \geq 3$: A number of approaches have been suggested for cases where M is equal to or greater than 3 and for flow or job shop formats.

Heller conducted an experiment to determine the distribution of alternative schedule times (completion time for entire schedule) for a set of N jobs and M machines.[5] The alternative schedules were generated randomly on a computer. In the first experiment, the dimensions of the problem were 100 jobs and 10 machines. The processing time for each job on each machine was generated from a uniform distribution with range 0 to 9. The sample size was 3,000 trials. Each trial consisted of a randomly selected permutation of the 100 jobs. The jobs were then sequenced through the 10 machines in the same order (flow shop) and the schedule length calculated. The results yielded a near normal distribution of the schedule times with a sample mean of 656, standard deviation of 20.8, and range of 606 to 707 (Figure 16.5). In another experiment, he compared the distribution of schedules for a flow shop with that for a pure job shop using the same job set. As we might expect, the mean and variance of schedule times for the common ordering of jobs was considerably less than for the case where the job ordering was independent and randomly generated for each machine.

It is important to note that the flow shop format does not imply that the ordering of the jobs on each machine must be the same. It does mean that all jobs must proceed through the same ordering of machines, but, again, the sequencing

[5] J. Heller, "Some Numerical Experiments for an $M \times J$ Flow Shop and Its Decision Theoretical Aspects," *Operations Research*, vol. 8, no. 2, March–April 1960.

of jobs on the machines may be different. Thus, one may find better schedules than those contained in the set of schedules with common job orderings. However, for the special case of M equal to 2 or 3, it can be shown that the optimal schedule is one in which the job sequence on each machine is the same.

In the case of the flow shop, Ignall and Schrage proposed the use of the branch and bound technique for determining the minimum completion time for the last job for the case $M = 3$. For $M > 3$ the method may be used but does not result necessarily in an optimal solution because of the restriction of common job ordering.[6] Their procedure is briefly as follows. Suppose there is a set of N jobs to be sequenced on a set of M machines; $N = 1, 2, \ldots, i, \ldots, n$; $M = a, b, \ldots, j, \ldots, z$. Each job must be processed once and only once by each machine in a flow shop format. Then, a given node in the tree will represent a particular ordering of a subset of jobs, $K = 1, 2, \ldots, i, \ldots, k$, where $1 \le k \le n - 1$. The subset $\bar{K}$ will contain the jobs yet to be assigned to the sequence, or $\bar{K} = N - K$. Each job will require a processing time $p_{i,j}$ on the jth machine. For simplicity, we now assume the case $m = 3$. Let $_kC_j$ be the completion time of job k, the last in the sequence, on Machine j. Then for each node in the tree, a lower bound is calculated for the set K:

$$
LB(K) = \max \begin{cases} _kC_1 + \sum_{\bar{K}} p_{i1} + \min_{\bar{K}}(p_{i2} + p_{i3}) \\[2mm] _kC_2 + \sum_{\bar{K}} p_{i2} + \min_{\bar{K}}(p_{i3}) \\[2mm] _kC_3 + \sum_{\bar{K}} p_{i3} \end{cases}
$$

For example, the processing time for a set of four jobs on three machines is

$$
P = \begin{array}{c|ccc}
 & A & B & C \\ \hline
1 & 13 & 3 & 12 \\
2 & 7 & 12 & 16 \\
3 & 26 & 9 & 7 \\
4 & 2 & 6 & 1 \\
\end{array}
$$

Figure 16.6 and Table 16.1 show the tree and the solution steps, respectively.

Various other approaches have been taken to solving both the flow shop and job shop situations. Giffler and Thompson[7] propose an algorithm for handling the more general condition of the job shop, where job routings are independent and the objective is to minimize the schedule time for the batch of jobs. Their algorithm systematically investigates a subset of feasible schedules. This subset contains the optimum, which is found by enumerating the subset or by sampling the problem if it is large. Brooks and White[8] elaborate on the previous algorithm

[6] E. Ignall and L. Schrage, "Applications of the Branch and Bound Technique to Some Flow Shop Scheduling Problems," *Operations Research*, vol. 13, no. 3, May–June 1965, pp. 400–12.
[7] B. Giffler and G. L. Thompson, "Algorithms for Solving Production Scheduling Problems," *Operations Research*, July–August 1960.
[8] George Brooks and Charles R. White, "An Algorithm for Finding Optimal or Near Optimal Solutions to the Production Scheduling Problem," *J. Ind. Eng.*, vol. XVI, no. 1, January–February 1965, pp. 34–40.

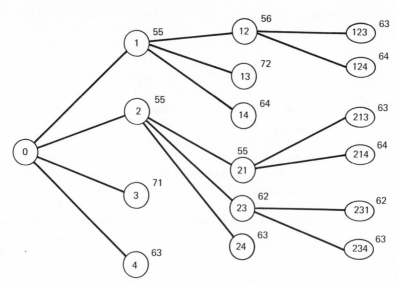

FIGURE **16.6**   Solution tree. From E. Ignall and L. Schrage, *Operations Research*, vol. 13, no. 3, May–June 1965, p. 402.

TABLE **16.1**   Solution steps.[a]

Node	Lower bound	$_kC_2$	$_kC_3$	Disposition
0	—	—	—	Branched from
1	55	16	28	Branched from
2	55	19	35	Branched from
3	71	35	42	
4	63	8	9	
21	55	23	47	Branched from
23	62	42	51	Branched from
24	63	25	36	
213	63	61	63	
214	64	57	64	
12	56	36	48	Branched from
13	72	48	55	
14	64	22	29	
123	63	61	63	
124	64	57	64	
231	62	60	62	An optimal sequence
234	63	51	63	

[a] From Ignall and Schrage.[6]

by using branch and bound to improve the search for optimum. We will not examine these methods in detail. In terms of an efficient method of solution, the general job shop scheduling problem still remains an unsolved problem for large values of M and N. However, the problem of scheduling a fixed batch size N is probably encountered less frequently in practice than the problem of dispatching jobs that arrive intermittently or randomly to a shop, a condition which we will now examine.

DISPATCHING RULES FOR QUEUE NETWORKS

We now relax the requirement that the N jobs are scheduled as a fixed number with common starting times. We will consider the shop or production system as a waiting line or queuing system of machines and jobs. The jobs arrive at the shop continuously in a regular or random pattern, and then each job is serviced by one or more of the machines in the shop.

Single-Machine Queuing System

Consider a single machine at which jobs arrive randomly to be serviced by the machine, and the processing time for each job is an independent random variable. This is a single-channel queuing system characterized by alternating periods of waiting jobs and idle machines.

The measures of the performance of the system are generally 1) the average job completion time, 2) the expected length of the waiting line or the average number of jobs in the system, 3) the machine utilization, and 4) the average waiting time for a job, which is the same as the average completion time minus the average processing time.

The single-channel system was examined by Cobham in terms of different dispatching priority rules.[9] He assumed an unsaturated queuing system (rate of service greater than rate of arrivals) with exponentially distributed interarrival times and arbitrary service time distributions. His method involved assigning one of a finite number of priority classes to each arriving unit by some priority rule. Expressions are given for the expected waiting time of a unit of priority p. Without going into the proofs, we summarize the result of Cobham's work by the following statements:[10]

1. If the expected service time is the same for each priority class, then the over-all mean waiting time and the mean system state (number of jobs in the system) are the same for all priority rules.
2. If a priority class can be divided into two subclasses, such that the expected processing time of one subclass is smaller than the expected processing time of the other class, and if a lower priority value is assigned to the subclass with the smaller expected processing time, both the over-all mean waiting time and the mean system state will be decreased.
3. If the expected service times of arriving units differ, then the over-all mean waiting

---

[9] A. Cobham, "Priority Assignment in Waiting Line Problems," *Operations Research*, vol. 2, no. 1, February 1954.

[10] R. W. Conway and W. L. Maxwell, "Network Scheduling by the Shortest-Operation Discipline," Dept. of Ind. Eng., Cornell Univ., Ithaca, N.Y., April 1961, p. 7.

time and the mean system state are *minimized* by numbering the priority classes in the order of expected service time.

4. If the expected service times of arriving units differ, then the over-all mean waiting time and the mean system state are maximized by numbering the priority classes in the opposite order as the expected service time.

5. If the waiting times of units of priority class p are weighted by a value v_p, the over-all mean weighted waiting time is minimized by assigning priority classes in the order of the ratio s/v: $s_1/v_1 \leq s_2/v_2 \leq \cdots$, where s_p is the expected service time of the pth class.

In the simple, single-channel queuing system, the shortest processing time rule is optimum among a limited class of time-independent priority rules and with respect to certain mean values of system performance. That is, the statements are true with respect to a classification of the products into priority classes, and the classes can be broken down such that each product is a class.

Multiple-Machine Queuing Network

The next logical step is to extend the analysis to a system of N jobs and more than one machine. In an early analytical work, Jackson showed that, under certain assumptions, the system "decomposed" into one of a network of independent individual-machine queuing systems.[11] The assumptions are:

1. The arrival times for each job arriving from outside the system are exponentially distributed.
2. The processing times at each machine are exponentially distributed.
3. The jobs are routed to a machine by a fixed probability transition matrix.
4. The priority rule at each machine is first come first served.

The results were based on the fact that with a first-come-first-served discipline, the output of a simple queue is exponential if the interarrival and service times are exponential. The output of one system becomes the input to the next in a network of queues.

"Job" Shop Simulation

The next step, after Jackson's original analytical work, was to examine the characteristics of the queuing network by sampling the output of a digital computer simulation. Various groups have pursued the study of scheduling job shops utilizing computer simulation techniques. We will consider here mainly the work of a group at Cornell University.[12]

The general purposes of early Cornell experiments were to pursue the matter of dispatching beyond the results obtained from purely analytical approaches. Computer simulations were run in an attempt to derive answers to the following questions.

---

[11] J. R. Jackson, "Networks of Waiting Lines," *Operations Research*, vol. 5, no. 4, August 1957.
[12] R. W. Conway, B. M. Johnson, and W. L. Maxwell, "An Experimental Investigation of Priority Dispatching," *J. Ind. Eng.*, vol. XI, no. 3, May–June 1960, pp. 221–29.

1. Can it be shown statistically that the shortest operation rule is different from various other priority rules with respect to aggregate measures of performance?
2. What is the magnitude of this difference, and to what extent does it depend upon the system parameters such as load ratio, number of machines, and nature of the transition matrix?
3. What is the sensitivity of the shortest operation rule to imperfect or imprecise a priori knowledge of processing times?
4. To what extent can the disadvantages of the shortest operation rule be alleviated by modifying the rule or combining it with other disciplines?
5. Can the optimality of the shortest operation rule, at least with respect to mean system state, be established?

GENERAL METHOD OF SIMULATION: This kind of simulation is a more complex version of the queuing simulator described on page 106. The function of the simulator is to generate a set of N jobs, release the jobs to the shop according to some arrival pattern, assign them to various machines according to their routing specifications, sequence from machine queues according to priority rules, and accumulate information about system measures of performance.

The general logic of a shop simulator is shown in Figure 16.7. The steps in the procedure are as follows:

1. *Job file*   The first major step involves a number of operations designed to generate information about each of N jobs. For each job,

   a. The arrival time to the shop is generated from an interarrival time distribution, and the job is assigned a code number to identify it.
   b. A routing is generated automatically by the computer using a probability transition matrix that assigns the probability of a job going to a machine j, given that it has just been processed on machine i. The form of the transition matrix is shown in Figure 16.8. If all probabilities p_{ij} are equal, then the matrix represents a pure job shop. When a job is assigned to the shop (In) it has an equal likelihood of going to any machine in the set M (other than Out). A flow shop format can be designed by permitting only one cell of each row of the matrix to have a positive probability. A limit can be imposed on the number of operations for a job in the job shop format by forcing it into the Out status after a maximum number of operations.
   c. A processing time will be generated for each operation from a service time distribution. We may assume that this distribution is constant for all job-machine assignments for the sake of simulation economy. However, one could use a different distribution for each machine or machine group.
   d. A due date is assigned by any one of a number of methods. These will be discussed in subsequent pages.

All of the above information is recorded on a card or tape. The deck comprising all jobs is called the job file.

2. *Study parameters*   Besides the parameters implied in the job file, other study

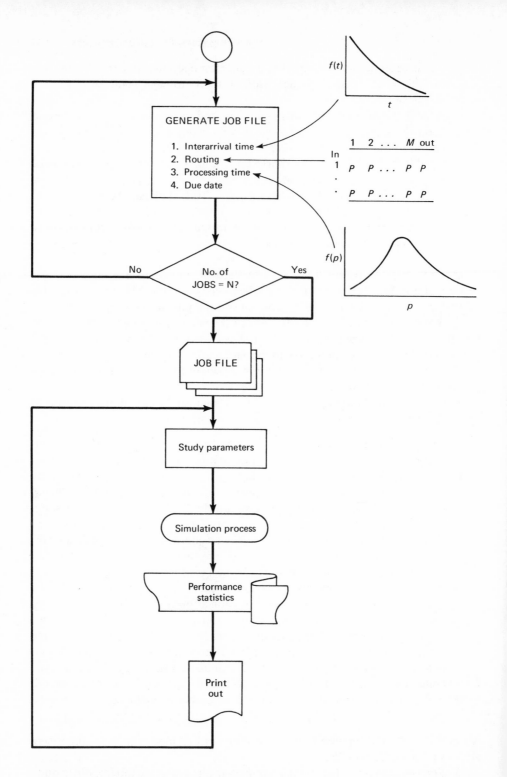

FIGURE **16.7** General method of job shop simulation.

$\diagdown$ j i $\diagdown$	1	$\cdots$	M	OUT	
IN	P_{I1}	$\cdots$	P_{IM}	0	$\sum\limits_{j=1}^{M} P_{Ij} = 1$
1	P_{11}	$\cdots$	P_{1M}	P_{10}	$\sum\limits_{j=1}^{OUT} P_{1j} = 1$
$\vdots$	$\vdots$		$\vdots$	$\vdots$	
M	P_{M1}	$\cdots$	P_{MM}	P_{MO}	$\sum\limits_{j=1}^{OUT} P_{Mj} = 1$

FIGURE **16.8**   Probability transition matrix for job routing.

variables include the number of times the computer will be interrogated to gather sampled statistics about performance parameters, the priority dispatching rule to be used in sequencing jobs through each machine queue, etc.

3. *Simulation process*   Each job is assigned to the shop in accordance with the interarrival time sequence. The computer advances in time until some event takes place, such as the completion of a job on a machine or the arrival of a job to the shop. At that point, the computer will update the shop status, assigning the completed job to its next operation (machine queue), recording accumulated job completion times, lateness, etc. It should be noted that initially some jobs may be used solely to overcome the transient phases of the queuing network to a point where steady-state conditions prevail. Once this stage is reached, the remaining jobs are used as the basis for shop statistics.

4. *Replication*   Once the N jobs have been read into the shop, the experiment may be repeated using a different priority rule or assigning other values to parameters of interest. It may be noted that one advantage of the job file is that each replication can use consistent job information.

A BASIC FLOW EQUATION: The theoretical underpinnings of the Cornell studies are based on a basic flow model or equation for a shop. This equation is[13]

$$\bar{C} = \bar{N}\bar{Y}$$

where

$\bar{C}$ = the average completion time of all jobs in the shop
$\bar{N}$ = the average number of jobs in the shop
$\bar{Y}$ = the average interval of time between the arrival of jobs to the shop

This relation holds true for any shop in steady state that is not saturated (i.e., the service rate is greater than the arrival rate) and is independent of:

1. The size of the shop, either in total number of machines or number of different types of machines.

---

[13] The term completion time and corresponding symbol C will continue to refer to the *interval* of time that a job spends in the shop. This is not to be confused with a completion date.

2. The arrival pattern or the manner in which jobs are released to the shop.
3. The distribution of processing times.
4. The manner in which jobs are sequenced through the machine network.
5. The manner in which the jobs are routed to machines.

Suppose we consider a time interval (O, T). We wish to determine the total time spent in the shop by all jobs during this time interval. At the end of the time interval, some jobs will be only partially completed. If we designate the last job to be completed in the time interval as job n, then some jobs in the shop that arrived earlier than n (i.e., jobs $1, 2, \ldots, n - 1$) will be partially completed, and some jobs that arrive while n is being completed (i.e., jobs $n + 1, n + 2, \ldots, r$) will be partially completed.

Now let R be the subset of jobs that arrive during the time interval between the arrival of the nth job and its completion, and let S be the subset of all jobs that arrive prior to n and are completed in the interval (O, T). Also, let a_i be the fraction of the completion time for the ith job, which falls in the interval (O, T) $0 < a_i \leq 1$. Now the total time spent by all jobs in the shop in the interval (O, T) is

$$B = \sum_{i \in S} C_i + \sum_{\substack{i \notin R \\ i \notin S}} a_i C_i + \sum_{i \in R} a_i C_i$$

The average number of jobs in the shop will be equal to

$$\bar{N} = B/T$$

where

$$T = \sum_{i \in S'} Y_i + C_n$$

and S' is the set of all jobs arriving prior to n. Dividing B by T and n, we have

$$\frac{\sum_{i \in S} C_i}{n} + \frac{\sum_{\substack{i \notin S \\ i \notin R}} a_i C_i}{n} + \frac{\sum_{i \in R} a_i C_i}{n} = \frac{\bar{N}(\sum_{i \in S'} Y_i + C_n)}{n}$$

If we let n increase, then

$$\frac{\sum_{i \in S'} Y_i}{n} \to \bar{Y} \quad \text{and} \quad C_n/n \to 0$$

The number of jobs in the set R does not change, so

$$\frac{\sum_{i \in R} a_i C_i}{n} \to 0$$

Since the fraction of jobs that are completed during the interval increases,

$$\frac{\sum_{\substack{i \notin S \\ i \notin R}} a_i C_i}{n} \to 0 \quad \text{and} \quad \frac{\sum_{i \in S} C_i}{n} \to \bar{C}$$

Therefore,

$$\bar{C} = \bar{N}\bar{Y}$$

From this basic equation, we may deduce the following. The first item is that any dispatching rule that minimizes the average completion time of jobs must also minimize the average number of jobs in the shop providing that the mean arrival rate is constant. Secondly, the average completion time is inversely proportional to shop utilization.

Let

$\bar{P}$ = mean processing time per job in time units

K = capacity of the shop in time units of work per time unit

$\bar{U}$ = mean proportion of capacity utilized under a given rule

$$\bar{Y} = \frac{\bar{P}}{K\bar{U}}$$

Now substituting for $\bar{Y}$,

$$\bar{C} = \frac{N\bar{P}}{K\bar{U}}$$

Therefore, any rule that reduces $\bar{C}$ also increases utilization of the shop.

AN EXPERIMENTAL COMPARISON OF PRIORITY DISPATCHING RULES: In an extensive computer simulation experiment, Conway examined 39 different priority dispatching rules. The major purpose of the experiment was to examine the effect of the various rules on job completion time, job lateness, and work-in-process inventories. The experiments were run on an IBM 7090 using SIMSCRIPT simulation language. Each trial run corresponded to five years of operating experience assuming that the mean machine processing time for a job was one hour. The experimental conditions are summarized below.[14,15]

Nine machines; continuous operation—no division into days or shifts, no provision for breakdown.

Processing times exponentially distributed with mean equal to 1. Same distribution for each machine.

Intervals between arrivals of jobs exponentially distributed with mean such that utilization is 88.5%.

Random routing between machines—each machine is equally likely to serve as a job's starting point, from which it is equally likely to go to any other machine, or out of the shop. The expected number of operations is 9.

Machines work on one job at a time—no overlap operation allowed. No provision for setup or transport. As soon as one operation is completed, the job is instantaneously available for next operation.

Once assigned, jobs are not interrupted, and with exceptions noted, a machine is never held idle when there is work waiting for it to do.

---

[14] See R. W. Conway, "Priority Dispatching and Job Lateness in a Job Shop," *J. Ind. Eng.*, vol. XVI, no. 4, July–August 1965, pp. 228–37.

[15] ——, "Priority Dispatching and Work-in-Process Inventory in a Job Shop," *J. Ind. Eng.*, vol. XVI, no. 2, March–April 1965, pp. 123–30

Sample size—10,000 jobs (five years experience if mean processing time is taken to be one hour). Data based on jobs 401–9100.

Sample jobs generated independently of the simulation; each different decision rule presented with precisely the same set of jobs.

1. *Job lateness*   We should recall that the lateness of a job is a function of its due date. Applying the general shop flow model, we note that

$$\bar{L} = \bar{C} - \bar{D}$$

where

$\bar{L}$ = average job lateness
$\bar{C}$ = average completion time
$\bar{D}$ = average due date[16]

Since

$$\bar{C} = \bar{N}\bar{Y}$$

then

$$\bar{L} = \bar{N}\bar{Y} - \bar{D}$$

Therefore, any rule that minimizes average completion time and work in process must also minimize average job lateness.

In examining job lateness, Conway considered four different ways of generating due dates for the experimental jobs. Each way reflected methods in common use in industry. These four methods were called *TWK* (total work content), *NOP* (number of operations), *CON* (constant), and *RDM* (random). In more detail:

TWK Due date equals the time the job entered the shop plus a constant times the sum of the processing times for the job. This rule reflects an "internally" set due date predicated on the work content of the job.

NOP Due date equals the time the job entered the shop plus a constant times the number of operations performed on the job. Again, this method reflects a due date set to correspond with the work content of the job. Both the *TWK* and the *NOP* methods might be used where the jobs represent parts that have to meet some final assembly schedule.

CON Due date equals the time the job entered the shop plus a constant. This corresponds to the case where, for example, the salesman might quote a delivery date that is standard for all items. In this sense, the due date is externally set.

RDM Due date equals the time the job entered the shop plus a constant times a random number selected from a uniform distribution with a range 0 to 1. In this case, the due date might correspond to a demand set by the customer that ignores both the work content of the job or any standard delivery period.

---

[16] To be consistent with the interpretation of completion time, the due date D should also be interpreted as an interval of time, namely the difference between the date the job is due to be completed and the date the job is introduced into the shop.

TABLE **16.2**

Priority Rule	Shop time[a]	Variance shop time	Average job lateness[b]	Variance of job lateness	Percentage of jobs positively late
FCFS	74.4	5739	−4.5	1686	44.8
SPT	34.0	2318	−44.9	2878	5.0
DDATE	63.7	6780	−15.5	432	17.8
OPNDD	69.0	28820	−9.9	14560	10.4
S/OPN	66.1	6524	−12.8	226	3.7

[a] This is the total time the job spends in the shop ($\overline{C}$).
[b] A negative value means the job was completed before the due date.

The study of job lateness consisted of examining the effect of a number of priority rules on job lateness and shop time for each of these four due-date generating methods. We will examine the results of five rules, namely,

FCFS first come first served at each operation.

SPT shortest processing time rule.

DDATE the job having the earliest due date given highest priority.

OPNDD each operation is given a due date. Equally spaced due dates are assigned to each operation at the time the job enters the shop.

S/OPN slack time per operation. The slack time is the remaining time to due date less the sum of the remaining processing times. The slack time divided by the number of remaining operations gives the S/OPN value.

For the TWK method of setting due dates, the results of using the five rules are shown in Table 16.2.

In general, four of the rules were better than first come first served due to both the decreased mean completion times and reduced variances. The S/OPN rule yielded the least percentage of jobs late, undoubtedly due to the small lateness variance. However, the shortest operation rule (SPT) again performed well due mainly to the low mean lateness. We might note that one advantage of the SPT rule is that it is not necessary to consider the due date in applying the rule.

The results of using four of the rules, in terms of percent of jobs late, for each of the due date methods are shown in Table 16.3.

We can make the following generalization. The shortest processing time rule is the best of all the due-date methods. That is, it is least sensitive to the due-date generating methods. All rules except FCFS become less effective to the degree that the due-date method deviates from a rational assignment of due dates. We use "rational" in the sense that the methods are not arbitrary. The relative merits of the rules are shown with respect to the total experiment. Examination of the details of the simulation results shows that these relative merits vary. Conway broke down the total set of jobs into subsets of 100 and examined the results of using the four

TABLE **16.3**   Percent jobs with positive lateness.

Priority rule	TWK	NOP	CON	RDM
FCFS	44.8	39.9	33.8	41.2
DDATE	17.8	26.7	43.9	48.8
SPT	5.0	6.2	11.0	19.8
S/OPN	3.7	21.6	48.1	52.6

rules for each subset. For example, the *S/OPN* rule was better for the *NOP* method than the *TWK* method under conditions of light shop load, whereas the total performance shows the opposite. This simply indicates that the performance of the rules for a given due-date method depends on the load on the shop. Replications of the total experiment for heavier shop load, for example, showed that the *SPT* rule seems less sensitive to shop load than the other rules for the *TWK* method.

2. *Work in process*   There are various measures of work in process. For a job shop system of machines and jobs, these could include:

1. Total number of jobs in the shop.
2. Total work content, which is the sum of the processing times for all the jobs in the shop.
3. Work completed, which is the sum of the processing times for all completed operations for all jobs in the shop.
4. Work remaining, which is total work content minus work completed.

Each of these measures may be appropriate under different circumstances. Numbers of jobs might be important in situations where there is a constraint on available space or where the existence of the job in inventory introduces an opportunity cost, such as when equipment in a repair shop is not producing revenue. The work content measures correspond to situations where the total amount of money tied up in inventory is important. Such rules assume that the work content measures are equivalent to the investment in inventories, which are both tying up funds and preventing or delaying income.

The problem is to find dispatching rules that minimize a particular measure of inventory. One might hypothesize the kinds of rules that would be used to decrease or minimize these measures. Since we already know that the number of jobs in the shop is a function of the job shop times (completion times), we would wish to use any rule that minimizes the shop time. This has been shown to be the *SPT* rule, and we would expect good performance from this rule as far as inventories are concerned. We might hypothesize that the number of jobs in queue would be minimized by giving priority to those jobs which will subsequently go to an operation that has the smallest queue or least amount of work. With respect to total work content, we would wish to expedite the jobs whose total work content was highest. The same applies to minimizing the work remaining.

In Conway's study of work in process, a variety of rules were examined. The following were important either as standards for comparison or as hypothetically good rules for a given measure of work in process.

Number of jobs in shop

SPT Since it is good for minimizing completion time, it should also tend to minimize the number of jobs in the shop.

NINQ Select the job that goes for its next operation to the shortest queue.

$aP + (1 - a)WKR$ Select the job that has the smallest weighted sum of processing time in the next operation plus work remaining, where WKR = sum of processing times on remaining operations and $0 \le a \le 1$.

$aP + (1 - a)XWQ$ Select the job that has the smallest weighted sum of processing time for the imminent operation and work in the following queue. XWQ equals the sum of the processing times in the queue of the next operation plus the processing times of jobs arriving soon to that queue, $0 \le a \le 1$.

Total work content

SPT

MWKR Select the job that has the most work remaining. This will be the sum of the job processing times for all uncompleted operations.

P/TWK Select the job that has the smallest ratio of next processing time to total work. Total work is the sum of all processing times for a given job.

Work remaining

SPT

$\dfrac{P}{(WKR)^a}$ Select the job that has the smallest "weighted" ratio of next processing time to work remaining. a is the weighting coefficient.

$aP + (1 - a)WKR$

The results for a few selected rules are shown in Table 16.4.

TABLE **16.4** Effect of priority rules on work in process measures.

Rule	Jobs in shop		Total work		Work remaining	
	Mean	Variance	Mean	Variance	Mean	Variance
SPT	23.25	41	545	19,129	297	6,730
NINQ	31.20	102			358	11,607
$0.015P + 0.985WKR$	22.98	40	552	19,800	309	7,556
MWKR	109.97	3,178			276	5,595
P/TWK	42.39	299	435	9,138	244	3,796
$P/WKR(1.00)$	62.94	879			220	2,765
$0.04P + 0.96XWQ$	22.67	39	536	18,212	293	6,439

For all three measures of work-in-process inventory, the *SPT* rule was in no case optimum, although its performance was good. The rule $0.04P + 0.96XWQ$ was found to be optimum for the number of jobs in shop. Total work content was minimized by the *P/TWK* rule and work remaining by the $P/(WKR)^{1.0}$ rule. We should note that the optimum rules were compound rules using the quality of the *SPT* rule in some combination with another rule. Again, the *SPT* rule looks good because of its performance and because of the relative ease of applying the rule in practice, as compared with applying the compound rules.

PRACTICAL ISSUES IN APPLYING THE *SPT* RULE: Because of the universally good performance of the *SPT* rule, Conway examined some of the possible practical objections to using the rule. The first objection is that the rule can discriminate against individual jobs, which could be intolerably delayed in the system. The second is that the rule depends on estimated times, which are subject to error.

The first objection can be partially overcome by substituting a compound *SPT* rule of the following types:

SPT-T(a) As long as no job in the queue from which selection is to be made has waited more than *a* time units in this queue, normal *SPT* selection is made. When a job has waited longer, it is given dominating priority.

FCFS*S(a) *SPT* selection is invoked for a particular queue whenever the queue becomes too long. If there are fewer than *a* jobs in queue at the time of selection, the earliest arrival (to the queue) is chosen. If there are *a* or more jobs, then the job with the shortest processing time is chosen.

The results of applying these two rules are shown in Table 16.5.

The results indicate that the *SPT-T(a)* rule is sensitive to truncation. For example, considering that the average processing time was 1 hour, the value of *SPT-T(32)* is not a severe constraint and yet results in a 41% loss in the efficiency

TABLE **16.5**   Results of using modified *SPT* rule on average number of jobs in queue.

Rule	$\bar{N}$	
SPT-T(0)	58.87	(*FCFS*)
SPT-T(4)	55.67	
SPT-T(8)	53.50	
SPT-T(16)	44.20	
SPT-T(32)	32.85	
SPT-T(∞)	23.25	(*SPT*)
FCFS*S(1)	23.25	(*SPT*)
FCFS*S(5)	29.49	
FCFS*S(9)	38.67	
FCFS*S(∞)	58.87	(*FCFS*)

TABLE **16.6**   Results of errors in estimates of processing
time on average number of jobs in queue.

Error	$\bar{N}$
SPT-0%	23.25
SPT-10%	23.23
SPT-100%	27.13

of the pure *SPT* rule. On the other hand, the use of the *FCFS*S(a)* rule to provide relief when the queue gets too long appears to have some advantage. With *FCFS*S(9)*, the *SPT* rule is invoked for a queue length of 9, resulting in a retention of 57% of the value of the pure *SPT* rule. As a basis for comparison, the mean queue length using a pure *FCFS* rule is 6.54 and 2.58 for the pure *SPT* rule.

As for the possibility of error in the estimate of processing time, Conway repeated the experiment using various degrees of error in the processing times. Errors in the times were generated from a uniform distribution with a range of $-E\%$ to $+E\%$. The true processing time was adjusted by the error to give the estimate used for the sequencing decisions. The *SPT* rule was applied in three cases, as shown in Table 16.6, where the rule is designated as *SPT-E%*:
These results indicate that the rule is quite insensitive to errors in the estimates of processing times.

SOME CONCLUSIONS: As a result of his rather extensive experiments, Conway[17] lists six conclusions:

1. There does not appear to be any reasonable measure of performance in this abstract model of a job shop that is invariant under the choice of priority rule. Even the work content measure, which is known to be constant for a one-machine shop, can be varied in a larger shop. For realistically high values of machine utilization these differences are large enough to have practical economic significance.

2. In many cases there appear to be important differences in performance between rules that are equally simple, reasonable and implementable.

3. The priority rule under which the job with the shortest processing time is selected (SPT) clearly dominates all the other rules tested. Its performance under every measure was very good, it was an important factor in each of the rules that exhibit a "best" performance under some measure, and it is simpler and easier to implement than the rules that surpass it in performance. It surely should be considered the "standard" in scheduling research, against which candidate procedures must demonstrate their virtue.

4. There is no basis for believing that highly precise estimates of processing times are required for scheduling purposes. Both scheduling and wage incentive systems are often cited as the reasons for conducting the time study of operations, but the quality requirements appear to be different by an order of magnitude. If a wage incentive system is not at issue, then much cruder estimating procedures would suffice.

---

[17] R. W. Conway, *J. Ind. Eng.*, vol. XVI, no. 2, pp. 129–30.

5. There are many ways of modifying the shortest processing time priority rule and of combining it with other rules. The "SPT influence" seems to be always beneficial. This should be considered an important building block in any scheduling procedure. It should at least be used to break ties, and resolve indifferences—all other things being equal (or immaterial), select the job with the shortest processing time.

6. These results suggest that it would be both worth-while and possible for manufacturing firms to rationally select a priority rule for job dispatching. This would be worth-while because there are significant differences between equally implementable rules—no elaborate data processing system is necessarily required. This would be possible because the technique employed here—simulated experimentation on a digital computer—can be used just as effectively to study the performance of various rules under the constraints and idiosyncrasies of specific real shops.

EXPEDITING

In the normal manufacturing shop, numerous exigencies occur with the result that no job is left to the mercy of a fixed schedule or even a flexible set of dispatching rules. A given job can assume a critical posture for various reasons. The delivery date on a job for an important customer is threatened, or final assembly is being held up for a delayed component, or inventory of a part is depleted, or a replacement part is critically needed. These conditions are inherent in most shops, and expediting is an important part of control systems.

Expediting is a common function of concentrating attention on the progress of a critical job through the production system. One extreme of a chaotic shop situation occurs when a large proportion of jobs are placed on an expedited status. Not only is there the implicit cost of disrupted schedules, but there is also the direct cost of the resources applied to the expediting function.

The expeditious progress of a critical job can obviously be assured by flagging the job order in some procedural manner. In some cases, human intervention is used in the form of expediter, whose job it is to personally guide the progress of the job from day to day.

Urgency Scales

Expediting can also be accomplished through the use of dynamic priority rules, which take into consideration updated information about the variables that reflect urgency. An obvious one is simply the updating of job due dates to reflect changes in inventory or final assembly schedules since the original release of the job to the shop. This is useful only if the normal dispatching function employs priority rules incorporating the due date as a variable.

A more elaborate urgency scale is used by a shop in the following way. The shop manufactures parts for an inventory from which the demands for final assembly are met. At the start of each month, the inventory is committed to meeting the scheduled or anticipated final assembly requirements for the month. In the meantime, the projected final assembly requirements two months hence are exploded to provide the basis for shop orders to replenish the inventory assuming about one month lead time for parts. During the course of the month, many things can happen to upset the planned final assembly schedule as well as the configuration of part removals from inventory. The production of defective parts, material failures, assembly line breakdowns, etc., will change the priority of assembly jobs. Therefore, the urgency of a part being made in the shop will depend on both the inventory status of the part (i.e., the ability to service final assembly) and the degree of change in final assembly schedules (changes in lead times). Under these conditions, an urgency ratio is calculated daily for each job in this way:

$$r = \frac{I/R}{L/A}$$

where

r = urgency ratio; the lower the number, the greater the urgency

I = current inventory status

R = inventory reorder point. This is a critical number corresponding to an anticipated one-month requirement for the part.

L = normal lead time to replenish inventory

A = adjusted lead time based on revisions in final assembly schedules

Jobs are then dispatched with the lowest urgency ratio having highest priority. If everything goes according to schedule, the ratio for a given part will be equal to 1.00. If adjusted lead time is shortened and inventory status is low, the ratio will shift to a lower value.

This kind of expediting requires an automated information system, since a large number of jobs is the usual characteristic of systems demanding this kind of expediting.

PROJECT SCHEDULING

In this section, we will investigate the problem of scheduling and managing the activities necessary to complete a project type of operation. Examples of such projects are the construction of a building, an integrated maintenance operation of a large facility, the design and development of a new product, or the actual layout of a shop, including the moving and installation of equipment. In each of these cases, the entire project can be dissected into a large number of *activities* or *tasks*, which, when completed in the aggregate, signal the end of the project. Some of the tasks are independent in their starting and completion times. Others must be performed in some time sequence. The general management problem is to develop an integrated program for all of the identifiable activities that comprise the project time schedule. This schedule indicates the anticipated starting and completion times for each activity, as well as the anticipated completion time for the project as a whole. A desirable scheduling method must not only indicate these data, but should also indicate the "criticalness" of each activity in terms of its influence on the completion time of the project as a whole. Furthermore, the method should permit the manager to assess the results of making changes in the rate at which various activities may be executed.

Network Models for Project Scheduling

Network models provide a way of structuring, analyzing, scheduling, and monitoring the operations or activities comprising a large-scale project. In general, the model shows the time relationship between activities, the degree of sensitivity of the project completion time to the various activity duration times, and the results in time and cost of making changes in the rate of performing activities.

The models that have been used have generically fallen under the heading of *PERT* (Program Evaluation and Review Technique) and *CPS* (Critical Path Scheduling). These two methods differ in their objectives in that the former is used to determine the expected duration of a project and the variance of the duration by considering variable time estimates for each activity, while the latter is concerned with determining the minimum cost for alternative and feasible schedules. However, both of these general methods have second- and third-order variations that have minimized their general differences. The literature of management science and engineering abounds in both the theoretical and practical aspects of these techniques. It will be our purpose here only to review the essential features of the techniques.

PROJECT NETWORK STRUCTURE: We will now consider the manner in which a project is structured in the form of a network of activities and events.

1. *Activities* The planning of a project commences with the description of the project in terms of activities. These are basic jobs, tasks, operations, or work elements that are well defined and have some precedence relationships. An activity implies the expenditure of resources to complete some segment of the project, or the enforced expenditure of time due to external circumstances. The degree of detail or the refinement of the breakdown into activities depends on the purpose of the planning activity, as well as on the ability to identify individual jobs.

2. *Events* An event is a definable point or state that signifies either the beginning or the end of an activity. Usually an event indicates the termination of one or more activities and the commencement of one or more activities that must follow. Events, therefore, are milestones in the progress of a project, or a section of it, and they must be clearly recognizable. Whereas activities imply a duration of time, events are points in time.

3. *Network diagram* Activities and events, as well as other pertinent information, are displayed in the form of a network diagram (arrow chart). Figure 16.9 shows a simple network of activities and events. The usual coding system is to designate the events as numbered circles or nodes and the activities as lettered directed arrows or arcs. The event signifies the completion of the activity, repre-

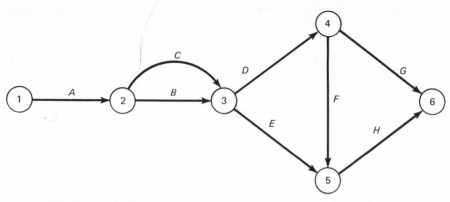

FIGURE **16.9** Network diagram.

sented by the arrow pointing to the event, and the start of activities, represented by the arrow originating at the event.

4. *Activity times* Associated with each activity is an estimated time of duration. We can make the general statement that this is the time to advance the project between the events connected by the activity. However, where more than one activity connects two events, such as in the case of *B* and *C* above, we may introduce a "dummy" event with a corresponding dummy activity with time zero, such as in Figure 16.10. Since time estimates are subject to error, activity time can be expressed as a distribution of values corresponding to some probability distribution. We will examine this facet of the problem in more detail later.

5. *Critical path* Suppose we have a network of events connecting a starting event *s* and an ending event *N*. Then a critical path is a given sequence of events

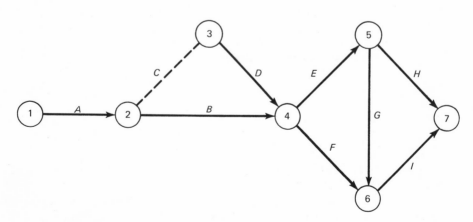

FIGURE **16.10** Dummy event and activity.

connected by activities, the times of which sum to a maximum. For example, the network has three possible paths connecting *s* and *N*.

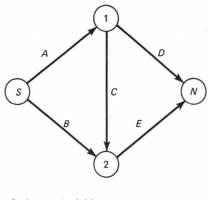

Path	Activities
s-1-*N*	*A, D*
s-1-2-*N*	*A, C, E*
s-2-*N*	*B, E*

The critical path is the path that yields the largest sum of the corresponding activity times. The activities included in the critical path are called the critical activities.

6. *Slack time* Any event that does not lie on the critical path can possibly have its completion date moved ahead to some point without affecting the project completion time. The maximum amount of advancement in time for an event completion before it becomes part of a critical path is called the slack time. We use the following example to clarify the basic structure of a project network.

EXAMPLE 16.2 Suppose that a plant has an overhead power conveyor material-handling system. An improvement in the layout of the assembly department requires that a new section of an overhead conveyor be installed. The project will consist of the following activities (which are simplified for the discussion).

Activity code	Activity
A	Prepare purchase orders for all necessary supplies and materials for the job.
B	Prepare initial work orders and hold preliminary conference.
C	Lead time on material order, receive, and inspect materials.
D	Remove pipelines from ceiling.
E	Move power materials to work site.
F	Install new power line.
G	Move materials and equipment to site.
H	Make some preliminary setups for testing.
I	Install conveyor.
J	Move some machines in the shop.
K	Trial run.

The events that signify the terminal points of the activities are listed below:

Event code	Event
1	authorization form to commence the project
2	material and equipment purchase order
3	material receiving and inspection reports
4	work Order No. 101 to remove pipe from ceiling
5	work Order No. 102 to install new power line
6	work Order No. 103 to install new conveyor
7	work Order No. 104 to move certain machines in the shop
8	trial and test-run authorization
9	production-run order

The network of events is shown in Figure 16.11.

We will now make an analysis of the network to determine the nature of the completion dates or times for the events and for the project as a whole.

EVENT TIMES: Each of the activities in the network has an associated expected time t_e, which is shown directly under the letter coding the activity. Each event has a bracket above it with two time values. The time value at the left is the earliest time T that the event can occur. Thus, for event 3, the earliest time is the sum of the earliest time for event 2 plus the time of the activity connecting events 2 and 3. Similarly, for event 7, the earliest time is $16 + 5$ or 21.

The earliest completion time for the project (event 9) is 42 and is determined by the critical path consisting of the event sequence 1-2-3-5-6-8-9. Any event that does not fall on the critical path has a slack time. For example, for event 7, the earliest time is 21. But the event completion time can be advanced to 26 without affecting the project completion time. Therefore, the right-hand number in the bracket is the latest event time T_L, the limit to which the event time can be advanced.

Both the critical path and slack times indicate where management effort should be directed in controlling or improving the project completion time. Improvements in activities bounding events with slack time yield no direct benefits in improved project completion time. Conversely, of course, efforts to reduce critical activity times can have an effect on the project completion time.

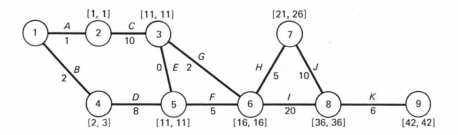

FIGURE **16.11**   Network for sample problem.

TABLE **16.7**   Time estimates (days) for sample problem.

Activity code	Most likely time (m)	Optimistic time (a)	Pessimistic time (b)	Expected time (t) $\dfrac{a + 4m + b}{6}$	σ_t^2 Variance $\left(\dfrac{b - a}{6}\right)^2$
A	1	0.5	1.5	1.0	0.028
B	2	1.0	2.0	1.8	0.028
C	10	8.0	15.0	10.5	1.360
D	8	6.0	10.0	8.0	0.445
E	0	0	1.0	0.2	0.028
F	5	4.0	8.0	5.3	0.445
G	2	1.0	3.0	2.0	0.111
H	5	4.0	8.0	5.3	0.445
I	20	15.0	30.0	20.8	6.250
J	10	5.0	12.0	9.5	1.360
K	6	4.0	10.0	6.3	1.000

VARIABILITY IN ESTIMATED TIMES: In the previous example, the activity times represented an expected value, but estimates are subject to error both in the raw data used and in the assumptions made by the estimator. Therefore, the time estimates can be expressed as a range of values corresponding to some distribution.

In specifying estimates for activity times, it is reasonable to assume that the estimator can provide three values. These are the "most likely" time, which is a measure of central tendency, an "optimistic" or minimum time, and a "pessimistic" or maximum time, designated m, a, and b, respectively. The first three data columns of Table 16.7 indicate these times for the previous example.

We now hypothesize that the estimated time is distributed in such a way that there is a low probability of the extreme values occurring and that the most likely value is represented by a single peak in the distribution, as shown in Figure 16.12.

In the PERT system, the activity times are assumed to be distributed according to the beta distribution, which has the general form $f(t) = K(t - a)^\delta (b - t)^\beta$. The form of the distribution depends on the parameters a, b, δ, and β.

We then assume that the standard deviation of the beta distribution for the time estimates is $\sigma_t = \frac{1}{6}(b - a)$ and that the mode is equal to m. In the original

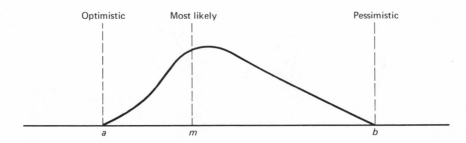

FIGURE **16.12**   Activity duration.

determination of the model used in PERT, these two assumptions permitted the derivation of the values for δ and β. The expected value of the distribution was then approximated by the function

$$t_e = \tfrac{1}{6}(a + 4m + b)$$

This approximation, in turn, permitted the calculation of the expected time in terms of the three known parameters for each activity.

While the exact distribution of the activity times is usually unknown, use of the beta model with the specific parameters indicated above can be justified on several grounds. The variable is continuously and unimodally distributed with non-negative extreme values. The mean and variance are calculated from the specified values of m, a, and b, and m may take any relative position between the limits a and b.

The last two columns of Table 16.7 indicate the expected times and variances for each of the network activities.

EXPECTED ELAPSED TIMES AND VARIANCES FOR EVENTS: The expected elapsed time $E(T_n)$ for an event n at any stage in the network is the sum of the expected activity times for the activities comprising a critical path to that event. For the last event, the end of the project, the expected elapsed time for the whole project is 44.1, the sum of the activity times in the critical path.

If we assume that the activity times are independent of each other, the variance of an event time σ_T^2 is the sum of the variances of the activity times for the activities in the critical path leading to that event. Thus, for our example, the standard deviation of the project completion time is 3.02 days.

PROBABILITY OF MEETING A SCHEDULE: Assuming that the distribution of event completion times is approximately normal, we can determine the probability of meeting a scheduled completion time for an event. For example, suppose we want to know the probability of completing the whole project in 38.5 days or less. Then, according to Figure 16.13, this probability will be about 0.03.

Summarizing the characteristics of an activity network in general terms, let

t_{ij} = expected estimated time for the activity represented by an arc connecting event i with event j

$\quad = \tfrac{1}{6}(a + 4m + b)$

where

$\quad a$ = optimistic time estimate
$\quad b$ = pessimistic time estimate
$\quad m$ = most likely time estimate

Also,

$\quad \sigma_{ij}^2$ = the variance of t_{ij}

$$\quad = \frac{(b - a)^2}{36}$$

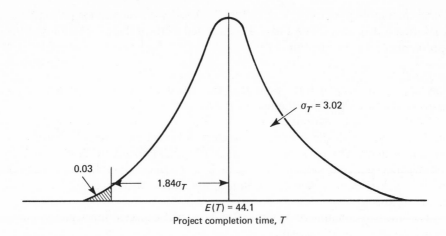

FIGURE **16.13** Distribution of project completion times.

Now let K be a set of activities comprising a directed path from the starting node s to a given node n.

$$E(T_n) = \text{expected time of event } n$$
$$= \sum_K t_{ij}$$
$$V(T_n) = \sum_K \sigma_{ij}^2$$

assuming that the activities are independent. Then the probability that an event n will be completed no later than a specified time T_n' will be

$$P[T_n \leq T_n'] = f\left(\frac{T_n' - E(T_n)}{\sqrt{V(T_n)}}\right)$$

Suppose that for an event n we have a set P of directed paths $p_1, p_2, \ldots$ leading from event s to event n. For each path we calculate $E(T_n)_p$. Then the feasible $E(T_n)$ is Maximum $\underset{P}{\{E(T_n)_p\}}$. This is now referred to as the earliest expected time for the event n.

An event may be delayed for a specific time, called the slack time, without affecting the time for the project completion $E(T_N)$. The latest expected completion time for an event n will be $E(T_n)_L$. Given a set of P paths $p_1, p_2, \ldots$ leading backward from event N to event n, each path having a set K_p of activities, then

$$E(T_n)_L = E(T_N) - \text{Maximum} \underset{K_p}{(\sum t_{ij})}$$

Then the slack time for event n will be

$$_sT_n = E(T_n)_L - E(T_n)$$

Sources of Error in Project Estimates

MacCrimmon and Ryavec[18] have made an analytical study of PERT assumptions to determine the sources of error in both activity and project network time estimates. We quote a summary of their analysis of network time estimates to emphasize the need to exercise judgment in using complex models of this kind. We note that the term "PERT calculated mean or variance" refers to time estimates for the project or events in the network.

The PERT-calculated mean will always be biased optimistically, but the PERT-calculated standard deviation may be biased in either direction. Precise statements about the magnitude of the errors, however, cannot be made, since errors in the project mean and standard deviation vary with different network configurations. If there is one path through a network that is significantly longer than any other path, then the PERT procedure for calculating the project mean and standard deviation will give approximately correct results. However, if there are a large number of paths having approximately the same length, and having few activities in common, errors will be introduced in the PERT-calculated project mean and standard deviation. The more parallel paths there are through the network, the larger will be the errors. If, however, the paths share a large number of common activities, the errors will tend to be lower. The extent to which these two factors compensate depends on the particular network configuration.

The errors in the PERT-calculated project mean and standard deviation will tend to be large if many noncritical paths each have a duration approximately equal to the duration of the critical path. However, the more slack there is in each of the noncritical paths, the smaller will be the error.

Because of the possible errors in the PERT-calculated project mean and standard deviation, there may be correspondingly large errors in the probability statements that are based on these parameters.

It is suggested that for a stochastic model (such as PERT) a critical activity concept is more valid than, and probably as useful as, a critical path concept. This is based on the fact that the PERT-calculated critical path does not necessarily contain the most critical activities.

Critical Path Method (CPM)

In general, the PERT method focuses on the temporal relationships between events in a project network with the objective of determining network schedules. In project planning there are often major questions regarding the allocation of project resources to various activities. Given limited resources, one issue is the manner in which these resources are to be allocated, or scheduled, to the various activities. Then, if there are unlimited resources, a second issue is the degree to which these resources will be applied to achieve the event or project completion times.

The critical path method is directed to the problem of deciding on the degree

---

[18] Kenneth R. MacCrimmon and Charles A. Ryavec, "An Analytical Study of the PERT Assumptions," *Operations Research*, vol. 12, no. 1, January–February 1964, p. 36.

to which a project completion time should be changed by accelerating various activity times. If the duration time for an activity is to be compressed, this must usually be done at the expense of additional resources. If the activity is critical, then there will be a reduction in the project time or the avoidance of an unanticipated extension of the project duration. Therefore, there is a reduction or avoidance of costs related to the time of the project as a whole. While these costs may be indirect, they are nevertheless relevant to the acceleration decision.

ACTIVITY ACCELERATION: The reduction in project time is gained by accelerating critical activities. The problem is to choose the activity that is to be accelerated. We might anticipate that a critical activity's duration can be reduced by allocating more resources to the activity in one or more ways. Suppose that we have an activity A_{ij} connecting event nodes i and j. Under the normal plan for the activity, the expected duration is T_{ij}. We may reduce the duration to a new value t_{ij}. Let the normal cost of the activity be c_1. Then this cost will be increased to a new value c_2, as shown in Figure 16.14, due to the reduced duration.

Now let there be a cost coefficient

$$C_{ij} = \frac{c_2 - c_1}{T_{ij} - t_{ij}}$$

This cost coefficient is a measure of the rate of increasing the activity cost for a unit reduction in the activity duration time over the range $T_{ij} - t_{ij}$. In this case, we have approximated the cost-time relationship by a linear function. However, this need not be done; and it is possible to deal with a piece-wise linear relationship between cost and time when making the analysis for project costs.

MINIMUM PROJECT COST: Given a cost coefficient for each activity of a project,

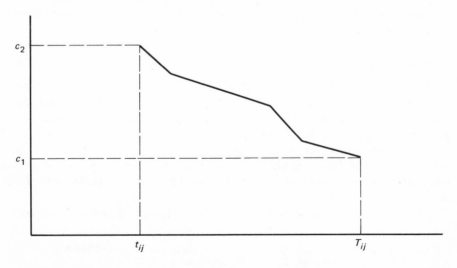

FIGURE **16.14**   Time cost curve for accelerating an activity.

TABLE **16.9** Cost coefficients for eleven activities.

Activity connecting events		Normal time T_{ij}	Accelerated time t_{ij}	Cost coefficient C_{ij}
i to j				
1	2	1	1	∞
1	4	2	1	10
2	3	10	6	5
4	5	8	4	4
3	5	0	0	8
3	6	2	2	∞
5	6	5	4	15
6	7	5	4	12
6	8	20	14	6
7	8	10	7	7
8	9	6	5	12

we are in a position to determine an optimal activity acceleration plan. Such a plan minimizes the cost of the project for some mix of activity acceleration.

In order to demonstrate the idea of project cost minimization, we will continue with the example used in the previous pages.

First, a study is made of each activity to determine its cost coefficient C_{ij}. In order to use our time economically, we might confine the analysis initially to the critical activities, but, as we will see, we will need to examine noncritical activities eventually. Table 16.9 shows the results of our analysis for all the activities.

We now proceed in the following manner:

Step 1. Determine the *normal* critical path. This is the critical path if all activities are performed at the normal time T_{ij}. This critical path is shown in Figure 16.15 in the form of a network diagram.

Step 2. Examine the cost coefficients for the critical activities and choose the minimum C_{ij}. In this case, the minimum C_{ij} is equal to 5 for the activity 2-3. We next accelerate activity 2-3 until either 1) another path becomes critical or 2) we have reached the minimum time for the accelerated activity. In our case, if we accelerate 2-3 by one time unit, the path 1-4-5 becomes critical. Referring to

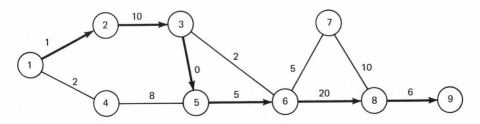

FIGURE **16.15** Network diagram for eleven activities showing normal critical path.

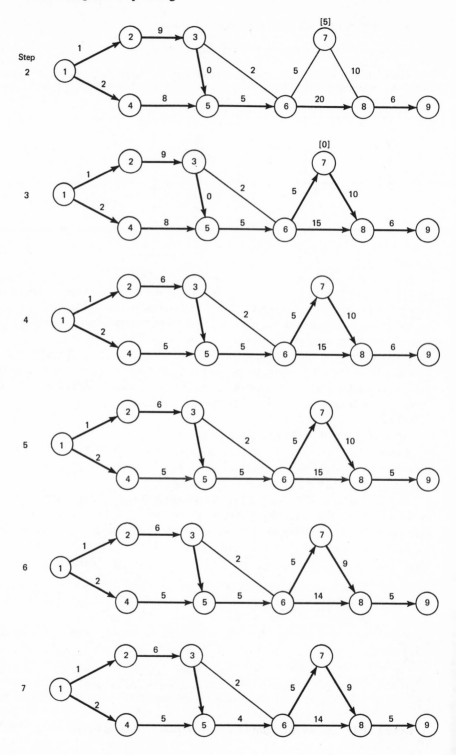

TABLE **16.10** Summary of acceleration steps.

Step	C_{ij}	Accelerated activity	Amount of acceleration Δt	$C_{ij} \times \Delta t$	$\sum C_{ij} \times \Delta t$	Project time
2	5	2-3	1	5	5	41
3	6	6-8	5	30	35	36
4	9	2-3	3	27	62	33
		4-5				
5	12	8-9	1	12	74	32
6	13	6-8	1	13	85	31
		7-8				
7	15	5-6	1	15	100	30

Table 16.10, we note that in Step 2, activity 2-3 is accelerated by 1 time unit at an additional cost of 5 units, resulting in a project time of 41.

Step 3. Considering the new critical paths, examine the cost coefficients for the critical activities and choose the minimum C_{ij}. In our case, since we have two critical paths, we have the option of reducing, simultaneously, the times for two or more activities. We may reduce 1-4 and 2-3 or 4-5 and 2-3, giving us the combined cost coefficients $(10 + 5)$ and $(5 + 4)$, respectively. Each of these is still larger than the alternative of accelerating 6-8 at a cost of 6 units. Therefore, we will accelerate 6-8 until the path 6-7-8 becomes critical. This is summarized in Step 3 of Table 16.10.

Step 4. We now again examine the alternatives. They are

Accelerate activities	Cost coefficients	Maximum amount of acceleration
1-4 and 2-3	$10 + 5 = 15$	1
4-5 and 2-3	$4 + 5 =\ 9$	3
5-6	15	1
6-7 and 6-8	$12 + 6 = 18$	1
6-8 and 7-8	$6 + 7 = 13$	3
8-9	12	1

Note that the acceleration limit is determined by the maximum of the minimum t_{ij}'s for the activities in each alternative. We will now accelerate 4-5 and 2-3 by 3 units.

Step 5. Continue in the above manner until no further activity accelerations can be made.

The above steps result in the series of network diagrams shown in Figure 16.16. The total project time has been reduced to a minimum of 30 time units with an increase of 100 in the direct costs. The steps also result in the project cost curve

FIGURE **16.16** Arrow diagrams corresponding to acceleration stops.

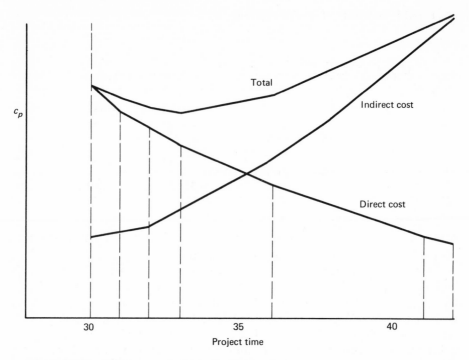

FIGURE **16.17**   Effect on cost of accelerating project.

shown in Figure 16.17, where the direct costs increase monotonically and piece-wise linearly as the project time is reduced. We assume that indirect costs are changed also. These would include rentals, bid penalties, administrative costs, etc. The resulting total of incremental costs is shown with a minimum occurring at the point where Step 3 is completed.

   The determination of a minimum project cost in the above terms is in practice a difficult task. An algorithm using the labeling-scanning procedure for maximizing network flow has been developed.[19] We will not duplicate the method here because of its relative complexity.

Planning Project Resources

   Critical path scheduling provides an insight into the effect of precedence rela-tions on the duration time of a project and its intermediate events. The critical path scheduling devices that have been discussed are tools in the solution of the more general problems of project planning. Project planning has much in common with the planning of any production system. For a given planning horizon, usually

---

[19] D. R. Fulkerson, "A Network Flow Computation for Project Cost Curves," *Management Science*, vol. 8, no. 2, January 1961.

the life of the project, resources such as labor, capital, and equipment must be allocated for efficient use without jeopardizing a reasonable completion time for the project.

It can be easily seen that a project schedule derived from activity network analysis ignores the effect of activity schedules on resource requirements. The sole scheduling criterion is the project completion time. We can imagine a highly variable response to the schedule resource requirements, causing the limitations in these resources to be exceeded at some times and inefficiently utilized at other times, a problem not unlike that encountered in a highly seasonal business.

Superimposing resource planning upon the normal or accelerated critical path schedule leads to a complex problem in which highly mathematical approaches are more academic than practical. At a less sophisticated level, we might expect the following steps to be involved in the formulation of a realistic project plan.

1. The study of basic jobs and tasks, the methods to be used, and the resource requirements are compiled by project engineers.
2. A basic activity network is constructed yielding both normal and accelerated activity times and event schedules.
3. Resource requirements (crew sizes, capital, equipment) for activities are translated into aggregate requirements by period, such as a day or week.
4. These aggregate requirements are compared with various constraints, and the schedule is adjusted to meet various criteria.

The criteria for making adjustments include a variety of things. It may be desirable to both level the demand for various labor skills and to concentrate their use within some constrained period to minimize both hiring and layoff during the course of the project. Similarly, it may be desirable to maximize the utilization of a heavy piece of capital equipment during an interval of time when the equipment is available and on site. Since partially completed projects may represent an inventory of accrued work subject to the normal inventory costs, it may be desirable to minimize this inventory, thus deferring costly operations as long as possible.

Adjustments to the schedule to conform with one or more of the above criteria may be effected in various ways. Certainly the major opportunity for adjustment resides in the event slack times. The slack permits the shifting of events, singularly or concurrently, to later than normal or earliest event times. Sometimes jobs or tasks may be split to be performed in partial units over an extended time to conform with resource constraints. Then, of course, normal activity times may be accelerated, if necessary, at the expense of one resource to gain some advantage in the use of another resource. For example, we may increase the rate of paving a new parking lot at an additional labor cost, but with the result of using a paving machine more economically.

A variety of methods have been proposed to analyze the conflict existing between resource requirements under normal or augmented schedules and resource constraints. Some of these cannot efficiently surmount the combinatorial difficulties of the problems. All of them utilize the computer in some manner.

Kelley[20] proposes a common-sense and probably highly practical method of handling this kind of problem. Jobs are serially arranged in the ascending order of the j index of the even pairs (i, j), which subtend the job arc. This assumes that the numbering of the events is such that $i < j$. Then, starting at the first event in the serial list, each job is analyzed to determine its earliest completion date and to schedule it accordingly. If the job cannot be scheduled because of insufficient resources, several alternatives are available. First, the job may be split into subsections and the split components scheduled ahead when the resources are available. Second, within a subset of jobs having the same j suffix it is possible to consider different permutations. Critical jobs within the subset should especially be given priority consideration in scheduling under constrained resources. Third, jobs may be reviewed at the point of scheduling to determine if the required resource allocation for the job can be altered either to more than scheduled, thus increasing utilization, or to less than scheduled. Fourth, jobs may be started with less than the scheduled resources (such as crew sizes) and then augmented with additional crew members as they become available. In this case, the original analysis of the jobs should include both lower and upper thresholds of resource size below which the job should not start and above which the full resource should not be applied.

Project planning and scheduling appear to be analogous to production planning and control. The detailed scheduling of a project, particularly on a short-term basis, may result in the application of tactical maneuvers, which cannot be anticipated in the original planning of the project at a more aggregate level. It is obvious that no planning, however bolstered by refined activity network analysis, can fully supplement the short-term control exerted by the line supervisor with his intimate knowledge of things as they exist.

Problems

16.1   Discuss the method of allocating jobs to machines by linear programing (pages 539–40) in terms of number of jobs and machines and the fact that all jobs will not have the same proportionality in production rates among machines—some jobs will not have alternative routings.

Problems 16.2–16.8 pertain to the case of a single machine $(1 \times N)$ system.

16.2   On page 541 is a list of six priority rules for dispatching jobs through a machine. Add to this list another eight rules.

16.3   Make a list of the 14 rules and classify each rule by 1) its ease of application in the sense that the information needed is readily available, 2) whether it is time dependent or independent, 3) whether it is local or global, and 4) whether it is simple or compound.

---

[20] J. E. Kelley, Jr., "The Critical Path Method: Resource Planning and Scheduling," in J. F. Muth and G. L. Thompson, Eds., *Industrial Scheduling*. Englewood Cliffs, N.J.: Prentice-Hall, Inc., 1963, Ch. 21.

16.4 A graduate student has five papers to submit by the end of the term, which is eight weeks away. Each paper is due for a different instructor. Each instructor will degrade the paper a certain number of points for each week the paper is late. The estimated time to write the paper and the number of degradation points are:

Paper	Estimated time to write (weeks)	Rate of point degradation per week
A	6	3
B	5	8
C	4	10
D	3	6
E	8	3

The student has decided to write the papers in the order *C-B-D-E-A*. What would you advise?

16.5 Suppose that *N* jobs are to be sequenced through a machine and the setup times are sequence dependent. What rule would be used to minimize the average completion time for the set of *N* jobs?

16.6 Consider Problem 16.4. Assume that there is an interrelation between the subjects covered by the papers. Therefore, the time to do some research for each paper will depend on the sequence in which the papers are researched and written. Below is an estimate of the research times as a function of paper pairs.

	Now	A	B	C	D	E
Now	0	2.8	2.0	2.7	2.8	2.4
A	0	0	3.2	3.3	2.8	3.2
B	0	3.1	0	2.5	1.2	4.1
C	0	4.1	1.6	0	3.4	2.2
D	0	1.2	2.8	2.8	0	3.4
E	0	0	2.7	3.9	1.2	0

Now is the current status of the student's research and study.

Assume that the estimated times to write the papers, not including the research time, are

A 3.5
B 2.5
C 1.5
D 0.5
E 5.5

How would you advise the student on the best sequence of paper writing, assuming that points degraded are prorated for a partial week late?

16.7 Devise two heuristic rules for solving the "traveling salesman problem." Try these rules out on the following matrices of paired job setup times, where Job 1 is the current status of the machine.

(a)

	1	2	3	4	5	6
1	0	4.1	1.9	1.3	4.4	3.5
2	0	0	3.8	1.6	4.5	3.0
3	0	3.0	0	3.1	2.9	2.0
4	0	3.1	3.6	0	3.9	2.6
5	0	4.1	1.7	0.8	0	2.2
6	0	2.8	0.5	1.0	5.2	0

Optimum sequence 142635; 10.8 hr

(b)

	1	2	3	4	5	6
1	0	3.2	2.0	2.5	2.4	1.8
2	0	0	4.3	4.4	3.2	3.5
3	0	2.1	0	1.4	1.9	2.2
4	0	4.2	3.0	0	3.8	3.2
5	0	2.3	3.3	2.3	0	3.3
6	0	2.0	3.2	3.6	0.6	0.0

Optimum 134652; 9.5 hr

(c)

	1	2	3	4	5	6
1	0	1.7	1.0	2.1	2.2	2.7
2	0	0	4.8	2.1	2.0	3.7
3	0	2.3	0	0.6	1.6	1.6
4	0	2.2	1.4	0	2.9	4.7
5	0	1.4	2.2	2.3	0.0	2.3
6	0	2.0	4.5	2.6	1.5	0.0

Optimum 136524; 7.6 hr

(d)

	1	2	3	4	5	6
1	0	2.9	2.6	2.7	1.3	2.1
2	0	0.0	3.7	2.8	1.3	1.8
3	0	1.7	0.0	2.1	2.7	4.7
4	0	1.6	2.8	0	3.3	2.9
5	0	2.3	3.0	0.3	0	3.4
6	0	1.9	3.4	4.1	0.8	0.0

Optimum 132654; 7.2 hr

16.8   This is an R matrix for Jobs 1, 2, and 3 and Machines A, B, and C:

$$R = \begin{array}{c|ccc} & A & B & C \\ 1 & A & B & C \\ 2 & B & A & C \\ 3 & C & B & A \end{array}$$

The following are P matrices. Determine a schedule of jobs to machines so as to minimize the completion time of the batch of jobs.

(a)

$$P = \begin{array}{c|ccc} & A & B & C \\ 1 & 3 & 1 & 4 \\ 2 & 6 & 2 & 5 \\ 3 & 1 & 5 & 4 \end{array}$$

(b)

$$P = \begin{array}{c|ccc} & A & B & C \\ 1 & 5 & 3 & 1 \\ 2 & 4 & 6 & 3 \\ 3 & 2 & 6 & 5 \end{array}$$

(c)

$$P = \begin{array}{c|ccc} & A & B & C \\ 1 & 2 & 3 & 4 \\ 2 & 3 & 4 & 5 \\ 3 & 4 & 5 & 6 \end{array}$$

16.9   The Morris Machine Company had a fire in one of its shops. Six machines were damaged by the fire. The machines are going to be recovered by sending each machine through the following operations in the sequence given.

Opn. 1   Unbolt machine from floor and move to repair shop.
Opn. 2   Dismantle machine, clean, and replace parts.
Opn. 3   Test machine.
Opn. 4   Put machine back in renewed shop.

The time to perform each of these operations on each machine is shown below.

Machine	Opn. 1	Opn. 2	Opn. 3	Opn. 4
1	4	8	1	12
2	2	6	5	6
3	1	4	2	2
4	10	20	8	20
5	5	25	1	8
6	3	10	12	5

Each operation is performed by a special crew. Your job is to schedule the machines to the crews in order to minimize the completion time of the last job, since all machines must be repaired before the shop can operate again.

16.10   In Problem 15.7, it was noted that the products were sequenced in an order that minimized the downtime of the machine. Now assume the following with respect to that problem. A setup time transition matrix for the five products is shown below. At the end of each production cycle, the processing machine is shut down and given a cleaning before the start of the next cycle. The cleaning takes a constant time of 10 hours. Assume the setup cost is $10 per hr.

	Clean	1	2	3	4	5
Clean	0	11.6	12.0	12.0	10.1	12.4
1	10.0	0	8.6	8.3	8.2	9.5
2	10.0	8.5	0	7.2	8.7	8.8
3	10.0	8.3	9.6	0	9.2	6.8
4	10.0	7.6	10.2	7.2	0	7.0
5	10.0	7.8	7.4	8.6	9.1	0

Optimum = 50.00 hours
clean-4-3-5-2-1-clean

Now suppose that there are a total of 2,300 hours in the year in which to meet the total demand. Determine if the optimum cyclic lot sizes can be scheduled in the limit of 2,300 hours. If not, what recommendations can you offer to meet this constraint?

16.11   The following products are to be allocated to production equipment. The higher its priority number, the earlier a product is to be "tried." For purposes of this problem, we will not attempt to balance labor requirements, but we will assume equipment is limited. Parts must be started before, or when, products are started and finished before the product they go into is finished. All machines are scheduled.

P hr/day

Product	Parts	Machine hours	Machine No.	Priority
1		12	1	6
	1*A*	12	2	
	1*B*	8	2	
	1*C*	4	3	
2		8	1	7
	2*A*	4	3	
	2*B*	4	2	
	2*C*	16	2	
	2*D*	8	3	
3		4	1	1
4		4	1	3
	4*A*	4	3	
5		4	1	5
	5*A*	4	2	
	5*B*	4	2	
6		4	1	2
7		4	1	4

(a) Make a Gantt chart of the allocation of these orders to facilities, trying them out in priority order and getting them out in the shortest time possible and with a minimum of machine idle time.

(b) Make a flow chart of your logical process for doing this. If you cannot, approximate your process. Assume that this process is to be automated.

16.12 (a) You are given a set of n jobs with the following attributes:

A_i = the arrival or ready-time of the ith job; this is 0 for all i

V_i = the dollar value of the ith job

P_i = the processing time of the ith job (known precisely in advance)

D_i = the due date of the ith job

Let C_i represent the time at which the processing of the ith job is completed.

Each of these jobs is to be processed on a single machine. Describe how you would sequence the jobs on this machine if your objective is to:

1. Minimize the average manufacturing interval $(C_i - A_i)$

2. Minimize the maximum manufacturing interval

3. Minimize the maximum lateness $(C_i - D_i)$

4. Minimize the average lateness

5. Minimize the total weighted manufacturing interval, where each $(C_i - A_i)$ is weighted by the dollar value of the job

6. Minimize the average number of jobs waiting to be processed

7. Maximize the average waiting time $(C_i - A_i - P_i)$ of the jobs

(b) Prove that your ordering for 1 or 7 is in fact the best ordering for the criterion given.

16.13 The following questions refer to a network of queues.

(a) According to the basic flow model, the average completion time of jobs is inversely related to the utilization of the shop [i.e., $\overline{C} = f(1/U)$]. Assume that the random priority rule is a standard for comparison. Make a list of priority rules that would tend 1) to decrease machine idleness; 2) to increase machine idleness.

(b) Consider the table of information (Table 16.2). Construct a hypothetical frequency distribution of job lateness for the case of using the *SPT* rule and the *DDATE* rule. That is, sketch the relative shape and position of the three distributions.

(c) Discuss some possible reasons why the mean completion time is relatively insensitive to errors in the estimate of processing times when using the *SPT* rule.

(d) In the use of the *FCFS∗S(a)* rule, the *SPT* rule is sacrificed to give some assurance that jobs will not remain in the queues for an inordinately long time unless congestion exists at the queue. What are the implications of this rule on job lateness?

(e) Suppose that jobs are dispatched according to the *S/OPN* rule, resulting in 5% of the jobs, on the average, being positively late. Due dates are set by adding a constant times the sum of the processing times over all operations for a job. If the constant multiplier is reduced, why might you wish to shift to using the SPT rule?

(f) Suppose you are interested in reducing the number of jobs in the shop (work-in-process inventory), as well as minimizing the number of jobs with positive lateness. Which of these two rules would you use, the *SPT* or the *S/OPN* rule?

16.14   The following are activities and events associated with preparations for the release of a new product to production. Make an activity network for this project. Determine the parameters of the time distribution for the arrival of parts to the assembly department.

Activity		Most likely time	Optimistic time	Pessimistic time	Event arc
A	Review estimated process layouts	2	1.0	4.0	1–2
B	Prepare tool orders	1	0.5	2.0	2–5
C	Prepare raw material requisitions	2	1.0	3.0	2–7
D	Prepare final process layout	3	1.0	5.0	2–4
E	Design and make tools	8	6.0	16.0	5–6
F	Review gauge requirements	2	1.0	3.0	3–8
G	Obtain gauges	6	4.0	8.0	8–9
H	Obtain purchased parts and raw materials	8	4.0	10.0	7–10
I	Deliver tools to manufacturing department	1	0.5	2.0	6–11
J	Deliver raw material and purchased parts to manufacturing department	1	0.5	2.0	10–11
K	Deliver final process layouts to manufacturing department	1	0.5	2.0	4–11
L	Deliver gauges to manufacturing department	1	0.5	2.0	9–11
M	Manufacture parts	6	4.0	8.0	11–12

Events

1. Engineering release to process engineering
2. Release process layouts to master manufacturing data
3. Release process layouts to quality control
4. Release final process layout to manufacturing department
5. Release tool orders
6. Tools approved

7. Order raw material and purchased parts
8. Order gauges
9. Gauges checked and approved
10. Raw material and purchased parts approved
11. Schedule start of production
12. Acceptable parts to assembly department

16.15   Determine a cost function for project duration for the following case.

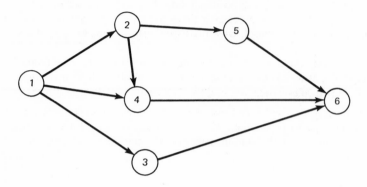

Arc	t_{ij}	T_{ij}	C_{ij}
1–2	4	6	8
1–3	4	8	9
1–4	3	5	3
2–4	3	3	∞
2–5	3	5	4
3–6	8	12	20
4–6	5	8	5
5–6	6	6	∞

16.16   A project consists of activities and events as shown in the activity network below.

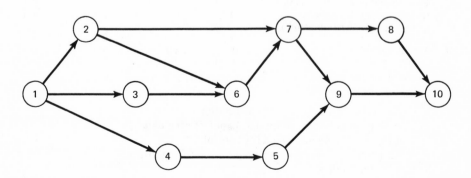

The following information about each activity is also available:

Activity (i, j)	Optimistic time	Most likely time	Pessimistic time	Accelerated time	Cost per time unit of acceleration
1–2	3	4	6	3	4
1–3	7	9	10	6	4
1–4	12	14	15	9	10
2–7	2	4	6	4	∞
2–6	7	10	12	7	2
3–6	9	11	14	6	9
4–5	5	6	8	6	∞
6–7	4	4	5	2	5
5–9	3	4	5	3	4
7–9	2	3	6	3	∞
7–8	14	15	16	12	9
8–10	3	3	5	3	∞
9–10	11	13	14	9	7

Given this information, determine the earliest and latest expected times for each event. Then construct a cost function showing the relationship between incremental project cost and accelerated project time.

Bibliography

General:

BOCK, ROBERT H., and WILLIAM K. HOLSTEIN, *Production Planning and Control.* Columbus, Ohio: Chas. E. Merrill Books, Inc., 1963.

MAGEE, JOHN F., and DAVID M. BOODMAN, *Production Planning and Inventory Control*, 2nd ed. New York: McGraw-Hill Book Co., 1967.

MUTH, JOHN F., and GERALD L. THOMPSON, *Industrial Scheduling.* Englewood Cliffs, N.J.: Prentice-Hall, Inc., 1963.

Single Machine Dispatching:

FIFE, DENNIS W., "Scheduling with Random Arrivals and Linear Loss Functions," *Management Science*, January 1965.

GILMORE, P. C., and R. E. GOMORY, "Sequencing a One State Variable Machine: A Solvable Case of the Traveling Salesman Problem," *Operations Research*, September–October 1964.

KARG, ROBERT L., and GERALD L. THOMPSON, "A Heuristic Approach to Solving Traveling Salesman Problems," *Management Science*, January 1964.

MC NAUGHTON, R., "Scheduling with Deadlines and Loss Functions," *Management Science*, October 1959.

ROOT, JAMES G., "Scheduling with Deadlines and Loss Functions on *k* Parallel Machines," *Management Science*, January 1965, Series A.

SCHILD, ALBERT, and IRWIN J. FREDMAN, "Scheduling Tasks with Deadlines and Non-Linear Loss Functions," *Management Science*, October 1962.

M × N Shop:

BROWN, A. P. G., and Z. A. LOMNICKI, "Some Applications of the Branch and Bound Algorithm to the Machine Scheduling Problems," *Operational Research Quart.*, June 1966.

DUDEK, R. A., and O. F. TEUTON, JR., "Development of *M*-Stage Decision Rule for Scheduling *n* Jobs Through *m* Machines," *Operations Research*, May–June 1964.

EASTMAN, W. L., S. EVEN, and I. M. ISAACS, "Bounds for the Optimal Scheduling of *n* Jobs on *m* Processors," *Management Science*, November 1964.

GIGLIO, R. J., and H. M. WAGNER, "Approximate Solutions to the Three-Machine Scheduling Problem," *Operations Research*, March–April 1964.

LIGTENBERG, EUGENE, "Minimal Cost Sequencing of *n* Grouped and Ordered Jobs on *m* Machines," *J. Ind. Eng.*, April 1966.

Queue Networks:

BULKIN, MICHAEL, JOHN L. COLLEY, and HARRY W. STEINHOFF, JR., "Load Forecasting, Priority Sequencing, and Simulations in a Job Shop Control System," *Management Science*, October 1966.

CONWAY, R. W., and W. L. MAXWELL, "Network Dispatching by the Shortest Operation Discipline," *Operations Research*, vol. 10, no. 1, 1962.

CONWAY, R. W., WILLIAM L. MAXWELL, and JAMES W. OLDZIEY, "Sequencing Against Due Dates," Dept. of Ind. Eng. & O. R., Cornell University, Ithaca, N.Y., 1966.

GERE, WILLIAM S., "Heuristics in Job Shop Scheduling," *Management Science*, November 1966.

JACKSON, J. R., "Jobshop-Like Queuing Systems," *Management Science*, October 1963.

LE GRANDE, E., "The Development of a Factory Simulation Using Actual Operating Data," *Management Technology*, vol. 3, no. 1, 1963.

LITTLE, J. D. C., "A Proof for the Queuing Formula $L = \lambda W$," *Operations Research*, vol. 9, no. 3, 1961.

PHIPPS, THOMAS E., JR., "Machine Repair as a Priority Waiting Line Problem," *Operations Research*, February 1956.

TRILLING, DONALD R., "Job Shop Simulation of Orders That Are Networks," *J. Ind. Eng.*, February 1966.

Project Scheduling:

BERMAN, E. B., "Resource Allocation in a PERT Network Under Continuous Activity Time Cost Functions," *Management Science*, July 1964.

CHRISTENSEN, BORGE M., "Network Models for Project Scheduling," *Machine Design*, May 10–July 19, 1962.

DAVIS, EDWARD W., "Resource Allocation in Project Network Models—A Survey," *J. Ind. Eng.*, April 1966.

KELLEY, J. E., JR., "Critical Path Planning and Scheduling: Mathematical Basis," *Operations Research*, vol. IX, no. 3, 1961.

MALCOLM, D. G., J. H. ROSEBOOM, C. E. CLARK, and WILLARD FAZAR, "Application of a Technique for Research and Development Program Evaluation," *Operations Research*, vol. 7, 1959.

MAYHUGH, J. O., "On the Mathematical Theory of Schedules," *Management Science*, November 1964.

ODOM, R. G., and EUGENE E. BLYSTONE, "A Case Study of CPM in a Manufacturing Situation," *J. Ind. Eng.*, November–December 1964.

PARIKH, SHAILENDRA C., and WILLIAM S. JEWELL, "Decomposition of Project Networks," *Management Science*, January 1965.

PHILLIPS, CECIL R., "Fifteen Key Features of Computer Programs for CPM and PERT," *J. Ind. Eng.*, January–February 1964.

SHAFFER, L. R., J. B. RITTER, and W. L. MEYER, *The Critical Path Method*. New York: McGraw-Hill Book Co., 1965.

WIEST, JEROME D., "Some Properties of Schedules for Large Projects with Limited Resources," *Operations Research*, May–June 1964.

17

Integrated
System Control

REQUIREMENTS

In this text, we have fractionated and dissected the subject of production management in order to expose a spectrum of problem areas. Most of these involve making "localized" or tactical decisions such as the choice of an improvement to a process or operation, the assignment of machines to locations, the replacement of individual facilities, the determination of inventory levels for individual parts, or the dispatching of jobs. This fragmented examination of the subject is necessary if we are to gain substantive knowledge about it, but it leaves us with the necessity and, hopefully, the desire to consider the integrative nature of the subject.

In the earlier sections, we extolled the virtues of a "systems" approach to management decision making and control. The systems approach implies the integration of the critical and interrelated variables of a problem while transcending the traditional boundaries of authority, responsibility, and function. The decision maker is interested in the impact of an alternative choice upon the welfare of an organizational entity such as a division, business, or institution as a whole.

Ignoring for the moment the problems of facilities design, the planning and control of a production system as an integrated whole is a subject of considerable current importance and interest for a number of reasons. First, there is the physical variety in products, processes, and materials. A characteristic of many new consumer products is that they precede successive generations of increasing variety. One has simply to refer to TV sets, cars, gasoline, and tires as examples of the evolution of variety in size, shape, price, color, etc. Similarly, technological innovation presents managers with a staggering array of choices in processing methods and materials, differing both in design problems and in the planning of facilities and inventories. The impact of variety can be avoided to some degree by policies of standardization and specialization, but optimal policies should be determined by economic analyses. In any event, this kind of variety introduces two problems in manufacturing control. Simply keeping track of sheer numbers of things poses problems of information storage and retrieval. Further, there is the problem of continual change imposed on the physical resources. New materials, alterations to machines, and product and part engineering changes require a continual updating and revision of information systems. This recurrent auditing of organization procedures can consume a significant proportion of the manpower devoted to designing and maintaining control systems.

Second, managers are forced to expedite their own decision making at a progressively faster rate. Under the impact of constant change, decisions must be made with minimum delay and often with inadequate information. Thus, there is a need to generate and maintain a "base" of current data and information about the firm's operations in its many ramifications. This information should be retrievable on short notice to assist in decision making and control.

Third, the high-speed electronic computer now provides the opportunity to implement the ingredients of a desirable integrated manufacturing control system. It not only efficiently stores what otherwise would be a hopeless morass of paperwork in jungles of file cabinets, but it can also process the information, permit random access, and even act upon the information by executing programed decision rules.

The requisites of an integrated manufacturing control system should include the following:

1. The system should clarify the kinds of decisions that must be made in controlling manufacturing operations and indicate the relative point in time when these decisions should be made. For each kind of decision, it is necessary to specify the critical variables, how they are interrelated, and where in the organizational structure the decisions should be made.

2. The system should supply the decision maker with the kind of information required to make the decision at the proper point in time. Redundant information should be minimized.

3. The decision maker should be provided with decision rules whenever possible. Automatic decision making should be programed for routine and repetitive types of operating decisions, thus leaving individuals normally burdened with these decisions for more creative work.

4. The system should clarify and generate measures of performance that demonstrate the effectiveness of control procedures and decisions. When these measures of performance are used to evaluate management effectiveness, they must be directly related to the manager's decision-making domain and be controllable by him. Furthermore, the system should indicate causes for both good and poor performance and perhaps even suggest courses for remedial action.

EVOLVING CONCEPTS

A half century ago, the tenets and methods of scientific management provided the manager with a rationale of organization, order, and system in the operation of complex production systems. The prerogative of daily shop control, including mainly the determination of work methods and the scheduling of work, was assumed by management rather than left to the machine operator or worker and his immediate supervisor. Order and control were provided by staff and auxiliary functions supported by communication systems and information storage. While order and system were established, the integration of separate departmentalized activities had to be left to a higher level of management. The specialization of management into functional authorities appeared good in theory, but in practice it was evident that integration suffered, and ultimately the final decision-making authority had to rest with line managers who could better assess the totality of a situation and coordinate diverse activities under their jurisdiction.

In the past two decades, management science and operations research have in turn centered attention on the decision-making process and the design of tools to assist the manager in making decisions about given types of operating problems. But much of this work has focused on the development of models for tactical decision-making situations without much reference to the practical problems of implementation and integration. However, these models will provide a basis for incorporating programed decision rules in automated control systems in the future.

In the past, integrated control has depended a great deal on the ability of the manager to evaluate a situation and perhaps subjectively consider and integrate the critical variables. Until the last decade, management scientists have paid too little attention to the behavioral aspects of decision making while focusing their attention on mathematical and other optimum seeking models. We probably need to know a good deal more about the reliability of the manager as a human integrator.

The computer has, of course, entered the picture as a data processor. While it has speeded up the preparation and display of operating data, these data have often reflected the traditional form of product or departmental performance costs. While this information is valuable, it nevertheless lacks the specificity production managers often need to make adjustments necessary if the production system is to react to current changes. More often, and at the local operating level, the manager needs to be guided by various measures of performance that are surrogates of profit and monetary costs. These include such performance indicators as degree of facilities utilization, facilities breakdowns, late shipments, material shortages, and part defects and spoilage.

While the automation of physical production processes has been proceeding at an increasing rate, it is becoming apparent that there will be a corresponding, but lagging, development of automated production or manufacturing control systems. The high-speed electronic computer and peripheral equipment will be at the core of these control systems. A highly developed system will collect, store, and display current information on a multitude of operating variables while making programed decision rules for routine portions of the management system. We will now consider some of the essential features of this kind of system.

AN INTEGRATED PRODUCTION CONTROL SYSTEM

An outline of an integrated manufacturing control system is presented in the following pages. There is no one system of control. The degree of sophistication, automation, and completeness depend, of course, on the size of the firm, management capabilities, physical production systems, etc. Our discussion centers on a multiproduct, job-shop type of producer. Let us envision a plant employing 1,500 to 2,000 people and which manufactures a large line of hand and powered tools for industrial and home use. Over 40,000 distinctive parts, components, and subassemblies are manufactured in the company shops. Final products are generally made for finished-goods inventory. Some final products are made to customer specification, and parts or subassemblies may be shipped directly to the customer or to field inventories as replacement parts. New products are continually generated by research and engineering.

The general control system relies on a number of computing facilities. The central facility is a time-shared general-purpose computer. Both input and output stations are located remotely in various sections of the company. Other special-purpose computers are available in specific areas of the plant, depending on their purpose and use. Data-processing systems such as payroll, customer billing, and other accounting functions have long been computerized and are normal functions.

The manufacturing control function is guided by organizational "groups." A department has meaning only for establishing an individual's "home base" for purposes of personnel guidance and control. Otherwise, an individual may be assigned to any group, depending on where his skills and experience are currently needed. Each group has an administrative manager responsible for the administration of the group and the maintenance of his part of the system.

The speed and utility of the system depend in part on the methods of information storage and retrieval. Storage by cards and tape is common, but they demand periodic handling and merging to obtain the information intermittently. Disk storage provides the added feature of random access to data, which is a prerequisite of a highly automated system. The ultimate in speed is a system of continuous on-line control, where operational information is continuously fed into a computer memory from remotely located transmission stations and information is in turn continuously fed to remote receivers upon demand. Much of the hardware for such systems has been developed and is operational in some cases. Continued implementation depends on the training and recruitment of personnel to install, operate, and manage these systems. The features of the system we will describe are intended to illuminate the concepts, rather than propose the details of a recommended system. The returns on the investment in man-years typically required to design, implement, and operate such systems are not easy to delineate in clear and precise terms. Such systems, of course, evolve into complexity. Many of the advantages and costs are indirect, and one can attempt to hypothesize their nature while considering the system features in the following pages.

Demand Analysis Group

Referring to Figure 17.1, we see that sales orders are originated at remote stations by salesmen, distributors, or warehouses and sent to the plant by long-distance transmitting facilities. Orders are temporarily electronically stored in a Current Customer Order File. Periodically, these orders are verified against a permanent Master Parts File. This file is a random-access file containing all pertinent information about every part handled by the company, including descriptive data, inventory status, lead times, lot sizes, and planned production orders by time periods. Verified orders are segregated into standard stock item and custom-made categories. The latter are sent to the Product Engineering Group for processing.

Orders for stock items are reconciled with the Master Parts File. If the order can be filled from current inventory, it is added to a Shipment Schedule. The

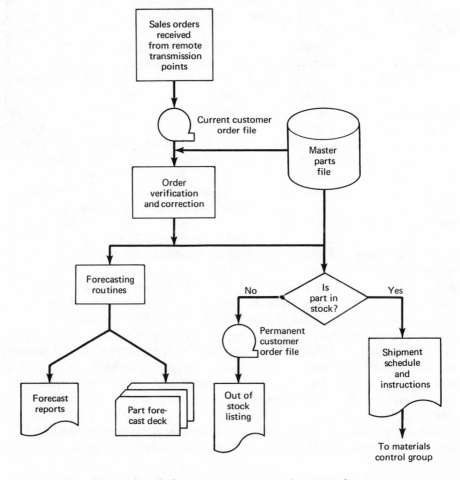

FIGURE **17.1**   Demand analysis group—customer order processing.

Shipment Schedule can be automatically transmitted to the Materials Control Group and includes the regrouping of customer orders into similar products, a listing of stockroom part locations, packaging configurations for individual orders, shipping instructions, type of carrier, and inventory requisition tab cards for subsequently updating inventory files.

Unfilled orders are added to a Permanent Customer Order File, which is a current backlog of unfilled orders. An inventory shortage listing is provided for management control.

Current daily demand is reclassified by product type and used to update daily, weekly, or monthly forecasts, which, in turn, are used for planning purposes. Significant changes in demand are flagged for management control purposes. Part forecast card decks or paper tapes are prepared and sent periodically to the Materials Control Group for updating inventory parameters and to the Manufacturing Control Group for product explosion and shop loading routines.

Materials Control Group

The Materials Control Group is responsible for maintaining and updating inventories of raw materials, fabricated parts, subassemblies, purchased components, and final products. Purchasing, materials receiving, packaging, shipping, and subcontracting administration are also carried out by this group.

Inventories are classified into *A*, *B*, *C*, groupings for variation in control procedures. Class *A* items include final products, their subassemblies and components, and high-turnover replacement parts. Their inventories are controlled mainly by the explosion of final product demand and future manufacturing schedules based on shop loading techniques. Class *B* and *C* inventories include slow-moving items, low-valued items, and indirect materials and supplies. These item inventories are controlled by economical lot size-reorder point or min-max schemes or by periodic replenishment of open-shelf items.

B and *C* items are issued on requisitions received at the time the items are required, unless they are open-shelf items. These requisitions are used to update a Class *B* and *C* inventory file, as shown in Figure 17.2. Semiannually or annually this file is updated for changes in inventory parameters considering price, cost, and demand changes. (Similarly, completed job orders or receiving reports are used to record additions to inventories.)

With respect to Class *A* items, the Part Forecast Deck is used as input to the Product Explosion Routine. A permanent Product Structure File contains the part makeup of all assemblies and subassemblies, with cross reference to the Master Parts File. These two files, together with the Forecast Deck, permit the development and listing of a Master Schedule of Parts Requirements by date. This schedule is fed back into the Master Parts File along with the Completed Job Orders Deck, thus updating the inventory section of that file. The updated inventory and order time series portion of the Master Parts List is shown in Figure 17.3.

Finally, Job Orders are prepared daily for Class *B* and *C* items as reorder or minimum points are reached, and for Class *A* items depending on the schedule of

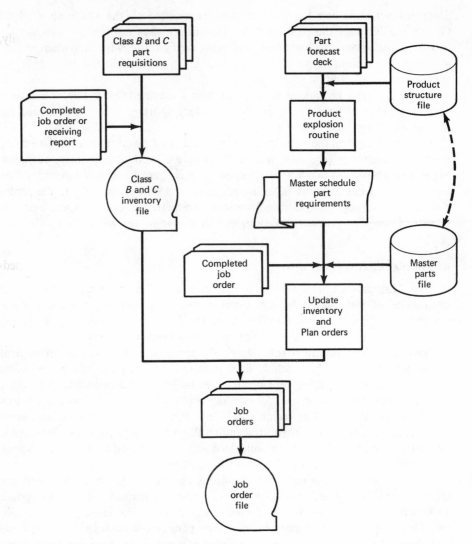

figure **17.2**   Material control group.

their requirements. These are added to the Job Order File, which is a permanent record of outstanding job orders.

Manufacturing Control Group

The functions of the Manufacturing Control Group are to prepare final part schedules and to control the actual shop performance on a short-term basis.

Job Orders currently received from the Materials Control Group are segregated into orders for assemblies, subassemblies, and fabricated components.

Inventory record

Period	Current	1	2	3	4	5	6
On hand	50						
On order			75	150			
Requirements	150	25	100	100	25		
Available for planning	50	25	0	50	25		
Lot size	75						

Planned order index

	Current			1			2			3			4			5			6		
	Stock date	Qty	Shop order	Stock date	Qty	Shop order	Stock date	Qty	Shop order	Stock date	Qty	Shop order	Stock date	Qty	Shop order	Stock date	Qty	Shop order	Stock date	Qty	Shop order
	0	75		0	75		2	75		3	75		3	75		3	75				

Lead time

Chain to bill of materials

FIGURE 17.3　Inventory time series record for Class *A* items. Courtesy of International Business Machine Corporation.

Assembly and subassembly orders are scheduled into the assembly section of manufacturing. Components and subassemblies used in the final assembly presumably will have arrived at the assembly department to mesh with the assembly schedule. On-line shortages will be noted; if they are severe, part lead times will be extended or parts will be held in temporary work-in-process inventories.

Job Orders for fabricated parts will be merged with the Master Route File to determine the approximate future load for shop facilities. This will be added to the Facilities Load File, which is a short-term prediction of facility loads in man or machine hours. This file will be used to anticipate capacity problems that might arise in the near future.

At the same time, a Shop Packet Deck is generated for each job. This deck includes

1. Job Identification Card to accompany the job in the shop.
2. Requisitions for materials and parts.
3. Completed Job Order Card for stockroom to report acceptance of finished parts.
4. Operation Tickets to report operation times and part counts.
5. Inspection Tickets.
6. Printed Shop Routing.
7. Tool Orders.
8. Microfilm part drawings and instruction sheets.

ON-LINE SHOP CONTROL SYSTEM: The core of manufacturing control is a continuous on-line system of shop control. Information from the shop floor and auxiliary functions is fed into it continuously or intermittently from remote input terminals (Figure 17.4).

The status of both jobs and facilities is determined from information inputs using the Shop Packet Deck. At the start of a given operation, the employee notes the starting time of the job and identifies his machine and himself by inserting the proper operation card and his badge in the transmitting station. End of operation information will be similarly transmitted. This information will be processed in a central computer and added to the appropriate files of current information.

A Job Status File contains complete and up-to-date information about the status of every job released to the shop. A Job is added to the file using the Job Order Card and the Master Routing File. The result is shown in Figure 17.5. This file is continually updated as the job progresses through the shop.

A Machine Status File indicates the current status of each production facility in the shop, and, similarly, an Employee Record indicates the current status of each shop employee. These two files are merged in the Operations Scheduling Routine. This routine creates the priority with which jobs are to be dispatched through each facility. Dispatching depends on a number of things, including the status of the jobs and facilities, the possibility of merging two jobs having current and similar operations, the original priority assigned to the job at the time it was released to the shop, the possibility of alternative routings, relation of current time to due dates, necessary rework, possibility of lot splitting, etc.

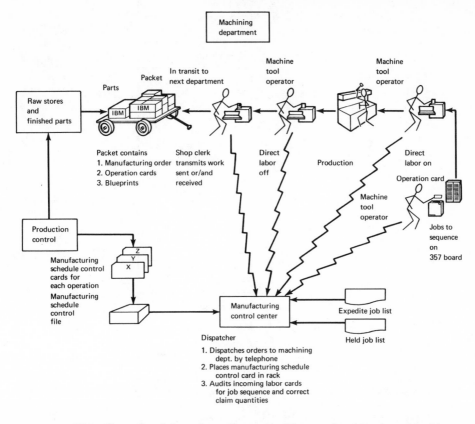

FIGURE **17.4**   Operational flow chart. Courtesy of International Business Machine Corporation.

An off-line Dispatching Simulator Routine is used to periodically simulate the shop under different priority rules using the current load on the shop. The results of dispatching are indicated in the Work Center Load File shown in Figure 17.6.

At the start of each shift, a Job Priority Assignment List is printed for each work center, indicating the current sequence of operations to be performed at that work center, as shown in Figure 17.7. Priorities may be altered during the day to correspond with more current information.

The core of the system is a high-speed random access computer. At any time, the random access files can be interrogated with such questions as:

Where is a certain order being worked?
Which men and machines are currently available?
What is the predicted completion time for a certain operation or job?
How many parts of a batch or order have been completed?
What are alternative routings for a given job?
What is the next operation to be performed on a job?

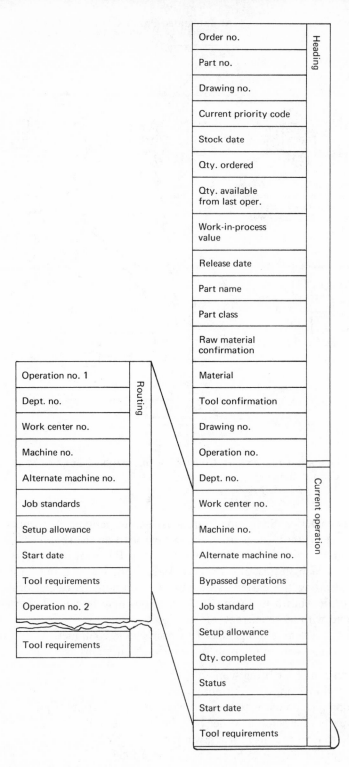

FIGURE **17.5** Job status file. Courtesy of International Business Machine Corporation.

Work center load file

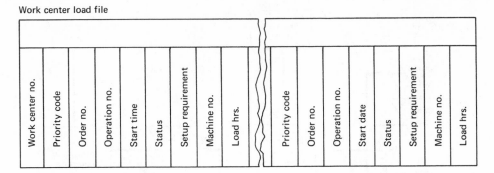

FIGURE **17.6**   Work center load record. Courtesy of International Business Machine Corporation.

XYZ Corporation - Springfield Plant

Task-To-Be-Assigned List

Date: 06/25/   Shift: 1   Work center: 42A

Order no.	Oper. no.	Part no.	Operation description	Suggested priority
39825	20	4X3951	Drill 5/8″ hole	1
56703	51	72A391	Drill 1/2″ & 3/16″ holes	2
43824	40	6A8392	Drill holes per dwg #6A8392-1	3
71163	10	73A642	Drill and ream	4
52931	30	7B7702	Drill and ream 1/2″ hole	5
52391	40	7B7702	Drill 7/64″ holes	6
43742	20	62A6031	Drill 5/32″ holes	48

FIGURE **17.7**   Task-to-be-assigned list. Courtesy of International Business Machine Corporation.

Manufacturing Engineering Group

The purpose of the Manufacturing Engineering Group is to convert a set of specifications for a product design into a set of detailed manufacturing instructions, including the routing of the part, the operational details, tooling requirements, and operation times standards.

The traditional approach to these functions is shown in Figure 17.8. Typically, the various functions are carried out by personnel experienced in shop lore and

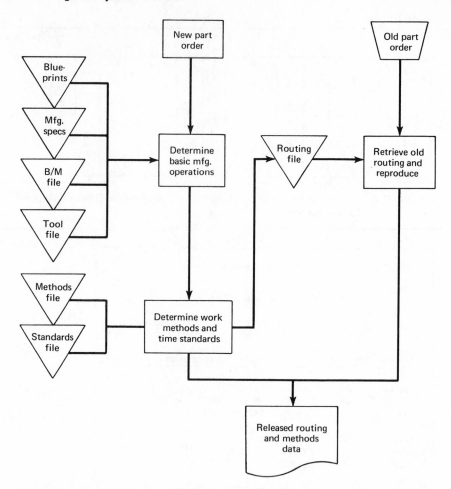

FIGURE **17.8**   Traditional approach to manufacturing planning. Courtesy of International Business Machine Corporation.

methods. New part specifications are converted into detailed manufacturing instructions by referring to past history as represented by files of information concerning machine capabilities, tool lists, methods and standard time data, plus original design provided by the engineer himself. Much of this work is tedious and should be transferred to mechanized data-handling systems. Beyond this, there is the possibility of converting some of the design structure into a computerized procedure that will replace much of the human action by more direct and automatic conversion of product specifications into manufacturing instructions.

The automation of the manufacturing engineering function is predicated on the assumption that there is some underlying logic involved in the conversion of product or part specifications into routing, methods, and time standards requirements. The essence of an automated procedure lies in the ability to define this logic and program it into computerized routines.

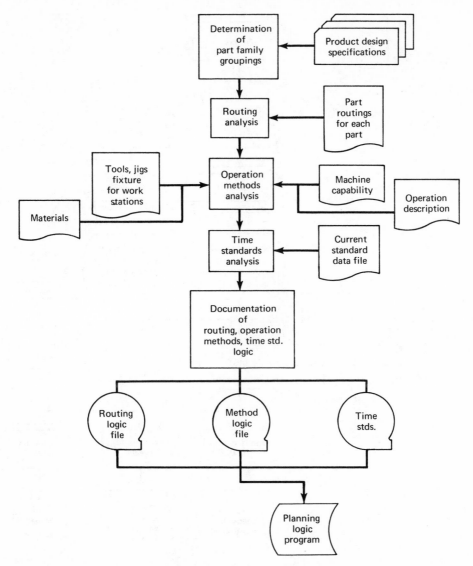

FIGURE **17.9**   Procedure for constructing planning logic program.

The preliminary phase of the program consists of a complete analysis of the present practice of production engineering. Referring to Figure 17.9, we may note that Product Design Specifications for current products are analyzed to determine "part families." The members of a family set include parts with similar design specifications or with similar processing requirements. Following this there are three major types of analyses. The first is a routing analysis, which consists of examining the routing of all members of a family set. The second is an analysis of

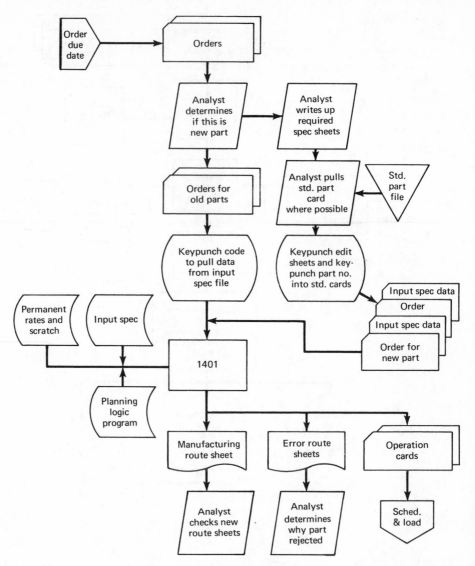

FIGURE **17.10** Automated manufacturing planning system. Courtesy of International Business Machine Corporation.

present operation characteristics, including machine capabilities, materials, tools, jigs, and fixtures, and operation descriptions. Finally, current standard data files are collected to construct a time standards analysis.

These analyses are used to construct the basic logic underlying the production engineering of the members of part families. The documentation of this logic is perhaps the most important and difficult part of the attempt to automate the function. With the use of the preceding analyses and exhaustive consultation with production engineers, the logic is documented and filed in Logic Files or Logic Tables and summarized in a Planning Logic Program.

The Planning Logic Program, together with data files for materials and tools, provides the core of the operational production engineering system. The input consists of the design specification for a new part, a given customer order, or an existing part that is to be verified. The output consists of the part routing, operator instruction sheets for each operation, tools lists, numerical machine control tapes, and any other pertinent manufacturing information. These are fed to the Manufacturing Control Group as Job Orders are released to the shop. Part routings are permanently stored in a Master Route File. These operational characteristics of the manufacturing engineering function are shown in Figure 17.10.

Future Implications

The future success of systems of automated manufacturing control will be difficult to assess initially in terms of monetary savings and profitability. The criteria of success will be in the improvement of local measures of performance. Certainly, there is an advantage in the development of current or up-to-date information that can be used to make decisions related to current changes in operating conditions. Decisions can be postponed for longer periods, thus permitting the accrual of more accurate information about a given situation. This is in contrast to forcing an early decision based upon inadequate information or making a late decision based on delayed information.

The generation of pertinent information, however, does not guarantee the improvement in measures of performance. Performance improvement depends on the development and use of decision rules and procedures, which reflect a systems viewpoint and attempt to optimize the critical variables. This implies more centralized decision making about functions that are normally controlled at the very local level by the foremen and supervisors, such as dispatching, short-term scheduling, and expediting. The payoff in the more centralized control of shop activities must be made evident, and we may expect that empirical research on actual shop behavior under different control methods will be required in the future to clarify the issue.

One potential advantage of systems of the kind discussed is a more rational choice of manufacturing batch or lot sizes. Typically, these may be determined by economical lot-size formulas or inventory replenishment requirements without consideration of the impact of the batch sizes and job orders on shop loads. We have suggested in earlier sections that the shop load is sensitive to changes in demand unless smoothing devices are used to dampen responses to the demand changes. In any event, manufacturing lead times will change with shop loads, especially if batch sizes are rigidly fixed by independent methods. A system of control should permit the adjustment of batch sizes to correspond with shop loads. In periods of heavy loading, batch sizes may be split or reduced in size, providing this does not have deleterious effects on shop capacity due to expanded setup requirements. Conversely, at points where capacity is underloaded, the batch sizes may be increased. Thus, batch sizes are influenced by the scheduling process. We already know that moderate deviations from economical lot-size quantities do not seriously affect the balance of setup and inventory costs structure, so that the net gains from better shop loading by batch size manipulation may be significant.

A continuous on-line shop control system would probably result in improvements in job completion times and correspondingly in work-in-process and average satisfaction of customer due dates. The priority dispatching theory that has to date been gained from hypothetical job shop simulation can be extended to include the knowledge gained from off-line simulators, which use actual shop conditions for data input. We may expect the manager of the future to periodically feed a simulator with current shop conditions and then evaluate alternative courses of action.

Changes in Management

The general theme of the text, as well as the more specific changes that will occur in manufacturing control systems, strongly suggests a future metamorphosis in management structure and control. We conjecture that some of the more important changes are the following:

1. There will be a continued increase in the ratio of persons in staff and auxiliary functions to those involved in direct line manufacturing. The design, planning, implementation, and maintenance of control systems will require a substantial labor force of programers, technicians, engineers, and planners. The differentiation between staff and line functions will grow more obscure. Line management authority for production will reside with individuals who will rely heavily on technical information systems and staff recommendations to support decisions. On-line computer control systems will be a line management tool. Systems Groups, such as Materials Control and Manufacturing Control, will be quasi-line organizations.

2. Departmental performance will assume a secondary role compared to the system performance as a whole. Operational goals will be spelled out for the system and not for the department, and responsibility for attaining these goals will rest with the Systems Groups and their managers, who will answer to a General Operations Manager. Whereas routine personnel functions will be handled by a department, the human and behavioral problems will be an integral concern of Group Managers. A computerized automated system of management cannot transcend the issues and problems of human relations that are a normal part of any group activity.

3. In general, managers will be expected to be more concerned with innovation and change. They will be rewarded for encouraging and sustaining innovation in their operations. Such innovation will be purchased from technical service functions within or without the firm, as well as coming more or less spontaneously from the members of the organization. This encouragement and sustenance of a

viable base for innovation and change will demand changes in management and supervisory methods.

4. Everyone will be paid a guaranteed annual wage. Incentive based on individual job effort and performance will disappear under the impact of automation and the annual wage. However, group incentives may be designed, but based on system measures of performance, such as scrap and spoilage levels, late deliveries, and facilities utilization. Such incentive schemes will have to be designed with great care, if they are employed, and we may expect grievances and arguments to occur over bonus payments.

5. Middle managers will have to become conversant with computer methods and systems just as they have to be today with the intricacies of the processing methods. Furthermore, they must understand the nature of tools of modern management science, although they will not need to be experts in their development and implementation. They will have to be able to converse with the operations researcher who will be attempting to translate a decision process into a model or a set of decision rules. Furthermore, they will have to be able to clarify for the organization the measures of performance that will be used to judge the system efficiency.

6. We may expect that the on-line control of a production operation will be centered physically in a control room, perhaps somewhat similar to the control center of a military operation. Managers will operate as teams rather than as separate individuals in private offices.

7. Engineering changes in part designs will be translated rapidly into changes required in other parts of the system. An engineering change in a part results in substantially a new part, and all parts of the system must be updated with that change.

Considerable labor will be required to maintain and audit the system. Probably 30% to 50% of the individuals involved in the system will be involved in making changes in the computer programs.

Problems

17.1   A small paint company makes industrial coatings to customer specifications. The company has been in business for over ten years, during which time about 200 distinct formulas have been made. A given customer's specifications are converted, by one of two chemists, into a production formula for ingredient mix, etc. A coating can be specified in terms of 20 factors, including such things as hardness, ease of curing, and impact resistance. Translating customer specifications to production formulas consumes about 75% of the chemist's time. The time to construct the formula is sometimes reduced by searching the customer files for the possibility of a previous duplicate order. As part of an over-all objective of improving the company's control procedures, what might be the elements of a system to "automate" the product design in this company?

17.2   Consider the circulation procedure at your college library. Could all or portions of this procedure be automated, and if so, what would be the basic features of the plan?

17.3 The Utilities Maintenance Company provides home appliance service. It acts as an intermediary between applicance manufacturers and consumers. The justification for this kind of service is based on the economics of scale, specialization in the training of technicians, and specialization in the management of shop maintenance operations. Some features are:

(a) There is a central plant that houses the company's vehicles, stockroom of parts, shop for in-plant maintenance of appliances, offices, and a small computer.

(b) There is a fleet of 100 trucks, each specializing in some type of service and manned by one or two men.

(c) Each day a certain number of "jobs" are assigned to the crew of each truck. A job consists of
1. an order to respond to a customer's call for repair,
2. an order to perform preventive maintenance according to a predetermined schedule, and
3. an order to install or remove an appliance at a given location.

Consider the features of an operational control system for this operation.

What specific areas need control procedures?

What kinds of operating decisions are involved?

What parts of the control system could be computerized?

Make a flow diagram indicating the concept of an automated operations control scheme.

Bibliography

BULKIN, M. H., JOHN L. COLLEY, and HARRY W. STEINHOFF, JR., "Load Forecasting, Priority Sequencing and Simulation in a Job Shop Control System," *Management Science*, October 1966.

CARROLL, DONALD C., "On the Structure of Operational Control Systems," Working Paper 167–66, Sloan School of Management, Cambridge, Mass.: Massachusetts Institute of Technology.

DESMONDE, WILLIAM H., *Real-Time Data Processing Systems*. Englewood Cliffs, N.J.: Prentice-Hall, Inc., 1964.

MALCOLM, DONALD G., "Real-Time Management Control in a Large Scale Man-Machine System, *J. Ind. Eng.*, March–April 1960.

MALCOLM, DONALD G., and ALAN ROWE, Ed., *Management Control Systems*. New York: John Wiley & Sons, 1960.

OPTNER, STANFORD L., *Systems Analysis*. Englewood Cliffs, N.J.: Prentice-Hall, Inc., 1960.

PARKER, R. W., "The SABRE System," *Datamation*, vol. XI, September 1965.

RHINE, RAMON J., "Development of an Operational Management System," Systems Development Corporation, April 16, 1963.

18

Logistics Systems

INTRODUCTION

Beyond the planning and tactical decision making within the context of intraplant production control lie the problems of controlling material flow in an inter-plant-warehouse-consumer logistics system. The design, planning, and control of material transportation and storage in these large-scale systems is a subject of considerable magnitude. We can do no more than consider a few selected topics, which are representative of the kinds of problems involved and the approaches taken to their solution.

Provided that we know something about the magnitude and location of ultimate consumer demand for a product or service, the major components of the logistics problem involve the following:

1. The determination of the capacity and location of both production and storage facilities.
2. The choice of methods to be used for transporting materials within the system.
3. The planning of procurement, production, and inventory levels for the system as a whole.
4. The operational scheduling and routing of fleets of proprietary vehicles for materials transportation.

The subject is not entirely new, since in Chapter 7 we devoted some attention to the location of economic activities as related primarily to transportation costs. However, once the issues of location, capacity, and methods of transportation have been satisfied, the problem is one of controlling production and inventory levels and transportation operations within the context of the multifacility situation.

What we have to say in the remainder of this chapter applies to a wide variety of industrial and institutional settings. However, unless advised otherwise, we will think in the context of a system of plants, warehouses, and consumers, such as suggested by Figure 18.1.

A set of factories, each producing some product mix, services a nation-wide

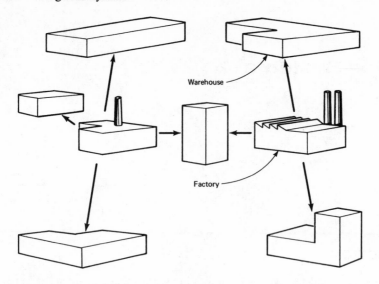

FIGURE **18.1**   Multiplant warehouse distribution system.

set of warehouses. Plant outputs are assigned to warehouses based on an allocation model. Now the issue becomes one of planning production and inventory levels in the system as a whole. Various specific questions arise.

1. What is an efficient aggregate production plan for each plant?
2. What minimum and maximum inventory levels are required at each warehouse?
3. How can customer demand patterns be translated into short-term production schedules for each plant?
4. How can short-term production scheduling be reconciled with aggregate production plans?
5. What kind of an information system is needed to effect a smooth and integrated operation of the distribution system?
6. Where in the organization should various production control decisions be made?

The answers to these questions lie in the ability to understand the interconnection between the system variables and then to utilize this knowledge in the design of an information and data collection system to facilitate decision making. But we must ask ourselves, what is it that we wish to accomplish in an integrated control system? Certainly, as in the case of planning and tactical control, we wish to minimize the costs of utilizing the resources of the system commensurate with satisfying consumer demand. We can agree that in distribution systems of this kind, we wish to provide expeditious service to the customer while at the same time effecting a smooth and predictable response throughout the system to the vagaries of ultimate consumer demand. It is this matter of stabilizing the system response that has been the subject of considerable research in the behavior of distribution systems and in the design of information systems and control decision procedures. We will now consider both aspects.

INFORMATION FEEDBACK SYSTEMS

The operational behavior of a multistage distribution system depends in part on the point in the organization at which decisions are made and the kind of information available to the decision maker. At a particular stage in the distribution system, the decisions to change resource levels are made in response to the demand for products at that same stage. We can extrapolate the discussion of intraplant multistage systems to the case of distribution systems. The integrated operation and control of such systems is preferable to operating each stage as an independent entity. For instance, permitting factories to operate independently in response to exogenous demands by warehouses can cause over-response to changes in the original source of demand, namely, the ultimate consumer. This can result in uneven and at times long lead times for replenishing warehouse needs, consequently large warehouse inventories, and highly variable use of resources at the factory.

UNCONTROLLED RESPONSE: Lippitt shows the behavior of a retail-wholesale-factory warehouse system under an assumed set of ordering and inventory rules, as well as delivery and communication lead times.[1]

1. *Lead times*   Figure 18.2 shows the time sequence of events in the distribution channels. These lead times include intervals required for the communication of information and orders, transporting and handling goods, organizational delays, and time to adjust production to new levels in response to orders from the factory warehouse.

2. *Normal inventory levels*   Retail levels are set at six times the average weekly sales over the previous six weeks. Distributor levels are six times the average weekly orders received over the previous six weeks. Factory warehouse levels are four times the average weekly orders received over the previous six weeks.

Considering these inventory policies and the indicated lead times, a sustained 10% increase in customer orders will result in the responses shown in Figures 18.3 and 18.4. The over-all sequence of events is spread out over two months and results in an over-response of the system to the increase in the original customer demand. Orders are placed progressively larger as the impact of the increased customer orders filters through the stages. The resulting large load placed on the factory is shown at the bottom of Figure 18.3.

MODERATING RESPONSES: The problem in both in-plant and multistage inventory systems is to moderate the fluctuation of orders placed at succeeding stages

[1] V. G. Lippitt, "Trade Inventories: Their Influence on Manufacturer Sales," College of Business Administration, University of Rochester, N.Y.

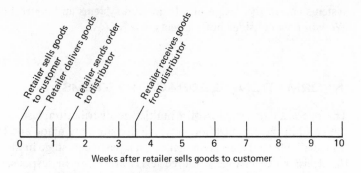

Retailer

Distributor

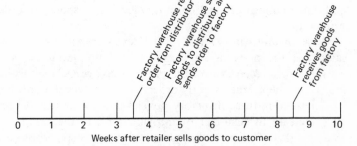

Factory warehouse

FIGURE **18.2**   Time sequence of events in distribution channels. From V. G. Lippitt, "Trade Inventories: Their Influence on Manufacturer Sales," College of Business Administration, Univ. of Rochester, N.Y.

in the system. One effective way is to reduce the lead times due to communicating sales information and order placements.

Figure 18.5 shows changes instituted in the communication of information in Lippitt's analysis. Under the new policy, the retailer sends retail sales data directly to successive stages in the system. For example, the distributor using the retail

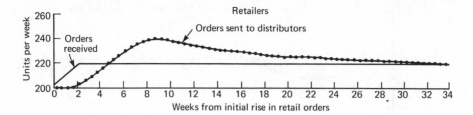

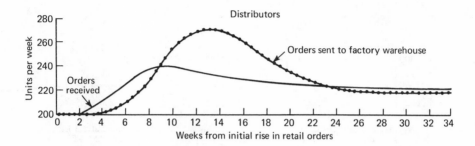

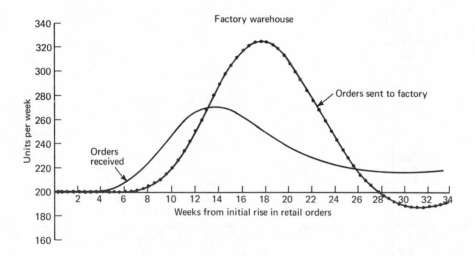

FIGURE **18.3**   Flows of orders at three stages of distribution in response to a 10%
rise in retail sales. From V. G. Lippitt, "Trade Inventories: Their
Influence on Manufacturer Sales," College of Business Administration, Univ. of Rochester, N.Y.

sales information as a guide sends his replacement order to the factory $1\frac{1}{2}$ weeks
after the retail sales are made. The effect of reducing these lead times is shown by
Model II, which is compared in terms of order flow with the original policy,
Model I (Table 18.1).

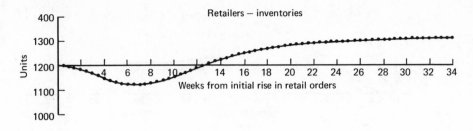

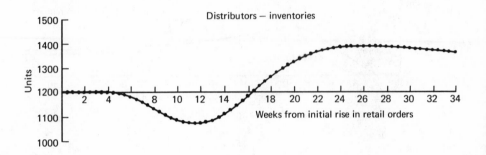

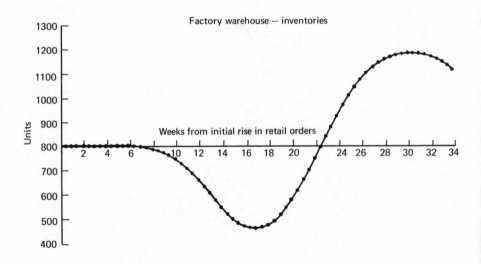

FIGURE **18.4**   Inventory changes at three stages of distribution in response to a 10%
rise in retail sales. From V. G. Lippitt, "Trade Inventories: Their
Influence on Manufacturer Sales," College of Business Administration, Univ. of Rochester, N.Y.

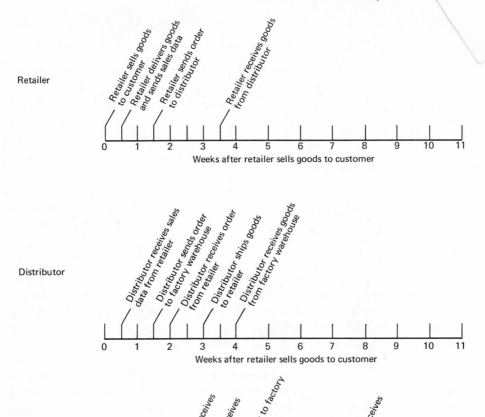

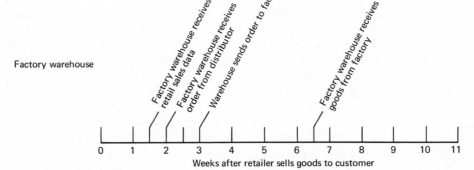

FIGURE **18.5**   Time sequence of events in distribution channels. From V. G. Lippitt, "Trade Inventories: Their Influence on Manufacturer Sales," College of Business Administration, Univ. of Rochester, N.Y.

Industrial Dynamics

Industrial dynamics is a formalized methodology and technique for modeling the information feedback characteristics of a complex business system. The concept and method were developed by Jay Forrester at M.I.T. The method is very sophisticated and involves the description of a dynamic system in terms of a set

TABLE **18.1** Comparison of fluctuations in orders and inventories for Models I and II.

	Orders sent			Inventories		
	Initial level	Peak level	% Rise	Initial level	Minimum level	% Decline
Retailers						
Model I	200	239	20	1,200	1,121	7
Model II	200	239	20	1,200	1,121	7
Distributors						
Model I	200	270	35	1,200	1,071	11
Model II	200	240	20	1,200	1,116	7
Factory warehouse						
Model I	200	325	62	800	465	42
Model II	200	243	22	800	650	19

of equations that express information and physical flows, as well as the interactions among the system variables. It is more than a theoretical approach to understanding system behavior, and its development included an early application to the business operations of an electrical equipment manufacturer.

Industrial dynamics can be applied to a wide variety of organizational situations, including production, distribution, research, and financial operations or combinations of these. The scope of the system to be studied is a matter of problem definition. Classically, the method was used to describe the interrelations among the elements of a factory-distribution system. The details of the method, especially as it was applied in the above context, are described by Jay Forrester.[2]

We will describe the basic features of the method using a deceptively simple example. This will be a retailer dealing in one product, which he receives from a distributor, inventories, and then sells to customers.

FLOW DIAGRAM: The first step is the construction of a flow diagram of the elements of the system, as shown in Figure 18.6. First, note that the system has been defined as a collection of elements under the domain of the retailer as distinct from those elements which would be included under the customer or distributor domains. It is important to understand that the system for study could include the latter two domains; however, we must limit our example.

The various symbols of the diagram will be explained as we progress. The variables of the system are a mixture of letters and numbers and represent either *rates*, *levels*, or *delays*.

To begin the flow, customer orders are received at a rate of *CDR* units per week. Orders are backlogged so that at any given point in time we will have a backlog level equal to the variable *BLL*. Note that levels are symbolized by a box

---

[2] Jay W. Forrester, *Industrial Dynamics*. Cambridge, Mass.: M.I.T. Press, 1961.

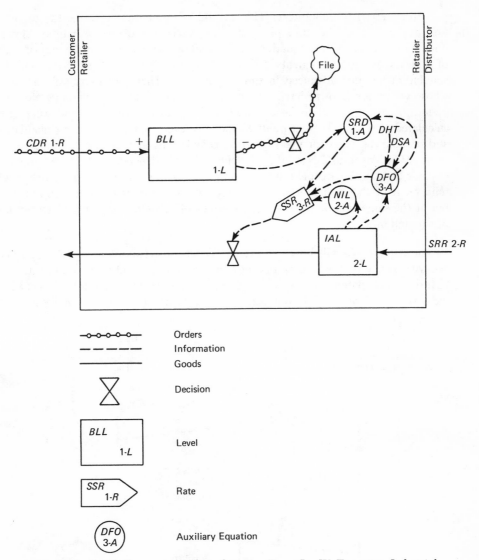

FIGURE **18.6**   Symbolic representation of system. From Jay W. Forrester, *Industrial Dynamics.* Cambridge, Mass.: M.I.T. Press, 1961.

with the variable in the upper left-hand corner, and the number of the equation by which the variable is calculated in the lower right-hand corner.

The other level is the actual inventory level, *IAL.* This level is determined by the rates at which shipments are both received *SRR* and sent *SSR.* The rates in the flow are either exogenous, such as *CDR,* or controlled by decision, such as *SSR.* The rate of shipments received *SRR* is obviously a controllable system variable that depends on the ordering policy of the retailer and the distribution system, which we are ignoring in this example.

SIMULATED TIME INCREMENT: The method of simulation involves the calculation of the changes that take place in rates, levels, and delays over time. This is done by using the system equations to calculate these variables at the end of each of a series of time increments *DT*. Referring to Figure 18.7, suppose that the simulation has just advanced in time to point *K*. There are two level variables whose values are known, having been calculated at *J*. The rate variables for the period *JK* are assumed to be constant during this time interval and were also calculated at time *J*. Then at point *K*, the new levels and new rates are calculated and become the basis for making future calculations at point *L*, one time increment *DT* in the future. Note that the choice of *DT* depends on both the amount of error that can be accepted in the assumption of rate linearity and the degree of refinement of the model. A small *DT* reduces the error if the rate is nonlinear, but at the same time it increases the amount of computation for a given period of simulation.

EQUATIONS: We will now express the system in terms of a set of equations. We will assume that we are at a point *K* in time and that all levels *J* and rates *JK* have been calculated. The equations represent the dynamic relationship between the system variables and in one sense are the heart of the approach. While our

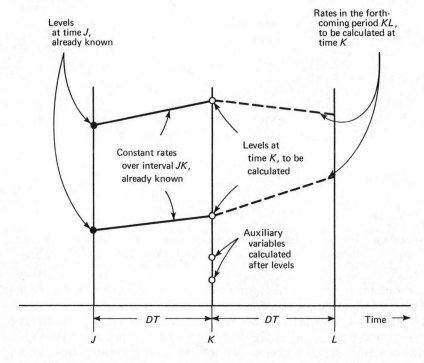

FIGURE **18.7**   Calculation of system variables at point *K*. From Jay W. Forrester, *Industrial Dynamics*. Cambridge, Mass.: M.I.T. Press, 1961.

equations are simple, a good deal of analysis can be involved in developing them. The first two equations determine the levels.

$$BLL.K = BLL.J + DT(CDR.JK - SSR.JK)$$ (1-L)

where

> $BLL.K$ = backlog level at time K (units)
> $BLL.J$ = backlog level at time J (units)
> $CDR.JK$ = customer demand rate during the interval of time from J to K, which equals DT (units/week)
> $SSR.JK$ = rate of shipments sent during the interval JK (units/week)

This says that the backlog level at time K will be equal to the level at J plus the number of units demanded by customers in time JK less the shipments made in time JK. Note that a dimensional check yields

$$\text{units} = \text{units} + \text{week} \left(\frac{\text{units}}{\text{week}} - \frac{\text{units}}{\text{week}} \right)$$

$$IAL.K = IAL.J + DT(SRR.JK - SSR.JK)$$ (2-L)

where

> $IAL.K$ = actual inventory level at time K (units)
> $IAL.J$ = actual inventory level at time J (units)
> $SRR.JK$ = shipments received rate during the interval JK (units/week)

We will now consider the rate equations.

$$CDR.KL = f(DT)$$ (1-R)

In this case, the customer demand rate CDR during the interval KL is simply noted as a function of DT. Since this is an exogenous variable, we will not concern ourselves with how this rate would be generated, except to note that a study of customer demand behavior would determine this function.

$$SRR.KL$$ (2-R)

Again, this rate would be determined by the ordering policy of the retailer and the way in which goods are delivered by the distributor. For our discussion, we will assume this to be part of a later expansion of the system study.

Now consider the rate of shipments sent, $SSR.KL$. Suppose we use the following equation:

$$SSR.KL = \frac{BLL.K}{DFO.K}$$

where $DFO.K$ = delay in filling orders. First, we note that the rate of shipments sent is not a function of other rates *during the time increment KL*. Changes in CDR, for example, will be felt *in the future* on BLL and indirectly on DFO. We will not try to justify this equation now, except to note that other relationships might be more appropriate.

The rate of shipments sent is constrained by the actual inventory level. That is,

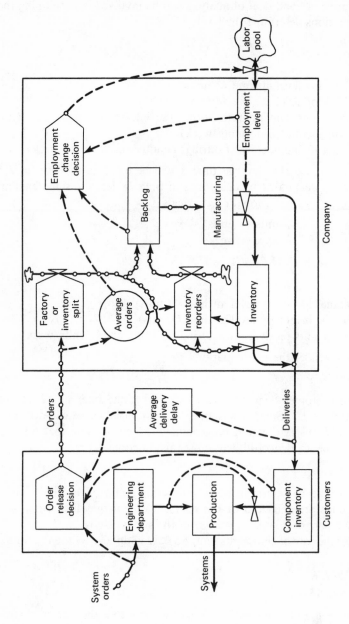

FIGURE 18.8   Company-customers system. From *Management Controls* by C. P. Bonini, R. K. Jaedicke, and H. M. Wagner. © 1964 by McGraw-Hill Book Company. Inc. Used by permission of McGraw-Hill Book Company.

it cannot exceed the limit IAL/DT. Therefore, two "auxiliary" equations are used to determine the limits on the rate of shipments sent.

$$SRD.K = \frac{BLL.K}{DFO.K} \tag{1-A}$$

where $SRD.K$ = desired shipment rate (units per week).

$$NIL.K = \frac{IAL.K}{DT} \tag{2-A}$$

where $NIL.K$ = negative inventory level at time K (units per week). Then,

$$SSR.KL = \begin{cases} SRD.K & \text{if } NIL.K \geq SRD.K \\ NIL.K & \text{if } NIL.K < SRD.K \end{cases} \tag{3-R}$$

Now we must consider the delay variable in filling orders, DFO. This delay consists of two components, namely, a constant time necessary to process the order and a time delay due to incurring a shortage condition. This later component is a function of the actual inventory level. Suppose we use the following:

$$DFO.K = \begin{cases} DHT + DSA & \text{if } IAL.K = 0 \\ DHT + \dfrac{DSA}{IAL.K} & \text{if } IAL.K > 0 \end{cases} \tag{3-A}$$

where

DHT = constant time to process an order (weeks)
DSA = constant delay time due to shortage (weeks)

At time K, these equations are solved in a certain order to determine the value of each variable, which, in turn, becomes the basis for calculations to be made at point L. The particular order in which the equations are solved is:

(1-L)	$BLL.K$
(2-L)	$IAL.K$
(1-R)	$CDR.KL$
(3-A)	$DFO.K$
(1-A)	$SRD.K$
(2-A)	$NIL.K$
(3-R)	$SSR.KL$

ENLARGING THE SYSTEM: The system may be enlarged to include further details at the retail level, such as smoothing incoming customer orders as a basis for formulating a desired inventory level or adding a purchasing decision for placing orders to the distributor. It can then be enlarged by adding to the system study the domain of the distributor and the factory. Furthermore, such flow variables as cash, people, and projects may be added.

Figure 18.8 shows an aggregate flow diagram for a consumer-producer system representing an industrial components manufacturer. Figure 18.9 shows the progressive improvement in certain system variables for this company. Through the use of industrial dynamics, in which the consumer sector was combined with the company sector, a significant reduction in manpower deviations and backlogs was

Men, Orders, Inventory (percent)
Backlog (percent)

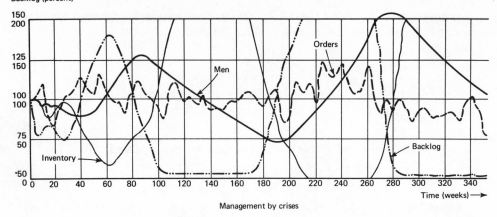

Management by crises

Men, Orders, Inventory (percent)
Backlog (percent)

Effects of management control systems

Men, Orders, Inventory (percent)
Backlog (percent)

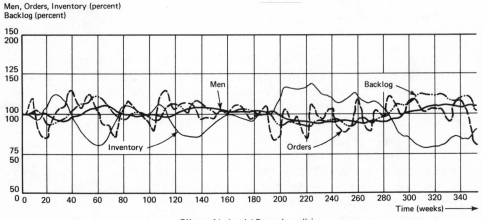

Effects of Industrial Dynamics policies

achieved. This was made possible by an understanding of the influence of factory lead time on the customer's ordering habits.

Industrial dynamics is a method for analyzing and understanding the behavior of complex systems. The knowledge gained can be used to improve system performance through changes in organization, decision rules, and system parameters. It is not, however, equivalent to an on-line computerized system for the continuous control of an existing and operating distribution organization.

CONTINUOUS CONTROL SYSTEM

The development of a continuous control device for a multiplant warehouse situation is a formidable task requiring a good deal of preliminary research. For example, imagine a large food processing company that produces several hundred food varieties in a dozen factories that ship to 50 nationally distributed warehouses. We wish to design a control system that will provide answers to the kinds of questions raised on page 614. Obviously the complexity of the situation precludes our drawing specific conclusions about how such a control system would work. We might, however, envision its basic structure along the following lines, which are summarized in Figure 18.10.[3]

1. *Allocation of factory output to warehouses*   For each kind of product, it must be decided which factory is to service a given warehouse. Each year, in advance of the fiscal period, allocations are made based on the use of a linear transportation programming model in which transportation costs are minimized. The aggregation of the results over all products is analyzed and adjusted, if necessary, to account for constraints on individual factory capacities.

This activity is supported by research in which location, capacity, and transportation factors are analyzed through the use of a computer simulator. Existing and new locations for facilities are examined in the light of trends in consumer demand. Studies are conducted on the routing and scheduling of truck fleets and on alternative modes of transportation. A continued analysis of costs is made to maintain a base of cost information and other data.

2. *Factory aggregate planning*   At the start of each fiscal year, each factory submits to a central control organization an aggregate production plan. This plan balances mainly the costs of deviations in employment levels and inventory. An annual forecast of warehouse requirements is made, based upon historical sales data, promotional schemes, market development, and other factors. A simple trial-and-error approach is used to determine the behavior of employment and

---

[3] The details of such a system are described in Paul A. Strassmann, "A Plant-Warehouse System with Variable Lead Times and Variable Re-order Levels," *Management Technology*, June 1962.

FIGURE **18.9**   Progressive improvements in control. From *Management Controls* by C. P. Bonini, R. K. Jaedicke, and H. M. Wagner. © 1964 by McGraw-Hill, Inc. Used by permission of McGraw-Hill Book Company.

inventory costs as a function of the deviation of production from a purely leveled form.

3. *Amended quarterly production plan* At the end of each quarter, an amended production plan for the next quarter is submitted, taking into consideration the

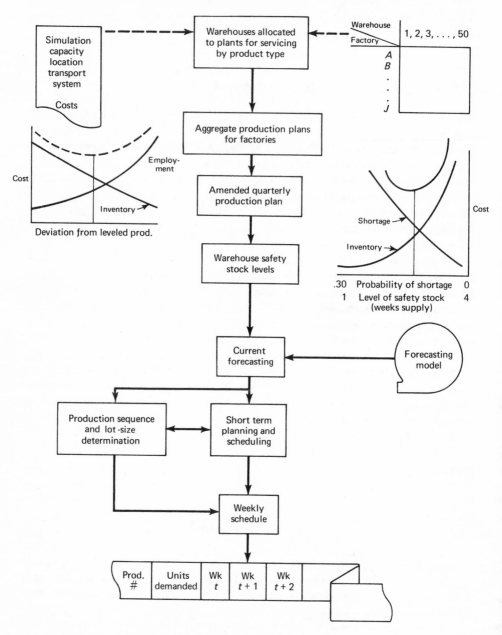

FIGURE **18.10** Continuous control system.

experience of the past quarter as well as more up-to-date forecasting information.

4. *Safety stock levels for warehouses* Safety stock levels for each product in each warehouse are established. Factory replenishment lead times are carefully analyzed along with lead time demand distributions based on forecasting error information. Shortages are measured as the multiplication of the number of units short times the number of days of shortage. A decision model attempts to balance the costs of safety stock versus the costs of alleviating an out-of-stock condition. The latter cost includes such elements as the cost of trans-shipments between warehouses, disruption of optimal production schedules, less-than-carload shipments, etc.

5. *Short-term planning and scheduling* Each week, for a given plant, a computer program forecasts the projected demand on each served warehouse for a given product. The projected demand, for eight weeks in the future, is cumulated by week and compared with current warehouse stocks and with desired safety stock levels. Production of the product is scheduled for the week in this future period when it appears that replenishment is necessary considering shipment lead times. Conditions demanding the expedition of a replenishment order are signaled when it appears that an out-of-stock condition is highly probable.

The results of forecasting are used to determine economical product sequencing on jointly used facilities and the determination of production lot sizes commensurate with the projected schedule.

For a given week in the eight-week period, the anticipated production schedules for all products are aggregated to indicate the short-term manpower and facility requirements. Similarly, gross product requirements are exploded to determine raw material needs and procurement planning. If projected demands are less than capacity, as predetermined in the quarterly plans, then surplus capacity is used to build inventories up to the predetermined planned maximum levels.

6. *Weekly production schedule* At the end of each week, a detailed production schedule is set forth for the coming week. This takes into consideration the warehouse requirements, the additions to inventories in slack periods, and the economics of product sequencing and lot sizes.

Bibliography

LIPPITT, VERNON G., "Moderating Swings in Manufacturing Sales," *Marketing Times*, General Electric Co., April 1960.

MAGEE, JOHN F., *Physical Distribution Systems*. New York: McGraw-Hill Book Co., 1967.

MC GARRAH, ROBERT E., *Production and Logistics Management*. New York: John Wiley & Sons, 1963.

ROBERTS, EDWARD B., "Industrial Dynamics and the Design of Management Control Systems," in *Management Controls*, Charles P. Bonini, Robert K. Jaedicke, and Harvey M. Wagner, Eds. New York: McGraw-Hill Book Co., 1964, ch. 6.

STRASSMANN, PAUL A., "A Plant-Warehouse System with Variable Lead Times and Variable Re-order Levels," *Management Technology*, June 1962.

Appendix

Appendix

PROBABILITY DISTRIBUTIONS

Discrete Distributions

Given a random variable X, the set of all possible mutually exclusive values of X is called the probability set of X. The probability of X is designated in a general sense as $f(x)$ or usually $P(X = x) = P(x)$ for the discrete random variable. The listing of the probability set, $X = \{x_i; i = 1, 2, \ldots\}$, together with the probability of each element of the set, is called the probability distribution of X. The cumulative probability distribution (or distribution function) of the random variable X is of the form $P(X \leq r) = \sum_{x=0}^{x=r} P(x)$.

BERNOULLI TRIAL: A basic discrete distribution is the Bernoulli Trial, in which the random variable assumes either the value 1 with probability p or the value 0 with probability q, and $p + q = 1$. The probability distribution is

X	1	0
$P(x)$	p	q

The mean or expected value of this distribution is $E(X) = p$, and the variance is $V(X) = pq$.

BINOMIAL DISTRIBUTION: Assume that we have a sample of n observations of a random variable, which is distributed as a Bernoulli trial. Let r be the number of observations yielding the value 1. Then r is binomially distributed:

$$P(r; n, p) = \frac{n!}{r!(n - r)!} p^r q^{n-r}$$
$$E(r) = np$$
$$V(r) = npq$$

POISSON DISTRIBUTION: The Poisson distribution is the limit of the binomial distribution as p approaches zero. Letting $\mu = np$, then

$$P(r; \mu) = \frac{\mu^r e^{-\mu}}{r!}$$

Table B in the Appendix is the Poisson distribution function for values of μ ranging from 0.02 to 10.0. For values of μ greater than 10, the Poisson distribution can be approximated by the normal distribution with mean and variance equal to μ.

HYPERGEOMETRIC DISTRIBUTION: Assume we have a population of N items, of which M items have the value 1 and $N - M$ have the value 0. A sample of n items is randomly selected from this population without replacement. The probability distribution of r, the number of sampled items having the value 1, is hypergeometric:

$$P(r; N, M, n) = \frac{\binom{M}{r}\binom{N - M}{n - r}}{\binom{N}{n}}$$

$$E(r) = \frac{(n)(M)}{N}$$

$$V(r) = \frac{N - n}{N - 1} \times n \times \frac{M}{N} \times \frac{N - M}{N}$$

Continuous Distributions

A random variable X, which is a continuous variable, has a probability function designated as $f(x)$. The distribution function is continuous and of the form

$$F(X \leq r) = F(x) = \int_{x=0}^{x=r} f(x) \, dx.$$

STANDARD NORMAL DISTRIBUTION: Let Z be a random variable whose possible range of values is $-\infty$ to $+\infty$. Z is called a *standard normal deviate* if the probability that $Z \leq z$ is

$$F(z) = \int_{-\infty}^{z} \frac{1}{\sqrt{2\pi}} e^{-Z^2/2}$$

$$E(Z) = 0.0$$
$$V(Z) = 1.00$$

The distribution function for Z is tabulated in Table A. A normally distributed random variable X may be converted into a standard normal deviate by the function

$$Z = \frac{X - E(X)}{\sqrt{V(X)}}$$

UNIFORM DISTRIBUTION: A random variable X is *uniformly distributed* if the function $f(x)$ is constant over a given range of X and zero otherwise. If $a \leq x \leq b$, then

$$f(x) = \frac{1}{b - a}$$

$$E(X) = \frac{a + b}{2}$$

$$V(X) = \frac{(b - a)^2}{12}$$

EXPONENTIAL DISTRIBUTION: A random variable X is exponentially distributed if, for $x \geq 0$, $f(x) = ke^{-kx}$. The mean and variance are $1/k$ and $(1/k)^2$. The distribution function is $F(x) = 1 - e^{-kx}$.

SINGLE-CHANNEL QUEUE

Consider a single-channel queue with Poisson arrivals with mean rate (λ) and exponential service time with mean $\left(\frac{1}{\mu}\right)$. We wish to derive the steady-state probability distribution of the random variable n, the number of customers in the system, where $n > 0$. Suppose we examine a small increment of time $t + \Delta t$. The system can be in state n if any one of the following four mutually exclusive possibilities takes place:

Possibility	Probability

I

1. The system was in state n at time t, *and* $\quad P(n)$
2. No arrivals take place during the interval Δt, *and* $\quad 1 - \lambda \Delta t$
3. No customers are serviced during the interval Δt. $\quad 1 - \mu \Delta t$

The probability of I is the joint probability of the three events $=$ $P(n)(1 - \lambda \Delta t)(1 - \mu \Delta t)$

II

1. The system was in state $(n + 1)$ at time t, *and* $\quad P(n + 1)$
2. One customer is serviced during the interval Δt, *and* $\quad \mu \Delta t$
3. No arrivals take place during Δt. $\quad 1 - \lambda \Delta t$

Joint probability $= P(n + 1)\mu \Delta t (1 - \lambda \Delta t)$

III

1. The system was in state $(n - 1)$ at time t, *and* $\quad P(n - 1)$
2. One arrival takes place in the interval Δt, *and* $\quad \lambda \Delta t$
3. No customers are serviced during Δt. $\quad 1 - \mu \Delta t$

Joint probability $= P(n - 1)\lambda \Delta t (1 - \mu \Delta t)$

IV

1. The system was in state n at time t, *and* $\quad P(n)$
2. One arrival takes place in the interval Δt, *and* $\quad \lambda \Delta t$
3. One customer is serviced during Δt. $\quad \mu \Delta t$

Joint probability $= P(n)\lambda \Delta t \mu \Delta t$

Since the four possibilities are exhaustive and mutually exclusive, the probability of n customers in the system during the interval $t + \Delta t$ is the sum of the four compound probabilities:

$$P(n) = P(n)(1 - \lambda \Delta t)(1 - \mu \Delta t) + P(n + 1)\mu \Delta t(1 - \lambda \Delta t)$$
$$+ P(n - 1)\lambda \Delta t(1 - \mu \Delta t) + P(n)\lambda \Delta t\mu \Delta t \qquad (1)$$

This reduces to

$$P(n) = P(n)[1 - \lambda \Delta t - \mu \Delta t] + P(n + 1)\mu \Delta t$$
$$+ P(n - 1)\lambda \Delta t + \sum f(\Delta t^2) \qquad (2)$$

The last term on the right-hand side of Equation (2) are higher order terms in Δt that are assumed to be negligible compared to those in Δt.

Dividing Equation (2) by Δt and reducing, we have

$$0 = P(n + 1)\mu + P(n - 1)\lambda - P(n)(\lambda + \mu); n \geq 1 \qquad (3)$$

Now we must consider the special case $n = 0$. The probability that there will be no customers in the system at the time $t + \Delta t$ is the sum of two compounded probabilities:

I. Probability of 0 customers in the system at time t and 0 arrivals during Δt $[P(0)(1 - \lambda \Delta t)]$.

II. Probability of 1 customer in the system at time t and 1 customer being serviced and 0 arrivals in Δt $[P(1)\mu \Delta t(1 - \lambda \Delta t)]$.

Therefore,

$$P(0) = P(0) - P(0)\lambda \Delta t + P(1)\mu \Delta t - P(1)\mu\lambda \Delta t^2$$

Dividing by Δt and neglecting the higher order term, we have

$$0 = -\lambda P(0) + \mu P(1). \qquad (4)$$

Equations (3) and (4) are difference equations and can be solved for $P(0)$, $P(1)$, $\ldots$, $P(n)$ by successive substitution and by utilizing $\sum_{0}^{\infty} P(n) = 1$. Thus,

$$P(0) = P(0)$$

$$P(1) = \left(\frac{\lambda}{\mu}\right) P(0) \quad \text{from Equation (4)}$$

$$P(2) = \left(\frac{\lambda}{\mu}\right)^2 P(0) \quad \text{by letting } n = 1 \text{ in Equation (3) and substituting } \left(\frac{\lambda}{\mu}\right) P(0)$$
$$\text{for } P(1)$$

Then,

$$P(n) = \left(\frac{\lambda}{\mu}\right)^n P(0)$$

or

$$\sum_{0}^{\infty} P(n) = P(0) \sum_{0}^{\infty} \left(\frac{\lambda}{\mu}\right)^n$$

But,

$$\sum_{0}^{\infty} P(n) = 1 \quad \text{and} \quad \sum_{0}^{\infty} \left(\frac{\lambda}{\mu}\right)^n = \frac{1}{1 - \lambda/\mu}$$

from the sum of an infinite geometric series

Therefore, we obtain

$$1 = P(0) \frac{1}{1 - \lambda/\mu}$$

and

$$P(0) = 1 - (\lambda/\mu)$$

Figure A.1 shows the distribution $P(n)$, which is a geometric series. The mean is

$$\bar{n} = \sum_{0}^{\infty} nP(n) = \frac{\lambda/\mu}{1 - \lambda/\mu}$$

Since the server is idle when no customers are in the system, the percent idle time for the server is $p = P(0) = (1 - \rho)$.

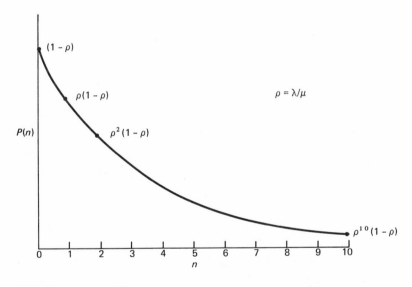

FIGURE A.1   Distribution of number of customers in queue system.

Tables

TABLE **A** Normal curve areas.

Area under the standard normal curve from 0 to z, shown shaded, is A(z).

Examples. If Z is the standard normal random variable and $z = 1.54$, then

$$A(z) = P(0 < Z < z) = .4382,$$
$$P(Z > z) = .0618$$
$$P(Z < z) = .9382,$$
$$P(|Z| < z) = .8764$$

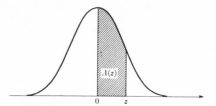

z	.00	.01	.02	.03	.04	.05	.06	.07	.08	.09
0.0	.0000	.0040	.0080	.0120	.0160	.0199	.0239	.0279	.0319	.0359
0.1	.0398	.0438	.0478	.0517	.0557	.0596	.0636	.0675	.0714	.0753
0.2	.0793	.0832	.0871	.0910	.0948	.0987	.1026	.1064	.1103	.1141
0.3	.1179	.1217	.1255	.1293	.1331	.1368	.1406	.1443	.1480	.1517
0.4	.1554	.1591	.1628	.1664	.1700	.1736	.1772	.1808	.1844	.1879
0.5	.1915	.1950	.1985	.2019	.2054	.2088	.2123	.2157	.2190	.2224
0.6	.2257	.2291	.2324	.2357	.2389	.2422	.2454	.2486	.2517	.2549
0.7	.2580	.2611	.2642	.2673	.2704	.2734	.2764	.2794	.2823	.2852
0.8	.2881	.2910	.2939	.2967	.2995	.3023	.3051	.3078	.3106	.3133
0.9	.3159	.3186	.3212	.3238	.3264	.3289	.3315	.3340	.3365	.3389
1.0	.3413	.3438	.3461	.3485	.3508	.3531	.3554	.3577	.3599	.3621
1.1	.3643	.3665	.3686	.3708	.3729	.3749	.3770	.3790	.3810	.3830
1.2	.3849	.3869	.3888	.3907	.3925	.3944	.3962	.3980	.3997	.4015
1.3	.4032	.4049	.4066	.4082	.4099	.4115	.4131	.4147	.4162	.4177
1.4	.4192	.4207	.4222	.4236	.4251	.4265	.4279	.4292	4306	.4319
1.5	.4332	.4345	.4357	.4370	.4382	.4394	.4406	.4418	.4429	.4441
1.6	.4452	.4463	.4474	.4484	.4495	.4505	.4515	.4525	.4535	.4545
1.7	.4554	.4564	.4573	.4582	.4591	.4599	.4608	.4616	.4625	.4633
1.8	.4641	.4649	.4656	.4664	.4671	.4678	.4686	.4693	.4699	.4706
1.9	.4713	.4719	.4726	.4732	.4738	.4744	.4750	.4756	.4761	.4767
2.0	.4772	.4778	.4783	.4788	.4793	.4798	.4803	.4808	.4812	.4817
2.1	.4821	.4826	.4830	.4834	.4838	.4842	.4846	.4850	.4854	.4857
2.2	.4861	.4864	.4868	.4871	.4875	.4878	.4881	.4884	.4887	.4890
2.3	.4893	.4896	.4898	.4901	.4904	.4906	.4909	.4911	.4913	.4916
2.4	.4918	.4920	.4922	.4925	.4927	.4929	.4931	.4932	.4934	.4936
2.5	.4938	.4940	.4941	.4943	.4945	.4946	.4948	.4949	.4951	.4952
2.6	.4953	.4955	.4956	.4957	.4959	.4960	.4961	.4962	.4963	.4964
2.7	.4965	.4966	.4967	.4968	.4969	.4970	.4971	.4972	.4973	.4974
2.8	.4974	.4975	.4976	.4977	.4977	.4978	.4979	.4979	.4980	.4981
2.9	.4981	.4982	.4982	.4983	.4984	.4984	.4985	.4985	.4986	.4986
3.0	.4987	.4987	.4987	.4988	.4988	.4989	.4989	.4989	.4990	.4990

From Frederick Mosteller, Robert E. K. Rourke, and George B. Thomas, Jr., *Probability and Statistics*. Reading, Mass.: Addison-Wesley, 1961.

TABLE **B**   Summation of terms of the Poisson Formula:

$$1{,}000 \times P(r \le c; \mu) = 1{,}000 \sum_{r=0}^{r=c} \frac{u^r e^{-\mu}}{r!}$$

$1{,}000 \times$ probability of c or less occurrences of event that has average number of occurrences equal to c' or np'

c μ or np'	0	1	2	3	4	5	6	7	8	9
0.02	980	1,000								
0.04	961	999	1,000							
0.06	942	998	1,000							
0.08	923	997	1,000							
0.10	905	995	1,000							
0.15	861	990	999	1,000						
0.20	819	982	999	1,000						
0.25	779	974	998	1,000						
0.30	741	963	996	1,000						
0:35	705	951	994	1,000						
0.40	670	938	992	999	1,000					
0.45	638	925	989	999	1,000					
0.50	607	910	986	998	1,000					
0.55	577	894	982	998	1,000					
0.60	549	878	977	997	1,000					
0.65	522	861	972	996	999	1,000				
0.70	497	844	966	994	999	1,000				
0.75	472	827	959	993	999	1,000				
0.80	449	809	953	991	999	1,000				
0.85	427	791	945	989	998	1,000				
0.90	407	772	937	987	998	1,000				
0.95	387	754	929	984	997	1,000				
1.00	368	736	920	981	996	999	1,000			
1.1	333	699	900	974	995	999	1,000			
1.2	301	663	879	966	992	998	1,000			
1.3	273	627	857	957	989	998	1,000			
1.4	247	592	833	946	986	997	999	1,000		
1.5	223	558	809	934	981	996	999	1,000		
1.6	202	525	783	921	976	994	999	1,000		
1.7	183	493	757	907	970	992	998	1,000		
1.8	165	463	731	891	964	990	997	999	1,000	
1.9	150	434	704	875	956	987	997	999	1,000	
2.0	135	406	677	857	947	983	995	999	1,000	

From *Statistical Quality Control* by E. L. Grant. Copyright, 1964, by McGraw-Hill, Inc. Used by permission of McGraw-Hill Book Co.

(Continued)

μ or np' \ c	0	1	2	3	4	5	6	7	8	9
2.2	111	355	623	819	928	975	993	998	1,000	
2.4	091	308	570	779	904	964	988	997	999	1,000
2.6	074	267	518	736	877	951	983	995	999	1,000
2.8	061	231	469	692	848	935	976	992	998	999
3.0	050	199	423	647	815	916	966	988	996	999
3.2	041	171	380	603	781	895	955	983	994	998
3.4	033	147	340	558	744	871	942	977	992	997
3.6	027	126	303	515	706	844	927	969	988	996
3.8	022	107	269	473	668	816	909	960	984	994
4.0	018	092	238	433	629	785	889	949	979	992
4.2	015	078	210	395	590	753	867	936	972	989
4.4	012	066	185	359	551	720	844	921	964	985
4.6	010	056	163	326	513	686	818	905	955	980
4.8	008	048	143	294	476	651	791	887	944	975
5.0	007	040	125	265	440	616	762	867	932	968
5.2	006	034	109	238	406	581	732	845	918	960
5.4	005	029	095	213	373	546	702	822	903	951
5.6	004	024	082	191	342	512	670	797	886	941
5.8	003	021	072	170	313	478	638	771	867	929
6.0	002	017	062	151	285	446	606	744	847	916

	10	11	12	13	14	15	16
2.8	1,000						
3.0	1,000						
3.2	1,000						
3.4	999	1,000					
3.6	999	1,000					
3.8	998	999	1,000				
4.0	997	999	1,000				
4.2	996	999	1,000				
4.4	994	998	999	1,000			
4.6	992	997	999	1,000			
4.8	990	996	999	1,000			
5.0	986	995	998	999	1,000		
5.2	982	993	997	999	1,000		
5.4	977	990	996	999	1,000		
5.6	972	988	995	998	999	1,000	
5.8	965	984	993	997	999	1,000	
6.0	957	980	991	996	999	999	1,000

(Continued)

μ or np' \ c	0	1	2	3	4	5	6	7	8	9
6.2	002	015	054	134	259	414	574	716	826	902
6.4	002	012	046	119	235	384	542	687	803	886
6.6	001	010	040	105	213	355	511	658	780	869
6.8	001	009	034	093	192	327	480	628	755	850
7.0	001	007	030	082	173	301	450	599	729	830
7.2	001	006	025	072	156	276	420	569	703	810
7.4	001	005	022	063	140	253	392	539	676	788
7.6	001	004	019	055	125	231	365	510	648	765
7.8	000	004	016	048	112	210	338	481	620	741
8.0	000	003	014	042	100	191	313	453	593	717
8.5	000	002	009	030	074	150	256	386	523	653
9.0	000	001	006	021	055	116	207	324	456	587
9.5	000	001	004	015	040	089	165	269	392	522
10.0	000	000	003	010	029	067	130	220	333	458

	10	11	12	13	14	15	16	17	18	19
6.2	949	975	989	995	998	999	1,000			
6.4	939	969	986	994	997	999	1,000			
6.6	927	963	982	992	997	999	999	1,000		
6.8	915	955	978	990	996	998	999	1,000		
7.0	901	947	973	987	994	998	999	1,000		
7.2	887	937	967	984	993	997	999	999	1,000	
7.4	871	926	961	980	991	996	998	999	1,000	
7.6	854	915	954	976	989	995	998	999	1,000	
7.8	835	902	945	971	986	993	997	999	1,000	
8.0	816	888	936	966	983	992	996	998	999	1,000
8.5	763	849	909	949	973	986	993	997	999	999
9.0	706	803	876	926	959	978	989	995	998	999
9.5	645	752	836	898	940	967	982	991	996	998
10.0	583	697	792	864	917	951	973	986	993	997

	20	21	22
8.5	1,000		
9.0	1,000		
9.5	999	1,000	
10.0	998	999	1,000

TABLE **C**   Random digits.

00000	10097	32533	76520	13586	34673	54876	80959	09117	39292	74945
00001	37542	04805	64894	74296	24805	24037	20636	10402	00822	91665
00002	08422	68953	19645	09303	23209	02560	15953	34764	35080	33606
00003	99019	02529	09376	70715	38311	31165	88676	74397	04436	27659
00004	12807	99970	80157	36147	64032	36653	98951	16877	12171	76833
00005	66065	74717	34072	76850	36697	36170	65813	39885	11199	29170
00006	31060	10805	45571	82406	35303	42614	86799	07439	23403	09732
00007	85269	77602	02051	65692	68665	74818	73053	85247	18623	88579
00008	63573	32135	05325	47048	90553	57548	28468	28709	83491	25624
00009	73796	45753	03529	64778	35808	34282	60935	20344	35273	88435
00010	98520	17767	14905	68607	22109	40558	60970	93433	50500	73998
00011	11805	05431	39808	27732	50725	68248	29405	24201	52775	67851
00012	83452	99634	06288	98083	13746	70078	18475	40610	68711	77817
00013	88685	40200	86507	58401	36766	67951	90364	76493	29609	11062
00014	99594	67348	87517	64969	91826	08928	93785	61368	23478	34113
00015	65481	17674	17468	50950	58047	76974	73039	57186	40218	16544
00016	80124	35635	17727	08015	45318	22374	21115	78253	14385	53763
00017	74350	99817	77402	77214	43236	00210	45521	64237	96286	02655
00018	69916	26803	66252	29148	36936	87203	76621	13990	94400	56418
00019	09893	20505	14225	68514	46427	56788	96297	78822	54382	14598
00020	91499	14523	68479	27686	46162	83554	94750	89923	37089	20048
00021	80336	94598	26940	36858	70297	34135	53140	33340	42050	82341
00022	44104	81949	85157	47954	32979	26575	57600	40881	22222	06413
00023	12550	73742	11100	02040	12860	74697	96644	89439	28707	25815
00024	63606	49329	16505	34484	40219	52563	43651	77082	07207	31790
00025	61196	90446	26457	47774	51924	33729	65394	59593	42582	60527
00026	15474	45266	95270	79953	59367	83848	82396	10118	33211	59466
00027	94557	28573	67897	54387	54622	44431	91190	42592	92927	45973
00028	42481	16213	97344	08721	16868	48767	03071	12059	25701	46670
00029	23523	78317	73208	89837	68935	91416	26252	29663	05522	82562
00030	04493	52494	75246	33824	45862	51025	61962	79335	65337	12472
00031	00549	97654	64051	88159	96119	63896	54692	82391	23287	29529
00032	35963	15307	26898	09354	33351	35462	77974	50024	90103	39333
00033	59808	08391	45427	26842	83609	49700	13021	24892	78565	20106
00034	46058	85236	01390	92286	77281	44077	93910	83647	70617	42941
00035	32179	00597	87379	25241	05567	07007	86743	17157	85394	11838
00036	69234	61406	20117	45204	15956	60000	18743	92423	97118	96338
00037	19565	41430	01758	75379	40419	21585	66674	36806	84962	85207
00038	45155	14938	19476	07246	43667	94543	59047	90033	20826	69541
00039	94864	31994	36168	10851	34888	81553	01540	35456	05014	51176
00040	98086	24826	45240	28404	44999	08896	39094	73407	35441	31880
00041	33185	16232	41941	50949	89435	48581	88695	41994	37548	73043
00042	80951	00406	96382	70774	20151	23387	25016	25298	94624	61171
00043	79752	49140	71961	28296	69861	02591	74852	20539	00387	59579
00044	18633	32537	98145	06571	31010	24674	05455	61427	77938	91936
00045	74029	43902	77557	32270	97790	17119	52527	58021	80814	51748
00046	54178	45611	80993	37143	05335	12969	56127	19255	36040	90324
00047	11664	49883	52079	84827	59381	71539	09973	33440	88461	23356
00048	48324	77928	31249	64710	02295	36870	32307	57546	15020	09994
00049	69074	94138	87637	91976	35584	04401	10518	21615	01848	76938

Reprinted by permission of the RAND Corporation, "A Million Random Digits With 100,000 Normal Deviates." Copyright 1955, The Free Press, Glencoe, Ill.

TABLE **D**   8% Compound interest factors.

	SINGLE PAYMENT		UNIFORM ANNUAL SERIES				
	Compound Amount Factor	Present Worth Factor	Sinking Fund Factor	Capital Recovery Factor	Compound Amount Factor	Present Worth Factor	
n	Given P To find S $(1+i)^n$	Given S To find P $\dfrac{1}{(1+i)^n}$	Given S To find R $\dfrac{i}{(1+i)^n-1}$	Given P To find R $\dfrac{i(1+i)^n}{(1+i)^n-1}$	Given R To find S $\dfrac{(1+i)^n-1}{i}$	Given R To find P $\dfrac{(1+i)^n-1}{i(1+i)^n}$	n
1	1.080	0.9259	1.00000	1.08000	1.000	0.926	1
2	1.166	0.8573	0.48077	0.56077	2.080	1.783	2
3	1.260	0.7938	0.30803	0.38803	3.246	2.577	3
4	1.360	0.7350	0.22192	0.30192	4.506	3.312	4
5	1.469	0.6806	0.17046	0.25046	5.867	3.993	5
6	1.587	0.6302	0.13632	0.21632	7.336	4.623	6
7	1.714	0.5835	0.11207	0.19207	8.923	5.206	7
8	1.851	0.5403	0.09401	0.17401	10.637	5.747	8
9	1.999	0.5002	0.08008	0.16008	12.488	6.247	9
10	2.159	0.4632	0.06903	0.14903	14.487	6.710	10
11	2.332	0.4289	0.06008	0.14008	16.645	7.139	11
12	2.518	0.3971	0.05270	0.13270	18.977	7.536	12
13	2.720	0.3677	0.04652	0.12652	21.495	7.904	13
14	2.937	0.3405	0.04130	0.12130	24.215	8.244	14
15	3.172	0.3152	0.03683	0.11683	27.152	8.559	15
16	3.426	0.2919	0.03298	0.11298	30.324	8.851	16
17	3.700	0.2703	0.02963	0.10963	33.750	9.122	17
18	3.996	0.2502	0.02670	0.10670	37.450	9.372	18
19	4.316	0.2317	0.02413	0.10413	41.446	9.604	19
20	4.661	0.2145	0.02185	0.10185	45.762	9.818	20
21	5.034	0.1987	0.01983	0.09983	50.423	10.017	21
22	5.437	0.1839	0.01803	0.09803	55.457	10.201	22
23	5.871	0.1703	0.01642	0.09642	60.893	10.371	23
24	6.341	0.1577	0.01498	0.09498	66.765	10.529	24
25	6.848	0.1460	0.01368	0.09368	73.106	10.675	25
26	7.396	0.1352	0.01251	0.09251	79.954	10.810	26
27	7.988	0.1252	0.01145	0.09145	87.351	10.935	27
28	8.627	0.1159	0.01049	0.09049	95.339	11.051	28
29	9.317	0.1073	0.00962	0.08962	103.966	11.158	29
30	10.063	0.0994	0.00883	0.08883	113.283	11.258	30
31	10.868	0.0920	0.00811	0.08811	123.346	11.350	31
32	11.737	0.0852	0.00745	0.08745	134.214	11.435	32
33	12.676	0.0789	0.00685	0.08685	145.951	11.514	33
34	13.690	0.0730	0.00630	0.08630	158.627	11.587	34
35	14.785	0.0676	0.00580	0.08580	172.317	11.655	35
40	21.725	0.0460	0.00386	0.08386	259.057	11.925	40
45	31.920	0.0313	0.00259	0.08259	386.506	12.108	45
50	46.902	0.0213	0.00174	0.08174	573.770	12.233	50
55	68.914	0.0145	0.00118	0.08118	848.923	12.319	55
60	101.257	0.0099	0.00080	0.08080	1253.213	12.377	60
65	148.780	0.0067	0.00054	0.08054	1847.248	12.416	65
70	218.606	0.0046	0.00037	0.08037	2720.080	12.443	70
75	321.205	0.0031	0.00025	0.08025	4002.557	12.461	75
80	471.955	0.0021	0.00017	0.08017	5886.935	12.474	80
85	693.456	0.0014	0.00012	0.08012	8655.706	12.482	85
90	1018.915	0.0010	0.00008	0.08008	12723.939	12.488	90
95	1497.121	0.0007	0.00005	0.08005	18701.507	12.492	95
100	2199.761	0.0005	0.00004	0.08004	27484.516	12.494	100

Taken from Eugene L. Grant, *Principles of Engineering Economy*, 3rd ed. Copyright 1950, The Ronald Press Company, New York.

TABLE **E** 10% Compound interest factors.

	SINGLE PAYMENT		UNIFORM ANNUAL SERIES				
n	Compound Amount Factor	Present Worth Factor	Sinking Fund Factor	Capital Recovery Factor	Compound Amount Factor	Present Worth Factor	*n*
	Given P To find S $(1+i)^n$	Given S To find P $\dfrac{1}{(1+i)^n}$	Given S To find R $\dfrac{i}{(1+i)^n-1}$	Given P To find R $\dfrac{i(1+i)^n}{(1+i)^n-1}$	Given R To find S $\dfrac{(1+i)^n-1}{i}$	Given R To find P $\dfrac{(1+i)^n-1}{i(1+i)^n}$	
1	1.100	0.9091	1.00000	1.10000	1.000	0.909	1
2	1.210	0.8264	0.47619	0.57619	2.100	1.736	2
3	1.331	0.7513	0.30211	0.40211	3.310	2.487	3
4	1.464	0.6830	0.21547	0.31547	4.641	3.170	4
5	1.611	0.6209	0.16380	0.26380	6.105	3.791	5
6	1.772	0.5645	0.12961	0.22961	7.716	4.355	6
7	1.949	0.5132	0.10541	0.20541	9.487	4.868	7
8	2.144	0.4665	0.08744	0.18744	11.436	5.335	8
9	2.358	0.4241	0.07364	0.17364	13.579	5.759	9
10	2.594	0.3855	0.06275	0.16275	15.937	6.144	10
11	2.853	0.3505	0.05396	0.15396	18.531	6.495	11
12	3.138	0.3186	0.04676	0.14676	21.384	6.814	12
13	3.452	0.2897	0.04078	0.14078	24.523	7.103	13
14	3.797	0.2633	0.03575	0.13575	27.975	7.367	14
15	4.177	0.2394	0.03147	0.13147	31.772	7.606	15
16	4.595	0.2176	0.02782	0.12782	35.950	7.824	16
17	5.054	0.1978	0.02466	0.12466	40.545	8.022	17
18	5.560	0.1799	0.02193	0.12193	45.599	8.201	18
19	6.116	0.1635	0.01955	0.11955	51.159	8.365	19
20	6.727	0.1486	0.01746	0.11746	57.275	8.514	20
21	7.400	0.1351	0.01562	0.11562	64.002	8.649	21
22	8.140	0.1228	0.01401	0.11401	71.403	8.772	22
23	8.954	0.1117	0.01257	0.11257	79.543	8.883	23
24	9.850	0.1015	0.01130	0.11130	88.497	8.985	24
25	10.835	0.0923	0.01017	0.11017	98.347	9.077	25
26	11.918	0.0839	0.00916	0.10916	109.182	9.161	26
27	13.110	0.0763	0.00826	0.10826	121.100	9.237	27
28	14.421	0.0693	0.00745	0.10745	134.210	9.307	28
29	15.863	0.0630	0.00673	0.10673	148.631	9.370	29
30	17.449	0.0573	0.00608	0.10608	164.494	9.427	30
31	19.194	0.0521	0.00550	0.10550	181.943	9.479	31
32	21.114	0.0474	0.00497	0.10497	201.138	9.526	32
33	23.225	0.0431	0.00450	0.10450	222.252	9.569	33
34	25.548	0.0391	0.00407	0.10407	245.477	9.609	34
35	28.102	0.0356	0.00369	0.10369	271.024	9.644	35
40	45.259	0.0221	0.00226	0.10226	442.593	9.779	40
45	72.890	0.0137	0.00139	0.10139	718.905	9.863	45
50	117.391	0.0085	0.00086	0.10086	1163.909	9.915	50
55	189.059	0.0053	0.00053	0.10053	1880.591	9.947	55
60	304.482	0.0033	0.00033	0.10033	3034.816	9.967	60
65	490.371	0.0020	0.00020	0.10020	4893.707	9.980	65
70	789.747	0.0013	0.00013	0.10013	7887.470	9.987	70
75	1271.895	0.0008	0.00008	0.10008	12708.954	9.992	75
80	2048.400	0.0005	0.00005	0.10005	20474.002	9.995	80
85	3298.969	0.0003	0.00003	0.10003	32979.690	9.997	85
90	5313.023	0.0002	0.00002	0.10002	53120.226	9.998	90
95	8556.676	0.0001	0.00001	0.10001	85556.760	9.999	95
100	13780.612	0.0001	0.00001	0.10001	137796.123	9.999	100

Taken from Eugene L. Grant, *Principles of Engineering Economy*, 3rd ed. Copyright 1950, The Ronald Press Company, New York.

Index

Index

Page numbers followed by *n* indicate references to footnotes.

649